VLSI: Technology and Design

OTHER IEEE PRESS BOOKS

VLSI: Technology and Design

Edited by

Otto G. Folberth

Director of Science and Technology
IBM Germany

Warren D. Grobman

Manager, Advanced Packaging Development
IBM General Technology Division

The Institute of Electrical and Electronics Engineers, Inc., New York

IEEE Order Number: PC01743

Library of Congress Cataloging in Publication Data
Main entry under title:

VLSI: technology & design.

A revision of 2 issues of Proceedings of the IEEE
originally published in 1983.
IEEE order no.: PC01743.
Includes index.
1. Integrated circuits—Very large scale integration.
I. Folberth, Otto G. II. Grobman, Warren D. III. Title:
V.L.S.I.
TK7874.V5663 1984   621.3819'5835   84-15848
ISBN 0-87942-180-0

Contents

Preface

THE PROCEEDINGS OF THE IEEE, the leading engineering journal in electrical and electronic science and technology, from time to time devotes an entire issue to a special topic. Usually, the Editorial Board nominates a Guest Editor, who is then responsible for the issue, including the selection of the author-team, which is key for the success of such an issue. With considerable effort and great care, the most qualified authors in the respective fields are invited to write and submit papers. Therefore, such an issue usually contains high-level tutorial material, which provides an authoritative state-of-the-art survey. In most cases such papers are understandable to technically sophisticated readers, who are nonspecialists in the particular fields.

In early 1983 two such issues were devoted to "Micron and Submicron Circuit Engineering" and "VLSI Design: Problems and Tools." Both issues were very well received by the technical community. This response stimulated a suggestion by the IEEE PRESS to combine and re-edit these issues, forming a book around them. The Guest Editors of the issues welcomed this suggestion and coedited this volume on "VLSI: Technology and Design." It primarily contains the individual papers of the two quoted special issues. For this purpose, the papers were regrouped into parts, and brief introductions to the various parts were written, using mainly the material of the "Scanning the Issue" introductions of the two issues. Two papers, however, too specialized for the envisioned broader readership, are not included in the book. On the other hand, some other topics were considered suitable for rounding out the book. Therefore, two additional papers—not from the special issues—have been added. These papers are written by the Editors of this volume themselves. These additions are "Status of X-ray Lithography," by W. Grobman, and the last paper, "Miniaturization of Digital Si-VLSI—Obstacles and Limits," by O. G. Folberth.

Foreword

THERE is a symbiotic relationship between system performance achieved through design advances and device and circuit technology. Each new development in technology makes possible further system advances, while the system advances lead to more aggressive, more highly integrated designs which in turn stimulate and require VLSI hardware technology improvements, both in integrated circuit chips and in system packaging.

This volume first looks at contributions in the areas of micron and submicron engineering of semiconductor chips, followed by a series of papers on VLSI design. It begins with two introductory papers covering the basic ideas of device scaling and design automation, which represent two of the fundamental driving forces behind the VLSI systems revolution.

The papers on engineering of high-density circuits are concerned with the fabrication of circuits at dimensions which approach and shrink below the 1 μm "barrier." The engineering of such integrated circuits has only recently succeeded in producing significant numbers of working chips with large numbers of devices per chip at these dimensions. Thus, the first half of this volume represents a review of this success. The first of the papers in this portion of the book are concerned with the lithography tools which permit micrometer circuit fabrication, and are followed by papers which explore experimental techniques which may lead to improved tools, processes, and devices. The circuit technology portion of the volume ends with papers which, most significantly, describe the application of these techniques to the design, fabrication, and testing of working micron and submicron circuits.

In the second half of this book, the papers describe aspects of VLSI design and its link to mathematical models of semiconductor devices. This portion of the book starts with papers on device and circuit modeling, which form the link between the physics of semiconductor devices, the engineering of circuits, and the mathematical discipline of design algorithms and automation. The next part consists of papers which describe algorithms for layout and circuit design, as well as the key area of testing methodology. Following this part is one on design systems in Japan and the developing countries. Finally, an outlook is presented for the future path of design systems as complexity increases, driven by the submicron capabilities of circuit engineering described in the beginning of this book.

Clearly, as is shown by the contents of this volume, the link between high-density circuit fabrication capability and high circuit count chips is a close one. We hope that the combination of papers from both areas will prove especially useful for this reason.

OTTO G. FOLBERTH
Boeblingen, Germany

WARREN D. GROBMAN
Yorktown Heights, NY

January 19, 1984

Part I
Overview

THIS overview contains two papers, representing device scaling and design automation, respectively. The first paper is by A. Reisman and describes the history and physics of device scaling. This paper sets the framework for many of the topics covered in the first half of this volume. Reisman discusses the evolution of circuit density over the last decade or so and considers the problems raised by a continuation of this trend. In particular, he describes reliability effects of Si-device shrinkage (e.g., hot-electron effects, soft-threshold-induced nonscaling of supply voltage which leads to large gate oxide field, etc.), and then reviews the process concerns and improvements which are an issue for continued circuit density improvements. This paper ends with an analysis of the effect of device scaling on circuit delays, and with a description of experimental results from real micron-scale Si FET circuits.

The next paper, by M. Feuer, is a sketch of the history, state of the art, and current key problems in the field of automation of design for VLSI circuits. The complexity of VLSI designs has grown to the extent that there are substantial doubts about the designers' ability to keep up with process capability. The implication is that future chips will be designed inefficiently in terms of silicon utilization or performance because of lack of time and design resources. The phrase "silicon is cheap" has always had a certain irony about it, but we may actually be coming to the point that silicon utilization is less important than design time. While the problems are serious, they are not insurmountable. Feuer discusses promising approaches for the solution of these design problems. Some of them are treated in more detail in further papers of this volume.

Device, Circuit, and Technology Scaling to Micron and Submicron Dimensions

ARNOLD REISMAN

Invited Paper

Abstract—From the discrete semiconductor component technology of the early 1960's, where the transition from the past focused on a major reduction in device size, i.e., from vacuum tubes to transistors, the emphasis from the late 1960's to the present has centered on integrating an ever-increasing number of devices on a chip. This trend has given rise to the acromyms SSI, MSI, LSI, and VLSI standing for small scale, medium scale, large scale, and very large scale integration, respectively. Following a discussion of the trends in device integration levels, four topics impacting our ability to achieve these levels are discussed from technological and engineering points of view. These are shrinking of conductor and device dimensions, known as scaling, reliability concerns in small structures, representative processes utilized in achieving small structures, and anticipated circuit delays for Insulated-Gate Field-Effect Transistors, IGFET's, at 1-μm design groundrules. The problems are numerous, and the potential solutions are even more numerous. However, it is not unreasonable to expect that these can all be sorted out during the 1980's. If this comes to pass, then one can expect IGFET integration levels of 10^6 bits of dynamic random-access memory, DRAM, storage on a 70-mm^2 chip, and logic circuit performance at the 1-ns level at room temperature and <0.5 ns at liquid nitrogen temperature. The logic numbers are in the context of maximum performance achievable at maximum circuit density, and at an acceptable power dissipation level of 2 W/chip or less (where the chip area is between 0.2 and 0.3 cm^2).

INTRODUCTION

THE HISTORY of semiconductor device and circuit integration on a single chip employing photolithographically delineated interconnections is about two decades old. To keep pace with an ever-increasing level of integration, acronyms intended to impart the magnitude of this level were born without specifying the size of the child. Thus we have SSI, MSI, LSI, and VLSI standing for small scale, medium scale, large scale, and very large scale integration, respectively. The beginning time frames for each of these, roughly, were the mid 1960's, the early 1970's, the mid 1970's and the early 1980's respectively. The picture is a little confusing, in that semiconductor device technology up to the late 1960's was primarily centered around bipolar technology. At that point in time we saw the emergence of insulated-gate field-effect transistors, IGFET's, and a concomitant rapid increase in levels of integration. The reason for this coincidence is that IGFET's dissipate much less power than bipolar devices, and can, therefore, be employed at much greater packing densities. For example, at 1-μm dimensions with each type of device otpimized for performance, chip density, and power dissipation, one might expect about 0.2-mW/circuit dissipation in IGFET's and about

Manuscript received September 1, 1982.

The author is with the IBM Thomas J. Watson Research Center, Yorktown Heights, NY 10598. He is now at the Microelectronic Center of North Carolina, P.O. Box 12889, Research Triangle Park, NC 27709, and the Department of Electrical Engineering, North Carolina State University, Raleigh, NC 27650.

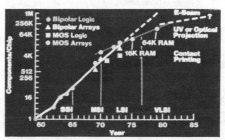

Fig. 1. Component density/chip versus time.

4 mW in bipolars. This factor of 20 translates directly into chip packing density differences unless one uses more sophisticated cooling in the case of bipolar chips. One such advanced cooling technique has been described recently [1]. It is based on heat removal with flowing water via heat fins built into a silicon chip, and is said to be able to remove approximately 800 W/cm^2 with a maximum temperature rise of 71°C. For a chip 8 mm on an edge, this translates into a heat dissipation capability of about 505 W/chip. For comparison, conventional packaged chips have a heat dissipation capability of about 2 W/chip, or in package terms, assuming a 25 mm on an edge package, about 0.3 W/cm^2. If such efficient package approaches become economically and technologically practical, bipolar technologies may become competitive with IGFET's in integration level. However, yields of IGFET's, especially at small dimensions, appear to be greater due to a lower process complexity, among other things. At any rate, when we talk of very large levels of integration today we generally refer to the status of IGFET's.

Beginning in 1960, it appears that the number of components on a chip has increased, more or less exponentially with time. For the case where we do not differentiate between bipolars and IGFET's, logic and memory, chip size, or minimum lithographic dimension, we have the progression shown in Fig. 1. The ordinate plots the number of components on a chip logarithmically to the base 2, while the abscissa plots the time linearly. The component chip density boundaries are also depicted in Fig. 1. The intervals arbitrarily chosen are 2^5. Consequently, beginning with the integration of two devices, e.g., 2^1, SSI covers the range 2^1-2^6 (2-64) components, MSI from 2^6-2^{11} (64-2048), LSI from 2^{11}-2^{16} (2048-65 536), and VLSI from 2^{16}-2^{21} (65 536-2 097 152). Depending how one counts, chip densities are now either at the end of the LSI era or the beginning of the VLSI era.

Fig. 2 is a little less diffuse than Fig. 1. It depicts the growth

Reprinted from *Proc. IEEE*, vol. 71, pp. 550-565, May 1983.

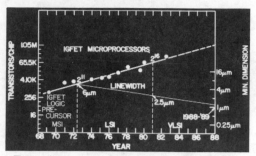

Fig. 2. Microprocessor component density/chip versus time.

in component count of microprocessor chips which are a mix of logic and memory elements implemented in IGFET's, but which contain no main memory. Fig. 2 is plotted in the same way as Fig. 1. Precursor microprocessor chips containing between 500 and 1000 components were being developed toward the end of the 1960's. Since then, there has been an approximate doubling of component count every two years. By 1981, the component count had exceeded 64 000, and by 1988 if the trend holds true, the component count will be up to 10^6/chip. Design questions will probably be more crucial, before such integration levels are achieved, than fabrication questions.

If we return to Fig. 1 and examine the RAM, random-access memory, curve, which was for a period of time the indicator of integration level, we see a close parallel to the microprocessor case. From a component count of around 4000/chip in 1971, this value for dynamic random-access memory, DRAM, had reached 64 000 by about 1977 (since each DRAM bit of memory consists of a transfer device and a storage capacitor, the 64 000 number is equivalent to 32 000 bits of DRAM). By 1981, experimental DRAM chips containing 0.25 Mbit/chip had been reported [2], and 64 000-bit DRAM's (128 000 devices) were in introductory production in several companies. By 1982, 64-kbit chips were the industry standard. The parallelism is interesting, since devices used in microprocessors are of the static type, and more difficult to lay out on a chip than the DRAM devices which are configured in the so-called "one device cell" version of the IGFET [3]. Fig. 2 also depicts the evolution in the shrinking of minimum lithographic dimensions that has accompanied the increase in integration level. As before, it appears that an exponential dependence on time is involved. In 1972, lithography tools were required to provide resolutions around 6 μm,[1] with a 3σ tolerance of ±30–40 percent. This was at the beginning of the LSI era by my arbitrary definition. By the end of this era in 1981, the minimum lithographic dimension had decreased to 2.5–3.0 μm with the same tolerance. This would imply that a more constrained definition for VLSI is that chip component counts are in excess of 32 000 bits of DRAM or 64 000 IGFET logic or static RAM elements and minimum lithographic dimensions are ⩽2.5 μm.

By the end of the 1980's, it is not unreasonable to expect that minimum lithographic dimensions in manufacturing will

have decreased to the 1-μm level, again with the same 3σ percentage tolerance. By the end of the 20th century, 0.25-μm minimum dimensions are anticipated and theoretical understanding of IGFET behavior at this dimension has already been reported upon [4]. Based on what we know today, if this shrinkage occurs without major innovation in device, circuit, and interconnection design, 0.25 μm may represent the end limit of useable linewidth shrinkage in IGFET technology. The main problem may not be the fabrication of small structures, but rather their reliability. This question will be addressed further below. One additional comment about device size reduction, which is termed "scaling" [5], relates to the type of lithographic tool needed to accomplish dimensional shrinkage.

During the SSI and MSI eras, contact printing was employed almost exclusively. The photographic mask was brought into direct contact with the silicon wafer which was overcoated with an ultraviolet (UV) light-sensitive emulsion called a photoresist, and the emulsion was exposed. During the LSI time frame, contact printing gave way to proximity and projection printing using shorter wavelengths of UV light. Proximity printing involves maintaining a gap between the mask and the wafer, and projection printing separates this distance futher. The latter may involve image-size reduction during projection, or may, as in contact and proximity printing, operate on a one-to-one basis. The LSI tool approach offers, as a great advantage, preservation of mask lifetime, since no contact between mask and wafer takes place. Contact, proximity, and projection exposure, as generally practiced, involve "full wafer exposure" with wafer sizes increasing from about 1 inch in 1970 to about 3–4 inches in diameter in 1981. This wafer size increase, coupled with dimensional shrinkage results, of course, in enhanced productivity. Because full wafer exposure, particularly in large wafers, and with shrinking line dimensions, makes overlaying subsequent levels for exposure more difficult, due in part to wafer distortion during processing, from the early 1970's on, a lot of work was done to develop step-and-repeat projection printers, S & R. In this technique, a unit cell is projected on only a portion of the wafer, and the wafer is then repetitively stepped across the projector's field of view to expose the entire surface. 10:1 image reduction is commonly employed in S & R exposure. It is claimed that in volume production, this technique is capable of line resolution down to the 1.25–1.50-μm level, with overlay from level to level of about ±0.5 μm 3σ, or better. Questions relating to overlay and resolution tolerances are both crucial in considering scaling to smaller dimensions. In order to achieve maximum benefits from reducing dimensions, i.e., in device density and performance, the aforementioned tolerances must scale proportionally. There is considerable uncertainty about the minimum nominal dimension, plus acceptable overlay tolerance that is achievable using light optical exposure techniques for volume production. A somewhat soft consensus is that the light optical resolution number is around 1–1.25 μm, while the 3σ overlay number is around ±0.4–0.5 μm. To achieve smaller dimensions, it is expected that direct writing step-and-repeat electron-beam, or step-and-repeat X-ray exposure using electron-beam generated masks will be required. The key to the economic feasibility of electron-beam exposure is wafer throughput, since electron-beam exposure, as it is currently evolving, utilizes serial writing techniques [6]–[10].

Before leaving the subject of lithography, it is worthwhile to bring up an economic subtlety, that concerned with productivity. In step-and-repeat optics, as well as with electron-beam exposure there exists a tradeoff between field size, the

[1] A resolution number implies that minimum features of this size, e.g., 1.0-μm lines and spaces, can be resolved. With a defined resolution as a starting point, the ability to superimpose mask levels, overlay, is an equally crucial number. In general, its 3σ value is about a factor of 2.5–3 smaller than the resolution number, e.g., at the 1.0-μm resolution level, overlay of the order of 0.3 μm (3σ) is achievable.

area that can be exposed without moving the stepping table, and resolution. In general, as field size increases, resolution tends to degrade. Thus to buy resolution, you must step the wafer past the optics more times to expose the entire wafer and a throughput penalty is incurred. This may, however, be a little myoptic since, as we shall see, wafer device productivity is proportional to the square of a scaling factor, while wafer throughput may not degrade by the square of the scaling factor. In other words, if device dimensions are shrunk by the scaling factor α, thereby increasing component density by α^2, wafer steps may not necessarily have to increase by α^2, but may increase by a smaller number.

Why this preoccupation with making devices smaller and achieving higher levels of integration on a chip? The answer is simple, To Reduce Costs. This reduction can manifest itself in two ways, processing costs and packaging costs. Thus if the cost of processing a wafer remains constant, or increases at a slower rate than the component density on a chip increases, productivity increases. Similarly, if the number of chips needed to achieve a given electrical function is reduced, the number of packages needed to contain these chips is reduced. The net is that computational and/or information storage costs are lowered, and wider potential markets are opened up. Attendant with increased productivity due to decrease in device dimensions, device-circuit performance improves. Consequently, one not only buys computational capability more cheaply, but also buys higher performance computational capability more cheaply. From Figs. 1 and 2, it is seen, using our arbitrary 2^5 partitioning rule that we are now at the gateway to the VLSI era. At present, as we have stated, this is synonymous with IGFET technology, although bipolars in so-called MTL or I^2L format [11]–[13] offer the potential to challenge the IGFET role. This IGFET role is determined to a great extent by the low power dissipation of circuits comprised of such devices. In optimized fashion at the 1-μm dimensional level, IGFET circuits dissipate power in the 0.1–0.2-mW range. Conventional bipolar circuits dissipate an order of magnitude more power. A second consideration relates to yield questions, and whether or not bipolar processes can achieve comparable yields to IGFET processes. MTL bipolar configurations, however, do not have the power dissipation problems of conventional bipolar designs, and are, in self-aligned configuration [11], competitive with FET performance. MTL technology is not as far along as IGFET technology and could have bipolar-like yield problems. Furthermore, like its genre, it cannot probably be operated much below room temperature. The 1980's should tell the story. At any rate, the final step needed to make the entrance into VLSI complete is to bring lithographic dimensions down below the 2.5–3.0-μm values of today. This is being pursued vigorously at dimensions down to 1.25 μm using step-and-repeat tools.

By the time 1-μm minimum dimensions are achieved in manufacturing, this could translate into memory unit component manufacturing costs of about 0.002 cent per bit in 1983 money, and memory packing densities of the order of about 1 Mbit of DRAM/70 mm^2. In other words, a chip approximately 6 mm on an edge will contain a million components (approximately half a million bits of DRAM). Logic performance will be in the 1-ns nominal delay range for typically loaded circuits operating at acceptable power levels at room temperature. Achieving these goals poses some obvious technology, and device and circuit challenges, and some less obvious, and perhaps more difficult challenges. Several

TABLE I
TECHNOLOGY CHALLENGES FOR VLSI

- High Resolution Precise Registration Lithography
- Scaled Tolerances
- Improved Etching Processes
- Reliable Thin Gate Insulators
- Shallow Implanted Doping Profiles
- Shorter Time/Lower Temperature Hot Processes
- Better Interconnection Technology in Terms Of
    - Contact Metallurgy
    - Electromigration Immunity
    - Higher Density, Lower Capacitance
    - Multiple Wiring Layers
- Removal of Process Induced Radiation Damage
- Enhanced Reliability

TABLE II
DEVICE AND CIRCUIT CHALLENGES FOR VLSI

- Coping with the Subthreshold Problem
- Power Distribution
- Power Dissipation
- VLSI Design Methodology
- Chip Testing
- Hot Electron Effects
- α Particle and Cosmic Ray Effects

obvious technology challenges are listed in Table I, and several device and circuit challenges are listed in Table II. Selected topics from among those listed in Tables I and II will be considered below in the appropriate section.

In order to approach the subject of VLSI in an orderly, albeit cursory fashion, the many ramifications of the subject will be considered in the context of four topics. There are

1) Scaling Implications
2) Reliability Issues
3) Processes
4) Performance.

The foci will be on the materials and device engineering aspects and the interplay between these.

SCALING IMPLICATIONS

Fig. 3 shows schematically the key elements in an integrated circuit. Simplistically, it is seen that what takes place is transport of a signal through an interconnection to a circuit site, manipulation of the signal at the circuit site, and finally, transport of the signal from the circuit site via another interconnecting link. Let us consider what the impact of geometric and electrical scaling using the same scaling factor for both leads to in the case of the conductors and devices separately.

Fig. 4 considers the impact of scaling of conductors from some initial dimensional configuration to a final one by some arbitrary scaling factor α. The left-most column of Fig. 4 lists several key electrical parameters, capacitance, resistance, time constant (the product of resistance and capacitance), and current density. The next column shows arbitrary values for these parameters prior to scaling, and the third column lists values for these parameters when the conductor structure is decreased in all dimensions by the scaling parameter α, and when current and voltage are also decreased by the same

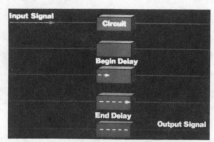

Fig. 3. Signal delay in a circuit.

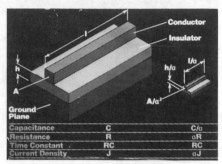

Fig. 4. Scaling of conductors.

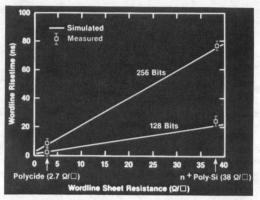

Fig. 5. Word-line rise time as a function of resistance.

scaling factor. Before going into the details, it is important to note that the conductor problem is most critical when considered in the context of the gate electrode in IGFET technology, when this gate electrode is made of heavily doped polycrystalline silicon having a resistivity of approximately 1000 $\mu\Omega$cm and this material is employed as a local interconnection metallurgy. The conductor concept is still valid for metallic conductors except that the R term in the RC product is always small. The RC product for device and conductor combined may, however, be quite large, e.g., the R term comes primarily from low width-to-length ratios in the device, while the capacitance term has a heavy contribution from both the device and conductor. Pedagogically, however, it is perhaps more informative to separate the conductor and device contributions. To continue, since the area of the conductor in contact with the insulator is decreased to $1/\alpha^2$ of its initial value (the length and width of the conductor are each decreased to $1/\alpha$ of its initial value), we might expect a capacitance reduction to C/α^2. However, the insulator thickness is simultaneously reduced to $1/\alpha$ of its initial value resulting in a capacitance increase of α. Coupled with the area decrease, the net is that the capacitance of the scaled conductor structure decreases to only $1/\alpha$ of its initial value. The resistance of the conductor, due to a reduction of cross-sectional area to $1/\alpha^2$ might be expected to increase by α^2. However, as the length of the conductor is also decreased to $1/\alpha$ of its initial value, the resistance increases only by the factor α. This is still an undesirable result, since the time constant of the scaled conductor remains precisely what it was prior to scaling. In other words, in the scaled structure, a proportionately larger fraction of the elapsed time is spent in moving signals from one place to another, since, as we shall see, the scaled circuit will manipulate the signals faster. We can envisage a situation where the bulk

of the elapsed time may be spent in signal propagation. The time constant is, of course, a function of both the line resistance and line capacitance. If insulator thickness is not fully scaled, the capacitance problem can be alleviated somewhat at the possible expense of increased technological complexity in the form of greater aspect ratios, and longer times at temperature during device processing to form the thicker insulator. The importance of conductor resistance would, however, still be significant. This resistance effect in nonmetallic interconnections can be seen with reference to Fig. 5 which depicts memory chip word-line rise time as a function of line resistance for two lines of different length. The upper curve shows the rise time for a word line twice the length of that whose rise time is depicted in the lower curve. Focusing on the bottom curve, it is seen that the polycide conductor [14], [15], a name given by this author to a structure comprising heavily doped polysilicon overlaid by WSi_2, or other refractory silicide, exhibits a rise time relative to the conventional polysilicon conductor, linearly proportional to the sheet resistivity ratios of the two, i.e., 2.7 $\Omega/\square$/38 $\Omega/\square$. The upper line represents the case with twice the line length (therefore, twice the line resistance) and twice the line capacitance. It shows a rise time increase of approximately four for both the polycide and polysilicon rise times. As a matter of interest, Table III lists the resistivities (in $\mu\Omega$cm) of some common silicides [16]. These are not all usable for polycide fabrication. For more details, the reader is referred to the tutorial on silicides [17] by F. d'Heurle.

It is obvious from Fig. 5 that because of the large RC time constant associated with polysilicon, the latter cannot be used extensively as an interconnection metallurgy. Even the polycide structure with its much higher conductivity is limited, since it has a resistivity an order of magnitude greater than aluminum, the most pervasively used conductor. Aluminum is potentially usable for extensive scaling, with one important caveat which is best seen with reference to Fig. 4 once more. The last entry in Fig. 4 deals with current-density changes accompanying scaling. Decrease in cross-sectional area to $1/\alpha^2$ would cause an increase in current density by α^2. As the current and voltage are each scaled by α, the current density increases only by the factor α. Unfortunately, no increase is tolerable, since one has to contend with the phenomenon of electromigration [18], [19]. Under the incessant bombardment of conductor atoms by electrons, these atoms tend to

TABLE III
APPROXIMATE RESISTIVITIES OF SOME COMMON SILICIDES,* Si, AND Al
METAL IN THIN-FILM FORM

Material	Resistivity $\mu\Omega$cm
Al	3
Si (heavily doped)	~1000
TiSi$_2$	15
ZrSi$_2$	35
HFSi$_2$	45
VSi$_2$	50
NbSi$_2$	50
TaSi$_2$	35
CrSi$_2$	~ 10^4
MoSi$_2$	90
WSi$_2$	45
FeSi$_2$	~ 10^6
CoSi$_2$	20
NiSi	15
NiSi$_2$	35
Pd$_2$Si	30
PtSi	28

*The values reported in the literature show
rather wide variations.

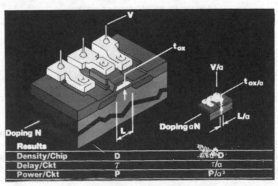

Fig. 6. Scaling of devices.

move, resulting ultimately in the breaking of conductor lines. What is even worse is that the susceptibility to electromigration may be linewidth and line thickness dependent, i.e., narrower and thinner lines may be more susceptible than wider and thicker lines.

This means that when we scale device structures downward, we may not be able to scale conductors fully. This implies a penalty in circuit density, and technologically leads us again to structures with larger aspect ratios than we would like. In other words, the height of the conductor increases relative to conductor center–center distance which poses undue challenges to the already challenged lithographic and etching processes employed.

While the interconnections pose problems when scaled, the picture with devices and circuits is outwardly more favorable. The device situation is shown in Fig. 6. The device cross section depicted is that of the IGFET. It is seen from Fig. 6 that the device is conceptually simple. Current flow between a source and drain region (see Fig. 15) is modulated by application of a field to the silicon surface, causing it to accumulate or invert. The voltage at which inversion occurs is called the threshold voltage, and it represents the voltage at which electrons start to flow from the source to the drain in a so-called n-channel device. One important performance determining parameter is the channel length L. Using the same approach employed with conductors, we focus here on the parameters density/chip, delay/circuit, and power/circuit. It is seen that with the scaling factor α applied, the density/chip increases by the factor α^2. The delay/circuit decreases to τ/α, and the power dissipation/circuit decreases to P/α^2.

The "goodness" associated with device and circuit scaling is mitigated to a degree by several conditions. Since the power dissipation/circuit decreases by the factor $1/\alpha^2$, owing to a simultaneous decrease in threshold voltage (therefore, to required power supply voltage) and current, and since the

circuit packing density increases by α^2, the power dissipation for the chip as whole remains constant. In other words, if there was no cooling problem associated with the unscaled chip, none should exist with the scaled chip. However, consider the following. Since power/chip is constant and the threshold voltage V_T is scaled, the total current/chip (as contrasted to the current/circuit) must increase so that EI unscaled $= EI$ scaled. This may pose a power distribution problem on the chip, since the total current must pass through smaller pads. If the number of such pads is increased to accommodate the increase in total current, this will require more pins/package upon which the chip is mounted, and existing packages may become pin limited. In addition, from both engineering and economic points of view, it may not be desirable to scale power supply voltages (therefore, threshold voltages) fully.[2] In such an event also, power dissipation/circuit will not decrease by the factor α^2, and the power dissipation/chip may begin to encroach on the limits of inexpensive module cooling techniques. To circumvent this problem, circuit solutions that utilize less standby power may have to be employed. A circuit type satisfying this requirement is known as CMOS (designating complimentary-metal-oxide-semiconductor circuits), in contrast to the primary type we have been considering which has the acronym NMOS (designating n-channel metal-oxide-semiconductor, and, where because of historical useage MOS and IGFET are synonomous). Such CMOS circuit solutions could impose a complexity problem in processing, since the complimentary circuits utilize n- and p-channel devices on the same substrate. In addition, they may be wasteful of space when maximum packing density is the goal. They may also pose yield problems. CMOS circuits are also subject to a phenomenon known as latch-up due to the inadvertent presence of parasitic surface bipolar devices created by proximity of adjacent n- and p-doped regions [20]. CMOS activity is extensive at present, and it is to be anticipated that the questions raised will be resolved satisfactorily.

One other aspect of the NMOS–CMOS question which is peripherally related to the power question is worth discussing. NMOS devices in normally employed circuit configurations

---

[2] We have assumed that geometric and electrical parameters scale by the same scaling factor α. In terms of the device, this implies constant field scaling relative to the gate insulator. If voltages are not scaled as assumed, then the scaling factor α is modulated, for example, by a second scaling factor κ which is the factor by which the potentials are scaled, and where $\lambda/\kappa > 1$ [4]. This means that the field is no longer constant and increases by λ/κ and could result in a reliability penalty.

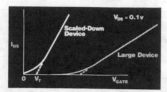

Fig. 7. Subthreshold scaling problem.

TABLE IV
PERFORMANCE OF LOGIC CIRCUITS
(Fan-In = Fan-Out = 3, with wiring delay)

Channel Length, L (μm) and Minimum Mask Dimension	4.0	1.0	0.25
Delay (ns)	4.0	1.0	0.25
Power Dissipation, (μW)/ckt.	2720	170	10.6

do not drive long lines very well, primarily because of device impedance considerations which we need not go into here. The net is that even for low-resistance aluminum interconnection lines, the device–interconnection time constant is not insignificant. To overcome this effect creates design problems in terms of width-to-length ratios of the devices and causes power dissipation levels to become too high. CMOS circuits do not have these problems. Consequently, they can be used more advantageously in the so-called Gate Array or Master Slice configurations in which interconnections and devices lay on orthogonal grid intersections which lend themselves to quick design turnaround times for LSI and VLSI of chips [21].

There exist three other potential device-related problems which must be contended with, as devices are scaled, expecially if liberties are taken with scaling. These are the short-channel effect, hot-electron injection (to be discussed under reliability issues), and subthreshold turn-on. The short-channel effect [22] manifests itself at a given channel length as a lowering of device threshold voltage with increasing source-drain voltage in the IGFET, and at constant drain voltage as a decrease in threshold voltage with decreasing channel length, and is due to merging of the junction depletion regions. If, however, substrate doping level and gate insulator thickness, Fig. 6, are properly scaled, this effect can be obviated. This assertion presupposes that the junction depths are also properly scaled. At dimensions below 1 μm, junction depth containment may require reduction of time–temperature cycles for oxidation and ion-implantation damage removal. Reduction of time-temperature cycles has been addressed using 600°C plasma-oxidation techniques [23]. Elimination of ion-implant damage may require dispensing with ion implantation and replacing such regions with polycide overlays from which shallow junctions are outdiffused. This is a drastic solution for a variety of reasons. One alternative, involving very rapid heating will be discussed subsequently, as will the reduced temperature oxidation technique.

The subthreshold scaling problem [5], [24] is perhaps the most fundamental of the device–circuit concerns. It is best understood with reference to Fig. 7 which is a plot of the drain current versus gate voltage for reference and scaled devices. It is seen that when the gate voltage is decreased to below the threshold value, the channel current does not drop linearly to zero, but, in fact, decreases exponentially. This rate of decrease in the subthreshold region (or weak inversion region, as it is sometimes called) is dependent on the value of the gate voltage, and is the same, independent of the channel length at a given temperature. Consequently, if the designed threshold of the scaled device is too low, the situation arises that when the gate voltage is reduced to zero, a significant amount of current continues to flow in the channel. The impact of this subthreshold current flow is that in a DRAM, the stored charge on the capacitor will leak off in-between refresh

cycles. This phenomenon precludes scaling of DRAM threshold voltages according to the dictates of scaling theory, and therefore precludes accurate scaling of power supply voltages. The net result is that as DRAM's are made smaller and gate insulators are made thinner, in order to avoid the subthreshold problem, it may be necessary, as indicated for the general case discussed earlier, to operate at higher fields across the oxide as compared to the unscaled device, incurring the possibility of a reliability problem, or to incur a performance penalty if the power supply voltage is scaled. Other solutions to the problem involve scaling operating temperature (which may not be an acceptable practical solution for obvious reasons), increasing the storage capacitor area to increase the total charge stored (which incurs a density penalty) replacement of the SiO$_2$ storage capacitor insulator by a higher dielectric constant material, or improving the dielectric breakdown characteristics of the SiO$_2$ insulator so that the increased fields can be tolerated in the gate insulator. The mentioned solutions, with the exception of temperature lowering and improved oxide integrity, each involve some penalty.

Thus from a device–circuits point of view, we see that aside from the sheer difficulty of making things smaller, line interconnections and device problems may mitigate, to a degree, performance and density advantages arising from device size reduction. Probably, the best solutions to the RC time constant and potential electromigration problems involve quasi-geometrical scaling of metal lines, substitution of polycide or equivalent structures for polycrystalline silicon, and the use of multilevels of wiring in which the upper level(s) involve dimensional expansion. The materials and technology ramifications of scaling deviations are complex. For example, if because of the subthreshold problem in DRAM's we do not scale the threshold voltage below a certain value, we require larger power supply voltages which result in increased current densities in the interconnection lines beyond even the fundamentally dictated increase in such current densities already mentioned. If we make the lines wider and thicker than is called for in scaling, we decrease current densities, but increase line capacitances, and pose a technology penalty due to increase in aspect ratios, etc.

Having injected a number of caveats let us consider some of the advantages of decreasing dimensions.

Table IV lists capacitively loaded IGFET NOR circuit delays and power dissipation values to be expected with scaling nominal channel length dimensions from 4 → 1 → 0.25 μm. Each of the performance numbers is a nominal value which degrades by a factor of approximately 2 in a 3σ worst case design.

Table V lists the density advantages associated with scaling, for a chip of fixed area, for both memory and logic applications. The range for logic circuit density refers to whether the logic devices are interconnected using a "master slice" approach [21] or are laid out in custom fashion. As mentioned, in the former,

TABLE V
DENSITY ADVANTAGES OF SMALL DIMENSIONS

Minimum Dimension	Memory Bits/Chip*	Logic Elements/Chip*
4	16K	800 - 2,000
2	64K	2,500 - 7,000
1	256K	8,000 - 20,000

*Chip Size = 15-20 mm²

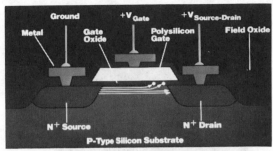

Fig. 8. Channel hot-electron injection and trapping.

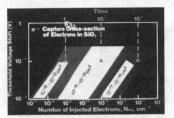

Fig. 9. Threshold voltage instability due to hot-electron trapping.

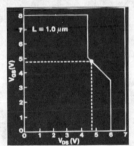

Fig. 10. Channel hot-electron voltage limits.

the device locations lay on a grid and are interconnected as needed. In the custom approach they are "squeezed" in wherever space is available. However, as also mentioned, because IGFET's do not drive capacitances well, master slice approaches to IGFET logic, while simplifying chip design, may result in significant performance degradation, in addition to providing lower circuit density/chip.

RELIABILITY

Aside from the questions raised by nonscaling of threshold voltages, and potential electromigration degradation of conductors, the "Hot-Electron" issue [25] is one to be monitored, especially if strict scaling is not adhered to, and especially if the nonscaling is associated with power supply voltages. From a technology point of view, the phenomenon is aggrevated if ionizing radiative processes are employed at the first metal level, e.g., electron-beam lithography, X-ray lithography, electron-beam metal evaporation [26].

The phenomenon is best understood with reference to Fig. 8 which depicts the cross section of an IGFET. A small fraction of the electrons moving from source to drain in the IGFET have sufficient energy to overcome the interfacial barrier height and are injected into the SiO_2. These injected electrons can be trapped in either positively charged or neutral defects, causing an upward shift in threshold voltage. Fig. 9 depicts the latter effect as a function of the number of injected electrons and the trapping center cross sections. In each defect cross-section range, the number of injected electrons required to cause a threshold shift of 0.1 V is shown as well as the relative time required to achieve such a shift. In terms of an arbitrary useful device lifetime of 10^4 on-hours, the concern is greatest with defect cross sections $\geqslant 10^{-15}$ cm². The radiation induced positively charged centers fall in the 10^{-12}–10^{-13} -cm² range, and the neutral trapping centers fall into the size range 10^{-13} cm² and smaller. These neutral trapping centers [26] pose somewhat of a special problem, since their presence is not felt electrically until they trap electrons. From a device–circuit point of view, the designer can evolve useful ranges of operation to minimize hot-electron effects as is shown in Fig. 10 for undamaged devices. The safe operating limits for gate and source–drain voltages are shown to the left of the boundary line.

From a materials point of view, one wants to minimize the defect density in the gate insulator, either native defects or radiation-induced defects [27]. A limitation in annealing such damage following metallization is the maximum time-temperature annealing cycle that can be tolerated by metallized devices. Elevated temperature stable contact metallurgies represent one route, albeit a difficult one, since not only must the metallurgy be able to function as a barrier metallurgy in the range 550–600°C, but it must exhibit good contact resistance characteristics and good mechanical characteristics. One recently reported method [28] for removal of such damage

involves the use of elevated pressures (50-atm forming gas). The results are best seen with reference to Figs. 11 and 12. The devices being examined were subjected to approximately 10^7 rads SiO_2 following metallization. The devices were then annealed either conventionally, or at eleveated pressure. This damage level approximates that resulting from either electron-beam exposure at the metal level during device fabrication or electron-beam evaporation of metal at the metal level during device fabrication. Figs. 11 and 12 show, respectively, source-drain current versus gate voltage characteristics of IGFET devices annealed conventionally, and at elevated pressures. Curve 1 of each figure depicts the current–voltage characteristic following device fabrication and damage, and annealing. Curve 2 depicts the threshold shift following intentional hot-electron injection to fill residual positive traps (cross sections greater than 10^{-3} cm²). Curve 3 depicts further threshold shift following an additional injection of 10^{16} electrons which fill all the residual neutral traps having cross sections greater than 10^{-15} cm². In Fig. 12, it is seen, based on the comparatively small threshold shifts following electron injection, that little residual positive traps remain following elevated pressure anneal, and much fewer neutral traps are present than in the conventionally

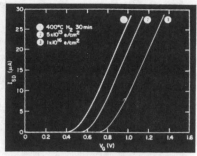

Fig. 11. Injection into the gate insulator after normal anneal at atmospheric pressure.

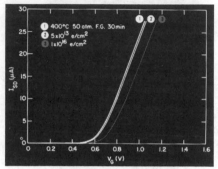

Fig. 12. Injection into the gate insulator after high-pressure anneal.

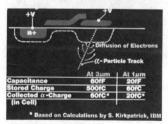

Fig. 13. Alpha-particle effects.

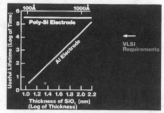

Fig. 14. Reliability of SiO$_2$ with Al and poly-Si electrodes.

annealed device depicted in Fig. 11. Both of these residual levels in elevated-pressure annealed samples approximate those observed in devices which have not seen ionizing radiative processes. Novel barrier-contact metallurgies involving Ti (see below) offer promise of high temperature stability, but these are too new to know how effective they will be. In any event, at dimensions down to 1 μm, process-induced radiation damage is more of an annoyance that can be designed around than a show stopper. At smaller dimensions this may no longer be true.

A phenomenon receiving considerable attention during the past several years, which is a reliability problem of sorts, deals with α-particle effects in both DRAM and logic IGFET's [29]. The effect is illustrated in Fig. 13. α-particles emanating from silicon chips, interconnections, packages, and the environment, upon striking the silicon can generate a few million electron–hole pairs. A fraction of the generated electrons can find their way to the storage plate of a DRAM, for example, leading to

so-called soft errors being induced. 1 femtocoulomb (fC) of stored charge represents about 6.2 $\times$ 10^3 charges, and at the 1-μm device level the total charge stored is only of the order of 3.7 $\times$ 10^5. At the 0.5-μm design level, the stored charge value can be as little as 1 $\times$ 10^5. Clearly, α-particle impact can, in either instance, lead to capture of sufficient charge to cause transient errors. One other possible effect due to α-particles is that the generated electrons can move across the depletion region of the IGFET into the gate insulator via a hot-electron mechanism causing permanent or hard error effects. Device design modifications, chip organization modifications, and device processing with extremely clean materials may all be required to contain such effects.

One other aspect of reliability which should be mentioned deals with the generic choice of polysilicon IGFET's in the first place. Prior to the use of polysilicon as a gate material, aluminum was used for this purpose. Three things mitigated against the evolution of the IGFET as we now know it, and the continued use of aluminum, as originally employed. When in direct contact with SiO$_2$ of diminishing thickness, data such as shown in Fig. 14 indicated that the reliability of aluminum gated devices was suspect [30]. It is seen that as the gate insulator thickness decreases, the useful lifetime of aluminum gated devices decreases linearly on a log–log plot, while that of polysilicon gated devices does not. A second consideration was that unlike the more refractory polysilicon, aluminum gates had to be positioned on the device after all elevated temperature processing steps had been completed. Because of lithography limitations, this resulted in large overlaps of the aluminum gates to source and drain regions, an undesirable electrical situation, and a concomitant decrease in potential packing density due to the lithographic laxity required in a gate "last" technology. Finally, the technology, as then practiced, could not make use of the wiring flexibility offered by the use of a conductor such as polysilicon which could be self-passivated. For the future, extensive modification of poly-gate technology looks mandatory, primarily because of conductivity limitations, and to a degree because of existing design inflexibility associated with the poly-gate–insulator work function. This will lead initially to the use of polycides, and then to a new device-materials structure termed SALICIDE [31] standing for self-aligned silicide. In this latter structure, not only will the gate electrode employ a silicide, but so will the source and drain regions. An excellent review of this topic and a fabrication approach appears in [32].

This leads us into a discussion of the process employed in the fabrication of 1-μm polysilicon-gated devices using direct-write electron-beam lithography, ion implantation for the formation of junctions, and plasma techniques for etching device structures [33]. The technology was initially evolved for logic-oriented applications, and has been extended to mem-

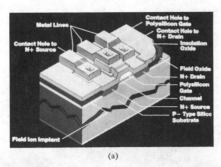

(a)

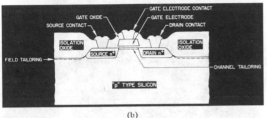

(b)

Fig. 15. Perspective of an n-channel MOSFET.

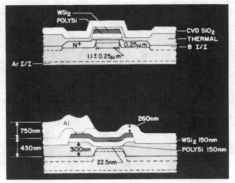

Fig. 16. Cross section of an n-channel MOSFET in a polycide structure.

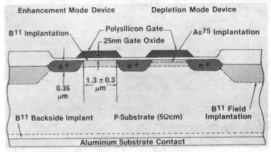

Fig. 17. Cross section of 1-μm minimum channel length polysilicon gate device.

TABLE VI
LITHOGRAPHY DIMENSIONS OF A 1-μm LITHOGRAPHY TEST VEHICLE

•Minimum Contact Hole Width	1.0	μm
•Minimum Linewidth	1.25	μm
•Minimum Poly-Si Linewidth	1.5	μm
•Minimum Diffusion Linewidth	1.75	μm
•Device Channel Length, L_{eff} =	1.3±0.3 μm 3σ	

ory useage in an even more aggressive 1-μm design, as well as to enhanced-logic-oriented applications.

Fig. 15(a) shows one such device construction in perspective, while Fig. 15(b) shows the cross section of a similar device. The devices shown are so-called n-channel devices, and are constructued in p-type silicon. The regions in Fig. 15(b) denoted as isolation oxide separate adjacent devices. The regions under the isolation oxides, known as field regions, and the channel region have additional p-type impurities incorporated within them to adjust their threshold voltages. In the case of the field regions, threshold voltages must be high enough so that the silicon in these field regions does not become conductive during device operation. Fig. 16 shows details in the channel cross section of a 1-μm-dimensional device in polycide form, and Fig. 17 shows such a device in poly-gate form. Table VI gives pertinent dimensions at the wiring level for the latter specifically. The logic-oriented experiment alluded to was undertaken to test the validity of scaling concepts at the 1-μm dimension and to explore the technological difficulties. It will be noticed from Table VI that the designation 1 μm refers to minimum lithographic dimension, not to all dimensions. The reason is that even if only one such dimension is needed, one must have a lithographic tool capable of providing it. One can with a poorer tool, using overetching of gate electrodes, for example, achieve 1-μm structures. However, packing densities will be different than obtainable with the proper tool set, and yields and performance will suffer if excessive etching biases are employed, since required tolerance control on such structures is difficult to achieve. Ideally, one desires minimal etching biases in order to achieve scaled tolerances.

Figs. 18 and 19 show the essence of an "n"-channel process sequence in cross section through the channel region. The fabrication sequence involves five mask steps (in this case data sets for driving an electron-beam system). The first mask is used to define alignment marks so that subsequent levels can be overlaid to these to register upper structural levels properly.

Having done this, a pad layer of SiO_2 is grown on the surface of the wafer to protect it from stress damage, and an oxidation-resistant layer of Si_3N_4 is deposited on this oxide pad layer to serve as an oxidation mask. The Si_3N_4 layer is patterned by applying photoresist over it, and writing a pattern on it. For the case in question, a "positive" photoresist was employed, i.e., the photoresist is developed away only where it is written upon by light, or in the present instance by electrons. The photoresist is developed, and a so-called liftoff process (to be discussed) is employed to cover the exposed silicon nitride with a layer of aluminum which is impervious to the etching gas used to etch unprotected Si_3N_4. Once this aluminum layer is in place, the top structure shown in Fig. 18 is delineated by a gas plasma etching process to be discussed below, and the aluminum protective layer is removed. The surface of the isolation or field regions of the structure are ion implanted to establish their threshold, and using the Si_3N_4–SiO_2 structure as a mask, the unprotected regions are oxidized to form interdevice isolation regions known as semi-ROX (semi-recessed oxide) structures. The Si_3N_4–SiO_2 protective structure is

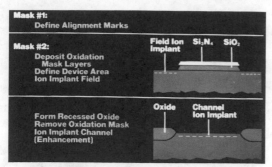

Fig. 18. "n"-channel process sequence for 1-μm devices.

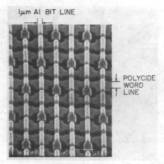

Fig. 20. Polycide–aluminum interconnections.

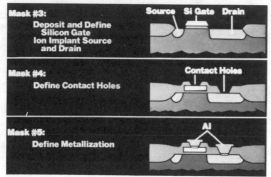

Fig. 19. "n"-channel process sequence for 1-μm devices.

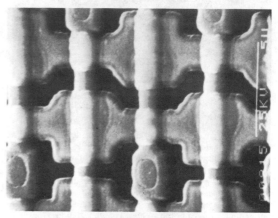

Fig. 21. Polycide–aluminum interconnections.

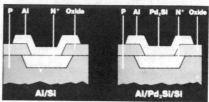

Fig. 22. Barrier metallurgy in contact opening.

then removed and the newly exposed device region, to be, is ion implanted to establish its desired device channel threshold as shown in the bottom structure of Fig. 18.

The next steps involve growth of the gate insulator, deposition of the polysilicon, and delineation of this composite using liftoff lithography again. This results in delineation of the gate region of the device and its critical channel length, Fig. 19. Once formed, this gate region serves as a mask for ion implanting the source and drain regions which are self-aligned to the gate region, Fig. 19, Mask 3. Once this is done, using a combination of oxidation and oxide chemical vapor deposition steps, the entire structure in encased in oxide, and contact holes are delineated using Mask 4. Aluminum is then deposited over the entire wafer and the interconnection and contact patterns are delineated, Mask 5. One such resultant structure viewed from the top where instead of polysilicon, a polycide structure has been used for the gate electrode is shown in Figs. 20 and 21. In Figs. 20 and 21 the more aggressive 1-μm groundrules, referred to, were employed than in the initial study being described.

In making contacts to shallow junctions, a barrier layer must be employed in the contact holes to prevent aluminum from penetrating the junction and shorting out the junction during subsequent annealing cycles. This is shown in Fig. 22. Use of Pd_2Si as a barrier layer is shown in the right-hand structure. It is formed in a rather simple procedure without the use of additional masks as follows. When the contact holes are opened, Pd is deposited on the entire wafer. The Pd reacts with silicon at 200°C to form Pd_2Si wherever it contacts it, but does not react anywhere else. The Pd_2Si is insoluble in

a potassium iodide, iodine solution which dissolves palladium. Unlike the case shown in the left-hand structure of Fig. 22, the presence of Pd_2Si causes Al to penetrate in planar fashion rather than along (111) planes, providing a reasonable degree of junction protection during annealing cycles. Pd_2Si represents a marginal barrier-contact metallurgy even at 1-μm design rules and considerable effort is being expended to evolve more efficient metallurgies. As mentioned, one such metallurgical barrier involves the use of Ti [34] which appears promising up to temperatures as high as 450°C. Another alternative involves the use of W [35].

The technique used for etching of the different structures shown in Figs. 18 and 19 involves either plasma or reactive ion etching (RIE) [36]. The relationship between these techniques and conventional sputtering is shown in Fig. 23. The latter uses a nonreactive gas, while the first two use reactive gases

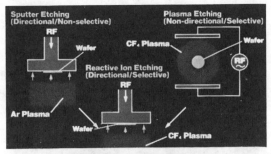

Fig. 23. Gas etching techniques.

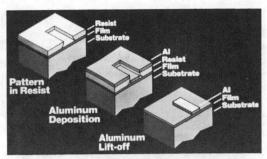

Fig. 26. Pattern transfer and liftoff.

Fig. 24. Linewidth profiles using different etching techniques.

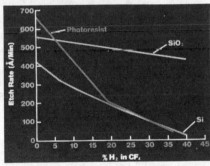

Fig. 25. Selectivity in RIE etching.

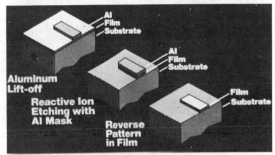

Fig. 27. Reactive ion etching using a pattern transfer mask.

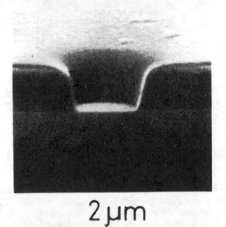

2 μm

Fig. 28. Contact hole in SiO_2 using a controlled profile RIE process.

(such as CF_4) which form volatile reaction products with the material to be etched. The basic differences in profiles obtained by different etching techniques is shown in Fig. 24. An even more sophisticated approach using two driven electrodes in a so-called flexible diode configuration has been reported recently [37]. It combines features of both plasma and RIE etching and enables tailoring of edge profiles over wide ranges.

Plasma-assisted etching techniques with their many advantages have certain problems. It is often difficult to develop selective etching processes as are readily available with wet chemical etching techniques. Fig. 25 shows the results of studies intended to define conditions for selective etching of SiO_2 relative to both photoresist and silicon in a mixture of H_2 and CF_4. Etch rates for Si, SiO_2, and photoresist as a function of percent of H_2 in CF_4 in an RIE system are shown. It is seen that with increasing H_2 concentration, the SiO_2 etch rate changes only slightly while the etch rates of both Si and photoresist decrease dramatically. Much further work is needed in studies of etching selectivity of metals and other materials used in processing. Part of the solutions to selectivity problems lie in the mode of use of the etching tools.

The techniques of pattern transfer and liftoff followed by RIE referred to earlier are depicted in Figs. 26 and 27. Basically these enable one, when required, to employ a positive photo-

resist when a negative photoresist would be more desirable. Liftoff procedures provide extremely good etching biases and tolerances when coupled with reactive ion or plasma etching. Fig. 28 shows a contact hole opened in SiO_2 using a controlled RIE process, while Fig. 29 shows two different profiles obtained in single-crystal silicon etching using pattern transfer and liftoff coupled with RIE.

The processes of oxidation, particularly for the thick field or isolation regions, and ion-implantation activation and damage removal, represent, in current IGFET fabrication processes, the most severe time–temperature processes. Based on the work described in [23], a multiwafer plasma oxidizer

Fig. 29. Single-crystal RIE etched silicon.

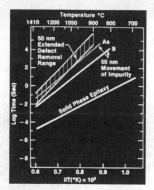

Fig. 30. A multiwafer plasma reactor.

Fig. 31. Relationships between defect removal and impurity motion as a function of time and temperature.

was evolved to enable formation of these field-oxidation regions at temperatures below 800°C, e.g., 500–700°C. Such a reactor is shown in Fig. 30. To make use of this technique in a device configuration like that shown in Fig. 18, the Si_3N_4–SiO_2 mask had to be replaced by MgO.

The ion-implantation damage removal question is at low temperatures or short thermal cycles being addressed using so-called "Short Time Annealing" [38], [39] techniques, STA. These can be carried out in a variety of ways, e.g., using arc, or other high-energy lamps, high-energy resistance heaters, laser, electron, and ion sources. Annealing times range between nanoseconds and few tens of seconds all of which are quite acceptable. At present, there is some question as to whether STA can in fact eliminate all impurity motion during the time required to remove extended defects resulting from the ion-implantation process. This concern is depicted in Fig. 31. In this figure, the lines marked As and B represent the time–temperature behavior for 50 nm of motion of these impurities. For shallow junction devices this is probably an

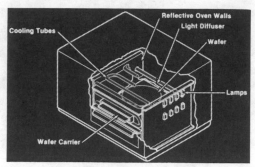

Fig. 32. A short time annealing apparatus.

upper allowable level of impurity motion that can be tolerated during the activation and defect removal process. The band marked extended defect removal represents the time–temperature requirements to remove extended defects of about 50-nm size. It is seen that the times at temperature to achieve this defect removal are greater than the impurity motion time, except at high temperature. Thus the key may be to make use of the different activation energies for the two processes. Alternatively, it may be the case that in short-term annealing processes, temperature gradients across a wafer might be smaller than in conventional furnace heating which could minimize extended defect size. At any rate, one such commercial apparatus involving high-energy output lamps is depicted in Fig. 32. It can handle a single wafer at a time, and is intended to provide a homogeneous thermal environment.

Because it is often necessary to deal with large aspect ratios in scaled structures to alleviate resistance problems, the so-called two-layer resist technologies [40] are most appropriate in lithographic applications. A thick bottom resist layer is used to planarize the surface, and a thinner top layer is employed as an *in situ* mask. The top layer is patterned and once developed serves as mask for the lower layer. This leads to better etch biases and tolerances in thick resist layers than can be generally achieved in single-layer resist approaches.

A version of this two-layer technique is called portable conformable masking (PCM) [41] and its operation is shown in Figs. 33 and 34. The top layer is exposed using electron-beam writing (or optical exposure), and the image is developed forming a top mask. This mask is then subjected to a blanket exposure, Fig. 34, using deep UV wavelengths to expose the underlying layer of thick resist. The top layer does not allow this UV to penetrate to the lower layer, except where the top layer has been patterned, thereby acting as a deep UV mask. Structures of extremely large aspect ratios can be delineated by such a technique, Fig. 35.

One problem associated with electron-beam direct writing deals with the phenomenon of backscattering. This can be seen with reference to Fig. 36. In addition to the primary beam resulting in exposure of the photoresist, a secondary backscattered "beam" exposes or "fogs" areas adjacent to the primary beam (dashed peak). Thus the interior of large structures receive additional spillover doses, while isolated small lines and spaces, and the edges of large structures do not. This requires providing "proximity" dosage corrections (longer exposures) to the beam when edges of large areas, etc., are exposed [42]. The effects are seen in Fig. 37.

Fig. 37(a) shows a structure where proper dosage is applied to develop the resist out of most of the large shape at the

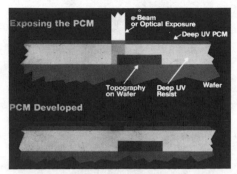

Fig. 33. Portable conformable masking (PCM).

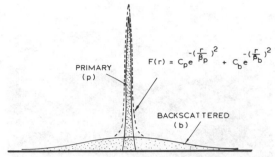

$$F(r) = C_p e^{-(\frac{r}{\beta_p})^2} + C_b e^{-(\frac{r}{\beta_b})^2}$$

Fig. 36. Gaussian proximity function approximation.

Fig. 34. Portable conformable masking (PCM).

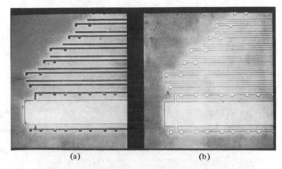

(a)   (b)

Fig. 37. The use of variable doses to clear resist patterns.

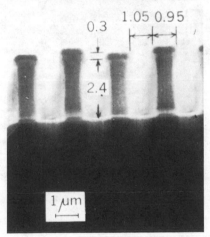

Fig. 35. Aspect ratios in photoresist using PCM.

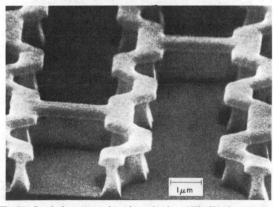

Fig. 38. Proximity corrected two-layer developed liftoff resist patterns.

bottom. It is seen that the resist in the isolated lines does not develop out completely, nor do the edges of the large structure. Fig. 37(b) shows the same pattern when additional electron-beam dosage (proximity correction) is given to these isolated lines, and to the edges of the large structure. In this case, all of the exposed regions clear out at the same time.

Using the exposure techniques described, one is able to evolve complex resist structures useful in liftoff or subetching

applications, such as shown in Fig. 38 (perspective) and Fig. 39 (cross section).

Having employed all of the processing techniques, briefly and somewhat simplistically described, let us now examine the results one can obtain. Fig. 40 shows part of an electron-beam lithographically delineated wafer containing three different part numbers prior to dicing. Fig. 41 shows one of these part numbers or dies, as they are sometimes called, of a microprocessor cross section designed to operate in dynamic mode (right-hand side of the chip), and Fig. 42 shows the same structure designated to operate in static mode. The left-hand

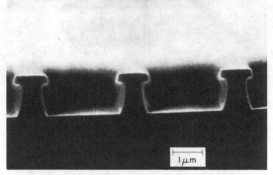

Fig. 39. Cross section of Fig. 38.

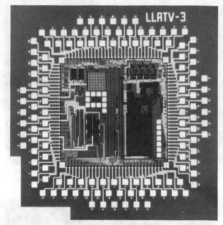

Fig. 41. Enlarged view of Fig. 40 showing dynamic microprocessor part number and ring oscillators.

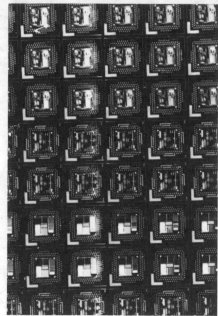

Fig. 40. Electron-beam exposed completed wafer.

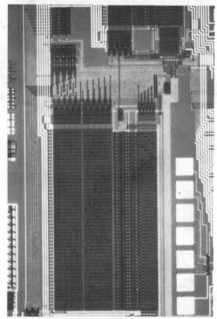

Fig. 42. Enlarged view of Fig. 40 showing static microprocessor part number.

side of the chip, Fig. 41, contains three different types of ring oscillators designed to test the devices under no load (a limiting case, not of practical interest, and often employed to impress an audience), realistic loading levels (the case of greatest practical interest), and heavy loading (to define the worst case situation). The loading referred to is primarily capacitive. The chip size, Fig. 41, is 2 mm on an edge, and including the pad array it is 4 mm on an edge. Fig. 43 shows the long width to channel ratio drivers in the dynamically operated microprocessor version (lower structures), as well as the associated clock generators (upper structures). Fig. 44 shows the Arithmatic Logic Unit (ALU) section of the microprocessor implemented in a Programmable Logic Array design (PLA). Fig. 45 shows a top interconnection view of the PLA showing aluminum interconnections (lighter structures) connecting to contact regions on the polysilicon. Fig. 46 shows a portion of the

unloaded ring oscillator. The 1-μm contacts are evident in this figure.

Finally, Table VII shows measured performance obtained for the different ring oscillators, and the static version of the PLA. Data for the ring oscillators are given for room temperature and liquid-nitrogen temperature operation. The numbers are within the context of realistic designs operating at acceptable power levels of 0.1–0.2 mW/circuit. Even more dramatic performance figures can be obtained with these circuits, but such performance would be at the expense of acceptable power dissipation levels, and would require operating in voltage re-

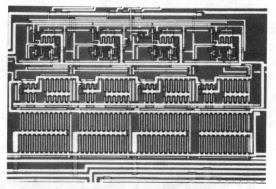

Fig. 43. Clock generators and drivers of Fig. 41.

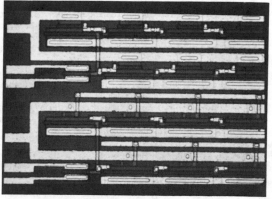

Fig. 46. Enlargement of portion of high-speed ring oscillator of Fig. 41.

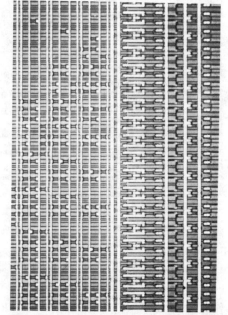

Fig. 44. Enlarged view of ALU of microprocessor of Fig. 41.

TABLE VII
MEASURED PERFORMANCE OF 1-μm FET CIRCUITS

	Delay/Circuit	
	R.T. (23°C)	L.N. (-196°C)
High Speed - No Wiring Load	0.23 ns	0.1 ns
Typical Wiring Load - Custom Layout	1.1 ns	0.46 ns
Heavy Wiring Load - Array Layout	1.7 ns	
	Cycle Time	
Static PLA	13 ns - 21 ns	

gimes in which hot-electron reliability would be degraded. One final point to be made concerns the PLA cycle time range. When wafers are processed, structured dimensions on a given chip generally track, i.e., they fall at some point within the 3σ tolerance range. What is shown are the measured cases for the channel length at 1 μm (13-ns operation) and 1.6 μm (21-ns operation), the 3σ device channel length tolerance range. The observed circuit performance at room temperature is improved by a factor of 2–2.5 by operating at liquid-nitrogen temperature.

Since the described performance is "high end," even though a "low end" technology is employed, it is not inconceivable that the day of a high end computer on a chip will be demonstrated in the 20th century. One of the most formidable engineering obstacles may well be automation of the design cycle, since design costs can become untenable. A second may involve testing of designs. The prime technological challenges, in this author's opinion, may well center on how well we can extend patterning techniques, and perhaps, of equal significance, on how well we can develop the technology of contacts having reproducible contact resistance and stability. The question of contact resistance has not been dwelt upon by us earlier, because it is not clear whether an ever-present problem of contacting small contacts is of fundamental origin, or is simply a reflection of "state of art" fabrication knowledge in 1982. If contact resistivity, for example, lies in the 10^{-6} Ωcm^2 range, then a 1-μm contact will exhibit a limiting resistance of about 100 Ω. A 0.5-μm contact will exhibit a limiting resis-

10 μm

Fig. 45. Metallization pattern of Fig. 41.

tance of 400 Ω. Both of these numbers would impact bipolar performance seriously. If not controlled tightly, they could impact the design in IGFET's also. Together with the previously discussed contact barrier and interconnection metallurgy problems, the overall contact problem poses a formidable challenge to the technologist-materials scientist.

We have indicated that, to a first approximation, extension of current process and engineering technology to 1-μm dimensions appears feasible and offers significant rewards. Extensions to the 0.5-μm level are being explored currently by a number of companies, and plans are in place to demonstrate prototypes at this dimension by the mid 1980's.

ACKNOWLEDGMENT

The author wishes to thank R. H. Dennard, and H. N. Yu of the IBM T.J. Watson Reserach Center and C. M. Osburn of the Microelectronics Center of North Carolina for their many valuable discussions during the preparation of this perspective on the requirements for very large scale integration.

REFERENCES

[1] D. B. Tuckerman and R.F.W. Pease, *IEEE Electron Devices Lett.*, vol. EDL-2, p. 126, 1981.
[2] T. Mano, K. Takeya, T. Watanabe, N. Ieda, K. Kiuchi, E. Arai, T. Ogawa, and K. Hirata, *IEEE J. Solid-State Circuits*, vol. SC-15, p. 865, 1980.
S. Matsue, H. Yamamoto, K. Kobayashi, T. Wada, M. Tameda, T. Okuda, and Y. Inagaki, *IEEE J. Solid-State Circuits*, vol. SC-15, p. 872, 1980.
[3] R. H. Dennard, U.S. Patent 3 387 286, July 4, 1968.
[4] G. Baccarani, M. R. Wordeman, and R. H. Dennard, "Generalized scaling theory and its application to a 1/4 micron MOSFET design," presented at the 40th Annual Device Res. Conf., IEEE, June 21-23, 1982, Colorado State U., Ft. Collins, in *Extended Abstracts*, abstr. IIA-1.
[5] R. H. Dennard, F. H. Gaensslen, H. N. Yu, V. L. Rideout, E. Bassous, and A. R. LeBlanc, *IEEE J. Solid-State Circuits*, vol. SC-9, p. 256, 1974.
[6] A. J. Speth, A. D. Wilson, A. Kern, and T.H.P. Chang, *J. Vac. Sci. Technol.*, vol. 12, p. 1235, 1975.
[7] A. D. Wilson, T.H.P. Chang, and A. Kern, *J. Vac. Sci. Technol.*, vol. 12, p. 1240, 1975.
[8] T.H.P. Chang, A. D. Wilson, A. J. Speth, and C. H. Ting, in *Proc. VII Int. Conf. on Electron and Ion Beam Sci. Technol.* (Washington, DC, May 1976), R. Bakish, Ed. Princeton, NJ: The Electrochem. Soc., p. 392.
[9] A. D. Wilson, A. Kern, A. J. Speth, A. M. Patlach, P. R. Jaskar, T. W. Studwell, and W. L. Keller in *Proc. VII Int. Conf. on Electron and Ion Beam Sci. Technol.* (Washington, DC, May 1976), R. Bakish, Ed. Princeton, NJ: The Electrochem. Soc., p. 361.
[10] W. D. Grobman, H. E. Luhn, T. P. Donohue, A. J. Speth, A. Wilson, M. Hatzakis, and T.H.P. Chang, *IEEE J. Solid-State Circuits*, vol. SC-14, p. 275, 1979.
[11] D. D. Tang, T. H. Ning, R. D. Isaac, G. C. Feth, S. Wiedmann, and H. N. Yu, *IEEE Trans. Electron. Devices*, vol. ED-27, p. 1379, 1980.
[12] H. H. Berger and S. K. Wiedmann, *IEEE J. Solid-State Circuits*, vol. SC-7, p. 340, 1972.
[13] K. Hart and A. Slob, *IEEE J. Solid-State Circuits*, vol. SC-7, p. 346, 1972.
[14] B. L. Crowder and S. Zirinsky, *IEEE J. Solid-State Circuits*, vol. SC-14, p. 291, 1979.
[15] M. Y. Tsai, H. H. Chao, L. M. Ephrath, B. L. Crowder, A. Cramer, R. S. Bennett, C. J. Lucchese, and M. R. Wordeman, in *Semiconductor Silicon 1981 (Electrochem. Soc. Proc.)*, vol. 81-5, p. 573.
[16] S. P. Murarka, M. Read, C. Doherty, and D. Fraser, *J. Electro-*

[17] chem. Soc., vol. 129, p. 293, 1982.
F. M. d'Heurle, in *Proc. 1st Int. Symp. on Very Large Scale Integration Science and Technology* (Electrochem. Soc., Oct. 17-22, 1982, Detroit, MI).
[18] F. M. d'Heurle, *Encyclopedia of Chemical Technology*, vol. 8, 3rd ed. New York: Wiley, 1979, p. 763.
[19] F. d'Heurle and P. Ho, in *Thin Films: Interdiffusion and Reactions*, J. Mayer, J. Poate, and K. Tu, Eds. New York: Wiley, 1978, p. 243.
[20] G. J. Hu, M. R. Pinto, and S. Kordic, presented at the 40th Annual Device Research Conf., Colorado State U., Ft. Collins, June 21-23, 1982, paper VA-5.
[21] *Electronics*, Nov. 17, 1981, p. 106.
J. Z. Chen. W. B. Chin, T. S. Jen, and J. Hutt, *IBM J. Res. Develop.*, vol. 25, p. 142, 1981.
[22] D. L. Critchlow, R. H. Dennard, and S. E. Schuster, *IBM J. Res. Develop.*, vol. 17, p. 430, 1973.
[23] A. K. Ray and A. Reisman, *J. Electrochem. Soc.*, vol. 128, pp. 2460, 2466, 2424, 1981.
[24] F. H. Gaensslen, V. L. Rideout, E. J. Walker, and J. J. Walker, *IEEE Trans. Electron Devices*, vol. ED-24 p. 218, 1977.
[25] T. H. Ning, P. W. Cook, R. H. Dennard, C. M. Osburn, S. E. Schuster, and H. N. Yu, *IEEE J. Solid-State Circuits*, vol. SC-14, p. 268, 1979.
[26] J. M. Aitken and D. R. Young, *J. Appl. Phys.*, vol. 47, p. 1196, 1976.
[27] B. E. Deal, *IEEE Trans. Electron Devices*, vol. Ed-27, p. 606, 1980.
[28] A. Reisman, J. M. Aitken, A. K. Ray, M. Berkenblit, C. J. Merz, and R. P. Havreluk, *J. Electrochem. Soc.*, vol. 128, p. 1616, 1981.
A. Reisman and C. J. Merz, *J. Electrochem. Soc.*, vol. 130, June 1983, to be published.
[29] T. C. May and M. H. Woods, in *16th Annual Proc. Reliability Physics 1978*, IEEE Cat. No 78 CH1294-8PHY, p. 333, 1978.
——, *IEEE Trans. Electron. Devices*, vol. Ed-26, p. 3, 1979.
T. C. May, *IEEE Trans. Components, Hybrids Manuf. Technol.*, vol. CHMT-2, p. 377, 1979.
J. R. Ziegler and W. A. Lanford, *Science*, vol. 206, p. 776, 1979.
D. P. Bouldin, *J. Elect. Mat.*, vol. 10, p. 747, 1981.
[30] C. M. Osburn and E. Bassous, *J. Electrochem. Soc.*, vol. 122, p. 89, 1975.
[31] T. Shibata, K. Hieda, M. Sato, M. Konaka, R.L.M. Dang, and H. Iizuka, in *IEDM Tech. Dig.*, p. 647, 1981.
[32] C. M. Osburn, C. Y. Ting, M. Y. Tsai, and S. Roberts, in *Proc. 1st Int. Symp. on Very Large Scale Integration Science and Technology* (Electrochem. Soc., Oct. 17-22, 1982, Detroit, MI).
[33] W. R. Hunter, L. M. Ephrath, W. Grobman, C. M. Osburn, B. L. Crowder, A. Cramer, and H. E. Luhn, *IEEE J. Solid-State Circuits*, vol. SC-14, p. 275, 1979.
[34] C. Y. Ting and B. L. Crowder, "Electrical properties of Al/Ti contact metallurgy for VLSI application," *J. Electrochem. Soc.*, in print.
[35] *Semicond. Int.*, vol. 7, p. 16, 1982.
[36] R. G. Frieser and C. J. Mogab, Eds., *Plasma Processing, (Electrochem. Soc. Proc.)*, vol. 81-1.
[37] L. M Ephrath and R. S. Bennett, in *Proc. 1st Int. Symp. on Very Large Scale Integration Science and Technology* (Electrochem. Soc., Oct. 17-22, 1982, Detroit MI).
[38] T. O. Sedgwick, in *Proc. 1st Int. Symp. on Very Large Scale Integration Science and Technology*, Electrochem. Soc., Detroit, MI, Oct. 17-22, 1982, in press.
[39] S. Shastas and A. Gat, Paper B-2 presented at the Electronic Materials Conf., June 23-25, 1982, Colorado State Univ., Fort Collins, CO.
[40] M. Hatzakis, *J. Vac. Sci. Technol.*, vol. 16, p. 1984, 1979.
[41] B. J. Lin, *J. Soc. Photo-Optical Instrum. Eng.*, vol. 174, p. 114, 1979.
B. J. Lin and T.H.P. Chang, *J. Vac. Sci. Technol.*, vol. 16, p. 1669, 1979.
B. J. Lin, *J. Electrochem. Soc.*, vol. 127 p. 202, 1980.
[42] M. Parikh, *J. Vac. Sci. Technol.*, vol. 15, p. 931, 1978.
W. D. Grobman, A. J. Speth, and T.H.P. Chang, in *Electron and Ion Beam Science and Technology, 1981*, vol. 80-6. R. Bakish, Ed. The Electrochemical Society, Pennington, NJ, 08534, p. 314.

VLSI Design Automation: An Introduction

MICHAEL FEUER, MEMBER, IEEE

Invited Paper

Abstract—This paper is a brief introduction to the automation of the design of very-large-scale integrated circuits (VLSI). The field of design automation has grown so large in the last twenty years that a complete treatment would require an encyclopedia. What follows, therefore, is only a sketch of the history, state of the art, and current key problems of the automation of VLSI design.

HISTORY

THE HISTORY of anything to do with VLSI is almost a contradiction in terms. Until recently, VLSI had always been thought of in the future tense. Integrated circuits (IC's), medium-scale integration (MSI), and large-scale integration (LSI) are historical terms, but not VLSI. Only with the advent of microprocessors with some half-million transistors on a chip has there been a grudging acceptance that VLSI may indeed have arrived. These acronymic labels are always applied after the fact, but VLSI was resisted longer than most. Extrapolating from the fact that early IC's contained several logic gates, MSI tens, and LSI hundreds, we might expect VLSI circuits to contain thousands of gates. By the same reasoning, today's 32-bit microprocessors would be examples of ULSI (the U for ultra). Maybe we are running out of acronyms and need to conserve. In any case, for this article, a chip with several thousand logic gates or more qualifies as a VLSI chip.

During the 1950's, Texas Instruments, Fairchild Semiconductor, and others developed the photolithographic process for the fabrication of transistors on crystalline silicon. The steps involved in the design of early IC's are still qualitatively the same today. The first step is the definition and optimization of the process by which the devices and interconnections are to be fabricated. The second is the electrical characterization of the circuit elements. These two steps together are sometimes known as technology definition. Third, the user of the technology generates a design (circuit or logic schematic) to be implemented. Fourth, this logical design is reduced to a series of geometric patterns through which materials are to be added or subtracted in the fabrication of the circuit. Finally, a set of test input signal patterns and responses is generated to detect fabrication defects. Testing is an integral feature of IC manufacture because a significant percentage of chips come off the line with at least one defect. These defects are detected by applying the test patterns to the chip inputs and comparing the output signals to those expected. Defective chips are discarded.

In the 1960's, these five steps were largely manual. Process parameters, such as diffusion temperatures, times, and pressures, and metal line widths and spacings were worked out

Manuscript received July 27, 1982; revised November 18, 1982.
The author is with California Automated Design, Inc., Santa Clara, CA 95051.

primarily through trial and error. Yields and electrical properties of the resulting devices were monitored. The process was characterized by a set of electrical and physical design rules for the user of the technology. For digital circuits, the switching characteristics were boiled down to rising and falling delays, fan-out rules, and the like. Physical design rules prescribed widths, spacings, and overlaps required to achieve acceptable yields.

The engineer–user would supply a circuit or logic schematic sketched on a piece of (yellow) paper. The correctness of the circuit could be verified by implementing the same circuit in discrete components ("breadboarding"). An expert layout designer then drew the mask patterns necessary to implement the circuit. The drawings were transferred to a red plastic material called rubylith which was cut away according to the drawing. This step was verified by a careful, independent visual inspection ("eyeballing"). The rubylith pattern was optically reduced to form photolithographic masks.

Testing was a manufacturing function. For small circuits, exhaustive functional testing was possible and ac characteristics could be measured.

As time progressed, the number of devices per chip started to double every year (Moore's law, [1]). This increased mask complexity, and in the early 1970's the rubylith patterns began to outgrow the space on laboratory floors. By the late 1960's this method began to give way to numerically controlled optical pattern generating machines. These required digitally encoded geometric patterns, and the layouts were transferred to data tapes by tracing over them with electromechanical digitizers. With the patterns now accessible to computer processing, the visual inspection could be enhanced with design rule checking (DRC) programs which detected shorts and spacing violations. Another advantage was that corrections to the drawing could be made much more easily than to the rubylith cutouts.

The next step was to display the patterns on a CRT screen, and interactive graphic layout was born—an activity almost synonymous with computer-aided design (CAD) for many years. Commercial turnkey graphics systems began to appear in the early 1970's, although large companies developed in-house systems earlier [2]. The power of interactive graphics was most evident for repetitive patterns such as memory arrays or gate arrays, where a set of geometric data called a cell could be replicated thousands of times in different positions and orientations on the array without having to be redrawn.

As the density of IC's increased, the need for circuit simulation programs became critical. Discrete circuits could be probed and monitored at all nodes, but IC's were inaccessible inside the chip. The only way to tell what they were doing internally was through circuit simulation and through effects

Reprinted from *Proc. IEEE*, vol. 71, pp. 5–9, Jan. 1983.

19

accessible at output pins. A series of programs was developed in the decade from the mid-1960's to the mid-1970's: CIRCAL, SCEPTRE, ECAP, ASTAP, SPICE, and others [3]. A by-product of circuit simulation was the availability of the circuit schematic in machine readable form. This network information was entered on punched cards, then through alphanumeric terminals, and lately as drawings on interactive graphics equipment. The network information made possible not only simulation, but also automatic verification that the layout interconnections indeed matched those of the input network.

Because it was impossible to modify a chip to correct a design error, it became important to verify the correctness of the design prior to releasing the chip to manufacturing. Since the simulation of the full analog behavior of large digital circuits became prohibitively expensive, logic simulation with discrete Boolean values became the dominant software verification tool. Switching-level or gate-level simulators evolved through a series of stages ([4] and [5]) until event-driven simulators capable of handling unique delays for several thousand logic blocks became standard tools.

The automation of the layout function began with techniques borrowed from printed circuit board design. Routing algorithms based on work by Lee [6] and Moore [7] were available for finding paths for metal interconnections between pins of logic functions on the chip. A distinction can be made between this sort of automatic design activity and the verification mentioned above: one is synthesis and the other analysis. To facilitate layout, certain constrained design styles such as gate arrays and standard cell arrays were developed in the late 1960's. These led to the invention of the channel router of Hashimoto and Stevens [8], an algorithm unique to IC's. Over the years, routing has become one of the richest areas in design automation in terms of available techniques, and algorithms have been developed to handle the interconnection problem in almost all conceivable situations.

The regularity of standard cells and gate arrays also facilitated the development of automatic placement algorithms of very high quality [9]. The standardization of the size and shape of the units of logic made the placement task more tractable than that of modules on printed circuit boards. Automatic placement and routing together formed a complete automatic layout system [10], [11].

The gate array, or masterslice, was recognized by the systems manufacturers, notably IBM, as a design style which reduced design time while still providing reasonable silicon area utilization compared to free-form layout. It became very important to understand how much routing space was required on a gate array to ensure the automatic layout of almost all designs using the array. Too much routing space reduced the gate count, while too little led to low utilization of available gates. This need led to theoretical work on routing space estimation which found substantial usage and payoff [12].

For designs consisting of large functional units of different internal structure, tools were developed for the automatic generation of PLA macros, register stacks, memory macros, and bit sliced data flow macros [13].

Test generation also soon outgrew the capabilities of manufacturing organizations. Exhaustive tests based on the input–output specifications of the circuit require an astronomical amount of time even for moderately large IC's. An exhaustive test requires that all possible input patterns be applied for each internal state of the circuit. For a static (dc) test this number is two raised to the number of primary inputs times two raised to the number of internal latches. Even for an early microprocessor, the Intel 8080, an exhaustive test set would contain over 10^{32} patterns; at 1 μs per input pattern, the test time would be more than 10^{20} years!

One solution was to save the simulation patterns used to verify the logic design and to apply them during test. Unfortunately, this functional testing did not provide a high level of confidence that other valid input patterns would not uncover defects missed by the test. To estimate this risk, researchers studied the circuit structure and classified the likely local faults. One model, appealing because of its mathematical tractability if nothing else, was the single-stuck fault model. With a fault dictionary it was possible to include fault grading into simulation to compute the number of faults which would be uncovered by a set of patterns. The designer could also see which faults would have been missed and could add more patterns to find them. With the single-stuck fault model, test patterns could be automatically generated for combinatorial unit logic using methods such as Roth's celebrated D-algorithm [14].

Extensions of automatic test pattern generation algorithms to sequential circuits met with only limited success up to about 5000 equivalent gates, and it became obvious that the test pattern generators would need more assistance from the logic designers. At least in the case of the large systems manufacturers, special circuitry was added to the chips to increase the ease of generating and applying tests. The best known of these is IBM's Level Sensitive Scan Design (LSSD) [15]. Today testability is recognized as one of the key responsibilities of the logic designer. An untestable design, even if otherwise correct, is worthless.

STATE OF THE ART

The status of VLSI design automation is particularly difficult to assess because so much of it is carried on inside large electronics companies on a proprietary basis. Most of these activities are reported in the literature, but, since the systems themselves remain inaccessible, others are forced to develop their own tools or to turn either to university sources or to the relatively small vendor design automation industry. This makes for a very uneven state of the art.

VLSI design practices vary from the fully integrated highly automatic gate array design systems of the large systems manufacturers to the computer-assisted largely manual methodologies of the designers of high-density custom MOS microprocessors. The following is a composite state-of-the-art design system:

Hardware

A design automation facility usually consists of a family of interactive terminals attached to each other and to a host mainframe computer by a communications network. Alphanumeric terminals are sufficient for messages, status reporting, and job control. A low-cost graphics terminal for logic entry is desirable in each engineer's office. For layout, a high-function color system is most efficient. The advent of inexpensive VLSI memories and microprocessors is revolutionizing the interactive graphics business. The trend has been to supply more and more processing power and memory at the terminals or work stations. The mainframe computer is reserved for long-running jobs such as simulation, test pattern generation, or design rule checking and for maintenance of the central data base. A high-speed plotter is useful for displaying the finished artwork.

Control and Release System

This is software to track design status, to coordinate the contributions of many designers, to control engineering changes and other levels of design, to ensure that updates do not invalidate previous verification steps, and to prepare data in standard form for manufacturing. Data integrity is the key to success in VLSI design. Not only is the number of devices per design staggering, but the design automation process itself produces volumes of intermediate data which must be controlled.

Multimode Hierarchical Data Base

This is not a data base in the usual sense of small interactive transactions. The data needed for automatic processing are rather large specially organized files. These files are related to each other in at least three ways. The first was already mentioned: they may describe different versions or levels of the same thing. The second is that they may describe a different aspect or mode of the same entity. Thus a shifter can have a symbolic form for documentation, a behavioral simulation model, another model for test pattern generation, an outline shape for floor planning purposes, a symbolic track description for automatic routing, detailed polygon mask shapes, and "fractured" rectangle shapes for pattern generation. The data base must maintain consistency among these data modes. These modes contribute to the volume of intermediate data mentioned earlier. The third relationship is hierarchy. The same shifter behavioral model can have an expansion to behavioral models of interconnected latches, which, in turn, can be expanded to simulation models of unit logic elements and, finally, to individual transistors. The associated shapes will display a similar hierarchical structure. In a large systems environment, the hierarchy will extend to all packaging levels as well as the chip. The data base must allow for this multiple nesting of design entities. The trend toward relational data base organization (e.g., Mentor Graphics, Portland, OR) also deserves mention. The advantages claimed are simplicity of use and ease of reorganization for future enhancements without invalidating existing programs. The traditional disadvantage of poor performance seems to be yielding to improved software and hardware techniques.

Unified Interactive User Interface

Any large design system must incorporate tools from various sources. It is important, however, that the user be presented with a consistent, well-designed view of the system. Nomenclature, menu layout, message style, and job submission commands should be consistent. The Bell Laboratories Designer's Workbench is an example of such a system [16]. Redundant data entry should be minimized. Errors, especially simple syntactic errors, should be trapped by the system in real time. Even better is a system to guide the user by presenting only options which cannot produce trivial errors.

Automated Verification

With VLSI this is the key function which a design automation system performs—the avoidance of errors. The beginning of the design process currently is the specification of external system behavior. The verification of system specifications is accomplished through design reviews, emulation on existing hardware, and simulation using general-purpose or specially written simulation systems. The state of the art here is understandably rather uneven. The next phase is the design of the system in terms of functional components. For computer systems, these might be ALU's, PLA's, registers, and busses. The verification of this design is usually done using simulators which contain behavioral models for these functional components. The results are examined for consistency with the system specifications. This comparison is typically not automatic because of the lack of precision of the usual specifications. At this point, the designer should also have a plan for partitioning and packaging the system. On single-chip systems, this is the so-called floor plan. Tools are under development to estimate the shape, area, power consumption, pin requirements, and routability of the partitioned subfunctions, but the verification of the feasibility of a partition or floor plan still depends largely on human judgement. The ensuing refinement steps of detailed logic design can all be verified automatically against the next higher level of design. Static verification of logical equivalence and static timing analysis can take the place of simulation. Where simulation is desired, a mixed-mode simulator capable of combining behavioral, unit logic and possibly switch level, and analog circuit level models is ideal.

Layout verification consists of a comparison with the logic and a check of internal consistency. In a hierarchical system, each level of the layout hierarchy can be checked for spacing violations with the boundaries specified at the next higher level. However, at the lowest levels of design, the verification that a given mask geometry will produce the desired analog devices, and that these, in turn, will perform the desired digital functions is only partly automated today. The usual practice is to limit the design to a specified library of basic structures, to analyze these exhaustively using device analysis and circuit simulation programs, and to generate the appropriate digital models.

Automated Design

Modern design automation systems provide powerful tools for the synthesis of VLSI circuits. Logic entry is necessarily an interactive task. It is supported by intelligent graphic engineering workstations. The automatic generation of detailed unit logic from register transfer logic has met with practical success. PLA minimization programs are in common use. Layout is either computer assisted on high-function color graphic workstations for free-form designs, or highly automated for more constrained design styles such as PLA's, gate arrays, standard cell arrays, and even standard floor plan chips. There is now a trend to mix these design styles on single chips, using automatic generators to produce customized PLA, register, RAM, ROM, and random-control logic macros [13]. Test pattern generation is another sophisticated synthesis problem. The most advanced methodologies use special design rules and additional hardware to subdivide the circuitry into manageable combinatorial sections, or to condense the results of long test sequences, or even to administer pseudo-random test patterns on the chip itself.

Such a composite system does not exist, of course, but each of its components does. Clearly, the development of a state-of-the-art automation capability for fast turnaround VLSI design is a very ambitious undertaking indeed.

PROBLEMS FOR THE FUTURE

Fortunately, there are still problems, or, rather, opportunities for creative work. How does one manage the complexity of VLSI design? What happens when computer runs exceed weeks? When tester times exceed hours?

21

The complexity of VLSI designs has grown to the extent that there are substantial doubts about the designers' ability to keep up with process capability. The implication is that future chips will be designed inefficiently in terms of silicon utilization or performance because of lack of time and design resources. The phrase "silicon is cheap" has always had a certain irony about it, but we may actually be coming to the point that silicon utilization is less important than design time.

While the problems are serious, they are not insurmountable. Clearly some very spectacular chips are being designed. 32-bit microprocessors such as the Intel iapx432, the Bell Laboratories BELMAC, and Hewlett-Packard's 32-bit microprocessor chip set [17] are all near the limit of fabrication technology. There is no reason to expect the next generation of microprocessors to leave any unused silicon either. Even so, these projects are costly (50-100 person-years) and therefore rare. If VLSI were as simple to deal with as modules on wire-wrap boards, many more products would appear.

The problem of handling complexity has come up in other disciplines, notably software engineering, and a variety of promising techniques have been proposed. Prof. C. Sequin has a very interesting discussion of this subject elsewhere in this issue. One technique for dealing with complexity has been to use regular structures such as PLA's rather than try to squeeze out every square micrometer through local optimization. This approach, advocated by C. Mead of Caltech [18], has broad implications. How does one obtain a library of useful regular structures or macros to include in one's VLSI design? To be useful to someone other than the designer, a macro must be general, well documented, and configurable to other technology ground rules and to other system environments. Such macros would necessarily be encoded primarily as programs and only secondarily as pictures. This again is a feature of the Caltech approach. To be useful, each of these macro generation programs should be accompanied by a simulation model as well. All this implies a level of interface standardization which has yet to be achieved. Thus one challenge is the invention and development of commercially available VLSI macro generators and the creation of an environment to facilitate their transfer.

A closely related challenge has to do with interactive graphics. We need to develop graphic techniques for specifying not only pictures, but families of pictures with given relationships among their components. Procedural design or algorithmic macro generation is inherently a problem of expressing shapes and their relationships, yet we must still use programming languages which are patterned on speech, rather than use the seemingly more natural medium of interactive graphics. Why can these programs not be specified by diagrams which express the number of repetitions of a shape in two dimensions, the required clearances and overlaps of related shapes, the fact that some can be extended as necessary, and so on? We can generate families of pictures from programs; how can we generate programs from pictures?

Reusing standard macros is one way to deal with design complexity. Another is to automate the design process so that the designer deals only with high-level entities and the machine handles all the details of converting and optimizing the design. In layout, as was previously mentioned, there are automatic design algorithms for gate arrays and standard cells. For such chips the time spent in logic design far exceeds the time spent in layout. There is a need for automated techniques for converting high-level functional descriptions to lower level logic

suitable for implementation. This logic synthesis task has always been thought of as impractical for large networks, but recent progress in optimization by local transforms [19] holds out the promise of a solution. The generation of functional chips from high-level functional specifications, whether for gate arrays with unit logic or for standard floor-plan MOS microprocessors, would be a true "silicon compiler" and a worthwhile goal.

The issue of simulation and test pattern generation run times is still a very real one. Despite the advances in static verification and other proofs of correctness, there is no better way to verify the initial specifications of a system than through real-time emulation or simulation. The designer often does not understand all the capabilities of a structure which he creates. A period of "playing around" with the design is required. Simulations of VLSI systems running even trivial test programs are almost prohibitively expensive. A potential solution is the hardware simulation engine—a large array of processors and memories tied together with a high-speed communications switching network. It can handle the number-crunching simulation operation at speeds thousands of times greater than a standard serial computer. These engines might have been included earlier in this article as part of the state of the art, but there are still too few of them in use, and their effectiveness in a production environment is undocumented. The simulation problem remains a major challenge.

Test pattern generation speed can also be significantly enhanced by using the same or similar engines. However, there is also the problem of applying the tests in fabrication. This is still a sequential process, carried out by expensive test equipment. One way to cut down both test pattern generation time and testing expense is to have the VLSI chip carry its own built-in tester. While self-test and other hardware-assisted testing techniques impose penalties on silicon utilization, the tradeoff appears favorable. In any case, if there are any fears about designers' ability to use everything the process people can provide, this added testing requirement should allay them.

The most exciting challenge of VLSI design is in the area of applications. There is enough capability today, both in technology and in design techniques, to create radically new electronic systems. In the 1950's computer experts were fond of speculating on the structure of the brain, on robots, and on automatic language translation. Then the IC revolution occurred, and most practical people turned to remapping Von Neumann's computer from one technology to the next.

Some of these questions are being revisited today. Indeed, the logic simulation engine discussed earlier is an example of a step in this direction. It uses the power of many concurrent processors to model the concurrent events in a digital system. The recognition and translation of speech are also composed of many inherently concurrent activities. The efficient searching of a data base is another example of inherently concurrent processing.

The technology exists to produce vast arrays of processing and memory elements. What is not clear is how to have them communicate with each other. The interconnect capability of integrated circuits is hopelessly outclassed by that of biological systems. The easiest arrays to build have interconnections only among nearest neighbors. When it is necessary for each processor to be able to communicate with any other, as it is in the logic simulation engine, the communication network quickly becomes a bottleneck.

Design automation can only play a supporting role in the

process of creating these new concurrent systems. Improvements in logic description languages and in simulation techniques will help researchers to study the properties of alternate architectures. On the other hand, these unconventional new VLSI systems will have profound effects on design automation techniques. Programming general-purpose multiprocessor computer systems will require new techniques, but the resulting code should execute thousands of times faster than on uniprocessors. Compilers may begin to understand subsets of natural language. Spoken input and output may develop into an important medium of communication between man and machine.

Design automation will be transformed by the VLSI products which it will have helped create.

ACKNOWLEDGMENT

The author would like to acknowledge the valuable advice and help of J. Werner of VLSI Design, B. Lee of Calma Co., and, especially, of Dr. R. Russo of IBM Corp.

REFERENCES

[1] R. N. Noyce, "Microelectronics," *Sci. Amer.*, vol. 237, no. 3, p. 65, Sept. 1977.
[2] J. S. Koford, P. R. Strickland, G. A. Sporzynski, and E. M. Hubacher, "Using a graphic data processing system to design artwork for manufacturing hybrid integrated circuits," in *Proc. Fall Computer Conf.*, pp. 229–246, 1966.
[3] W. M. van Cleemput, *Computer Aided Design of Digital Systems—A Bibliography*. Woodland Hills, CA: Computer Sci. Press, 1976, pp. 231–236.
[4] R. B. Walford, "The LAMP system," in *Proc. Workshop on Fault Detection and Diagnosis in Digital Circuits and Systems* (Lehigh Univ., Bethlehem, PA, Dec. 1970), p. 10.
[5] P. N. Agnew and M. Kelly, "The VMS algorithm," Tech. Rep.
TR01.1338, IBM System Products Div. Lab., Endicott, NY, 1970.
[6] C. Y. Lee, "An algorithm for path connections and its applications," *IRE Trans. Electron. Comput.*, vol. EC-10, pp. 346–365, Sept. 1961.
[7] E. F. Moore, "Shortest path through a maze," in *Annals of the Computation Laboratory of Harvard University*. Cambridge, MA: Harvard Univ. Press, vol. 30, pp. 285–292, 1959.
[8] A. Hashimoto and J. Stevens, "Wire routing by optimizing channel assignment within large apertures," in *Proc. 8th Design Automation Conf.* (Atlantic City, NJ, June 1971), pp. 155–169.
[9] M. Hanan and J. M. Kurtzberg, "Placement techniques," in *Design Automation of Digital Systems*, M. A. Breuer, Ed. Englewood Cliffs, NJ: Prentice-Hall, 1972, pp. 213–282.
[10] K. H. Khokhani and A. M. Patel, "The chip layout problem: A placement procedure for LSI," in *Proc. 14th Annual Design Automation Conf.* (New Orleans, LA, 1977), pp. 291–297.
[11] K. A. Chen, M. Feuer, K. H. Khokhani, N. Nan, and S. Schmidt, "The chip layout problem: An automatic wiring procedure," in *Proc. 14th Annual Design Automation Conf.* (New Orleans, LA, 1977), pp. 298–302.
[12] W. R. Heller, W. F. Mikhail, and W. E. Donath, "Prediction of wiring space requirements for LSI," in *Proc. 14th Annual Design Automation Conf.* (New Orleans, LA, 1977), pp. 32–42.
[13] R. Donze, J. Sanders, M. Jenkins, and G. Sporzynski, "PHILO—A VLSI design system," in *Proc. 19th Design Automation Conf.* (Las Vegas, NV, June 1982), pp. 163–169.
[14] J. P. Roth, "Diagnosis of automata failures: A calculus and a method," *IBM J. Res. Develop.*, vol. 10, pp. 278–291, July 1966.
[15] E. B. Eichelberger and T. W. Williams, "A logic design structure for LSI testability," in *Proc. 14th Design Automation Conf.* (New Orleans, LA, June 1977), pp. 462–468.
[16] L. A. O'Neill *et al.*, "Designer's workbench—Efficient and economical design aids," in *Proc. 16th Design Automation Conf.* (June 1979), pp. 185–199.
[17] J. W. Bayers *et al.*, in *ISSCC Dig. Tech. Papers*, pp. 128–129, Feb. 1982.
[18] C. Mead and L. Conway, *Introduction to VLSI Systems*. Reading, MA: Addison-Wesley, 1980.
[19] J. A. Darringer, W. H. Joyner, L. Berman, and L. Trevillyan, "Logic synthesis through local transformations," *IBM J. Res. Develop.*, vol. 25, no. 4, pp. 272–279, July 1981.

Part II
Lithography

LITHOGRAPHY plays a central role in the advance towards and below 1 μm minimum dimensions. The next four papers describe the tools and processes of micron lithography. The first of these is by D. R. Herriott, and gives an historically oriented review of the evolution and characteristics of lithography tools using light, electrons, X-rays, and ions as the resist exposure medium. This history starts with rubylith masters patterned by hand, progresses through a series of successively more acute optical systems which use masks produced automatically by pattern generators (at first optical, and then using electron beams), and then leads through the present and into the future with UV optics, direct-write electron beam, X-ray, and ion-beam techniques.

This succession of tools, driven by the changing nature of imaging as dimensions shrink, requires a succession of resist advances which accommodate several requirements: the changing nature of the exposing radiation, smaller dimensions, higher aspect ratio, and new process resistance requirements. This resist evolution is surveyed in an overview by M. Hatzakis, which gives a historical description of changing resist technology as time, circuit smallness, and semiconductor fabrication processes evolve.

One of the keys to lithography is pattern generation. As was briefly described in Herriott's paper, electron-beam systems play a central role in all present or future high-resolution circuit fabrication. These systems either make the masks which are then imaged by one set of lithography approaches, or they represent a system which writes directly in resist on the product wafer. The former role is especially appropriate when the cost of mask making is amortized over large product volume (e.g., memory), while the latter approach is especially used where flexibility and low volume coexist (i.e., personalization or exploratory device fabrication). In all cases, scanning electron-beam systems must be carefully engineered to satisfy the requirements of system speed, high resolution, pattern flexibility, high accuracy, level to level registration precision, and large workpiece size which permit large numbers of submicrometer aligned circuit images to be written. This difficult electron-beam tool engineering task is described in a paper by A. D. Wilson, who describes in detail the set of approaches and tradeoffs which are used in developing a high-resolution high-accuracy scanning electron-beam system.

Finally, the lithography part of this book closes with two chapters on X-ray lithography. The first is a short review of alternative approaches in X-ray lithography by W. D. Grobman. Then we include a paper by B. B. Triplett and R. F. Hollman, describing the application of X-ray lithography to VLSI device fabrication. The finished devices previously reported by the authors and their colleagues, using X-ray lithography, are bubble-memory chips, but in this paper the emphasis is the application of X-ray lithography to multilevel, semiconductor circuit production. The authors concentrate on resist and conventional source technologies, and also on mask technology. For the latter subject, they review the stability of masks produced by various approaches and the relation of these specifications to aligned device production.

The Development of Device Lithography

DONALD R. HERRIOTT, SENIOR MEMBER, IEEE

Invited Paper

Abstract—Lithography has been the principal pacing element in the development of complex integrated circuits. Although major programs in electron-beam lithography and X-ray lithography have developed new systems with smaller feature capability, the optical systems remain the only candidates for large-volume device production. Scanning and step-and-repeat optical systems have been developed for the next generation of devices with 1-μm features. Electron beams are used for mask fabrication and direct exposure of special devices of exceptional value or for prototypes. X-ray and ion systems are being developed for future devices.

INTRODUCTION

DEVICE LITHOGRAPHY has been the principal pacing element in the growth of very large scale integrated circuits. In spite of a tremendous development effort, the resolution, registration between levels, and defect density of the lithography have limited the device complexity. This is not to say that the lithography has not improved. The complexity of integrated circuits has almost doubled every year since the early 1960's when they were invented, so that 500 000 active components is a reasonable goal for new devices today. There is a major economic value in increased scale of integration in eliminating interconnection cost, reducing system device cost, and increasing system reliability. During the past ten years, integrated electronics systems cost has been reduced by one hundred and the reliability increased by the same factor for a given function.

This paper presents a general review of the mainstream of lithographic system developments of integrated circuit patterning. It is neither detailed nor complete but will give a general background for the papers that follow in this issue.

INTEGRATED CIRCUITS

Integrated circuits grew out of the previous transistor technology when a means of isolating two or more transistors on a single substrate of silicon, and interconnecting them to perform a more complex function, was developed. The planar geometry, with layers on a flat silicon surface, permits the use of device lithography to pattern the successive layers that make up the three-dimensional structure. A layer of insulator, conductor, or mask material to control the diffusion of impurities into the silicon is deposited on the surface of the wafer and covered with a radiation-sensitive resist (commonly a photoresist). After the resist is exposed with the pattern for the layer of the device, the developer solution dissolves the pattern regions leaving a mask to control etching of the layer beneath. This process is used for six or more accurately registered layers to form the discrete transistor areas, isolate them

Manuscript received September 9, 1982; revised November 18, 1982.
The author is with the Perkin-Elmer Corporation, Norwalk, CT.

from each other, and interconnect them to form the desired circuit.

The features in early integrated circuits had minimum dimensions of five or ten thousandths of an inch (before metric) and a chip was as large as a tenth of an inch across. The pressure for more complex circuits has pushed the feature size down to a few thousandths of a milimeter and the chip to as large as 10 mm on a side. Thus the features have shrunk by a factor of ~60 in each dimension and grown by ~10 in area permitting the growth in complexity.

When the size of the features goes down and the area of the chip increases, both the defect density and the size of the defects must go down to achieve an adequate yield of good devices.

HISTORICAL DEVELOPMENT

The history of lithographic system development contains a continuing series of bottlenecks that have limited performance. As new development has cleared each of these problems, it has moved the bottleneck to another area of the technology.

The early integrated circuits were patterned with contact printing on photoresist using printing industry techniques to prepare the mask. Each layer of the device was laid out on graph paper at between 50 and 500 times final size and then cut into a plastic material called Rubylith. A red layer on the transparent substrate was cut so it could be peeled off in the pattern areas. The pattern was then backlighted with the mercury lamps in a printing plate camera and reduced to 10 times final size on photographic glass plate. This 10X reticle was then reduced to final size in a special step-and-repeat camera that exposed an array of identical images. A 10X microscope objective was commonly used for the reduction lens in these cameras.

Contact copies of this master mask were then used in a contact printer to expose the photoresist coated wafers. The masks were pressed hard against the wafer using vacuum to even out the flatness errors in both substrates and obtain good contact. Where the mask emulsion and photoresist were pushed hard together, particles of emulsion adhered to the photoresist leaving particles on the wafer and holes in the mask that were propagated with further exposures. The probability of having a fatal defect on small chips with large features was small enough to give adequate yields. As chip size grew and defects became more critical, each mask copy was used for fewer exposures; as low as 10 wafers in critical cases.

Pattern Generators

As the device patterns increased in complexity, the layout of the devices and cutting of Rubylith became a bottleneck. Automatic plotters and coordinatographs with knives were

Reprinted from *Proc. IEEE*, vol. 71, pp. 566–570, May 1983.

developed to cut the Rubylith from data on punch cards, but the patterns still had to be peeled.

Photographic pattern generators were later developed that used an *X–Y* table and an adjustable rectangular aperture illuminated with a flash lamp to expose photo artwork from computer tape inputs.

Projection Printing

As the defect density and yield became a critical problem, two systems were developed to avoid contact defects. One system is proximity printing, where the spacing between the mask and wafer was increased to ~10 μm. This results in lower contrast and some distortion of features because of diffraction effects. Proximity printing was very successful on the less critical levels.

Projection printing was tried using a lens at 1–1 magnification to image a standard mask onto a small wafer. The resolution was poor and the resulting linewidth errors caused as much yield loss as the contact defect density. The best conventional lens will resolve about 10^8 pixels over its field, so that it can well resolve a single chip but not a whole wafer pattern.

Micralign System

A novel optical system was developed in 1973 that changed this resolution limit. A system of spherical mirrors was used to form a narrow ring of aberration-free imagery. The wafer was moved past an arc of this ring image while a mask was moved in synchronism at the object end. An arc of the mask was illuminated and imaged onto the wafer so that by scanning once across the wafer, the whole image was exposed. This system was extended over the years so that it would image 2-μm features over a 4-in diameter wafer at a rate of ~40 wafers/h. This is 5×10^4 linear resolutions or 25×10^8 pixels in the whole image. These Micralign systems quickly became the principal lithographic tool in the industry because of the uniformity of resolution and illumination as well as the high throughput (see Fig. 1).

With the lower defect density provided by projection printing as well as improvements in the materials and processing of the wafer, chip complexity increased to the point where many hours were consumed in producing the initial reticle pattern for the chip, and defects introduced in the photographic materials used in the many steps of this process became significant in terms of yield.

Electron-Beam Pattern Generation

Electron beams have long been considered an obvious technology for high-resolution direct wafer exposure and this will be considered later in this paper, but electron beams were first applied to the pattern generation problem (see Fig. 2).

An electron-beam system (EBES) was developed in 1972 that highlighted the speed and accuracy of electron beams for patterning a final mask in a single step with lower defects on an economical basis. The speed of deflection and blanking of the electron beam combined with the ease of coupling the electron-beam system to computers contributed to the high throughput of the system for very complex patterns.

The use of a small deflection field combined with a laser interferometer measured stage achieved the dimensional accuracy required for the more complex and smaller feature devices. A raster scan on a continuously moving stage was used to write at a 40-MHz address rate directly on the electron resist over a chrome-coated mask substrate. These electron-beam

Fig. 1. The scanning projection printer has been the principal wafer exposure tool.

Fig. 2. An electron-beam mask exposure system can generate complex patterns efficiently.

pattern generators were used to push defect density down to ~2/cm^2 and write most final masks in the late 1970's in ~20 min. Since that time, the machines have been upgraded to give 0.1-μm address capability in addition to the previous 0.25 or 0.5 μm and accuracies of 0.05 μm to keep up with new requirements. The larger number of 0.1-μm addresses in a 5-in mask area and the complexity of ~5 million features per chip is pushing up exposure times. Improved systems are continually being developed.

LITHOGRAPHY FOR TODAY

The forefront of commercial lithography today is at 2-μm minimum features on 5-mm to 1.0-cm long chips on a 4- to 6-in wafer. The older Micralign machines that have been the mainstay of the industry are pushed to the limit to meet the submicron registration required between levels. The next generation of devices will shrink to 1–1.5-μm features and will require a new generation of lithography that is now emerging.

Step-and-Repeat Optical Lithography

In anticipation of the tighter requirements, many companies have developed step-and-repeat cameras for direct wafer expo-

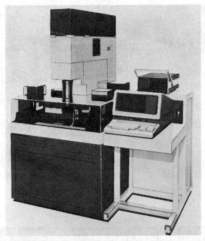

Fig. 3. A high-technology Censor Step-and-Repeat camera uses alignment on every exposure.

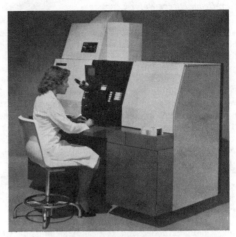

Fig. 4. A new scanning printer will expose 100 5-in wafers per hour with adjustable magnification.

sure (see Fig. 3). These systems use a very-high-quality lens to image as small as 1-μm features over a chip area of about 1 cm square at 10 times reduction. A fast stepping table with laser interferometer measurement is used to expose at rates in excess of one field per second. The high numerical aperture of the >13-element lens gives a better ultimate resolution than the Micralign systems can. Registration accuracy can be achieved using a single alignment over the wafer and dependence on the interferometer for stage position control, or alignment can be done on each chip of the wafer. The reduction ratio of the lens makes the reticle generation easier.

The problems with step and repeat are in defects and throughput. Any defect on the reticle will be printed onto every chip on the wafer. Thus if there is a particle of dirt or fatal defect on the reticle for exposure of any level of the wafer, the yield may drop to zero. Thin transparent pellicles mounted over the mask can eliminate the dirt problem. On recent systems a reduction ratio of 4 or 5 has been used so that two adjacent patterns can be written on the reticle and compared for defects in an automatic inspection system.

The throughput of step-and-repeat systems is limited because of the large number of steps required to fill the wafer. If the chip size exceeds a quarter of the area of the field, it may be necessary to expose them one at a time, pushing up the exposure time. A throughput of 30 to 40 5-in wafers per hour is about the best that can be expected in usual commercial production.

New Micralign Systems

Two new Micralign systems have been developed to meet the new requirements. The optics for the Micralign systems has been improved using phase measuring interferometry to reduce the registration tolerance to below 0.5 μm for exposure of 4-in wafers.

A new Micralign system has been developed to cover a 5-in wafer with better registration and to permit automatic adjustment of magnification in both coordinates, as part of the automatic alignment procedure. The machine uses a double optical system of the concentric spherical mirror type with some fused silica elements to obtain a wider annulus of aberration-free imagery. This reduces the exposure time so the system will

expose 100 5-in wafers per hour with 0.5-μm registration tolerances (see Fig. 4). Because the numerical aperture is less than the step-and-repeat lenses, the minimum feature is 1.25 μm in visible light, but the system can be used with UV exposure for submicron features. The use of UV also results in greater depth of focus compared to visible light systems of the same resolution.

TOMORROW'S LITHOGRAPHY

It has been assumed, since the early 1970's, that optical systems were at the limit of their performance and would be replaced within a few years. Since resolution was assumed to be the basis for that limit, shorter equivalent wavelength systems were proposed and developed. In actual practice, the limits turned out to be in registration and linewidth control. It is clear that the choice of the next generation will be between the optical step-and-repeat and scanning systems. The major problem is economic. Semiconductor manufacturers have a surplus of lithographic capacity but very little capacity for the next generation. Step-and-repeat cameras and advanced Micralign systems each cost about a million dollars with automatic alignment and loading. This is in comparison to $20k for a contact printer in the early days and $200k for a projection printer a few years ago.

Industry is being forced to commit funds to new systems because the capacity in the equipment industry will not be able to supply the demand when business turns up. At these costs, the lithography has become the most expensive part of the process. Step and repeat has somewhat more resolution in the visible, but the scanning systems have a clear edge in capacity per dollar.

ALTERNATE TECHNOLOGIES

Alternate technologies have been in development for many years. Many electron-beam systems have been designed for production use including beam scanning systems, image projection, and array systems with multiple sources. X-ray sensitive resists, sources, and exposure systems have been developed along with the critical X-ray masks. Ion systems are newer but have promise.

Electron-Beam Direct Wafer Exposure

Electron beams have long been the wave of the future for wafer exposure. The high resolution of electron beams, combined with fast deflection and computer control, all favor this technology.

Experiments were done in the late 1960's using scanning electron microscopes to expose a few high-resolution devices with excellent results. The electron beam was used to sense alignment marks and registration was superior to that of any other lithography. Many groups developed systems aimed at practical commercial production of devices.

Electron optics, with deflection fields of 5 to 10 mm at high deflection speeds, were developed. Variable beam shaping systems to expose an adjustable rectangular spot at one time were devised. Vacuum stages for rapid and accurate positioning of the wafer with laser interferometer measurement were designed. Data systems to describe the device features and feed signals to the system at the required rates were constructed.

There were some limitations on the performance of these systems. LaB_6 cathodes and thermal field emission sources were developed to achieve very high writing rates, but electron interactions in the beam limit the total current that can be used. Proximity correcting computer programs were required to compensate for the scattering range of the electron in the resist and back from the substrate to avoid distortions of the features below 2 μm.

The majority of these systems write at address rates between 40 and 500 million addresses per second and will expose up to ~6 wafers per hour with ~1-μm features. The systems have been used to make special devices that have extraordinary value because of device speed, small volume custom devices, or prototype devices for design confirmation (see Figs. 5 and 6).

The cost of these systems, in the range from 1–4 million dollars, and the moderate throughput limits their ability to economically produce catalog circuits. Further, there would not be enough capacity to produce such systems or capital to fund such systems to meet a significant fraction of the device production capacity in the foreseeable future.

Some electron-beam systems attempt to form the image of a mask rather than modulate a scanned beam. ELIPS is a system using a photocathode as the patterned source with a homogeneous magnetic and electrostatic field to image the electrons onto the resist-coated wafer. The system has improved continually for over 10 years but has always missed the moving target in resolution and registration.

A number of systems have been developed that use an array of parallel beams on a wafer or an array of lenses to form multiple images of one beam to write the array of identical chips on the wafer. These systems are a possible solution for the future but many practical problems make them improbable. There is a need for more invention in this field.

X-ray Systems

X-ray lithographic systems use the beam diverging from a small X-ray source to form a shadow image of an X-ray mask onto an X-ray-sensitive resist-coated wafer. At the X-ray wavelengths, the wafer can be spaced up to 50 μm from the mask to avoid contact. Wavelengths between 4 and 20 Å are used to have sufficient transparency in the mask substrate, sufficient opacity of the mask pattern, sensitivity of the resist and, in some cases, enough transmission through a beryllium window in the X-ray tube and through a helium atmosphere to permit exposure at atmospheric pressure. Many mask materials have been used as the substrate including silicon, boron nitride,

Fig. 5. The IBM EL-3 system is used for fast turnaround in electron-beam patterning of prototype devices.

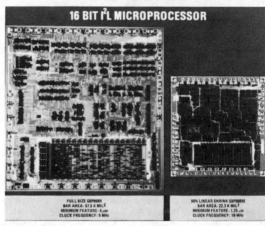

Fig. 6. Texas Instruments uses electron-beam exposure to achieve smaller features, more chips per wafer, and faster device operation.

and other polycrystaline films, metal films, and plastic films. Most substrates are only a few microns thick and must support a 1-μm-thick pattern of gold or other metal.

Some X-ray masks are transparent in the visible so optical alignment techniques can be used. The scattering range of the X-ray-generated photoelectron in the resist is only ~500 Å so resolution can be higher than electron lithography.

The major problem has been in devising a sensitive enough resist combined with a reliable bright source to give exposures of less than a minute. Also, small uncontrolled distortions in the mask substrate during and after patterning have caused significant distortions in the pattern.

X-ray systems have been used to make many devices with 2-μm features and a few in the 1-μm range. As the resolution and registration tolerances have tightened to keep ahead of the growing optical technology, the X-ray mask distortions for full field exposure have improved, but have continued to be a problem. With current registration tolerances in the 0.1–0.2-μm range, smaller X-ray masks with step-and-repeat exposures of large wafers are being studied.

The use of step and repeat will complicate the X-ray system and increase its cost compared to that of other lithographic systems.

Ion Exposure Systems

Ion beams can be used to expose resists in both the scanned beam system, comparable to electron beams, and in mask exposure systems, using crystaline substrates as in the X-ray systems. The critical question is the flux of ion beam and the sensitivity of the resist. Ions should have a shorter range in the resist and not suffer from the proximity effects as much as electron beams.

There is the possibility to use ion beams of desired materials for direct implanting of impurities in the silicon substrate. With existing beam intensities, this would be limited to a small fraction of the area to be economical. Ion systems are in a very active stage of development and results are awaited with great interest.

FUTURE DIRECTIONS

Once again the next lithography will depend on optical systems because the alternate systems are not ready. At some point, the optical resolution will be insufficient and other technologies will be required. The VHSIC military program supporting electron and X-ray lithography for making large, complex, fast processors for military applications may bring these technologies to the point of successful commercial application and extend the lithography once again.

Resists for Fine-Line Lithography

MICHAEL HATZAKIS

Invited Paper

Abstract—Resists are radiation-sensitive materials used in the fabrication of integrated circuits (VLSI) for imaging the desired pattern onto the silicon wafer. Most resists in use today consist of polymeric solutions that are spin-coated onto the silicon wafer, exposed in a lithographic tool, developed, and completely removed after the pattern has been transferred to the substrate. This paper presents a historical development of resist materials, present uses of resists, and future requirements, dictated primarily by developments in lithographic tools.

INTRODUCTION

THE NEED for decreasing the device dimensions in memory and logic circuits has been emphasized already in numerous papers, including papers in this issue. This need is driven by two primary factors; decrease in cost by increasing the number of devices per chip and/or the number of chips per silicon wafer, and improvements in circuit performance by reducing the device capacitance and shortening propagation delay time. One of the primary limitations in the manufacturing of smaller devices has always been lithography, which includes lithographic tools and resists and processes.

Manuscript received January 24, 1983.
The author is with IBM Thomas J. Watson Research Center, Yorktown Heights, NY 10598.

Since lithographic tools are quite adequately covered in a separate paper in this issue, I will attempt to cover the development of resists and processes that have contributed significantly to micrometer and submicrometer device fabrication. Although large-scale fabrication of micrometer-size device circuits is not yet a reality, resists and processes are being extended to submicrometer device dimensions and the limitations today lie in economic factors, lithographic tools and masks, and device design optimization.

RESIST DEFINITIONS

Resists are temporary layers applied onto the workpiece only for imaging purposes. After pattern transferring onto the active layer (insulator or semiconductor material), the resist is removed (stripped) in a solvent or an oxidizing solution. The most common resists are organic solutions applied on the workpiece (wafer) by spinning and dried by baking at a suitable temperature, referred to as "prebake temperature." The thickness of the dried resist layer depends largely on the concentration of solids in the solution and on the spinning speed.

After baking of the resist-coated wafer, the desired pattern is exposed in a lithographic tool, and the resist is developed. The most important distinction between resists concerns the

Reprinted from *Proc. IEEE*, vol. 71, pp. 570–574, May 1983.

pattern polarity after development. "Positive" resists refers to resists in which the areas exposed in the lithographic tool are removed during development while "negative" refers to resists in which the exposed areas remain after development. Another important distinction concerns the form of radiation used in the lithographic tool. "Photoresists" refers to resists which are sensitive to UV photons of wavelengths between 200 and 400 nm. Further subdivisions of photoresists have been used recently as the trend in lithographic tools is to push UV sources towards shorter wavelengths in order to improve resolution. Thus photoresists have been divided into "near-UV" resists sensitive in a wavelength range around 400 nm, "mid-UV" resists centered around 300 nm, and "deep-UV" resists intended for wavelengths around 200 nm. Other important categories include electron resists, sensitive to electron-beam radiation, and X-ray resists, intended for use with X-ray lithographic tools operating in a range of wavelengths between 4 and 20 Å.

In general, resists undergo chemical changes on exposure to the appropriate radiation, which render them soluble (positive resists) or insoluble (negative resists) in the exposed area relative to the unexposed area. Most resists, with some recent exceptions, are developed in a solution which could be a mixture of organic solvents or an inorganic solution. Measures of quality in resists include the following:

1) Sensitivity, which refers to the minimum incident exposure dose required to adequately differentiate between exposed and unexposed regions. This dose is measured in millijoules per centimeter square (mJ/cm^2) in UV and X-ray resists, and coulombs or microcoulombs per centimeter square (C/cm^2 or $\mu C/cm^2$) in electron- and ion-beam resists.

2) Resolution, referring to the ability of the resist to faithfully reproduce the size of the image that the lithographic tool can expose on it. The minimum linewidth that can be obtained in the resist, assuming that the lithographic tool is not the limiting factor, depends on the thickness of the resist and the shape of the resist profile (sidewall angle). In general, it is desirable to keep the resist at least 1 μm thick, and for maximum fidelity in the pattern transfer process, close to vertical resist profiles are necessary.

3) Compatibility with the pattern transfer process, which includes resist adhesion to the substrate, temperature stability, resistance to wet or dry etching processes, etc.

For a resist to be acceptable in a manufacturing process, it must satisfy all of these conditions, that is, its sensitivity must be adequate so that it does not impose a throughput limitation on the lithographic tool. Its resolution must also exceed that of the lithographic tool and it must be compatible with all the manufacturing processes.

HISTORICAL DEVELOPMENT

Semiconductor device fabrication using the planar process started in the 1950's and the term "lithography" was borrowed from the printing industry. Similarly, the first resists used were of the same type as the ones used in the printing industry. The most common of these was a negative photoresist supplied by Kodak under the name of KTFR and composed of cyclized isoprene with a bis-azide as sensitizer [1]. This resist is very sensitive to UV light in the wavelength range of 360–400 nm. Its resolution and temperature stability, however, are limited due to the rubber-like nature of polyisoprenes.

The most important development in photoresists was the introduction, in the early 1960's, of the AZ-1350 series by the Shipley Company through a licensing agreement with Azoplate

Corporation. These resists are positive in tone and contain phenol formaldehyde resin and a benzoquinone diazide as a sensitizer [1]. These resists also respond in the range of 400-nm UV and are developed in aqueous alkaline solutions, unlike the negative photoresists which require organic solvent developers. Many other positive photoresist systems have been produced by various manufacturers since then with similar composition and properties.

The most important contribution of these resists to the semiconductor industry was the fact that resolution was now limited by the lithographic tool and not by the resist and that the pattern linewidth could be modified after exposure by longer or shorter development time. After this realization, the burden was passed on to the lithography tool manufacturers to improve image resolution.

During the mid-1960's, it was felt that optical (UV) lithography tools would not be able to achieve resolution better than 2-μm minimum line dimensions, and therefore, other forms of radiation should be investigated. It was also known that electron-beam probes of diameter smaller than 1000 Å (100 nm) could be rather easily achieved, as the just emerging scanning electron microscope (SEM) developed at Cambridge University (UK) was demonstrating. Experiments were initiated in various laboratories, such as IBM Research, Westinghouse Research, Hughes, and Texas Instruments, to investigate the possibility of using electron beams as lithographic tools. The first step to that goal, however, was to identify a resist that would be able to resolve patterns of similar dimensions as the electron-beam probe size. One of the most important breakthroughs in the mid-1960's was the discovery that polymethyl methacrylate (PMMA) was a positive electron-beam resist with high-resolution capabilities [2]. In addition, it was discovered that, after exposure at 15–25 kV accelerating potential and development in a mixture of methyl–isobuty–ketone (MIBK) and isopropanol (IPA), the profiles produced in PMMA resist exhibited an undercut feature [3]. This observation led to the development of a new metallization technique that became known as "liftoff" [4]. The new technique made it possible to produce metal lines for semiconductor interconnections with micrometer and submicrometer dimensions. Such resolution could not be achieved previously due to undercutting effects, unavoidable with any wet chemical etching technique of thick aluminum. Micrometer and submicrometer devices, including silicon bipolar, FET, surface acoustic wave transducers, superconducting weak links, etc., were produced in many laboratories using PMMA and electron-beam exposure tools [5]–[9].

In addition to PMMA, it was discovered at Westinghouse Research that polystyrene can be used as a negative electron-beam resist of very high contrast, and therefore, submicrometer resolution could be also obtained with this resist. In the same paper, the fundamental principles of crosslinking and scission occuring during electron-beam exposure of negative and positive polymeric resist were summarized [10]. This paper indicated that, for negative resists, sensitivity increases as the initial molecular weight of the polymer increases. This was shown to be the case also with positive resists in a subsequent paper from IBM [11].

By the early 1970's, work was also initiated at Bell Laboratories with the objective to produce more sensitive electron-beam resists since PMMA and polystyrene, although capable of high resolution, were rather insensitive, requiring an exposure dose of approximately 10^{-4} C/cm^2 (100 $\mu C/cm^2$).

TABLE I
A Partial List of Lithographic Resists

COMPANY/ MATERIAL	TYPE	RADIATION/ SENSITIVITY	RESOLUTION	THERMAL STABILITY	REF.
KODAK KTFR - MICRONEG.	NEGATIVE	UV~4000Å E-BEAM 5×10^{-7} Coul/cm^2	2μm	~100°C	1
BELL LABS P(GMA-co-EA)	NEGATIVE	E-BEAM 5×10^{-7} Coul/cm^2	2μm	~100°C	13
HITACHI EPOXIDIZED POLYBUTADIENE	NEGATIVE	E-BEAM 10^{-8} Coul/cm^2	2-3μm	~100°C	14
SHIPLEY AZ-1350J	POSITIVE	UV~4000Å E-BEAM 5×10^{-5} Coul/cm^2	1μm	120°C	1,15
KODAK 809	POSITIVE	UV~4000Å	1μm	120°C	17
POLYCHROME PC-129	POSITIVE	UV~4000Å	1μm	120°C	17
BELL LABS PBS	POSITIVE	E-BEAM 10^{-6} Coul/cm^2	0.5μm	80°C	12
PMMA	POSITIVE	E-BEAM 8×10^{-5} Coul/cm^2	<0.05μm	120°C	3,4
PHILIPS RESEARCH CROSSLINKED PMMA	POSITIVE	E-BEAM $2-4 \times 10^{-5}$ Coul/cm^2	0.5μm	160°C	18
IBM P(MMA-co-MAA)	POSITIVE	E-BEAM 2×10^{-5} Coul/cm^2	0.1μm	160°C	19
BELL LABS POLY(CHLORO-ACRYLATES)	NEGATIVE	X-RAY ~10mJ/cm^2	1-2μm	~100°C	20
DAIKIN KOGYO CO JAPAN FBM	POSITIVE	E-BEAM $0.5-1 \times 10^{-6}$ Coul/cm^2	0.5μm	<100°C	21
SOMAR KOGYO CO JAPAN SEL-N	NEGATIVE	E-BEAM 1×10^{-6} Coul/cm^2	1-2μm	~100°C	22
TOKYO OHKA CO JAPAN ODUR-1014	POSITIVE	DEEP UV	-	-	23

Work at Bell Labs produced two very sensitive resists: a positive poly(butene-1-sulfone) (PBS) and a negative poly(glycidyl methacrylate-co-ethyl acrylate) (COP), both with electron-beam sensitivities in the range of 1 μC/cm^2 [12], [13]. Many more electron resists were announced from laboratories in the US, Europe, and Japan in the 1970's. Table I lists a small selection of these with the associated references.

Electron-beam exposure systems were designed and built by TI, IBM, Westinghouse, Bell Labs, Mullard (now Phillips Research), etc., both for experimental device fabrication and for production, on the assumption that optical (UV) lithography tools could not achieve sufficient resolution to fabricate devices with dimensions below 2 μm. By the late 1970's, however, most manufacturers changed this way of thinking primarily because of two factors. One was the excessive cost of populating the semiconductor factory with electron-beam tools, all of which required a dedicated fast computer with large memory capacity, and second was the advancements in UV lens design which allowed optical step-and-repeat systems to be built with at least 1-μm resolution capability. In addition, Perkin-Elmer promised the introduction of one-to-one optical scanning systems operating at shorter wavelengths

(310–250 nm) with also 1-μm capability. These factors shifted the emphasis from electron resists back to near-UV, mid-UV, and deep-UV resists.

Present Status of Resists

A. Resists for UV Tools

Current resist development is largely influenced by the trends in lithographic tools. Today most semiconductor manufacturers are using Perkin-Elmer's Micralign systems at 400-nm wavelength for down to 2.5-μm device geometries because of the high throughput of these systems. The most common resists for these systems are Shipley's 1350-J, one of the 1350 series of 400-nm resists, or similar types produced by Kodak, Hunt, and others in the United States and Japan. For higher performance circuit designs with linewidths of 1.5 μm, step-and-repeat optical tools, with 10X, 5X, or even 1X reduction and refractive imaging elements (lenses), are being utilized. These systems are available today from GCA Mann, Optometrics, Sensor, Ultratech, and others and are, in general, operating in the same wavelength range as the PE Micralign systems (400–435 nm), so that the same photoresists are being used as in the Micralign systems. Perkin-Elmer is also trying to increase the resolution of the new Micralign tools by improving the quality of the optical system and reducing the wavelength to 310 or even 254 nm. This new generation of PE tools will require new resists, designed for shorter wavelengths, since the existing photoresists absorb heavily at shorter UV and are difficult to expose in relatively thick layers (1–2 μm). As a result, many chemical companies in the US and Japan are trying to formulate new resist compositions that are less absorbing at 254 and 310 nm. Ultimately, the shortest wavelength that can be used in air is approximately 200 nm, but since conventional mercury or xenon lamps radiate much smaller amounts of power at deep UV (200–254 nm), resists designed for these wavelengths will have to be considerably more sensitive than conventional photoresists, in addition to being less absorbant.

B. Resists for Electron-Beam and X-Ray Tools

Electron-beam tools will probably not be used for mass production of VLSI circuits with minimum linewidth of 1 μm. However, because of the pattern generation capability of electron-beam systems, they are indispensable as mask generators for UV tools. Bell Lab's EBES systems manufactured under license by several companies today has become the industry's standard mask generator for original mask segments of IX mask plates. Very high sensitivity electron resists are required for these systems due to their low current density, so that Bell Lab's PBS and COP resists are almost exclusively used. Higher current density and throughput electron-beam systems such as IBM's EL-III will be used for direct device fabrication only in selected processes like personalization of master-slice logic chips. For the system's higher resolution, resists will be required with sensitivity between 1 and 5 μC/cm^2. For this application, resist requirements are much more stringent than for chrome mask fabrication; for instance, temperature stability, reactive-ion etch resistance, and other processing qualities are necessary for direct device fabrication.

X-ray systems will be useful when circuits with minimum device dimensions of 0.5 μm or less are ready for mass production. This probably will not happen until the 1990's, after 1-μm device circuits have been mass produced for several years using optical (UV) tools. Resists for X-ray systems will de-

<table>
<tr><td colspan="3" align="center">TABLE II
RESIST WISH LIST</td></tr>
</table>

TABLE II
RESIST WISH LIST

1. **RESIST SENSITIVITY OBJECTIVES:**

   UV RESISTS   220–440 nm   10–30 mJ/cm^2
   (deep UV–UV)

   X-RAY RESISTS $Alk_\alpha (E_{max}=1KeV)$ 1–10 mJ/cm^2

   E-BEAM RESISTS   20–25 KV 10^{-6} $Coul/cm^2$

2. **THERMAL STABILITY OBJECTIVES**

   NO PATTERN FLOW AT 180–220°C

3. **REACTIVE ION ETCH RESISTANCE**

   RESIST SHOULD ETCH AT 1/2 TO 1/5 OF ETCH RATE OF Si OR SiO_2

4. **DRY DEVELOPED RESISTS**

   COMPLETELY DRY PROCESS (NO LIQUID DEVELOPERS)

   DEVELOP IN OXYGEN, ARGON OR OTHER GAS PLASMA

TABLE III
MULTILAYER RESIST SYSTEMS

Resist System	Exposure Tool	Application	Reference #
PMMA HIGH Mw PMMA LOW Mw	E-Beam	Lift-off Process	24
P(MMA-co-MAA) PMMA	E-beam	Lift-off Process	25,26
Chlorobenzene soaked AZ1350-J	UV	Lift-off Process	27
AZ1350-J PMMA	UV/E-Beam	Lift-off or RIE	28
AZ1350-J or PMMA siloxane AZ1350-J	UV/E-Beam	High Temperature Lift-off	29
Hunt 204 SiO_2 Hunt 204	UV	RIE	30
$Ag_2Se/GeSe$ Hunt 204	UV	RIE	31
Siloxane AZ1350-J	UV/E-Beam	RIE	32

pend on the X-ray wavelength used and on the flux available from the source. If synchrotron radiation sources are used, then resist sensitivity is not a critical problem and the same resist used for electron-beam tools can also be used for X-rays. With conventional X-ray sources, however, very high sensitivity and resolution X-ray resists are required.

Table II is a "wish list" of the desirable properties of resist for the lithographic tools considered so far. For UV and X-ray tools, it is assumed that conventional sources of energy (UV lamps and electron-beam excited X-ray targets) are used.

FUTURE DIRECTIONS IN RESISTS

Resist requirements for future applications will be dictated as much by the transfer process conditions, which is defined as the process that follows resist exposure and development, as by lithographic tool requirements. Some of the important trends that may have significant effects on resist and process designs are as follows:

1) Due to wafer topography at the later stages of processing and due to current density problems in conductors used on chips and packages, the developed resist pattern aspect (height-to-width) ratio is increasing as lithographic dimensions decrease. This means that with some processing steps, 1-μm linewidth patterns will have to be developed in as thick as 2 μm of resist. This requirement places severe demands on resist and exposing tool contrast and it is doubtful whether a workable process can be realized.

2) Resist temperature stability and reactive-ion etch resistance requirements are increasing due to demands for hot processing in high-temperature liftoff and reactive-ion etching processes. Again, it is doubtful whether a resist can be found that can satisfy the sensitivity, temperature stability, and low RIE rate requirements.

For these reasons, multilayer resist systems are being very actively pursued in research and development laboratories. With multilayer systems, the image is first defined in a thin top sensitive resist layer by the exposure tool and then transferred onto a thick polymeric layer under it by either a second flood exposure or by reactive-ion etching. Many important advantages are realized by use of multilayer resist systems,

both for lithography and for the image transfer process onto the workpiece. These advantages include the following:

a) The resolution and linewidth control of all lithographic tools is significantly increased by the fact that only a very thin (2000–4000-Å) resist layer is exposed and developed.

b) Standing-wave effects in UV lithography tools are virtually eliminated by the fact that the thick polymeric underlayer can be made opaque and, therefore, nonreflecting for UV.

c) Resist thickness variations are eliminated since the thick underlayer planarizes any topography on the workpiece. This greatly improves linewidth control with all lithography tools.

d) The thick planarizing layer can be selected for optimum qualities such as adhesion, temperature stability, low RIE rates, etc., since it does not have to be an active resist.

e) Proximity effects in electron-beam lithography can be significantly reduced since backscattering from carbonaceous materials (polymers) is much less than from silicon or metals.

A partial list of multilayer resist systems is shown in Table III. Other important developments include recent attempts to restrict the use of solvents in resist processings for environmental reasons as well as improved process control. Plasma-developed resist processes have been reported by G. Taylor and coworkers at Bell Laboratories [33], and M. Tsuda and S. Oikawa of Ciba University in Japan [34], while an all-dry process, including resist deposition, exposure, development, and etching, has been reported by S. Hattori and coworkers of Nagoya University in Japan [35]. In addition, a new resist system that undergoes self-development during exposure and, therefore, requires no further processing, has been reported by H. Ito and G. Wilson of IBM [36]. These developments constitute a preview of what appears to be a revolution in resist materials and processing in the near future.

CONCLUSIONS

Resist materials and processing will, by necessity, follow the trends of lithographic tool development for improvements in resolution and throughput. It appears that optical (UV) tools will continue to dominate the silicon chip factory for at least the next decade until a 1-μm minimum linewidth is achieved. Electron-beam lithography tools will be used primarily for optical and X-ray mask fabrication and for special devices, as for example, personalization of logic chips. X-ray tools will be used only after the need arises to reduce the device dimensions to 0.5 μm or less. For these reasons, UV resists operating in the wavelength regions of 200–400 nm will continue to be developed with emphasis on increasing contrast, sensitivity, and process control. Also, work on multilayer and dry developable resists will continue with the objective to obtain the ultimate resolution, aspect ratio, and process control.

REFERENCES

[1] W. S. DeForest, *Photoresist, Materials and Processes.* New York: McGraw-Hill, 1975.
[2] I. Haller, M. Hatzakis, and R. Srinivasan, "High resolution positive resist for electron beam exposure," *IBM. J. Res. Devel.,* vol. 12, pp. 251–256, 1968.
[3] M. Hatzakis, "New method of observing electron penetration profiles in solids," *Appl. Phys. Lett.,* vol. 23, no. 1, pp. 7–9, 1971.
[4] ——, "Electron resists for microcircuit and mask production," *J. Electrochem. Soc.,* vol. 116, pp. 1033–1037, 1969.
[5] S. Magdo, M. Hatzakis, and C. H. Ting, "Electron-beam fabrication of micron transistors," *IBM J. Res. Devel.,* vol. 15, pp. 446–451, 1971.
[6] F. Fang, M. Hatzakis, and C. H. Ting, "Electron-beam fabrication of ion implanted high performance FET circuits," *J. Vac. Sci. Technol.,* vol. 10, no. 6, pp. 1082–1085, 1973.
[7] M. Sopira and P. Malmberg, "Fabrication of integrated CMOS transistors using electron lithography and ion implantation," *J. Vac. Sci. Technol.,* vol. 10, no. 6, pp. 1086–1089, 1973.
[8] A. Williamson, T. Brewer, R. Robbins, and G. Arnell, "Electron beam fabrication of high density CMOS RAM cells," in *Proc. 7th Int. Conf. on Electron and Ion Beam Science and Technology* (Electrochem. Soc.), R. Bakish, Ed., pp. 417–426, 1976.
[9] F. Ozdemiz, W. Perking, R. Yim, and E. Wolf, "Precision electron beam microfabrication," *J. Vac. Sci. Technol.,* vol. 10, no. 6, pp. 1008–1011, 1973.
[10] H. Ku and L. Scala, "Polymeric electron beam resists," *J. Electrochem. Soc.,* vol. 116, no. 7, pp. 980–985, 1969.
[11] M. Hatzakis, C. Ting, and N. Viswanathan, "Fundamental aspects of electron beam exposure of polymeric resist systems," in *Proc. 6th Int. Conf. on Electron and Ion Beam Science and Technology* (Electrochem. Soc.), R. Bakish, Ed., pp. 542–579, 1974.
[12] M. Bowden and L. Thompson, "The evaluation of poly(butene-1-sulfone) as a positive electron beam resist," *J. Appl. Polymer Sci.,* vol. 17, pp. 3211–3216, 1973.
[13] L. Thompson, J. Ballantyne, and E. Feit, "Molecular parameters and lithographic performance of poly(glycidyl methacrylate-co-ethyl acrylate)," *J. Vac. Sci. Technol.,* vol. 12, no. 6, pp. 1280–

1283, 1975.
[14] T. Hizai, Y. Hatano, and S. Nonogaki, "Epoxide-containing polymers as highly sensitive electron-beam resists," *J. Electrochem. Soc.,* vol. 118, pp. 669–672, 1971.
[15] R. Matta, "High resolution electron-beam exposure of photoresists," *Electrochem. Technol.,* vol. 5, pp. 382–385, 1967.
[16] J. Shaw and M. Hatzakis, "Performance characteristics of diazo-type photoresists under electron-beam and optical exposure," *IEEE Trans. Electron Devices,* vol. ED-25, pp. 425–430, 1978.
[17] M. Hatzakis and J. Shaw, "Diazo-type photoresist systems under electron-beam exposure," in *Proc. 8th Int. Conf. on Electron and Ion Beam Science and Technology* (Electrochem. Soc.), R. Bakish, Ed., pp. 285–302, 1978.
[18] E. D. Roberts, "Rapid direct formation of siliceous diffusion barriers by electron beams," in *Proc. 3rd Int. Conf. on Electron, and Ion Beam Science and Technology* (Electrochem. Soc.), R. Bakish, Ed., pp. 370–376, 1968.
[19] I. Haller, R. Feder, M. Hatzakis, and R. Spiller, "Copolymers of methyl-methacrylate and methacrylic acid and their metal salts as radiation sensitive resists," *J. Electrochem. Soc.,* vol. 126, no. 1, pp. 154–161, 1979.
[20] G. Taylor, G. Coquin, and S. Sasson, "Sensitive chlorine-containing resists for X-ray lithography," in *Ref. Technol. Conf., Soc. of Plastics Eng.,* pp. 132–168, 1976.
[21] M. Kakuchi, S. Sugawara, K. Muzase, and K. Matsuyama, *J. Electrochem. Soc.,* vol. 124, pp. 1648–1651, 1977.
[22] H. Ochi, *Denshi Zaizyo,* vol. 18, no. 10, pp. 70–74, 1979.
[23] T. Matsuzawa and H. Tomioka, *IEEE Electron Device Lett.,* vol. EDL-2, pp. 90–91, 1981.
[24] W. Moreau and C. Ting, "High sensitivity positive electron resist," US Patent 3 934 057, 1976.
[25] M. Hatzakis, "High sensitivity resist system for lift-off metallization," US Patent 4 024 293, 1977.
[26] ——, "PMMA copolymers as high sensitivity electron resists," *J. Vac. Sci. Technol.,* vol. 16, no. 6, pp. 1984–1988, 1979.
[27] M. Hatzakis, B. Canavello, and J. Shaw, "Single-step optical lift-off process," *IBM J. Res. Develop.,* vol. 24, no. 4, pp. 452–460, 1980.
[28] B. J. Lin and T.H.P. Chang, "Hybrid e-beam/deep UV exposure using portable comfortable masking (PCM) technique," *J. Vac. Sci. Technol.,* vol. 16, no. 6, pp. 1669–1671, 1979.
[29] J. Havas, "High resolution, high temperature lift-off technique," *Electrochem. Soc. Extended Abstracts,* vol. 76-2, pp. 743–744, 1976.
[30] J. Moran and D. Maydan, "High resolution, steep profile resist patterns," *J. Vac. Sci. Technol.,* vol. 16, no. 6, pp. 1620–1624, 1979.
[31] K. L. Tai, W. Sinclair, R. Vadimsky, and J. Moran, "Bilevel high resolution photolithographic technique for use with wafers with stepped and/or reflecting surfaces," *J. Vac. Sci. Technol.,* vol. 16, no 6, pp. 1977–1979, 1979.
[32] J. Shaw, M. Hatzakis, J. Paraszczak, J. Liutkus, and E. Babich, "Organosilicon polymers for lithographic applications," in *Proc. Regional Tech. Conf., Soc. of Plastics Eng.,* pp. 285–295, 1982.
[33] G. Taylor and T. Wolf, "Plasma developed X-ray resists," *J. Electrochem. Soc.,* vol. 127, p. 2665, 1980.
G. Taylor, T. Wolf, and M. Goldrick, "A negative-working, plasma-developed photoresist," *J. Electrochem. Soc.,* vol. 138, no. 2, pp. 361–366, 1981.
[34] M. Tsuda and S. Oikawa, "Plasma developable photoresist containing electronic excitation energy quenching system," in *Proc. Regional Conf., Soc. of Plastics Eng.,* pp. 397–423, 1982.
[35] S. Hattori, S. Morita, M. Yamada, J. Tamano, and M. Ieda, "A breakthrough to the plasma deposited dry-developable e-beam resist," in *Proc. Regional Conf., Soc. of Plastics Eng.,* pp. 311–328, 1982.
[36] H. Ito and G. Wilson, "Chemical amplification in the design of dry-developing resist materials," in *Proc. Regional Conf., Soc. of Plastics Eng.,* pp. 331–354, 1982.

Electron-Beam Systems for Precision Micron and Submicron Lithography

ALAN D. WILSON

Invited Paper

Abstract—This paper discusses the engineering of electron-beam systems for the generation of micron and submicron lithography. Design objectives and options for the electron-beam column, X-Y workpiece stage, laser interferometer, pattern generator, software, and general engineering are the major topics.

I. INTRODUCTION

ELECTRON-BEAM SYSTEMS for the fabrication of micron and submicron size devices have evolved from the early SEM-based instruments to sophisticated computer-controlled systems that run automatically. Scanning electron microscope research at Cambridge University and elsewhere was the cornerstone for the first electron-beam fabrication experiments. Research in electron-beam technology at several major companies, notably Bell Laboratories, Hughes Research, IBM, Thompson CSF, and TI during the late 1960's and early 1970's paved the way for the development of full systems for the generation of VLSI chips by electron-beam pattern writers [1]–[5].

The electron-beam pattern generators have evolved in two major directions: systems for direct device and mask fabrication above 1-μm minimum linewidth and high-resolution research-type instruments for generation of patterns whose minimum linewidths are below 1 μm. Most of the commercial electron-beam systems are used to make chrome masks for 1X optical projection printers and NX optical reduction step-and-repeat printers. The advanced electron submicron beam systems have been employed in the making of high-resolution 1X optical and X-ray masks and zone plates as well as directly writing advanced microstructures on a variety of substrates.

As a way of a review, we will briefly discuss the major electron-beam systems that have been discussed in the literature. There are many options available to the systems designer for his selection in configuring a particular system. Some of the options are, for example, 1) a round Gaussian probe versus a shaped beam; 2) a step-and-repeat table versus a continuously moving table; 3) electron source: a tungsten filament, or LaB$_6$ emitter, field emission tip, a single source versus multiple sources (and images); 4) proximity correction (corrections given to a shape because of electron dose received due to forward beam scattering and backscattering by the resist and substrate): by dose, by linewidth control, or by a combination of linewidth and dose; and 5) finally, beam energy or voltage, 5–100 kV.

Manuscript received January 26, 1983.
The author is with the IBM Thomas J. Watson Research Center, Yorktown Heights, NY 10598.

Some of the selections made in well-known pace setting systems are discussed next.

The Vector Scan system designed at IBM by Chang and his coworkers is composed of a round Gaussian probe, an LaB$_6$ source at 25 kV with proximity correction achieved by dose correction during shape writing, and a step-and-repeat table. The field size is variable and the probe size is also variable within some limits.

The original EBES system designed at Bell Laboratories by Herriott and his coworkers and an improved versions of this system now marketed by ETEC–Perkin-Elmer Corp. under the code names MEBES and by Varian-Extrion under the code name EEBES is also a round Gaussian probe, a tungsten source at about 10 kV, and a continuous moving table. The early systems at TI, and the Cambridge Instruments and Phillips (Eindhoven) systems are similar to a round-beam Gaussian Vector Scan system.

A major departure from the round Gaussian probe is the IBM manufacture system EL3 [6] and its predecessors. These manufacturing type systems use a step-and-repeat table, a tungsten source, but irradiate the substrate with an electron-beam probe shaped to the final shape to be written, or if the shape is very large such as a wiring pad, a significant portion of the shape is written at one time. This shaped-beam approach has been adopted by several other groups in Japan and elsewhere because it significantly increases the throughput of a single size round Gaussian beam probe system. Throughput enhancements of the order of 16 to 100 are potentially possible with the shaped-beam approach. A major problem with these systems is the writing of nonrectangular shapes such as angled lines or circles. Another problem is the large probe current which results in significant strong electron–electron interactions as the electrons traverse the column. Performance can be degraded by these interactions. The breaking up of a large shape into a group of smaller shapes for the inclusion of dose correction because of proximity effects somewhat defeats the advantages of the shaped-beam concept. At the present time, the shaped-beam systems are geared more to applications such as quick turn-around time (QTAT) personalization rather than submicron pattern generation. However, for many high-throughput applications, the shaped-beam system is very attractive. For the generation of micron and submicron linewidths we turn our attention to the design of an ideal or optimum laboratory type system.

Except for the round Gaussian beam based systems with proximity correction, such as Vector Scan, very few complex

Reprinted from *Proc. IEEE*, vol. 71, pp. 575–584, May 1983.

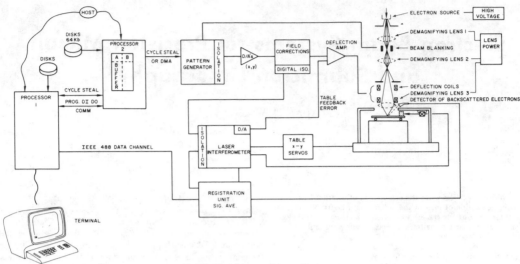

Fig. 1. Electron-beam lithography system.

micron or submicron device patterns have been generated because there is poor control of line/space dimensions on dense patterns written with shaped-beam systems or with other round Gaussian beam systems without proximity correction.

Some very interesting extra-fine submicron lithography has been achieved on a few special SEM and high-resolution electron-beam systems (Broers [7], Coane [8]). Because this activity is in the tens of angstroms to tenths of micrometers and is more novel than directed toward device making, we will not delve deeper into the methods used to fabricate these remarkably small structures.

We next discuss the selection of options that yield a good electron-beam system for the fabrication of micron and submicron geometries for either direct device fabrication or the making of 1X masks for optical and X-ray lithography. We will also discuss some of the engineering details that make a system really perform to its full potential. Extensions can be judiciously made.

II. Elements of a Basic System

The basic elements of a general electron-beam fabrication system are: 1) a column consisting of an electron source and accelerating electrode, condensing lens system, beam-blanking unit, a final lens assembly, and detector of backscattered electrons; 2) a mechanical subsystem comprising a workpiece chamber and X–Y stage, vacuum pumping hardware for both the column and chamber, a vibration isolation platform, a laser interferometer system with an optical mirror on the stage and reference column for control of the workpiece stage and sample carriers; 3) an electronic subsystem which includes a computer-control system, a pattern generator to "draw" a shape defined by the commands/data in the CAD pattern file, digital-to-analog hardware to convert the digital representation of the shape into some drive voltage for the deflection coil drive amplifier, a field correction unit to size, shift, and rotate the written field for proper registration of one pattern to a previously

written one, and a registration device for analysis of the backscattered registration electron-beam signal and last, but certainly not least, is a good software control program. A sketch of the "ideal" systems we will discuss here is illustrated in Fig. 1.

The architecture of the column determines the remainder of the system. For the fabrication of submicron and micron devices and structures, a good system is the round Gaussian beam system with proximity correction. The column is comprised of an electron source, a condenser and beam-blanking region, and a final lens with deflection yokes.

As of today, the shaped-beam systems generally have not progressed to the point of routinely making good lines down to the submicron region for real device structures and chips. This may come later, but for now let us direct our attention to the necessary elements of a basic electron-beam system that can draw a variety of submicron structures and devices.

A. Electron Source

The source to use in our "ideal" system is an LaB_6 (lanthanum hexaboride) cathode because of its high brightness and long lifetime. Brightness is the number of electrons emitted into a unit of solid angle per unit of source surface area. It is preserved through an optical system and is thus an important measure of the usefulness of a source. The brightness of LaB_6, a chemically active material, that has finally been tamed as a reliable source of electrons, ranges from 10^5 at 1600 K to 3×10^6 A/cm² sterad at 2000 K as compared to incandescent tungsten whose brightness is 10^5 when heated to ~3400 K. Tungsten at this temperature has a very short lifetime due to the thermal evaporation of the tungsten. A filament lifetime of a few hours to at most 20 or so is not unusual for such a tungsten filament where the lifetime of a properly designed LaB_6 source can be over 500 h. Therefore, the source for our ideal system is clearly LaB_6 because of its brightness and lifetime. A typical lifetime brightness product for LaB_6 versus tungsten is approximately 200 to 1. Hohn has published [9] a typical design of a reliable LaB_6 electron-gun source, and similar devices are being used more and more in commercial electron-beam systems. Considerable attention must be given to the thermal effects during the design of the gun so that movement of the emitter tip is minimized during the operation and lifetime of the gun cell.

We next select the type of illumination to be used which is either Koehler or "critical" and it is important to consider the integration of a beam-blanking unit and the condenser(s) lenses into one unit. The blanking unit and the gun cell including the grid or "Wehnelt" and the anode should be designed for operation over a wide range of beam energies, for example, 10 to 60 kV, so that we have an option for operating the system at more than one beam voltage (energy) which may be desirable for certain resist reasons or proximity effect correction.

The vacuum vessel should be very clean in the gun area so that contamination of the LaB_6 emitter does not occur. A pressure in the neighborhood of 10^{-8} torr is adequate for the gun region and 10^{-6} or below for the chamber area. Caution must be exercised in the design of the column drift spaces and apparatus (apertures, beam monitors) regions with attention given to the problem of vacuum pumping these somewhat confined regions of the system.

B. Column

In general, the column should be rigid because any shift of the source point during exposure will be reflected in the final image. Likewise, any unwanted movements of the electron beam due to charging of surfaces in close proximity to the beam must be minimized. Charging can result from insulating layers near the beam collecting a charge. Again, a good vacuum pressure in all regions of the column is essential.

Because the electrons are charged particles, they are acted upon by both electrostatic and magnetic fields and while this is very useful and employed in many areas of the column, it is also a troublesome effect. We must be careful to properly shield the column and workpiece chamber from external magnetic fields. Low-frequency or slowly varying fields are most troublesome. Particular attention must be given to 50–60-Hz fields from both the shield point of view and from the amount of field present in the physical location that the system is going into. Shielding of the external fields can be best accomplished by using magnetically soft iron and mumetal shields. It is probable that several thin mumetal shields will be more effective than one single one of a thickness equal to the sum of all the thinner ones. Proper handling of the shields must be observed at all times so that they do not lose their effectiveness.

Great precision must be achieved in the manufacture of the column elements, lenses, spacers, etc. Doing this minimizes the number of extra alignment devices, such as coils, that must be added to compensate for poor design or manufacture. Such coils are one source of beam lateral movement or noise shift if they are not properly driven electrically and, because it is not advisable to put such a coil in the high vacuum, the method of including them in a system is crucial to an overall good design. Between the gun crossover point and the final aperture at least one set of double deflecting alignment coils is advised and usually necessary to align even the simplest column correctly.

The condenser system can be of either a single or double condenser lens system. Its sole purpose is to illuminate or fill the final projection lens aperture. At some point in the system it is necessary to have an aperture which limits the solid angle of the beam. This aperture must not charge and should be very stable mechanically and thermally.

One of the most important sections of the column is the final lens and the deflection coils that are usually located in the final lens proper. Some general characteristics of the final lens are: 1) that it will have a focal length long enough to allow the placement of a detector between the bottom of the lens and the workpiece and allow some additional clearance space, 2) it will probably have ferrite pole pieces [3] to minimize the generation of eddy currents when the electron beam is deflected quickly during the writing of a chip pattern, 3) it may have to be water cooled to minimize both distortion of the ferrite and the workpiece (particularly true in precision mask making) due to lens heating, 4) it will form part of the vacuum wall and thus special considerations will have to be made to pump the lens and get the electrons down through it without having nearby surfaces charge up, 5) it will have to be made with great precision and will, with all the attachments, such as coils, detectors, etc., be quite expensive in both money and time to fabricate. Changes are difficult to make, so all the critical points must be carefully planned at the onset.

A typical lens focal length is 50 mm. A compromise must be made between the bore of the lens, that is, the diameter of the bore, and the allowed static field from the lens as well as the allowed dynamic field generated by the deflection coils. These two "stray" fields have important effects on the patterns being written. Too small a lens bore causes unwanted field curvature and too large a bore causes high stray fields. First, consider the dynamic fields. Inside the lens great care must have been taken to eliminate eddy currents generated by the rapidly changing deflection fields because if this is not done then it will not be possible to quickly draw a pattern. The deflection coil in a typical electron-beam system usually consists of two low-inductance orthogonal coils, one for X and one for Y deflection currents. These two coils may be of one or at most a few turns, carefully wound to minimize any self-inductance. Saddle coils and toroidal coils are two types that are used. The actual deflection coil may be of the "double-deflection type" which tends to keep the beam more parallel to the optical axis through most of its traverse down through the final lens and into the space between the lens and the workpiece. A beam landing at normal incidence on the workpiece is desirable to minimize magnification errors due to substrate nonflatness.

Unfortunately, it is necessary to have a sizeable magnetic field generated by the deflection coils to move the high-energy electron beam (10 to 100 keV). This deflecting field penetrates any metallic material in the final lens area and, consequently, an eddy current is generated to counteract the imposed field. This eddy current causes the beam to be deflected to some point other than that intended and to change the beam position as a function of time as the eddy current decays. To minimize this effect, extensive use of ferrites, plastics, and thin metallic coatings are used in the fabrication of deflection yokes and final lenses interior sections. The deflection yokes are not, however, within the vacuum system. The lens itself is a focusing element and is made of soft iron and many turns of copper wire. The thin metallic or conductive oxides such as tin oxide coatings are applied to the plastics and ceramics to prevent charging but, because of their thinness, the eddy currents generated in these films are small and decay quickly. We next look at the stray static fields.

C. Magnetics Effects of Static Field from Final Lens

If the bore of the final lens is made large, then the electron beam can be deflected over a large area without experiencing excessive deflection errors such as pin cushion or barrel distortions, to name two common field errors, or suffering significant deflection aberrations and defocus. However, if the bore is very large, then the deflection field as well as the static lens focusing field will leak or stray into the workpiece area. If the deflection field is any appreciable amount in the workpiece area, the workpiece, its carrier and even the supporting X–Y stage can have eddy-current problems and these structures will have to be fabricated from nonmetallic materials plated with a thin conducting layer or film to prevent charging. It is not desirable to have to fabricate these structures from a restricted list of materials. Therefore, a compromise is made between the deflection aberrations and stray fields external to the lens.

The focussing of electrons by the final lens is accomplished by a strong axial field within the bore of the lens generated between the two lens pole pieces. This field may be as high as a few thousand gauss. To minimize the deflection aberrations, it is customary to make the bore opening of the lower or outer pole piece quite large, a bore up to a few inches in diameter is not unusual. This large bore or hole in the final pole piece, while it tends to keep deflection aberrations down, also lets the magnetic flux generated in the final lens "leak" out into the space usually occupied by the sample and stage system. The leakage flux for a typical lens is illustrated in Fig. 2. Fig. 2(a) illustrates the axial field for a lens with a 100-mm and a 50-mm bottom pole piece bore. We can see that for the smaller bore, the on axis field decays quickly as a function of axial position (positive Z for regions exterior to the lens). At a distance, 35 mm from the bottom of the lens, the field ratio for the two lens designs is 8:1. The distribution of this field in a plane (35 mm from bottom) is shown in Fig. 2(b). From this figure we note that not only is the field axial value much lower for the smaller bore, but it also decays faster in the radial direction by a factor of about 2 resulting in a significantly smaller integrated magnetic interaction effect: eddy current, and static.

The effect of this leakage field on the precision or accuracy of the electron-beam system is in two parts. The first and more dominant effect is a shift of the beam when the stage is moved caused by the interaction of the leakage field with the magnetic or paramagnetic material in the stage system or sample carrier. (Any magnetic material in the carrier or stage which is magnetized will also cause a beam shift even if no additional field is present from the final lens.) Because the stray leakage field may be quite large, a few hundred gauss for example, significant beam shifts are noted when this field interacts with a 10-in^2 piece of "nonmagnetic stainless." In this case, the beam shift was on the order of 3 to 4 μm as the material was moved under the beam focal plane. To minimize this unwanted effect, keep the final lens bore size to that required for acceptable field deflection distortions for the "important" field to be written and select carefully the materials used in the stage and the sample carrier from the point of view of magnetic and paramagnetic materials.

When magnetic materials in the stage are moved in the static

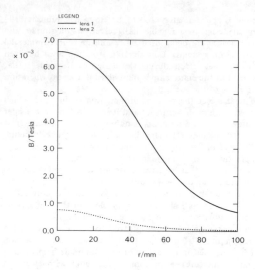

Flux density in a plane 35 mm below bottom pole piece for 100 mm (lens 1) and 50 mm (lens 2) pole piece bore

(a)

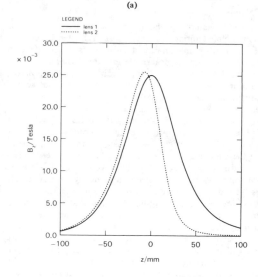

Axial flux density for 2 lenses with 100 mm (lens 1) and 50 mm (lens 2) diameter of bottom pole-piece bore

(b)

Fig. 2. (a) and (b) Lens flux density versus bore size.

field of the lens, distortions or changes are caused in the distribution of this stray leakage field and because the electrons are charged, their flight path is altered from what it was prior to the presence of the magnetic material. The beam position on the substrate is thus changed and absolute accuracy is lost. In step-and-repeat lithography with registration, this is not a problem because the registration at the next chip site corrects for any unwanted beam shift between chips, but in absolute mask making, beam shifts due to stray magnetic field interactions with the stage cause a loss in accuracy.

The second effect is eddy currents introduced by the interaction of the stationary final lens leakage or stray field and the moving stage metal parts, i.e., a Faraday generator. These eddy currents, while potentially possible, are small but as stage velocities increase they could become more of a problem. The voltage generated in the stage can, in principle, be computed from the equation of induction

$$V = \int (\boldsymbol{v} \times \boldsymbol{B})\, dL.$$

We can see that the generated voltage is proportional to stage velocity $\boldsymbol{v}$ and lens flux $\boldsymbol{B}$.

D. Magnetic Effects of Stage

A second effect associated with stray magnetic fields is in two parts. The first is the interaction of the magnetic stray field from the final lens with any magnetic material in the stage or workpiece carrier. For large-bore final lenses, the stray magnetic field can be on the order of 100 G or more and thus, if the stage has any magnetic properties, the beam position on the substrate will be adversely affected. For example, it is common to make the roller ways of aluminum X-Y stages from tool steel. These large steel bars will have different positions with respect to the final lens stray field as the stage is moved in the course of writing a mask or wafer. This will cause an overall slowly varying beam shift with table location and upset the absolute accuracy of the system with a specific "footprint" of the electron-beam system table. A similar effect will be noted if any magnetic parts are used in the stage itself, in the vacuum wall feedthroughs, etc. Reduction of residual magnetism to less than several milligauss in the stage system should be achieved in electron-beam systems intended for precision mask making and metrology measurements. In the machine shop use care in the selection of tool and work areas so as not to embed any magnetic particles in the final parts. This has been found to be quite a problem to control and without attention to this aspect the best design can become a source of unexplained problems. Care is also taken so as not to unduly workharden materials like brass, copper, Be, Cu, and aluminum. We have noted that some paramagnetic effects occur when this happens. Selection of the original materials is very important. Brass must be selected that is free of iron. Titanium, aluminum, Be, Cu should be carefully screened to make sure that they are magnetic free. Most stainless steels are slightly magnetic. Fasteners like screws and bolts likewise must be screened for magnetism. Magnetic free carbide can be used for hard surfaces and stage ways. Low-expansion glasses such as Corning Cer-vit have also been used as nonmagnetic and nonmetallic stage components successfully. Precautions must be taken, however, to insure against beam-induced charging or buildup of static charge of the glass components.

III. X-Y Stage

To minimize the contamination and heating problems, the prime movers (motors) for most of the electron-beam states have been located outside the chamber. Magnetic feedthroughs for rotary motion are extensively used. The shafts of these

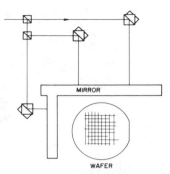

Fig. 3. Laser interferometer arrangement for stage "yaw" measurement/control.

feedthroughs should be made nonmagnetic and are shielded to minimize the coupling of the feedthrough magnetic fields into the chamber. Many successful electron-beam systems have been built with X-Y stages within the workpiece chamber. A few manufacturing oriented systems such as EBES from Bell Laboratories and its commerical derivatives place the stage outside the chamber and couple an arm for the workpiece under the final lens via a series of bellows. This is a fairly bulky technique, however, it has also proven to be satisfactory.

The stage must have very flat travel, otherwise, corrections for stage out of flatness will have to be made. (In my opinion, the fewer corrections that have to be imposed on the beam the better because they always seem to induce some additional complexity to the system. The more complex invariably means a more costly system to build and maintain.) A stage flatness of 1–2 μm is attainable and satisfactory. The stage should have a reasonable straightness, something on the order of a few microns is adequate because this will be automatically corrected by the laser interferometer feedback to the column. The angular variations of the stage are very important and the roll, pitch, and yaw should not exceed a couple of arc seconds. If the interferometer mirrors are near the plane of the workpiece, then these roll and pitch errors are effectively minimized. The yaw error can be compensated for by having two laser interferometer paths or beams tracking one rigid straight mirror as illustrated in Fig. 3. The drive to the stage should be as near to the center and as "smooth" as possible. Step-and-repeat stages should have a low mass but be designed to be stiff so that the stage does not distort during stepping. Both threaded and threadless lead screws have been used, however, I prefer the threadless type because of the greater choice of materials that can be used and the best threaded screws seem to be slightly magnetic.

IV. Laser Interferometer

A. Mounting of the Interferometers

The mounting of the laser interferometer reference mirror or corner reflector is a crucial decision in the design of the laser interferometer system. An attempt should be made to minimize the Abbe offset errors. The laser interferometer is the major element of the total system that provides an absolute and repeatable length measurement standard. A poor design of the optical system can negate the attributes of the laser interferometer. At the present time, there is really only one

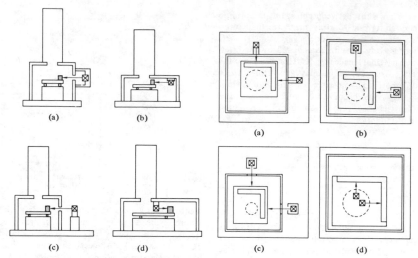

Fig. 4. Laser interferometer mounting options.

practical choice for a vendor of the laser interferometer and that is H.P. When properly applied this is a fine system.

There are four major choices for the mounting of the laser reference surface. These are depicted in Fig. 4. The choices are as follows:

(a) mount the laser interferometer "cube" to the sidewall of the chamber;

(b) mount the laser cube to the same top plate that the final lens is attached to;

(c) mount the interferometer to the base plate;

(d) mount the laser interferometer to the final lens and use an inside-out mirror arrangement (excellent mounting arrangement but may be difficult to fabricate as a single piece mirror).

Of the above choices, I prefer (b) because we can use a single piece mirror and by proper selection of materials for the lens/chamber top plate compensate for many thermal expansion effects between the lens support and the stage itself. Layout (d) is also good, however, a larger stage is usually required. A single piece mirror in (b) configuration is easier to fabricate than one for (d).

B. Mounting of the Mirror to the Stage and Mirror Selection

A diagram of the optical arrangement being discussed and the mounting of the mirror to the stage is shown in Fig. 5. A large "L" shaped single piece mirror from either metal (sintered chrome–carbide) or low-coefficient-expansion glass, square and optically flat to tolerances similar to those of individual mirrors, have been fabricated. The mirror itself should have a straightness and flatness on the order of $\lambda/20$ to $\lambda/40$ (250 to 125 Å).

It is important in mounting the mirror to the stage not to distort the mirror initially and not to introduce any additional distortion in the mirror as the stage is moved through its motions. If the stage is a classically roller or ball V-way stage, built by stacking two linear stages on top of each other, then it

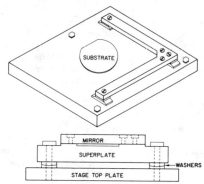

Fig. 5. Single-piece mirror mounting to stage.

is probable that if the mirror is simply clamped to the top of the stage the mirror will shift in time because of plastic or slipping action between the stage slider and the mirror and its relation to the substrate will have a "character" induced by stage motion. It is better to design the substrate carrier holding device and the mirror mount as integral parts mounted to top stage slider and at three points so that the relative position between the mirror and the substrate is not changed as the stage is moved from one location to another. This is illustrated in Fig. 5. The super plate used Vector Scan is a 1.5-in-thick aluminum plate which has been honeycombed to reduce its mass. The mirror is clamped only at its apex. The end holes are there just to prevent gross rotation in case the mirror comes loose.

C. Mirror and Substrate Carrier Mounting

The mirror is attached to the "super plate" at its apex in the case of an "L" shaped and single piece mirror. For mask and wafer writing with stitching, it is very important to attach the substrate carrier firmly to the super plate so that the relative position between mirror and substrate does not change during the writing time and also during the table move time, either continuous or stepping. Also, the substrate should not be deformed in any way by the means used to clamp the carrier to the stage. Three-point mounting techniques using balls, flats, "V" grooves, and the like are usually employed to kinematically hold the carrier rigidly but without distortion to the mirror super plate or carrier. Unfortunately, it is often the case that the carrier and loader device are designed and a large capital investment is made prior to discovering the problems of proper carrier mounting. One is then limited in the correct solution by the previously induced constraints of the loader and other attendant hardware.

D. Elastic Mounting of Mirror Super Plate

In cases where it is imperative to have the most precise writing system, it may be necessary to mount the mirror and substrate holder on a rigid plate that is elastically mounted to the stage top surface or upper ways. If this is done, then the relationship between the substrate and reference mirror is not affected or changed as the stage traverses back and forth. Stages constructed from crossed slides usually cause some distortion of the mirror mounting plate if it is simply bolted to the stage top surface. By elastically mounting the super plate, the mounts "give" as this stage is moved and thus the mirror-substrate mounting plate is not distorted. Flexure type mounts are adequate for the elastic mounting. It is not very important to prevent the super plate from moving with respect to the stage in the X–Y direction because the laser interferometer corrects for this, but if the interferometer is not correcting for stage "yaw," then the rotation must be controlled.

E. Substrate Mounting

For precision lithography, it is essential that the substrate not be distorted when placed in the carrier and that the substrate as well as the carrier not move relative to the stage mirror when doing the writing. Add to this the requirement that the carrier be loaded and unloaded automatically and you have a formidable task ahead to design a system that meets all three requirements.

A sketch of the system we have found to work best is illustrated in Fig. 6. Here the mask plate is clamped between two spherical surfaces with a couple of pounds of force. The spheres are flexure mounted. The substrate carrier is held kinematically on the stage super plate by a combination of balls, flats, and "Vees" spring loaded. It is also very important to have the substrate parallel to the stage travel and this can be accomplished by adjusting ball height "h."

For fast moving tables, the acceleration experienced by the carrier can approach a "g" and thus the clamping forces must be high enough to hold all objects in place while not distorting the fixtures. The location of the spherical balls for clamping the glass mask plates should be far enough from the edge to avoid the "roll-off" region of the glass. This ball clamp must also electrically ground the plate, otherwise another grounding strip will have to be attached. One-eighth-inch diameter balls seem to press through the resist to ground the plate effectively. How critical is the necessity of holding the mask plate without distortion? In precision mask making, we have found it

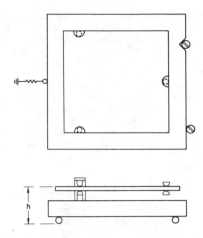

SUBSTRATE CARRIER
Fig. 6. Substrate mounting to carrier.

necessary to examine the mask holders carefully for substrate distortion—distortion induced by the holder itself. This is determined by taking a good master mask substrate and measuring its figure on, for example, a Zygo interferometer before and after clamping it in the mask carrier. Carriers were developed that did not change the mask plate figure both at writing time and subsequent use in an optical device.

Distortion of the plate in the out-of-plane direction by clamping torques, for example, can cause a surprisingly large amount of in-plane image movement, as follows. Assume a plate of thickness t and length L is deflected at its center a distance ω. This is, for example, a typical plate sag. What we wish to know is the lateral shift of the outer surface of the plate relative to the neutral axis. If the plate is distorted at the time of writing it in the electron-beam system and we are trying to generate an absolutely accurate reference plate, where each image is known to be placed on an absolute grid, what is the shift in the image absolute locations from center as we move toward the edges of the plate? It can be shown that the elastic deformation of the plate causes a shift ΔS according to the following approximation:

$$\Delta S = \frac{4t\omega}{L}.$$

If we let the plate be 4 mm thick and 100 mm across and it is deflected/distorted by 10 μm at its center, then the outer images will be 1.6 μm from the absolute grid relative to the plate center! From this simple calculation, it is evident that the substrates should not be distorted either in writing or using if absolute image placement is important.

It is difficult to support clamp wafers in a vacuum system with a high degree of flatness unless an electrostatic chuck is used [10]. However, because the wafers are thinner, a larger out-of-plane distortion can generally be tolerated, provided that the depth of field is sufficient.

The design of the wafer carrier is very important from the

point of view of autoregistration because the better prealigned the wafer is prior to being inserted into the electron-beam system, the easier it is to perform the alignment task, and, if good prealignment can be achieved, then no extensive search/coarse alignment concepts need to be implemented in the system and thus throughput will be higher. The wafer carrier I prefer clamps the wafer to an intermediate block and is then manipulated with respect to the "V and flat" mounting surfaces by an external manipulator on the alignment microscope. When the wafer is "aligned" the intermediate block is locked to the base of the carrier and the wafer can be considered located within a micron or better of its desired location. Grounding of the wafer is essential and can be a problem because of thick SiO_2 on the wafers.

V. MECHANICAL VIBRATIONS AND THERMAL EFFECTS

Mechanical vibration of the system parts can be caused by a combination of factors such as X-Y stage motion and vacuum-pump vibrations. Because of the rotary motion of turbo type vacuum pumps, I would not use them in a system to maintain the vacuum while writing patterns. They are fine for creating the initial vacuum quickly, but it is impossible to eliminate the vibrations introduced by these type pumps. Ion, cyro, or oil diffusion pumps are the better choice for sensitive electron-beam systems. Stage-induced vibrations can and should be minimized by judicious choice of the acceleration and deceleration curves for the stage motors and drive train. It is important to analyze carefully the effect of motor reactive forces on its mount and not to have this force cause an unwanted motion of the electron-beam column. Traditionally, we have installed motors directly to the sidewall of the workpiece chamber, but such a mounting can induce sidewall bending which, when translated to the column, can result in a shift of the column with respect to the stage.

The antivibration system on which the whole electron-beam system is resting is a critical part of the system and must isolate the system from *vertical* and *horizontal* floor vibrations whose frequency may range from a few hertz or less to several hundred hertz. Horizontal vibrations may be isolated by supporting the column platform on thin wires and then floating on air columns the platform with respect to the rods. Mechanical isolator resonances around 1 Hz are attainable and hence they isolate well above a few hertz. Precision pattern generation can be accomplished only if the environmental room temperature of system temperature is well controlled. Thermal expansion of system elements on the substrate itself can cause placement errors on the order of micrometers. For example, assume the laser interferometer is mounted on a steel plate and that the temperature of this plate changes by $0.3°C$ during the writing of a mask plate. Further assume that it is 30 cm from the laser interferometer center to the column center. The linear coefficient of thermal expansion is $\sim 10 \times 10^{-6}/°C$ for iron. The change in interferometer to column center distance is ~ 1 μm. This illustrates the need for good temperature control, judicious selection of materials, and mechanical and optical design which minimizes thermal effects.

VI. ELECTRONIC SUBSYSTEMS

A. Deflection Electronics

Two major types of beam-deflection principles have been used in electron-beam lithography: magnetic and electrostatic. In some systems only one or the other type is employed to deflect the beam. However, some, more complex, systems use combinations of magnetic and electrostatic. IBM's EL3 is one of these systems. For precision lithography, it is best to use only one type of deflection and have the deflecting element deflect the beam to the origin of a shape and also "fill this shape." Such an approach minimizes the calibration errors in systems using both magnetic and electrostatic deflection simultaneously. High-speed systems require many beam deflections per second and thus the natural choice is electrostatic deflection for these small but fast deflections. However, to cover a large writing area it is usual to use magnetic deflection. The electronics for these two types of deflection are vastly different. In either case, to attain a high degree of deflection accuracy, the deflection driver will have to have a high degree of stability, sufficient dynamic range to cover the field of interest, and the ability to do this in a time commensurate with the throughput requirements of the system.

The precision electron-beam writers we have built all use magnetic deflection. The amplifier is of a special type with emphasis placed on a precision approaching one part in 30 000 and with a bandwidth of several megahertz. When using single- or a few-turn deflecting yokes, it is necessary to drive several amperes of current to the coil to achieve the necessary beam deflection.

B. Pattern Generator/Data Paths

The pattern generator (PG) in the electron-beam system is a critical element that deserves much more attention than it can be given here. We will just touch on the highlights. The PG must be a device that is fast, flexible, and reliable. The role of the pattern generator is to take data from the CPU which describe in some compacted form the type of shape to be written, its location in the deflection field, and the dose including proximity correction and execute the shape quickly with little overhead. For experimental or R and D pattern writers, it is probably sufficient to design the data paths to be as shown in Fig. 1 where the major pattern data reside on a fast disk and are taken by DMA techniques from disk to memory and from memory to the pattern generator.

An alternative is to put between the CPU a large memory which can dump data to the PG as needed. In most R and D instances, it is not judicious to do this because no matter how large the memory is at the time the system is configured, VLSI circuit patterns to be written within the lifetime of the system will surely begin to exceed the memory size and then for each chip site the memory will have to be reloaded, a slow process. I think a better approach is to use a dedicated CPU to handle the pattern generator and optimize the data path from a large capacity fast disk, typically 64 Mbyte. Manufacturing systems should use the other large memory approach where the product plans are well in place prior to constructing the system and, if the memory is too small at a later date, a manufacturing strategy will motivate and have sufficient support to expand the memory as needed. This is not the case in R and D laboratory type systems and environment. Once the PG has received the pattern data from the CPU memory, it executes the shape or shapes and drives D/A converters that cause the beam to be deflected by either magnetic or electrostatic deflection.

The PG should have a "cache" type memory and obtain data from double buffers in the CPU. A microcoded PG is very useful because it is easy to experiment with different filling routines, i.e., shape paint-in algorithms as well as angled line methods of filling. Pattern generators for R and D need not be as fast as systems for manufacturing. To minimize the noise introduced by the PG into the deflection system, it is imperative that radiation from fast circuits be confined to the PG and that conductive noise be limited by extensive use of optical isolators and RF filtering. In many instances, a slow logic circuit will suffice in place of a Schottky unit. Use only fast logics where essential. It is good to have two modes of operation one for test and diagnostics where extra LED's and test points are driven active and another mode where all this extra circuitry can be turned off—this is the writing mode.

C. Noise and Grounding

Grounding of the column and electronics is very important and somewhat more of an art than a science. We have found that large welding cable, composed of many fine wires, is the best because of its flexibility and high conductance to high frequencies. Noisy cables should not be "run" alongside deflection lines and other sensitive cables. Vibrations induced by the cabling must be given adequate attention. All racks and chassis units should be explicitly grounded together. The deflection analog circuits should not be grounded and when switching from one mode of operation to another, no change in the ground condition should occur because this would result in a ground shift error affecting overlay.

D. Field Corrections and Registration

To obtain the correct size deflection field and correct for mirror or deflection coil imperfections such as mirror orthogonality, a field correction must be made either in software or hardware. For simple R and D systems that need to make a reasonable number of exposures per day the hardware approach is preferred. Corrections up to and including the cross product of X and Y are necessary. Thus the corrections are offset, magnification, rotations, and trapezoidal. These corrections are at most a few percent of the field, except for perhaps the magnification where it is desirable to have a continuously variable field size from 100 to 200 μm. The field size should be changed as close to the deflection yokes as possible so that the deflection noise is decreased with smaller fields. The control of these field corrections should be as passive as possible with all sources of noise disabled after the corrections have been implemented.

Registration in electron-beam lithography is a fairly easy task. The systems choices are numerous. One set of options that we have taken, and that has been proved workable over 10 years of experience, is the detection of backscattered electrons from pedestals for the marks (verses trenches) at a beam voltage of 25 kV. The automatic system makes a computer selected number of scans of the mark and averages this in real time in a special signal averager. The signal-to-noise ratio is improved to the point that the registration mark can be detected with an allowable error depending on the "rise time" of the mark signal. Pedestal marks are better than trenches because the scattered electrons have to traverse much less resist to escape from the sample and be detected. A combination of topographic and atomic number change makes a superb registration mark. Tungsten silicide on silicon is a typical mark material which has been excellent. The actual alignment accuracy between two different device levels for several runs over a period of time, in a typical but good R and D laboratory type system, is between 0.2 and 0.3 μm 3 sigma plus mean which includes all system errors and wafer distortions. This is for 1-μm groundrule devices.

E. Computer Control

The digital computer control functions for the electron-beam system should be implemented in a passive manner. That is, once the control function has been performed, no additional transactions should be performed unless essential. The purpose is to make the system as digitally quiet as possible while still providing all necessary control functions such as table move, registration, etc. Optical isolators should be used to keep analog and digital grounds separated.

VII. Software

A great deal of attention must be given to the development of control software for a successful electron-beam system. This cannot be overstated. The control software becomes an integral part of a complex system and the overall system is no better than the weakest part of all the elements which make up the total system. The control software functions are numerous but a few key ones are the following:

System initialization.
Laser and field correction feedback gain settings.
Wafer mapping (the measuring and mapping of the orientation and size, orthogonality, etc., of the wafer as chucked in the system).
Stitching control—the exact sizing of the fields to be written under laser feedback control (discussed below in more detail).
Multiple part number capability during exposure with a variable chip grid.
Setup of a "run" with ease and good correlation between input instructions and the physical wafer/mask to be written.
Measurements capability of the software so the electron-beam probe combined with the laser interferometer can be used as a measuring system to check the system itself as well as measure features on masks and wafers.
Utilities for the management of pattern data, loading data from large host facilities, linking of data sets, and the generation of control information for the table and pattern generator so that the correct pattern is placed on the correct substrate site.
A command language for manual testing of all I/O devices and operating the system in a manual to mode, or to do something unusual or to test out a new automation function.
Automatic control functions so that once hardware and software are operating, the system can be left to run a series of substrates fully automatically performing complex operations without the attendance of a full time operator.
Good modular system software, fully documented, with all interrupts and processor/processor communications done in a straightforward manner.
Frequently used software such as registration mark detection to be written in assembly language and high-level control commands to be written in a high-level command language with computations done as required in either assembly or a high-level language such as Pascal.

As an example, I would like to discuss the software required to set up the system for field stitching. Because chips tend to grow both in physical size and complexity, i.e., number of fabricated lines or cells per unit length, the electron-beam system should be capable of precision stitching of small subfields into the desired final large chip pattern. It is very difficult to achieve, in a single electron-beam field, both the chip size and fabricated lines requirement if the chip is over about

5–7 mm^2 and the number of fabricated lines exceeds 5000. In other words, 1-μm lines over 5 mm is about the practical limit.

To precisely stitch two or more fields together requires that the electron-beam field be precisely calibrated to the stage step-and-repeat distance. Calibration of the stitching field requires the laser feedback gain set to the correct value so that if the mechanical table has some positional error the electron beam is deflected to compensate for the table error. If we are going to stitch 1.6-mm fields, then the table is moved such that a corner of the field is 0.8 mm from the column center in both x and y directions. A single registration mark is required on the substrate and the table is moved so this reference mark is precisely located at the field corner. Next, the electron beam is deflected to that corner and the mark location is measured in beam steps. Then the table moves the reference mark to the next corner and the beam is deflected to the mark again. This repeats for all four corners and then based on the x and y locations of the four marks the electron-beam field is corrected to make it exactly match the intended stitching size. The laser interferometer is the reference, and with a good system the field can be sized to the limit of the laser interferometer, which is about 0.01 μm. Stitching with this technique of field sizing on the substrate to be written at the time of writing results in stitching errors which often cannot be detected.

VIII. Summary

Electron-beam-written masks and wafers can be made with good linewidth control and accurate image placement. With proximity correction and high-contrast positive resists, linewidth control of ±0.1 μm is achievable. Somewhat better control can be obtained in special situations for linewidths around 1 μm and below. Absolute image placement and plate to plate or wafer overlay is a strong function of column stability and the characteristics of the laser interferometer controlled mechanical stage. An absolute image placement over 10 × 10 cm area of 0.1 μm or better than most measuring systems are capable of measuring can be obtained.

Acknowledgment

The author would like to acknowledge discussions with D. Kern, W. Grobman, F. Hohn, and P. Coane in the preparation of this paper and the specific contribution of D. Kern which is Fig. 2, the influence of lens bore size on stray magnetic fields.

References

[1] D. R. Herriott et al., IEEE Trans. Electron Devices, vol. ED-22, p. 385, 1975.
[2] F. S. Ozdemir et al., in Proc. 13th Symp. on Electron, Ion and Photon Beam Tech., J. Vac. Sci. Technol., p. 1246, May, 1975.
[3] T.P.C. Chang et al., in Proc. 7th Int. Conf. on Electron and Ion Beam Science and Technology (Electrochem. Soc.), R. Bakish, Ed., p. 392, 1976.
[4] G. L. Varnell et al., in Proc. 12th Symp. on Electron, Ion and Photon Beam Tech., J. Vac. Sci. Technol., p. 1048, May, 1973.
[5] J. Trotel, in Proc. 14th Symp. on Electron, Ion and Photon Beam Tech., J. Vac. Sci. Technol., p. 872, 1977.
[6] R. D. Moore et al., J. Vac. Sci. Technol., vol. 19, p. 950, Nov./Dec. (Proc. 16th Symp. Electron, Ion, and Photon Beam Tech.).
[7] A. N. Broers and T. P. Chang, Microcircuit Engineering, Nixon and Ahmed, Eds. Cambridge, UK: Cambridge Univ. Press, 1980, p. 73.
[8] P. Coane et al., Microcircuit Engineering Conference, Grenoble, 1982 (in press).
[9] F. Hohn et al., J. Appl. Phys., vol. 53, p. 1283, Mar. 1982.
[10] G. A. Wardly, IEEE Trans. Electron Devices, vol. ED-11, p. 414, 1975.

Status of X-Ray Lithography

WARREN D. GROBMAN

Abstract—This paper will review some of the current approaches to X-ray lithography technology for device and circuit fabrication. Recent results in source, mask, process, and alignment research will be surveyed. A special emphasis will be placed on the differences in approach using full wafer, conventional source systems compared with those which are based on step and repeat and which may use a storage ring source.

Systems which use a full wafer approach can compete with full wafer optical lithography at minimum circuit feature dimensions greater than about $1\frac{1}{2}$ μm. Their resolution is also competitive with that of optical wafer steppers, but the overlay achievable with wafer steppers is potentially better. If the resolution achievable with X-rays ($\ll 1$ μm) is combined with the local control over alignment obtainable with a step-and-repeat approach, then a lithographic technology compatible with dense submicron circuits is potentially obtainable. However, this case will need the increased exposure speed which is achieved most easily by use of a synchrotron radiation source.

CURRENT X-RAY LITHOGRAPHY TECHNOLOGY

X-RAY lithography [1] (XRL) consists of proximity printing of a mask onto a wafer. In this approach to pattern definition, the mask is generally a thin continuous substrate on which a pattern of X-ray absorber has been fabricated. This technique has been extensively reviewed in the literature [2]–[5], and has several fundamental advantages compared with the competing techniques of electron beam or optical lithography [6].

One advantage is that of resolution and process simplicity for the high aspect ratio resist patterns required for dense circuits with linewidths $\lesssim 1$ μm. Such resist patterning requires complex pattern transfer processing of multilevel resist systems for electron beam lithography, due to electron scattering. In the case of optical lithography, whose intrinsic resolution is not as high as that of electron beam lithography, such complex processes are also required for linewidths near 1 μm in thick resist, due to diffraction effects.

Another significant potential advantage of XRL over scanning electron beam lithography is that the former is a serial while the latter is a parallel writing process. For this reason, the throughput for XRL can be substantially better than that for scanning electron beam systems.

A major conclusion of this work (discussed in detail in [7] and [8]) is that much of the potential throughput advantage of XRL may be lost if overlay consistent with dense circuits is required, and if conventional X-ray sources are used. For overlay which is a fraction of the linewidth, XRL will likely require a step and repeat approach in which an array of chips is stepped in the x- and y-directions to cover the entire wafer [5], [7], [8]. This reduction of mask size, required in the case of imperfect mask stability or mask-wafer separation control, is analyzed in the next section. There we show that conventional sources do not have enough flux for high throughput in such a stringent overlay regime due to the stepping, even when high sensitivity, complex layered resist systems are used [9], [10].

The author is with the IBM Thomas J. Watson Research Center, Yorktown Heights, NY 10598.

In order to recover the potential throughput of XRL in such a case, a storage ring source [7], [11] can be used. This approach not only provides higher throughput than any other lithography approach for dense, high resolution circuits, but also has the great advantage of requiring a simpler alignment system than that required with a conventional source.

Before analyzing the throughput and resolution of conventional and storage ring based XRL systems, we summarize briefly the current state of the art in several components of the technology.

Masks

XRL masks [2], [3], [12]–[15] are typically formed by first covering the front of a Si wafer with a film of a low-Z compound (e.g. a boron-doped layer, SiC, $Si_xO_yN_z$, etc.). The wafer is then etched from the back (with an annular rim masked from the etch), to form a free standing membrane [16]. An absorber pattern of a heavy element is then formed on this substrate. An additional step may consist of formation of a film of polymer on top of the wafer to form a composite structure [14], [17]. The mask also may be attached to a thick annular ring (quartz or some other material) to ensure flatness [14], [16]. An ingenious alternate approach, utilizing Ti films, has also been described recently [18]. Two types of parameters characterize the overlay potential of X-ray masks; those specifying flatness, and pattern stability. Several recent studies of these quantities have been performed [14], [17], [18], but much more detail is needed in this area as the analysis of the next section will emphasize.

Alignment Approaches

Approaches using both X-rays and visible light as the signal sensing radiation have been discussed in numerous articles [2], [3]. X-rays do not appear currently to be the method of choice, both due to the low contrast of X-ray alignment marks, and also due to the low flux available from most sources. Several recent techniques involving visible light have recently been described. Some of these involve an external optical system which images both the mask and the wafer, and then analyzes the signal in the image plane [19], [20]. Other types of techniques involve optical elements (such as gratings [21] on linear Fresnel zone lenses [22]) on the mask. These techniques in principle can generate signals with the precision required for submicron device fabrication. However, a total system for achieving this result has not yet been described.

Sources

The conventional source for X-ray lithography is a water-cooled anode bombarded by electrons with energy <10 KeV, yielding predominantly soft characteristic radiation [23]–[26] (e.g. Al_{K_α} with $\lambda = 8.3$ Å). Other recently described (pulsed)

Reprinted from *IEEE Int. Electron Devices Meeting*, Dec. 1980, pp. 415–419.

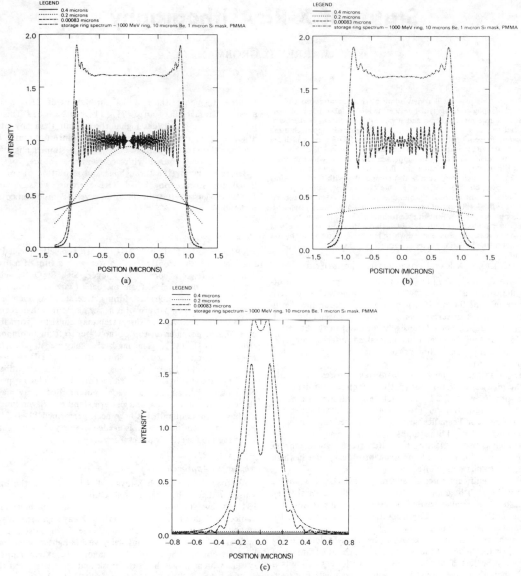

Fig. 1. (a) Fresnel diffraction thru a 2 micron slit 20 microns from the resist. (b) Fresnel diffraction thru a 2 micron slit 50 microns from the resist. (c) Fresnel diffraction thru a 0.5 micron slit 50 microns from the resist.

sources include laser-induced metal plasmas [27], and capillary spark discharge sources [28]. The former suffers from a debris and intensity problem, while it is difficult to get enough X-rays in the XRL range ($6 \lesssim \lambda \lesssim 15$ Å) with the latter source. A recent paper on pulsed argon plasma experiments may provide ultimately another route for new sources of characteristic X-rays [29]. Finally, the electron storage ring [7] provides a d.c. source of X-rays in a continuous spectrum which can match well the requirements of XRL, and which is unique in the magnitude and collimation of the flux which it produces.

COMPARISON OF CONVENTIONAL AND STORAGE RING BASED SYSTEMS: RESOLUTION AND THROUGHPUT

Resolution

As noted in several papers, the resolution of the exposed resist distribution in XRL depends both on the photoelectron range, and on Fresnel diffraction. For $\lambda \approx 10$ Å, the latter effect predominates and can be simply calculated [3] for the case of exposure of a line of width w, for a mask a distance S from the resist. Fig. 1 shows the results of imaging a line using four sources; three of these are monochromatic sources of wavelengths λ = 0.4, 0.2, and 0.00083 μm. The fourth source is a 1000 MeV storage ring spectrum, weighted as a function of λ by the transmission $T_W(\lambda)$ of a 10 μm thick Be window, by the transmission $T_S(\lambda)$ of a 1 μm thick Si mask substrate, and by the absorption coefficient $\mu(\lambda)$ for PMMA resist [7].

In Fig. 1(a), these results are plotted for the case of a line of width w = 2 μm, positioned a distance S = 20 μm from the resist. In this figure, the first three curves reproduce the results of [3], while the fourth curve shows that much of the high spatial frequency exposure inhomogeneity of a monochromatic 8.3 Å source is averaged out by using the continuous storage ring spectrum. In practice, penumbral blur due to the finite source size in a conventional system will eliminate the very high spatial frequency oscillations near x = 0 in Fig. 1(a) for λ = 8.3 Å. Nevertheless, there will still be significant dosage dips near the edges of the line for this wavelength. These are completely eliminated for the storage ring spectrum. For a larger mask-wafer separation S = 50 μm, Fig. 1(b) shows these results again for a line with w = 2 μm. At this printing distance, the nonmonochromaticity of the storage ring spectrum is again effective at eliminating undesirable dose oscillations. This advantage of a storage ring is even more dramatic for the case of a line of width w = 0.5 μm at distance of S = 50 μm, as shown in Fig. 1(c). In this case, the monochromatic radiation yields a highly non-uniform dose, with a 50 percent dip in the center of the image. The storage ring dose remains much more nearly constant in the center of the line.

These calculations expand on previous ones involving Fresnel diffraction by monochromatic radiation, and show a new advantage of storage ring XRL which has not been discussed previously. The wide range of wavelengths found in a continuous storage ring spectrum significantly reduces the amplitude of dose variations across a line which are due to Fresnel diffraction. For this reason, XRL obtains increased process simplicity for narrow lines when using a storage ring source compared with a conventional source which emits characteristic, relatively monochromatic radiation. Alternatively, one may say that the effective resolution of a storage ring exposure is significantly better than that of a conventional source.

Throughput

This section uses the results discussed in detail in [7] and [8] to give examples of the throughput difference for conventional and storage ring based systems with stringent overlay constraints.

We assume that patterns on the X-ray mask have random placement errors of size η_r, and that in addition, the mask pattern size does not quite match the wafer pattern size due to thermal expansion or wafer hot processing distortion [31]. That is, for a mask of radius R_m, a pattern at the edge of the mask suffers a placement error fR_m. This error will be cancelled in our conventional source analysis by adjusting mask wafer separation S, but cannot be adjusted for the storage ring due to the large value of the mask-source distance D_o (Fig. 2). Lack of perfect mask-wafer separation, of magnitude δS, occurs due to lack of perfect alignment system control of the quantity S, as well as due to imperfect flatness of the mask and wafer, leading to an additional overlay error $R_m \delta S / D_o$ at the mask edge. Finally, the mechanical system which is aligning the mask and wafer laterally is assumed to have a statistical error

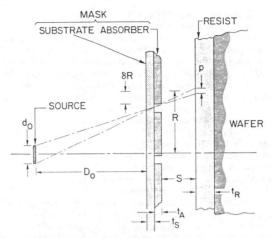

Fig. 2. Illustration of the X-ray lithography proximity printing process, showing the method by which various quantities determine image magnification and penumbral blurring.

A. The final overlay Δ which is achieved is assumed to be the square root of the sum of the squares of all of these errors:

$$\Delta^2 = \eta_r^2 + f^2 R_m^2 + A^2 + \left(\frac{\delta S}{D_o} R_m\right)^2. \tag{1}$$

This equation determines the maximum permissible mask size required to achieve the device overlay groundrule Δ, given the mechanical alignment error A, and the mask and wafer stability imperfections η_r, f, and ΔS. It therefore determines the number of steps per wafer, and consequently the system throughput.

For the storage ring, D_o is typically so large that the term involving δS is negligible. Ignoring this term, solving (1) for R_m in terms of the other quantities, and approximating the number of steps required to cover the wafer of radius R_w by $(R_w/R_m)^2$, we obtain

$$N_{SR} = \frac{R_w^2 f^2}{\Delta^2 - \eta_R^2 - A^2} \tag{2}$$

for the number of steps required to print the full wafer for a storage ring source.

For a conventional rotating anode source, the number of steps N_{RA} is determined in a similar manner. However in this case, we assume that S is adjusted so that the term involving f in (1) is negligible. The advantage of a conventional source, its ability to have the magnification adjusted, is used to eliminate the linear mask distortion term. Then, solving (1) for R_m in this case, the number of steps is:

$$N_{RA} = \frac{R_w^2 (\delta S/D_o)^2}{\Delta^2 - \eta_R^2 - A^2}. \tag{3}$$

As in the storage ring case, the number of steps depends on a factor $R_w^2/(\Delta^2 - \eta_R^2 - A^2)$, and is then multiplied by a second factor unique to this type of source. The ratio of the number of steps in the two cases is simply

$$\frac{N_{RA}}{N_{SR}} = \frac{\delta S^2}{D_o^2 f^2}.$$

Typical numbers for f, δS, and D_o of 10^{-5}, 2 μm, and 20 cm respectively would give an equal number of steps for both cases. The wafer throughputs would then simply be in the ratio of the exposure plus step and align time per step. A time of four seconds for storage ring exposure of relatively insensitive resist ($\sim$mJ/cm^2) can easily be achieved, while exposure times of about 60 seconds may some day be achievable with conventional systems only with difficulty, using extremely sensitive negative resists in a complex multilayer pattern transfer process [9], [10], [30]. For a step and align time of three seconds, the ratio of throughputs would then be about 10—one order of magnitude higher for a station at a storage ring. (In the concluding section, we show that for linewidths of 0.6–1.0 μm, one specific set of values for Δ, η_r, and A gives storage ring throughputs of 80–30 4" wafers/hour, compared with 9–3 wafers/hour for a conventional system.)

This rough estimate has been made conservative in favor of the conventional system, using an expensive pattern transfer process for that case. Reduction of f by a factor of two, for example by predicting the linear [31] hot processing wafer distortion and by then writing masks which begin to match this distortion would give a station at a storage ring a factor of 40 advantage in throughput.

Finally, it must be emphasized that in the storage ring case, only crude control of S is required, so that the alignment/wafer stepper system for a storage ring beam line is much less complex than for a conventional system. This point is made stronger by emphasizing that S must be kept small in a high throughput conventional system in order to minimize penumbra p (Fig. 2). Thus a conventional system must step the wafer near the mask N_{RA} times with a separation S of the order of 5–20 μm, leading to potential difficulties with catastrophic mask/wafer contact during stepping.

Conclusions

We have reviewed the current status of XRL and have showed that for the production of dense (stringent overlay) circuits with linewidths $W \lesssim 1$–1.25 μm there are significant throughput, resolution, and process simplicity advantage to XRL using a storage ring source. Such an approach combines the intrinsic advantage of XRL of low scattering in thick resist and parallel pattern element exposure with a source whose collimation, power, and spectrum [7] are ideally suited for high speed printing of small masks in a step and repeat mode. For example, using the formulae above, we can estimate the wafer throughput of the two approaches as a function of linewidth as shown in the following table.

The conventional system throughputs given here assume complex resist processing, with negative resists of a sensitivity which has not yet been demonstrated, while the storage ring source uses more conventional thick resists. If less sensitive negative resists are available, and if some of the linear mask/wafer distortion difference is reduced as described above, then the difference in throughput in the two approaches is even more dramatic.

Table I gives throughputs calculated using (1)–(3), which assume that total wafer fabrication time depends only on stepping, alignment, and printing time. Additional overheads such as wafer load/unload time will decrease the achievable throughput below these values.

As the second section of this paper has shown, most of the components of XRL have been demonstrated. Assembling them in a manufacturing system with auto-align step and re-

TABLE I
4" Wafer Throughput for Conventional and Storage Ring Source Systems

	Linewidth		
	1.0	0.8	0.6
Δ (μm – 3σ)	0.4	0.3	0.25
η_r (μm – 3σ)	0.25	0.20	0.15
f		10^{-5}	
A (μm – 3σ)	0.25	0.20	0.15
δS (μm)		2	
Conv. Source D_o (Cm)		20	
Storage Ring Throughput (levels/hour)	80	45	31
Conventional Source Throughput (levels/hour)	9	5	3

peat will, however, be a formidable development task. Some of the requisite technology may be taken from that used for optical step-and-repeat systems.

Finally, the cost of a storage ring for XRL is likely to be a large fraction of $10 [7]. Such an investment in a storage ring source, illuminating many exposure stations simultaneously, will only be acceptable if large production volume is required (e.g. for RAM). In the event that such an investment is justified by the production volume, there are still unique unanswered questions concerning mask inspection and the logistics of a mix of circuit patterns. The relative maturity of electron beam technology will play a significant role in solving these problems.

References

[1] D. L. Spears and H. I. Smith, Electron Lett. 8, p. 102–4, 1972. D. L. Spears and H. I. Smith, Solid State Tech. 15, No. 7, p. 21, 1972.
[2] B. Fay, "X-Ray Techniques and Registration Methods," in Microcircuit Engineering, Ed. H. Ahmed and W. C. Nixon, Cambridge University Press, London, England, p. 323.
[3] P. Tischer, "Advances in X-Ray Lithography," in Electronics to Microelectronics, Ed. W. A. Kaiser and W. E. Proebster, North Holland, 1980.
[4] E. Spiller and R. Feder, "X-Ray Lithography," in X-Ray Optics, Ed. H. J. Queisser, Springer Berlin, p. 35, 1977.
[5] H. I. Smith and D. C. Flanders, J. Vac. Sci. Technol. 17, p. 533, 1980.
[6] A. N. Broers and T.H.P. Chang, "High Resolution for Microcircuits," in Microcircuit Engineering, Ed. H. Ahmed and W. C. Nixon, Cambridge University Press, 1979.
[7] W. D. Grobman, "Synchrotron Radiation X-Ray Lithography," in Handbook on Synchrotron Radiation, Ed. E. E. Koch et al, North Holland, 1981. In Press.
[8] D. Hofer and W. D. Grobman. "Throughput in X-Ray Lithography Systems," to be published.
[9] J. M. Moran and G. N. Taylor, J. Vac. Sci. Technol. 16, 1979.
[10] J. R. Maldonado, et al, J. Vac. Sci. Technol. 16, p. 1942, 1979.
[11] E. Spiller et al, J. Appl. Phys. 47, p. 5450.
[12] L. Csepregi and A. Heuberger, J. Vac. Sci. Technol. 16, p. 1962, 1979.
[13] D. Hofer et al, J. Vac. Sci. Technol. 16, p. 1968–1972, 1979.
[14] D. Maydan et al, J. Vac. Sci. Technol. 16, p. 1959–1961, 1979.
[15] R. K. Watts et al, Proc. 8th Int. Conf. Electron Ion Beam Science and Tech., Ed. R. Bakish, The Electrochemical Society, Inc., Princeton, NJ, p. 453–457, 1978.
[16] D. C. Flanders and H. I. Smith, J. Vac. Sci. Technol. 15, p. 995–997, 1978.
[17] F. Yamagishi et al, Proc. 9th Int. Conf. Electron and Ion Beam Science and Tech., Ed. R. Bakish, The Electrochemical Society, Princeton, NJ 1980. In Press.
[18] W. D. Buckley et al, Proc. 9th Int. Conf. Electron and Ion Beam Science and Tech., Ed. R. Bakish, The Electrochemical Society, Inc., Princeton, NJ, 1980. In Press.

[19] G. M. Dubroeucq and M. Lacombat, "Automatic Alignment for Wafer Steppers," in *Microcircuit Engineering*, Ed. H. Ahmed and W. C. Nixon, Cambridge University Press, 1978.

[20] S. Yamazaki *et al*, J. Vac. Sci. Tech. *15*, p. 987–991, 1978.

[21] S. Austin *et al*, J. Vac. Sci. Tech. *15*, p. 984–986, 1978.

[22] B. Fay *et al*, J. Vac. Sci. Technol. *16*, p. 1954–1958, 1979.

[23] P. A. Sullivan and J. H. McCoy, J. Vac. Sci. Tech. *12*, p. 1325–1328, 1975.

[24] J. S. Greeneich, Appl. Phys. Lett. *27*, p. 579–581, 1975.

[25] G. A. Wardly *et al*, Proc. Int. Conf. Microlithography, Paris, p. 217–220, 1977.

[26] J. R. Maldonado *et al*, J. Vac. Sci. Technol. *16*, p. 1942–1945, 1979.

[27] M. C. Peckerar *et al*, Proc. 8th Int. Conf. Electron Ion Beam Science and Tech., Ed. R. Bakish, The Electrochemical Society, Inc., Princeton, NJ, p. 432–443, 1978.

[28] R. A. McCorkle and J. J. Vollmer, Rev. Sci. Instr. *48*, p. 1055–1063, 1977.

[29] C. Stallings *et al*, Appl. Phys. Lett. *35*, p. 524, 1979.

[30] G. N. Taylor *et al*, Polymer Engineering and Science *17*, p. 420–429, 1977.

[31] D. Maydan *et al*, J. Vac. Sci. Tech. *16*, 1979.

X-Ray Lithography for VLSI

BAYLOR B. TRIPLETT AND RICHARD F. HOLLMAN

Invited Paper

Abstract—In order for any lithography to become the preferred technique for the production of very large scale integrated circuit (VLSI) devices, the technique will have to 1) achieve the required resolution and registration and 2) become more cost effective in this capacity for large volume production than its competitors. The advent of advanced lithographic techniques for LSI production has been postponed by substantial advances in conventional lithography. However, integrated circuits with feature sizes of 1 μm or smaller seem to have significant performance and price advantages over current devices. Such submicron feature sizes press noncontact optical lithography up against the laws of physics. Meanwhile, advances in X-ray lithography have occurred and continue to occur at a promising rate. This paper discusses our experience with X-ray lithography at Intel. Most of our X-ray experience is with the Intel 1-Mbit bubble memory because of the small minimum feature size (1.2 μm) and the defect and alignment tolerance of this device. However, this discussion will be geared toward general VLSI applications of X-ray lithography.

INTRODUCTION AND BACKGROUND

LITHOGRAPHIC TOOLS in use for integrated circuit (IC) fabrication can be conveniently divided into two groups. The first group uses conventional ultraviolet (UV) light or shorter wavelength electromagnetic radiation such as deep UV or X-rays to produce resist exposure in conjunction with a "mask" to define the feature pattern. The second group uses a charged-particle beam (such as an electron beam) to achieve the desired resist exposure. In the case of the second group, the feature patterns are generally defined without the use of a "mask" but with precision wafer and beam locations controlled by a computer. Although electron-beam lithography is extensively used for mask production today and direct-write electron-beam systems are being readied for submicron IC development and low-volume fabrication, X-ray lithography offers a strong economic advantage over electron-beam lithography for high-volume applications. The present paper concentrates on the development and application of X-ray lithography for large-volume VLSI production and focuses on the similarities and differences between X-ray and deep-UV lithography for this application.

X-ray lithography is a proximity lithographic patterning technique in which the mask and wafer are typically separated by a gap of about 50 μm. Unlike conventional UV lithography, the resolution of X-ray lithography is not limited by diffraction effects because of the relatively short wavelength of the exposing radiation (7 Å in the Perkin-Elmer rotating tungsten source [2] and 4.4 Å in the Bell Labs fixed palladium source [3]). With conventional (nonsynchrotron) X-ray sources, inherent resolution is usually limited by the ratio of the effective source spot size to working distance according to the equation

Manuscript received September 29, 1982.
The authors are with the Intel Magnetics Inc., Santa Clara, CA 95051.

$$\delta = g \cdot s/D \qquad (1)$$

where δ is called the image penumbra and g, s, and D are the gap spacing, the spot size, and the source-to-wafer working distance, respectively. Thus the resolution of a conventional X-ray source can be improved simply by decreasing the source spot size. However, one generally pays for this improved performance with longer exposure times due to the reduction in the total flux emitted from the source spot. (Synchrotron radiation sources emit almost parallel X-ray beams and thus are not subject to the constraint mentioned above because $D = \infty$ in (1).) However appropriate synchrotron sources may be to well-developed, very large volume production lines of the future [4], the high capital cost of these systems suggests that research, prototype development, and first-generation production with X-ray will largely be done with the conventional sources (rotating anode, fixed anode, and plasma). Accordingly, this paper focuses on the issues involved in using these sources and our experience with the Perkin-Elmer tungsten rotating anode system [2] in particular.

X-ray lithography is similar to conventional UV lithography in the sense that the X-ray source is simply electromagnetic radiation emitted from a small spot (at least with conventional sources). However, X-rays interact with matter very differently than conventional light and are either transmitted or absorbed by materials depending on the material thickness and atomic number. Thus one inherent advantage of X-ray lithography over conventional UV is the transparency of small defects such as the organic or silicon-based debris commonly found in wafer fabrication areas. However, problems in fabricating the mask and resist arise from the intrinsic nature of X-ray interaction with matter. First, in order to be sufficiently X-ray transmitting, the X-ray mask substrate must be fabricated from a thin layer (typically 1- to 6-μm thickness) of a low-atomic-number material which is reasonably inert or carefully protected from deterioration or tension changes induced by the environment. High optical transmission is also desirable because many alignment techniques require an optically transmitting substrate. Secondly, in order to be sufficiently X-ray absorbing, the mask pattern must be fabricated from a reasonably thick film ($\sim$6000 Å) of a high-atomic-number material such as gold or platinum. The development of fabrication techniques to produce defect-free features with the required steep wall slopes was and still is substantially more time consuming and capital intensive than the development of techniques to pattern thin chrome layers ($\sim$1000 Å) on conventional photomasks or reticles. Finally, the low X-ray absorption of organic matter suggested that electron-beam resists, already developed and under development for the production of electron-beam photomasks and electron-beam

Reprinted from *Proc. IEEE*, vol. 71, pp. 585–588, May 1983.

direct write, might have to be modified or doped with more absorbing elements in order to provide exposure times consistent with the high wafer throughputs required for production lithography [5].

The above problems and their solutions can be conveniently divided into 1) the source–resist technology and 2) the mask technology; and they will be discussed in this order in the following sections.

SOURCE-RESIST TECHNOLOGY

X-rays are typically generated less efficiently than their UV and deep-UV counterparts and the question of exposure time with conventional X-ray sources received substantial attention a few years ago. At least two approaches have led to systems in this country that are currently in use for fabricating devices having minimum feature sizes near 1 μm. The two approaches are 1) the tuned resist approach as developed [5] extensively at Bell Labs with a low-power 4-kW palladium source and 2) the high-power source approach useable with a larger number and variety of resists. The two approaches are not exclusive and may well be combined in the production system of the future. If it is assumed that a viable system must achieve exposure times of 30 s or less with devices having about 1-μm minimum feature size, both approaches seem to be viable. Zacharias (Bell Labs) reports [6] the resolution of 0.5-μm gaps with a dry processed tuned resist exposed for 30 s. Conventional wet developed resist patterns require 240-s exposures with the DCOPA resist [6]. At Intel Magnetics, our present working resolution of 0.75 μm is achieved in a number of conventionally wet developed electron-beam resists often using the trilevel resist scheme described by Maydan [5] to enhance step coverage and resolution. Exposure and alignments are achieved with the prototype tungsten rotating anode system built by the Perkin-Elmer Corporation [2]. Exposure times for 20-kV excitation at our current 12-kW operating power are 60 s for Eastman Kodak EK88, 120 s for Somar Sel-N, Type A, and 100 s for Somar Sel-N, Type EX. (These exposure times become 36, 72, and 60 s respectively, at the operating power limit of 20 kW.) All of the above resists achieve our 0.75-μm working resolution but we have only used Sel-N, Type A[1] extensively at this time. The exposure time for a sensitive dry developed resist is indicated [7] to be about 6 s in our system. However, we have not put effort into attempting to develop high resolution or high throughputs with this process simply because the exposure time overhead is not a serious problem for full field exposures. More effort in this area will probably be appropriate before X-ray step-and-repeat systems become available [2].

Shorter exposure times are also possible within conventional floor space areas and with conventional wet developed resists with the plasma X-ray sources under development at Physics International [8] and Maxwell Laboratories [9]. These sources will not be considered further here because we have not yet evaluated them.

Both the Bell and Intel Magnetics (IM) groups have previously summarized [1], [10] their experiences with device fabrication using the two exposure systems described above. Some additional information about our experience with the system at IM seems warranted. The Perkin-Elmer rotating anode system at IM is an intrinsically higher power but more complex approach

[1] Somar Manufacturing Co., Ltd., 11-2, Ginza 4-Chome, Chou-Ku, Tokyo 104, Japan.

to X-ray flux generation than fixed-anode systems. The system installed at IM has been in operation for almost three years. During the three years only two periods of unscheduled downtime occurred. First, the vacuum system cryopump motor failed after 2.4 years of operation and had to be rebuilt. This failure is consistent with the expected operating life of the component. Second, a 25-μm-thick Be window developed a small vacuum leak after 2.6 years. Our current electron-beam gun has 250 h of operation at 20-kV excitation and 12-kW power. Since a failure of this gun design has not been observed at IM, we cannot comment on its expected mean time to failure.

Although properly designed rotating anode systems are quiet and reasonably vibration free, one potentially significant problem with rotating anodes for lithography is vibrational blurring of resolution due to coupling between the rotating anode and the mask–wafer cartridge. This effect was studied on the prototype system at IM by attaching a sensitive accelerometer to the cartridge frame to monitor the vibrational level of this component and then mechanically shorting the anode support frame to the cartridge. Under this direct short condition, a deterioration to 1.5-μm resolution was observed. By introducing partially damped couplings between anode and cartridge and plotting root mean square vibrational amplitude of the cartridge versus resolution, it was possible to quantify the effect of vibrational shorts on resolution. The vibration level measured with an accelerometer attached to the cartridge frame and with the anode in motion is approximately three times the room background level. The estimated resolution limitation due to this vibrational level is 0.1 μm or of order a factor of three less than we are capable of observing with our 0.75-μm resolution masks.

In summary, we have had no difficulty with the Perkin-Elmer prototype source. Furthermore, exposure times with the sensitive resists listed above do not seem to be an impediment to the development of production X-ray lithography. The prototype Perkin-Elmer system has a separate proximity aligner that requires [11] a sequence of manual operations. Although throughputs with this arrangement are adequate for development work, second-generation systems with more automation are required for production throughputs [2].

The enhancement of resolution/step coverage with multilevel resist schemes has been extensively discussed for both optical and X-ray lithography. Submicron optical lithography requires such multilevel structures because of diffraction and depth-of-focus limitations. X-ray lithography, on the other hand, may require such schemes primarily because of swelling and lack of dry process resistance with the sensitive X-ray resists currently in use and, secondarily, because of limited resist X-ray absorption and the image penumbra effects described by (1). The use of multilevel techniques has substantial manufacturing implications for volume production [12]. Steep resist profiles have been reported in conventional resists such as AZ or PMMA by using the intense X-ray output from synchrotron storage rings as a source. Using this observation, Maldonado has argued [4] that such a lithographic storage ring used in conjunction with single-level conventional resists may provide a more economical large volume production alternative to multilevel X-ray with conventional sources. Thus while optical lithography must use multilevel schemes in order to do production submicron lithography, X-ray lithography can consider either multilevel or single-level approaches depending on source, resist, and processing equipment developments in the future. We pattern the first layer of the Intel 1-Mbit magnetic bubble memory with a single-level thickness of 6000 Å Sel-N, Type A, but have not yet attempted to process single-level X-ray lithographic patterns over features with significant step heights.

MASK TECHNOLOGY

Our experience with fabrication of the Intel Magnetics 1-Mbit bubble memory using X-ray lithography has been described previously. The first working device passed test in October 1981 and the process has been undergoing prototype evaluation since that time. Since a commercial supplier of X-ray lithographic masks does not yet exist, we were forced to develop our own technology, and the fabrication of masks having sufficient quality to do VLSI device development work was found to be the most difficult task to date in our experience with X-ray lithography. Our mask patterning technology evolved over a two-year period into a process reasonably similar to the one described by the Bell group [5]. The Intel Magnetics megabit bubble memory is an ideal initial evaluation tool for the technology because of the high resolution required (1.2-μm minimum feature size) together with its defect and alignment tolerance (defect density and dimensional stability being the major shortcomings of early X-ray masks). Although our early experience indicated the defect density issue was the more troublesome of the two issues in our prototype development mode, continuous progress was being made by improvements in our processing. A learning curve of defect density versus time showed a factor-of-five reduction in defect density in 1981 to 15/cm^2 in December 1981 [1]. Progress since that time has slowed somewhat because of less effort on the defect issue alone and more on dimensional stability as described later. However, the corresponding curve for 1982 shows a factor-of-three reduction per year and indicates that LSI silicon device evaluation at Intel could start (at $\sim$5/cm^2) as soon as the end of 1982. The Bell Labs effort, which started several years before ours, reports defect densities on masks fabricated with similar techniques of 1 to 2/cm^2. Low defect densities on X-ray step-and-repeat reticles are achieved more easily because of the smaller area involved. Thus as pointed out by Fencil and Hughes [2], an 18-percent yield of perfect 4-cm^2 reticles for X-ray step and repeat is achieved with defect densities of 0.5 defects/cm^2.

Although X-ray step and repeat looks attractive for future X-ray production systems, it seems likely that the feasibility of X-ray for production lithography will be evaluated first on full field exposure systems. The use of full field X-ray masks poses a potential problem for LSI silicon device evaluation. The mask-to-mask overlay desired for LSI silicon device fabrication is generally $\frac{1}{5}$ to $\frac{1}{10}$ the minimum linewidth size. We have previously reported X-ray mask feature movement during fabrication of 0.5-μm maximum and 0.2-μm rms distortion in 75-mm fields on 1-μm-thick titanium membranes. Although perfectly adequate for bubble memory device fabrication where overlays can be comparable to minimum feature size, the above distortions would limit the yield of fine-line silicon devices. A preferred substrate would be a thicker film with a high Young's modulus.

In addition to titanium, boron nitride, silicon nitride, silicon dioxide, silicon carbide, and composite structures of these materials have all been proposed [13] as stable mask substrates for X-ray lithography. Boron nitride films fabricated by low-

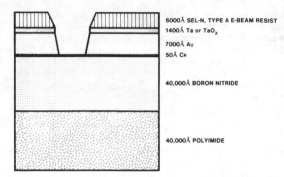

Fig. 1. X-ray mask structure of Eaton boron nitride substrate.

pressure chemical vapor deposition (LPCVD) and coated with polyimide organic films for additional toughness and durability have the advantage of being X-ray transmitting to most potential X-ray sources in thicknesses as great as 6 μm or more (compared with the maximum thickness of 1 μm allowed for titanium with the Perkin-Elmer tungsten source). Originally developed for X-ray use at Bell Labs [5], similar films have recently been fabricated at Eaton Corporation [14]. Several masks with the structure shown in Fig. 1 were recently fabricated at Intel Magnetics on substrates kindly made available by Eaton Corporation. The major difference from the Bell approach to this mask substrate is the use of the boron nitride surface as the lithographic working surface on which thin films are deposited and the X-ray mask patterns subsequently fabricated. Our reasons for preferring this surface to the polyimide surface used by Bell are twofold; 1) the low defect density attained after scrubbing this surface on the Eaton membranes, and 2) the superior flatness believed to be attainable with substrates fabricated with this surface facing up. The thin-film layers on the mask are deposited in the sequence:

1) 50-Å evaporated chrome
2) 7000-Å evaporated gold
3) 1400-Å sputtered Ta or TaO$_x$
4) 6000 Å of the electron-beam resist Sel-N, Type A (also our X-ray resist).

Next, the electron-beam resist is patterned in the manufacturing electron-beam exposure system (MEBES-I).[2] The Ta or TaO$_x$ layer is etched with a reactive ion etch (RIE) process and the gold layer is sputter-etched in a different chamber using the Ta-based film as a durable sputter-etch mask. Details of the process have been given previously [1]. Although we generally anticipate problems with a new process, the first masks fabricated on boron nitride showed significantly smaller feature movements than the best previous masks on titanium substrates.

Fig. 2 shows a so-called MARKET plot of the feature distortions resulting from the fabrication of mask features on this Eaton boron nitride substrate (4-μm boron nitride plus 4 μm of polyimide). The MARKET plot shows a matrix of mask locations on which the electron-beam system patterned reference marks called MARKET crosses during the original mask writing process. After the mask was completely fabri-

[2] Perkin-Elmer Etec., Inc., 3392 Investment Blvd., Hayward, CA 94545.

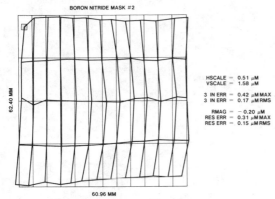

BORON NITRIDE MASK #2

HSCALE = 0.51 μM
VSCALE = 1.58 μM

3 IN ERR = 0.42 μM MAX
3 IN ERR = 0.17 μM RMS

RMAG = −0.20 μM
RES ERR = 0.31 μM MAX
RES ERR = 0.15 μM RMS

62.40 MM

60.96 MM

Fig. 2. MARKET plot showing patterning distortion on Eaton boron nitride substrate.

cated (resist development, RIE, and gold sputter-etch), it was reinserted in the MEBES and the positions of the MARKET crosses remeasured. The movement of the crosses from the original matrix locations is plotted on a greatly expanded scale defined by the parameters HSCALE and VSCALE. An expansion or contraction of the mask features having radial symmetry can be removed in X-ray lithography by changing the mask-to-wafer separation. This correction is listed on the MARKET plot as RMAG. After this correction is removed, the maximum and rms residual distortions are listed as RES ERR values. The analysis shown is for all matrix locations inside a 3-in-diameter circle and thus excludes the two points most distant from centers on all four corners of the array. (The point in the upper left corner is actually located on the 3.45-in inner diameter support ring structure and not the free-standing membrane.) The results shown in Fig. 2 were achieved without taking great care to achieve complete mask thermal equilibration. On the basis of our prior experience in this area, we feel further improvements can be achieved with modest attention to detail.

A substantial asset to cleanliness in wafer or mask fabrication is the ability to scrub the lithographic surface and thus effectively remove loose defects. The additional rigidity derived from the use of 4-μm boron nitride membranes as opposed to 1-μm titanium greatly improved our ability to remove such defects by scrubbing. The starting defect level on these substrates (before deposition of the thin-film layers) has been evaluated using X-ray exposures through the substrate and found to be about 0.5 defects/cm^2. The implication of this measurement is that mask defect densities of order 1 defect/cm^2 can be achieved only by cleaning up the thin-film deposition and patterning processes.

In summary, pattern distortions on full yield X-ray masks with 3-in-diameter active patterning area are approaching the level of MEBES pattern reproducibility (typically 0.1 μm) and there is good reason to believe progress will continue. Mask defect density is also improving and will continue to improve with effort.

CONCLUSION

In spite of the progress made by individual laboratories and companies in developing aspects of X-ray lithography, it seems clear that the total package (mask, source-aligner, and sufficiently sensitive resist) must be available to be attractive to prospective users. Eventually, X-ray must satisfy the requirements of 0.5-μm VLSI circuit devices. Perkin-Elmer has described X-ray step-and-repeat concepts which satisfy the overlay requirements of these devices [2]. The development of such systems requires time, money, and eventually, quality reticles. A key component inhibiting both the development of full field and step and repeat in the future is a commerical vendor of quality X-ray masks. Moreover, the most difficult aspect of this quality is just what a mask vendor achieves best—low defect density. Until commercial masks are available, it appears probable that X-ray lithography will remain in development laboratories except for well-matched applications such as the 4-Mbit bubble memory and production of very-high-speed integrated circuits. However, the sum total of the accomplishments to date in X-ray, coupled with the increasing obstacles faced by optical lithography, suggests that the resolution of the mask obstacle for VLSI volume production is only a matter of timing and capital, the key technology developments are here now.

ACKNOWLEDGMENT

The authors wish to thank Eaton Corp. and the Perkin-Elmer Corp. for essential technical help with this work

REFERENCES

[1] B. B. Triplett and S. Jones, "X-ray lithography: Fabrication of masks and very large scale integrated (VLSI) devices," *Proc. SPIE Microlithography VII*, vol. 333, p. 118, 1982.
[2] C. R. Fencil and G. P. Hughes, "X-ray lithography: Technology for the 1980's," *Proc. SPIE Microlithography VII*, vol. 333, p. 100, 1982, and references therein.
[3] A. Zacharias, "X-ray lithography exposure machines," *Solid-State Technol.*, vol. 24, pp. 57–59, 1981.
[4] J. R. Maldonado, "Trends in X-ray lithography," *Proc. SPIE Microlithography VII*, vol. 333, p. 131, 1982.
[5] D. Maydan, "X-ray lithography for microfabrication," *J. Vac. Sci. Technol.*, vol. 17, pp. 1164–1169, 1980.
[6] A. Zacharias, "X-ray lithography for integrated circuit development and manufacturing," *IEEE Trans. Components, Hybrids, Manufact. Technol.*, vol. CHMT-5, pp. 118–121, 1982.
[7] G. P. Hughes, private communication.
[8] S. M. Matthews and R. S. Cooper, "Plasma sources for X-ray lithography," *Proc. SPIE Microlithography VII*, vol. 333, p. 136, 1982.
[9] J. S. Pearlman and J. C. Riordan, "X-ray lithography using a pulsed plasma source," *J. Vac. Sci. Technol.*, vol. 19, pp. 1190–1193, 1981.
[10] E. N. Fuls, "X-ray lithography applied to the fabrication of 1 μm n-channel metal oxide semiconductor (NMOS) circuits," *Proc. SPIE Microlithography VII*, vol. 333, p. 113, 1982.
[11] W. D. Buckley, M. P. Eisenberg, G. P. Hughes, D. H. Kittell, and J. L. Kreuzer, "An X-ray lithography alignment system," *J. Electrochem. Soc.*, vol. 128, pp. 1111–1116, 1981.
[12] P. H. Lamey, Jr., "Manufacturing implications of multilevel resist processing," *Proc. SPIE Microlithography VII*, vol. 333, p. 59, 1982.
[13] P. Tischer, "Advances in X-ray lithography," in *From Electronics to Microelectronics*, W. A. Kaiser and W. E. Proebster, Eds. Amsterdam: North-Holland, 1980, p. 47, and references therein.
[14] D. L. Brors, "X-ray mask fabrication," *Proc. SPIE Microlithography VII*, vol. 333, p. 111, 1982.

Part III
Devices and Processes

THE engineering of VLSI circuits requires the coordination of processes and device structures which at first were developed as fundamental and individual technology experiments. The next two papers survey current work in two laboratories in which the theme is to explore the basic science and technology of microfabrication in order to provide the foundations for micron and submicron circuits in which large numbers of small devices are connected.

E. D. Wolf, T. Everhart, and their collaborators review such work in progress at NRRFSS—the National Resource Facility for Submicron Structures, at Cornell University. An overview of active research at this facility is presented as a series of vignettes covering work in the following areas: Nanolithography (M. S. Isaacson and A. J. Muray), Ion Sources and Lithography (B. M. Siegel and G. R. Hanson), Dry Etching for Submicron Structures (E. D. Wolf, I. Adesida, and J. D. Chinn), Microfabrication of Structures for Guided-Wave Optics (J. M. Ballantyne and G. J. Sonek), Molecular Beam Epitaxy for Microwave Devices (L. F. Eastman, C. E. C. Wood, and G. W. Wicks), Process and Device Technology (J. P. Krusius), Device Physics and Simulation and Analysis of Latch-Up in CMOS IC's (J. Frey),

and Superconducting Josephson-Junction Device Research (R. A. Buhrman).

Work at another fundamental technology research laboratory is then summarized by N. P. Economou of Lincoln Laboratories. He reviews research there in submicron lithography and processing, materials growth, and circuit architecture, all being developed especially as techniques which are extendible to and form a basis for submicron circuit construction. This chapter ends with a discussion of the permeable base transistor—a device which achieves high-speed operation due to its use of submicron gate structures of an unusual geometry. Experimetal results of the construction and operation of high-speed GaAs and Si devices are reported.

The final paper of this part is on process modeling and its use to guide the design of the vertical small device structures so as to minimize fabrication difficulties due to severe topography. In this paper A. R. Neureuther models lithography, deposition, and dry and wet etching techniques used for small ground rule thin-film processing. These models form a basis for tradeoffs which reduce the problems caused by increasing nonplanarity (aspect ratios) as device size decreases.

Advanced Submicron Research and Technology Development at the National Submicron Facility

Edited By
EDWARD D. WOLF, FELLOW, IEEE

Invited Paper

Authors

The authors are with Cornell University, Ithaca, NY 14853.
Ilesanmi Adesida—Research Associate and Lecturer at NRRFSS
Joseph Merrill Ballantyne—Director and Professor of Electrical Engineering
Robert Allan Buhrman—Associate Professor of Applied and Engineering Physics and an Associate Director of NRRFSS
Jeffrey D. Chinn—Graduate Student
Lester F. Eastman—Professor of Electrical Engineering
Thomas E. Everhart—Joseph Silbert Dean of the College of Engineering and Professor of Electrical Engineering
Jeffrey Frey—Professor of Electrical Engineering and an Associate Director of NRRFSS
Gary R. Hanson—Senior Research Associate at the NRRFSS
Michael S. Isaacson—Associate Professor of Applied and Engineering Physics
J. Peter Krusius—Associate Professor of Electrical Engineering
Andrew J. Muray—Graduate Student
Benjamin M. Siegel—Professor of Applied and Engineering Physics
Gregory J. Sonek—Graduate Student
Gray W. Wicks—Research Associate
Edward D. Wolf—Professor of Electrical Engineering and Director of NRRFSS
Colin E. C. Wood—Senior Research Associate (Now with General Electric Corporation, Wembly, Middlesex, HA9 7TT, England.)

Introduction

EDWARD D. WOLF, FELLOW, IEEE, AND
THOMAS E. EVERHART, FELLOW, IEEE

The National Research and Resource Facility for Submicron Structures (NRRFSS) is a national research center for microstructures science, engineering, and technology located on the campus of Cornell University, Ithaca, NY. Dedicated to discovering the concepts, techniques, and materials for the next generation of electronic devices, the facility remains the only microstructures science and engineering laboratory in an American university with a proven half-micrometer and below, multilevel processing capability that is open to visiting researchers from other universities, government, and industry.

The facility was established in 1977 by a 5-year grant from the National Science Foundation to provide a university research focus on the fabrication and research of submicrometer structures and to make the research resources available nationwide through a users' research program. Cornell University was responsible for the design, construction, and financing of the new Lester B. Knight Laboratory which houses the new facility with Class 10 processing capabilities and a low vibration and EMI ambient. The Facility research and resource program is currently supported by a renewed grant from the National Science Foundation and industrial sponsors.

The three main objectives of the national Facility are to promote and carry out research to advance (the state of) the art of submicron fabrication technology and to train engineers and scientists in this field; to provide a resource for the academic community to use to fabricate advanced devices or research structures which require submicron dimensions; and to stimulate innovative research in fields other than the electrical engineering device community which can benefit from the use of the Facility or which will shed light on fundamental physics or materials problems which affect or limit the application of submicron technology.

Facility research now involves about 200 researchers, including nearly 110 M.S./Ph.D. students from across the nation, representing 37 Cornell faculty members from eight departments, 16 faculty members and their students (included in the 110) from other universities, 12 industrial and government scientists, and 25 research associates. The latter includes nine full-time equivalent facility staff members who operate, maintain, develop highly specialized experimental equipment and processes, and assist visiting and resident users.

The Facility promotes an intensive vertically integrated graduate research program in advanced lithography (electron, ion, and X-ray), several kinds of dry pattern transfer processes, thin-film deposition, growth, and modification/conversion and analysis, and several advanced device technologies. Using linewidth as a measurement of minimum feature size, the research

Manuscript received December 16, 1982. The National Research and Resource Facility for Submicron Structures is supported in major part by the National Science Foundation Program on Solid State and Microstructures under Engineering Grant ECS-8200312, Dr. Ronald J. Gutmann, program director.
E. D. Wolf is with the National Research and Resource Facility for Submicron Structures, Knight Laboratory, Cornell University, Ithaca, NY 14853.

Reprinted from *Proc. IEEE*, vol. 71, pp. 589–600, May 1983.

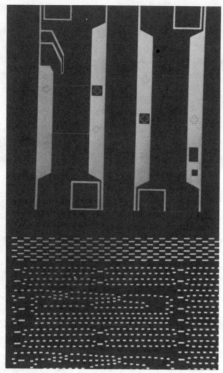

Fig. 1. Transmission optical micrography of an electron-beam exposed and wet-etched chrome mask for bubble-memory device fabrication. Minimum dimension in this work is 0.5 μm [1].

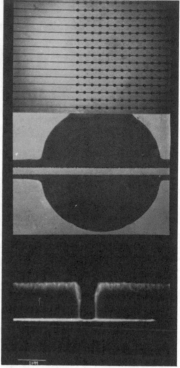

Fig. 2. Scanning electron photomicrographs of an array of microelectrodes (top), top view of a single cell (center), and the cross section of a 75-μm-diameter electrode (bottom) [2]. Dimension marker applies only to the bottom photo.

within the facility spans several orders of magnitude—from 1 μm down to nearly 1 nm. Among the areas in which significant technical accomplishments have been made are the use of molecular-beam epitaxy in the synthesis of GaAs and related compound semiconductors, the development of SOS MESFET logic, the production of superconducting devices, the fabrication of bubble-memory devices [1] (Fig. 1), the development of high-speed photoconductive detectors, the fabrication of deep-ultraviolet wire polarizers, the fabrication of microelectrode neural-recording arrays, micro-thermisters, submicrometer-diameter electrodes for electrochemistry experiments [2] (Fig. 2), and infrared notch filters [3] (Fig. 3).

Prospective users of NRRFSS facilities submit a proposal after discussion with the Director of NRRFSS, for review by outside reviewers, and by the NRRFSS Program Committee, which includes a majority of non-Cornell members from prominent positions in the microstructures science and technology community of the United States. Long-range policy and planning for the Facility is conducted by the NRRFSS Policy Board, also composed of members from within and outside of Cornell University, and chaired by the Dean of College of Engineering at Cornell.

NRRFSS is continually seeking ways to expand and strengthen its function as a national resource. These plans include increased accessibility of NRRFSS through its outreach program, including solicitations for qualified engineers and scientists to use Facility resources both as short-term users and as long-term visitors. A summer research program for

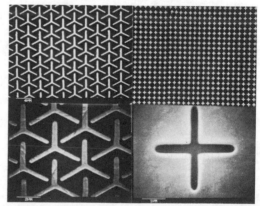

Fig. 3. Sections of infrared filter arrays using both tripoles (Al) and dipoles (slots on Al) on CaF_2 [3].

visiting faculty will be offerred in 1983. In addition, the Facility has begun to sponsor "short courses" to familiarize potential users and others of the potentials of this technology, and of Submicron Facility resources, to their research. The first of these courses was given in August 1982 and will be expanded and repeated in June of 1983, and will cover such topics as "Electron-Beam Lithography," "Reactive-Ion Etching Techniques," and will feature visiting lecturers from industrial and other academic laboratories.

What follows is a brief representative summary of some of the research currently being conducted at NRRFSS. The research described consists of both user projects and "Facility Development Research"—the latter projects have the goal of establishing NRRFSS with state-of-the-art research capabilities in a broad spectrum of microfabrication, thin-film growth, and microanalytical technologies, which can then be accessed by the national user community. Readers wishing more detailed information on NRRFSS and the User Program should write to E. D. Wolf at the adress provided above.

Nanolithography

MICHAEL S. ISAACSON AND ANDREW J. MURAY

We have started a program with the objective of exploring the limits of electron-beam microfabrication at the nanometer scale. Our aim is to determine how far conventional resist technology can be pushed (e.g., [4], [5]) and to investigate new, novel materials which can be directly modified by an electron beam *in situ*.

Initial experiments [6] have concentrated on alkali halides (e.g., NaCl, LiF, KBr) and to a lesser extent on other halides such as MgF_2, CaF_2, $AgCl_2$. The attractive features of these materials are as follows:

1) They can be etched *in situ* by an electron beam. Thus a pattern can be etched directly into the resist without additional processing.

2) They can be vacuum sublimated or evaporated and some of the fluorides (e.g., CaF_2) can be grown by MBE techniques [7]. In fact, CaF_2 has a lattice constant within 1 percent that of Si.

3) These materials are all of relatively low molecular weight (~100 Daltons) and thus of small molecular size compared to commonly used polymer resists. One might expect an inherent "grain size" of the exposed material to be of the order of the molecular size, so there would be possibilities of resolutions below a nanometer.

4) Since the etching mechanism may be due to surface desorption as opposed to a bulk interaction event, proximity effects might not be as serious as with larger molecular weight resists. Therefore, high aspect ratios may be possible.

A disadvantage of some of these materials may be that the exposure dose is larger than that for more conventional resists. For example, for complete etching of a 20-nm-thick film due to 100-keV electrons, the exposure varies from 10^{-3} C/cm^2 for LiF to almost 10^3 C/cm^2 for NaCl. This is to be compared to a dose around 10^{-3} C/cm^2 for negative exposure of PMMA. However, the advent of reliable field emission source technology alleviates some of this problem. In our lithographic system, which is a VG Microscopes HB-5 field emission scanning transmission electron microscope, we can obtain nanoampere currents in half nanometer diameters probes, so exposure of 1 C/cm^2 can be obtained in as little as 10 μs.

In Fig. 4, we show micrographs indicative of the size of structures that can be etched through some alkali halides. The apparent discontinuous nature of the LiF etched lines is due to the fact that in order to obtain the micrograph we need to use a dose that is almost 30 percent of that needed to etch the lines in the first place. At present, we have not been able to etch

Fig. 4. Patterns etched into alkali halide films by direct electron-beam vaporization using 100-keV incident electrons. In the upper left composite micrograph we show an intact tobacco mosaic virus taken at the same electron-optical magnification as the pattern below it, which has been directly etched into an NaCl film. The width of the lines in the pattern is less than 2 nm. In the micrograph on the lower left, we show lines etched into 100-nm-thick LiF films. The troughs (white areas) are about 2 nm wide, etched completely through the film and are separated on the average by 3.8 nm center to center. In the micrograph on the right, we again show lines etched into an LiF film. The horizontal scale of this micrograph is 450 nm and the lines are separated by 4 nm center to center.

lines in alkali halide resists closer than on 3.5-nm center-to-center distances and the narrowest width lines have been about 1.5 nm. It is not clear whether this limit is due to the range of secondary electrons in the material or the nonlocalization of the primary inelastic scattering event (which is of the order of 1 nm) [8].

We are trying to utilize such resists as masks for ion milling. For example, the argon-ion etch rate of LiF to gold is about one to three, thus 100-nm films of LiF can be used as a resist for etching through 100 nm of gold even if the troughs are not completely etched through the entire LiF film by the electron beam.

Ion Sources and Lithography

BENJAMIN M. SIEGEL AND GARY R. HANSON

Ion-beam lithography (IBL) can be expected to have at least three advantages over electron-beam lithography (EBL): 50–100X greater resist sensitivity, no proximity effects, and maskless processing. This means that very-high-resolution configurations could be structured by direct-write ion-beam lithography using single resist layers on thick substrates or with no resists at all with the proper ion sources. It is our task to develop the instrumentation required to produce high-resolution, high-current-density probes that could be used to investigate the interactions of ions with resists and substrate materials, to evaluate the potential and feasibility of ion-beam

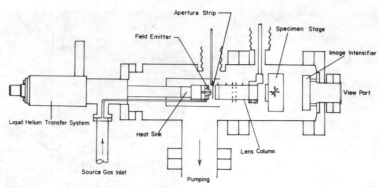

Fig. 5. Schematic of the Field Ion Probe System (FIPS-I) currently being developed.

lithography, and to produce structures and devices with dimensions in the range of 10 to 100 nm [9].

We have concentrated our efforts on developing the ion-beam lithography capability so we could investigate direct writing with high-resolution ion probes. Our approach and the instrumental developments that we have made are based on the use of the H_2^+ gaseous field ion source that we are developing here at Cornell. This source repesents an important breakthrough in providing a very-high-brightness ion beam of low-mass ions, H_2^+, with high angular current density and an energy spread of only 1.0 eV. Measured angular current densities of 10 to 20 μA/sr have been obtained. The ion optical systems we have designed should be able to focus this beam to probes of 100–300-Å diameter with current densities greater than 100 A/cm^2. The effective brightness of this probe is thus on the order of 1×10^8 A/cm^2/sr at 50 keV. Research on improved source performance and the development of sources to produce beams of other ion species continues to be carried out in NRRFSS.

In the development of the instrumentation for investigating the characteristics and potential of IBL, we have first built a relatively simple experimental probe system designated as the Field Ion Probe System 1, FIPS I (see Fig. 5). The optical system for the FIPS I was developed using a computer-aided design (CAD) program that provides a rapid, interactive method for trying many configurations to determine the one that gives the desired optical characteristics. Using this method, a five-element lens with double octupole deflectors has been designed, giving calculated probe diameters of 102 Å deflected over a 0.2×0.2 mm field (2×10^4 beam diameters) without dynamic correction. Taking the angular current $dI/d\Omega = 10 \mu$A/sr and 20 μA/sr, the current density in this 102-Å diameter probe calculates to be 150 and 300 A/cm^2, respectively. This ion optical system has been incorporated in a chamber that attaches to the existing H_2^+ field ion source. The chamber has a stage with x, y, z motion and an UHV specimen exchange lock.

This system will be used for making the initial studies on H_2^+ ion–resist interactions. A systematic investigation will be made of the sensitivities of various resists to the ion beam, development characteristics, and resolution limits. With the very-high current densities expected in the probes, very-short exposure times will be required.

A more advanced field ion probe system has also been under development. This system was designed to provide a complete ion-beam lithography research capability for structuring high-

resolution devices. This past summer (1982) we received a major equipment grant from Hewlett-Packard (HP) that has greatly enhanced the level at which we will be able to carry out the ion column instrumentation development. The HP grant consisted of one of their prototype high-speed, precision electron-beam lithography systems ("HERMES") for our work on ion-beam lithography. We are converting this instrument to an ion-beam lithography system by replacing the electron source and electron optical column with the field ion source and ion optical system that we have designed and developed. With the availability of this instrument we are now able to develop a more advanced ion-beam lithography capability utilizing the major part of the electronics, high-accuracy interferometer-controlled stage, UHV vacuum system, and mechanical structure. A column is now being designed that will house the source and the ion optics and will set in the same port of the work chamber that now takes the electron-beam column of HERMES. This instrumentation development for the ion-beam lithography system is funded under a separate contract with DARPA/ONR.

Dry Etching for Submicron Structures

EDWARD D. WOLF, FELLOW, IEEE,
ILESANMI ADESIDA, MEMBER, IEEE, AND
JEFFREY D. CHINN, STUDENT MEMBER, IEEE

Dry-etching techniques such as plasma etching (PE) and reactive–ion etching (RIE) have become an important tool in the process of microelectronics device fabrication. Among other factors, dry-etch methods were developed to produce anisotropic profiles and good dimensional control which conventional wet-etching methods were not capable of. These properties are especially desired for transferring high-resolution patterns created with electron, X-ray, or ion-beam lithography.

Some of our studies have been directed at understanding these novel etching methods and their applications to pattern transfer at submicrometer dimensions. We have studied the etch resistance of polymethylmethacrylate (PMMA), a high-resolution resist, under RIE and its use as an etch mask for etching various dielectrics [10]. It was found that by using a fluorine deficient fluorcarbon gas such as CHF_3, a reasonable selectivity could be obtained between PMMA and silicon dioxide. This has been used to etch lines with highly anisotropic profiles into silicon dioxide, as shown in Fig. 6. A rela-

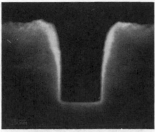

Fig. 6. Scanning electron micrograph of etched profiles in SiO$_2$ using PMMA as an etch mask.

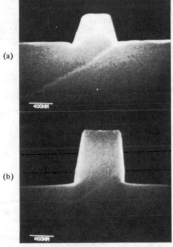

(a)

(b)

Fig. 7. Scanning electron micrographs of GaAs profiles etching in (a) chlorine-ion beam and (b) chlorine-ion beam in the presence of background chlorine gas.

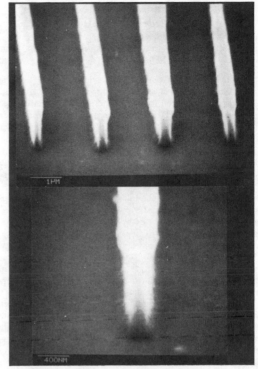

Fig. 8. Scanning electron micrograph of submicrometer lines in silicon implanted PMMA which was developed by oxygen RIE.

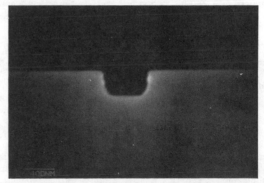

Fig. 9. Scanning electron micrograph of electron-beam exposed and conformal etched submicrometer line in SiO$_2$.

tively new technique is reactive ion-beam etching, which offers additional advantages over RIE in that several parameters such as ion energy, ion current density, and background gas composition can be varied independently [11]. We have recently investigated the etching of GaAs with an inert and a reactive ion beam in the presence of background molecular chlorine impinging on the specimen either from the ion beam or from the background gas. It was also found that an increase in the background chlorine partial pressure altered the wall profiles from an overcut slope found predominantly in physical etching mechanisms to a nearly vertical wall (see Fig. 7). Fig. 7(a) shows the GaAs profile obtained with an ionized CCl$_4$ ion beam (CCl$_3^+$) while Fig. 7(b) shows a profile obtained with the same ion beam in the presence of background chlorine gas. Note that the overcut slope in Fig. 7(a) is now vertical in Fig. 7(b), and that the trenching has been eliminated.

In work parallel to that described by Siegel earlier in this paper, we have also been investigating other forms of ion-beam lithography in which resist development can be performed using dry etching. Our approach has been to implant low-energy, high-dose ($\sim 1 \times 10^{15}$/cm^2) silicon ions into resists, followed by RIE in an oxygen plasma [12]. During the RIE process, the thin layer of implanted silicon reacts with the ambient oxygen to form SiO$_2$, which then inhibits further etching. Etch ratio between exposed and unexposed areas of

greater than 11 have been obtained. Using silicon thin-film transmission masks, resist structures down to 0.3 μm in line-width have been fabricated, as shown in Fig. 8. Another microlithographic pattern transfer technique that does not require resist development has also been studied [13], [14]. This involves the diffusion of gaseous HF and water vapor through an exposed resist and the selective etching of the underlying silicon dioxide. Etching was found to be conformal in that it proceeded only where the resist was in contact with the SiO$_2$ underneath. Application of this technique to submicrometer fabrication is shown in Fig. 9.

Microfabrication of Structures for Guided-Wave Optics

JOSEPH MERRILL BALLANTYNE, SENIOR MEMBER, IEEE, AND GREGORY J. SONEK

Structures for guided-wave optical devices often pose special lithographic problems in microfabrication which are different from those encountered in the production of integrated electrical circuits [15]. Examples of requirements for optical structures which are of lesser importance for integrated circuits include edge-roughness of waveguides (on the order of 20 nm), aspect ratios of waveguides (length/width of 10^4 or greater), gratings with periods down to 100 nm with accurate groove-to-groove spacing (1 to 0.01 percent of spacing), and high absolute accuracy in average period (to 0.05 percent).

A single lithographic technology which meets all of these requirements does not exist yet, but some of these specifications have been met on a case-by-case basis. In the following paragraphs we give a few examples from NRRFSS and related work of various high-resolution structures for guided-wave optics.

Periodic structures are of great interest because of their applications as frequency-selective filters, resonators, mirrors, couplers, phase-matching structures, etc. Laser holography is the preferred method for fabricating gratings because of its high accuracy in period-to-period spacing and absolute value of the average period, and because of its ability to make large-area gratings (many square centimeters) [16]. By exposing through a high refractive-index prism, periods down to 100 nm have been made and applied to semiconductor-distributed feedback lasers [17], [18]. Periods down to 75 nm have been made by starting with holography and then applying period division [19]–[21]. One example of such a structure, which consists of a 230-nm period high-aspect ratio grating whose effective period for UV light was halved to 115 nm by angle-evaporation of Al on both sidwalls, is shown in Fig. 10(a). The 115-nm period array of Al plates covers an area of many square centimeters and is effectively a series of parallel-plate waveguides which act as a polarizer for UV light (extinction ratio of 0.41 at $\lambda_0 = 200$ nm) by cutting off the guided wave with polarization parallel to the plates. The high-aspect ratio grating in the quartz substrate was formed by a combination of holography and sputter, wet-chemical, and RIE through the AZ resist and Cr etch mask [20].

Holographic gratings suffer from a lack of flexibility (they are not useful for generating complex patterns) and inconvenient registration of small gratings. Therefore, substantial work has been done on gratings produced by electron-beam lithography. The first small ($\sim$1-mm^2) diffraction-limited gratings produced by this technique were announced in 1972 [22]. Periods as small as 236 nm have been produced on GaAs using this technique (cf. Fig. 10(b)) [23]. Drawbacks of the electron-beam technique are the difficulty in setting the absolute period of the grating, and holding the groove-to-groove spacing constant. With analog deflection, absolute average period accuracies of 0.2 percent (1 nm) and groove-to-groove accuracies of 0.1 percent have been demonstrated [23]. The effects of fluctuations in period on grating filter performance are shown in Fig. 11 [24]. These can become serious when digital deflection is used, since a $\pm\frac{1}{2}$ LSB 16-bit digital-to-analog converter has resolution sufficient to specify length of an individual period to only 1 part in 32 for a 2048-line grating

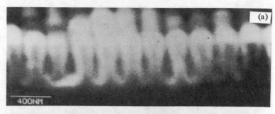

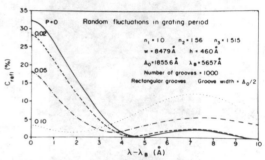

Fig. 10. (a) Holographic 230-nm period quartz grating, after an angle evaporation of 25 nm of Al on each sidewall. The Al waveguide structures have an effective period of 115 nm [20]. (b) Edge view of a 330-nm period grating formed by electron-beam lithography in PMMA on GaAs [23].

Fig. 11. Reflection coefficient versus wavelength deviation from the Bragg wavelength λ_B for a first-order grating filter with rectangular grooves [24]. Curves are symmetric about λ_B. P is the random maximum fractional fluctuation in the grating period on either side of λ_0.

which fills the entire field (or about 3 percent in Fig. 11). The situation is worse for gratings with more lines or which are smaller than the field size.

For some integrated optics applications, waveguides or grating grooves are desired which have large radii of curvature and smooth edges. These types of patterns are often not conveniently produced on electron-beam lithographic systems which generate the rectangles useful for integrated circuit work. This limitation was recognized early [25], and is illustrated in Fig. 12, which shows two types of planar waveguide diffraction lenses made by Chang et al. [26] on the NRRFSS EBMF-2. Note that for one lens, the smoothly sloping lines had to be constructed as a series of parallel rectangles. The other lens had a geometry compatible with the pattern generator and did not suffer this problem. A similar situation exists when the EBMF-2 is used for waveguide fabrication. In Fig. 13, we see that it is adequate for making both orthogonal and diagonal waveguides down to 2 μm in width and many centimeters long, but suffers from pattern generator limitations when used to draw narrow, slightly curved waveguides. Part of this limitation can be removed by using the electron-beam lithography system to make a reticle for later printing in a reduction optical projector. Fig. 14 shows a waveguide and horn which was patterned in a 7059 glass

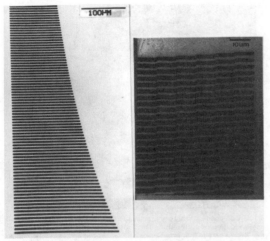

Fig. 12. Two geometries of wavguide diffraction lenses produced on the NRRFSS EBMF-2 by Chang *et al.* [26].

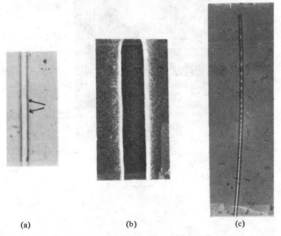

(a)   (b)   (c)

Fig. 13. Waveguide structures produced on the EBMF-2 by Sonek. (a) Butt joint in a 2-μm-wide guide, parallel to deflection axis, crossing edge of field. (b) Definition of a waveguide running at 45° to deflection axes. (c) Curved 1-μm-wide guide.

Fig. 14. Horn and waveguide made in Corning 7059 glass on GaAs photoconductive detector by projection optical lithography (after Gammel *et al.* [27]). Narrow gate match is 1 μm wide.

film by a 10 : 1 projection lithography [27]. Rough edges are smoothed by the resolution limits of the projector, but field size is now limited to about 1 cm² for the entire optical circuit. The approximate 1-μm resolution limit of the projector is still adequate for most waveguide work. In some geometries,

proximity effects can be used to smooth the ragged edges which result from the incremental pattern generation in electron-beam exposures.

Another technique useful for patterning high-resolution guided-wave optical structures was developed recently by Kurmer and Tang [28]. They have applied ion implantation to produce both waveguides and periodic structures. This approach provides an undistorted, smooth surface and low-temperature processing which are advantages over alternative methods.

In summary, a variety of techniques exist in NRRFSS which are useful for patterning guided-wave optical structures. These include electron-beam and optical-projection lithography; holography; wet, sputter, ion-beam, plasma, and reactive-ion-beam etching; ion implantation; and thin-film deposition by various means. Some examples of typical structures produced have been given.

MBE/Microwave Devices

LESTER F. EASTMAN, FELLOW, IEEE, COLIN E. C. WOOD, AND GARY W. WICKS

Advanced materials and structures grown by molecular beam epitaxy (MBE) for microwave and optical devices are being studied in Professor Lester Eastman's group (which includes the co-authors and others). A heterojunction bipolar transistor structure with an n-type $Al_{0.25}Ga_{0.75}As$ emitter, a p-type GaAs base, and an n-type GaAs collector has been investigated [29]. In this transistor, electrons are injected into the base at higher velocities than the maximum diffusion velocity, and will maintain high velocities as they traverse the thin (approximately 2000–4000-Å) base. Early results give a transition frequency f_T for this structure of 14 GHz.

Also under investigation is a "vertical" Schottky gated GaAs transistor [30]. In this device the critical distance, the source-to-drain spacing, is determined by the thickness of an MBE layer rather than by lithography as in a standard FET, thus small lengths and better control are possible. Devices have been fabricated with 5000-Å source-to-drain spacings and 1500-Å gate widths. Transconductances are 80 and 47 mS/mm at channel dopings of 5×10^{16} and 7×10^{15} cm⁻³, respectively. At the higher channel doping, current densities of 10^5 A/cm² have been achieved. At the lower channel doping, average electron velocities have been as high as 3×10^7 cm/s.

Also investigated for microwave FET's were modulation doped structures in the AlGaAs/GaAs material system as well as in the $Al_{0.48}In_{0.52}As/Ga_{0.47}In_{0.53}As$ material system. Liquid nitrogen mobilities in excess of 100 000 cm²/V·s for the AlGaAs/GaAs structure and in excess of 50 000 cm²/V·s for the AlInAs/GaInAs structure were obtained.

Planar doped barriers (PDB's) have been grown in both GaAs and GaInAs, and used as launchers for ballistic electrons as well as optical detectors. As optical detectors, PDB have exhibited gains up to 10 000 [31].

Double-heterostructure lasers have been fabricated with GaInAs active layers and AlInAs cladding layers [32]. With a 4500-Å active layer thickness, room-temperature thresholds of 4.3 kA/cm² were obtained. These lasers emitted at a wavelength of 1.64 μm at room temperature. In an effort to obtain optical emitters at the more useful wavelengths of 1.55 and 1.3 μm, quantum well structures in GaInAs with AlInAs barriers were studied. As shown in Fig. 15, it was found that 4K photoluminescence could be varied from wavelengths of 1.55

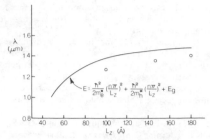

Fig. 15. Variance of wavelength with width of quantum well.

to 1.27 μm by varying the width of the quantum well. Subsequently, a quantum well LED which emitted at 1.34 μm at 77 K was constructed.

Process and Device Technology

J. PETER KRUSIUS, MEMBER, IEEE

The objectives of the research into submicron silicon process and device technology are to explore the processes, the feasibility of fabrication, the physical properties of individual devices and integrated circuits with minimum feature sizes as small as 1000 Å. In order to meet these objectives, the actual research includes elements of process development, process modeling and simulation, device and circuit fabrication, device physics and simulation, and device and circuit characterization and simulation. Routinely employed design and processing tools in the submicron device and integrated circuit area include equipment for VLSI layout design, direct electron-beam writing, plasma and reactive-ion etching (RIE), ion implantation, electron-gun evaporation for refractory metals and silicides, and scanning Auger microanalysis. Advanced silicon processing systems constitute a recent thrust area. New capabilities for ultrapure thin thermal oxides based on HCl and TCA, and for silicon nitride based on low-pressure continuous vapour deposition, are currently being set up together with an ultra high vacuum dual electron-gun evaporator for refractory metals and silicides.

Current research into process technology includes various aspects of downscaled conventional MOSFET and MESFET devices and circuits as well as new multilayer device structures based on silicon molecular beam epitaxy (MBE). This research is supported both by government (mainly NSF) and industrial (mainly Semiconductor Research Corporation) sources. Since small devices are inherently two- to three-dimensional, conventional fabrication techniques have to be re-examined and new ones developed. For example, a three-dimensional process simulator was developed in order to understand multidimensional implanted and annealed doping distributions for arbitrary mask edge profiles [33]. Recently, alternatives for self-aligned gate line-patterning techniques were investigated for linewidths down to 1000 Å. A novel fine-line patterning technique based on three-layer resists, electron-beam lithography, RIE, and local oxidation of aluminum has emerged from this effort [34]. Silicide gate lines with linewidths down to 1500 Å have been demonstrated. Fig. 16 shows, as an example, a patterned composite refractory metal–silicide gate line of Mo–Ta–PtSi with a linewidth of 5000 Å. The fundamental linewidth limitations of this technique are yet to be explored. Integrated circuit (IC) technology development has, for example, resulted in a full silicon-on-insulator MESFET

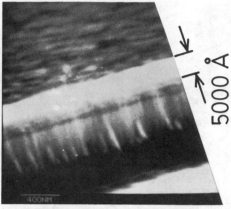

Fig. 16. Composite refractory metal–silicide gate line based on RIE and local oxidation of aluminum. The width of the self-aligned gate structure shown here is 0.5 μm.

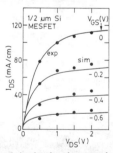

Fig. 17. Divide-by-two circuit realized with a silicon-on-insulator MESFET technology with $\frac{1}{2}$-μm design rules.

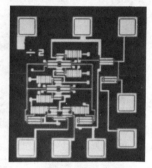

Fig. 18. Comparison of simulated and measured current–voltage characteristics for a $\frac{1}{2}$-μm gate length silicon-on-insulator MESFET. Simulation results are based on a local high-field transport model for thin films and realistic boundary conditions.

logic technology with $\frac{1}{2}$-μm design rules [35]. Average gate delays compatible with 3-GHz operation, for a fan-out of 2 and voltage swing of the order of 1 V, seem possible with this technology. A divide-by-two circuit realized with this technology is shown in Fig. 17.

Extensive work has been done both in the areas of two-dimensional device simulations and device models for circuit simulations. High-field transport in thin active layers and generalized boundary conditions at device interfaces have been investigated and successfully incorporated into an advanced time-dependent two-dimensional device simulator. Excellent agreement between simulated and measured data has been achieved, for example, for silicon-on-insulator MESFET's with 0.5-μm physical gate lengths (Fig. 18) [35]. Extensions to small MOSFET's are currently under way. In the area of device models for circuits simulation approaches based on general nonlinear networks in universal tensor product splines representations are currently being pursued. This technology-independent device modeling approach has been applied to several IC technologies, such as CMOS and MESFET's with excellent results [36]. The associated software will be released shortly. Current research is focused on the high-frequency and macromodeling aspects of this novel approach.

Device Physics and Simulation and Analysis of Latch-Up in CMOS IC's

JEFFREY FREY, SENIOR MEMBER, IEEE

Professor Jeffrey Frey's research group is studying the physics of submicron devices, using both simulation and experimental test structures; and is also involved in the analysis and prediction of latch-up in CMOS IC's.

Early work in the area of two-dimensional device simulation by this group included development of the Cornell University Program for Integrated Devices (CUPID), suitable for describing the physics of short-channel Si and GaAs MESFET's [37]. CUPID, now generally available, utilizes steady-state velocity-field curves for its calculations, and so does not include the effects of velocity overshoot [38], which are important in submicron-scale compound and semiconductor devices. To extend our understanding of these devices into the submicron-size range, the program COOPID was developed [39]. This program follows the two-dimensional flow of electron temperature in doing its simulations, and can lead to surprisingly different results for very-short-channel devices than its earlier steady-state counterpart. An example of such a difference is shown in Fig. 19, in which the results with overshoot included are compared to those obtained by the steady-state program. An array of MESFET design information has been obtained from the application of COOPID [40].

A summary of the evolution of MESFET and MOSFET simulation programs at Cornell is given in Fig. 20. In addition to the programs described above, this chart includes PUCEL, a one-dimensional GaAs MESFET simulator; MIMICS, a program containing simple models for GaAs MESFET's intended to facilitate process-tolerant design of microwave monolithic IC's; and LUSTRE, a one-dimensional bipolar process and device simulator for the HP41CV microcomputer, which are being developed.

Latch-up studies are being pursued by development of the PATHFINDER program (for "PATHological element FINDER") [41], intended to provide IC designers with a CAD tool that identifies active and passive parasitic elements in IC designs on the basis of both layout (horizontal geometry) and processing (vertical topology, and junctions) information. For example, in a CMOS circuit, the active parasitics found by PATHFINDER are lateral and vertical bipolar transistors; the passive parasitics include spreading resistances and those capacitances, such as the well-to-substrate capacitance, which lead to the flow of relatively large displacement currents. PATHFINDER is flexible enough to analyze such circuits as I^2L and ISL bipolar logic gates as well as

CMOS. The output of PATHFINDER is an equivalent circuit for the IC as designed, including both intentionally placed and parasitic devices; this circuit is suitable for analysis using standard circuit simulation programs, such as SPICE or ASTAP.

An example of the output of a PATHFINDER/SPICE simulation for the current through the most critical parasitic lateral bipolar transistors in a 26 (MOS) transistor frequency divider circuit, when a pulse is applied to the drain supply, is shown in Fig. 21. The current through $Q27$ (the lateral with the higher gain) takes off due to the displacement current triggering; while that through $Q39$ drops at the onset of latch-up.

The equivalent circuit parameters of the parasitic devices uncovered by PATHFINDER cannot be obtained from a simple stored tabulation, since the geometries of these devices will depend on the layout analyzed. Determination of these parameters therefore requires either fairly exact simulation, or extrapolation from a table of measured data obtained from prototype (test) structures. In an effort complementary to that on PATHFINDER, a parametric semiconductor device characterization system, and techniques for its use in extraction and extrapolation of parasitic circuit element parameters from test structures are being developed. Test wafers are being fabricated which include special structures for measurement of speading resistance and lateral transistor gain; the structures are typical of those to be found on VLSI CMOS IC layouts. The accuracy of various extrapolation techniques will be tested by comparison of extrapolated values with values measured from other test devices.

In an attempt to fill a large gap in the understanding and modeling of VLSI-scale bipolar devices, a study of the physics and simulation of these devices is being conducted. Band-gap narrowing, field-aided diffusion and drift; and transient transport effects in the VLSI-scale bipolar device's very narrow base are being studied to determine the effect of device shrinkage on the performance of vertical and lateral devices; and on the performance of inverted devices. Experiments on shallow-junction heavily doped p^{++}-n diodes are being done over a range of doping and temperatures in order to obtain a definitive data base for this study.

The modeling of submicron-scale MOS devices is being studied in this group in two ways: first, an assessment of currently available two-dimensional modeling programs, such as MINI-MOS, GEMINI, CADDET, etc., is being made in order to determine for which types of devices, and in what regions of operation, each program provides the best cost/accuracy ratio; second, the models used in each program to describe the high-field transport of electrons in the inversion layer are being examined both from the point of view of basic transport physics, and by comparison with experiments performed on submicron-scale devices. Inconsistencies in the use of such programs over a wide range of device sizes and bias levels may be traceable to the use of curve-fitting empirical "velocity-field" relationships, valid only for a particular device or bias range, and unrelated to the physics of operation of the device; this work is intended to bring basic physics back into the description of submicron MOSFET's, and therefore enhance the generality of application of the modeling programs.

Finally, a program aimed at studying the systems implications of multilevel IC technology is beginning. Both systems architecture developers and device technologists will be brought together to consider the possible applications for this technology, which might include such concepts as systolic processing, interleaved memory and logic circuits, etc. Power dissipation and the influence of parasitic elements will be investigated, and simple prototype circuits will be fabricated.

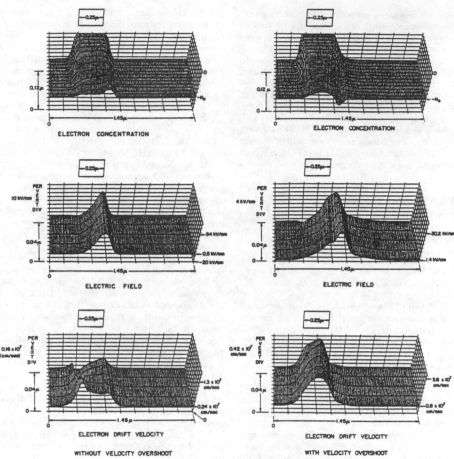

Fig. 19. Comparison of COOPID two-dimensional electron-flow simulation with earlier, steady-state counterpart.

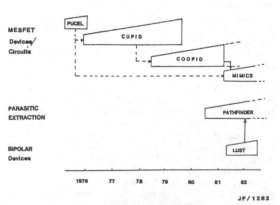

Fig. 20. Summary of evolution of MESFET and MOSFET simulation programs at Cornell.

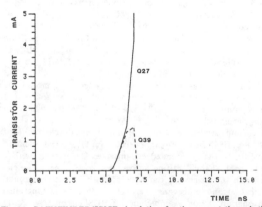

Fig. 21. PATHFINDER/SPICE simulation for the current through the most critical parasitic lateral bipolar transistor in a 26 (MOS) transistor frequency divider circuit.

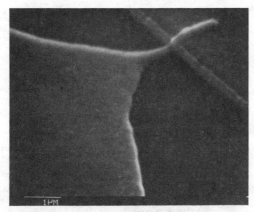

Fig. 22. An Nb–Nb_2O_5–PbBi Josephson tunnel junction formed by electron-beam lithography. In the micrograph, the electrode on the left is PbBi. It contacts the Nb film only on its exposed edge where a thin oxide layer has been grown by reactive ion-beam oxidation. The top of the 100-nm Nb film is insulated from the PbBi by a ~100-nm Al_2O_3 film.

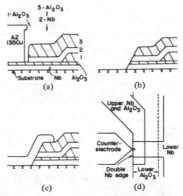

Fig. 23. Double-edge junction fabrication process. (a) Angled and normal depositions of the top layers. (b) The double edge created by ion milling. (c) Two closely spaced junctions are formed on the Nb edges after the counterelectrode deposition. (d) A top view of the finished device.

Superconducting Josephson-Junction Device Research

ROBERT ALAN BUHRMAN

Objectives of this program are to apply submicron fabrication technology to the field of superconducting Josephson-junction device research, and thereby improve the quality of Josephson junctions, both in terms of junction performance and reliability, and to employ these junctions in a number of very-high-speed digital device and high-sensitivity electromagnetic sensor experiments.

Recently, A. W. Kleinsasser and R. A. Buhrman developed a novel technique for fabricating quite high-quality and very stable Nb–Nb_2O_5–PbBi tunnel junctions [42]. This new technique is based on using a reactive O_2^+ ion-beam source to grow the very thin (~2-nm) Nb_2O_5 oxide layer. This reactive ion-beam oxidation (RIBO) technique routinely yields junctions with I–V characteristics suitable for essentially all current Josephson device applications.

Since in general it is desirable that a Josephson junction be a high-impedance, high-speed device, it must be quite small so as to minimize the junction capacitance. This is particularly true for Nb–Nb_2O_5–PbBi alloy junction due to the very high dielectric constant ~30 of Nb_2O_5. Consequently, a technique has been developed by which tunnel junctions can be easily formed on the faceted edge of an Nb film. In this technique, the top of the film is covered with an insulating layer and only the edge exposed where the junction is formed by RIBO and conventional photolithography or by electron-beam lithography. Using photolithography, junctions with areas as small as 1×10^{-9} cm^2 can be formed with good control, with electron-beam lithography [43] very good quality junctions with areas as small as 2×10^{-10} cm^2 can be readily fabricated. An example of such junctions is shown in Fig. 22.

A quite new development in the Josephson area is the effort

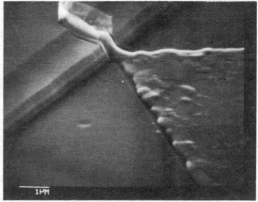

Fig. 24. SEM micrograph of a double Nb edge device with a 0.1-μm-thick PbBi counterelectrode.

to produce a three-terminal Josephson-type device with significant power gain. The idea here is to fabricate two tunnel junctions with one electrode shared between both junctions. The device operates by injecting electrons through one junction into the shared electrode. The effect of the hot, injected electrons on the shared electrode modifies the I–V characteristics of the second junction giving, under appropropriate conditions, the desired signal gain. For speed considerations, it is essential however that both the junctions and the size of the shared electrode be quite small. B. D. Hunt and R. A. Buhrman have devised a technique that meets this criterion by fabricating two edge junctions, one on top of the other. This procedures is shown in Figs. 23 and 24. In this geometry, the shared PbBi electrode is injected with hot electrons from the top edge junction. These electrons affect the I–V characteristic of the bottom detector junction. The result to date of this preliminary work [44] has been a power gain of ~3 in a device with an indirectly measured switching speed of $\lesssim$50 ps. Work is proceeding and higher gain levels are expected.

References

[1] R. L. Smith, A. Thiele, A. Das, D. Thomas and M. H. Kryder, "A major–minor loop memory organization with invisible redundancy," to be presented at Inter. Mag. Conf. (Philadelphia, Apr. 1983), and to be published in *IEEE Trans. Magn.*

[2] J. Osteryoung, *Science*, vol. 218, pp. 261–265, Oct. 1982.

[3] C. M. Rhoads, E. K. Damon, and B. A. Munk, *Appl. Opt.*, vol. 21, p. 15, 1982.

[4] A. N. Broers, J. Cuomo, J. Harper, W. Molzen, R. Laibowitz, and M. Pomerantz, in *Electron Microscopy 1978, Vol. III (Proc. 9th Int. Congr. on Electron Microscopy*, Toronto, Ont., Canada, 1978), p. 343.

[5] R. E. Howard and D. E. Prober, in *VLSI Electronics–Microstructure Science, Vol. V*, N. Einspruch, Ed. New York: Academic Press, 1982.

[6] M. Isaacson and A. Muray, *J. Vac. Sci. Technol.*, vol. 19, p. 1117, 1981.

[7] R.F.C. Farrow, P. W. Sullivan, G. M. Williams, G. R. Jones, and D. C. Cameron, *J. Vac. Sci. Technol.*, vol. 19, p. 415, 1981.

[8] M. Isaacson, J. Langmore, and H. Rose, *Optik*, vol. 41, p. 92, 1974.

[9] B. M. Siegel, G. Hanson, M. Szilagyi, D. Thomas, R. Blackwell, and H. Paik, "Ion beam lithography system using a high brightness H_1^+ ion source," in *Proc. SPIE*, vol. 333: *Submicron Lithography* (Santa Rosa, CA, 1982), p. 152.

[10] J. D. Chinn, I. Adesida, E. D. Wolf, and R. C. Riberio, *J. Vac. Sci. Technol.*, vol. 19, p. 1418, 1981.

[11] D. F. Downey, W. R. Bottoms, and P. R. Hanley, *Solid-State Technol.*, vol. 24, p. 181, 1981.

[12] J. D. Chinn, A. Fernandez, I. Adesida, and E. D. Wolf, in *Proc. 29th Meet. Amer. Vac. Soc.* (Baltimore, MD, Nov. 1982), to be published in *J. Vac. Sci. Technol.*, 1983.

[13] I. Adesida, J. D. Chinn, L. Rathbun, and E. D. Wolf, *J. Vac. Sci. Technol.*, vol. 21, p. 666, 1982.

[14] J. R. Ma, K. H. Shen, E. D. Wolf, and T. E. Everhart, *J. Vac. Sci. Technol.*, vol. 19, p. 1385, 1981.

[15] J. M. Ballantyne and C. L. Tang, "Microfabrication of integrated optical components using the scanning electron microscope," in *Proc. Electro-Optical Systems Design Conf.*, pp. 467–474, 1975. Published by Industrial and Scientific Conference Management, Inc., Chicago, IL.

[16] M. L. Dakss, L. Kuhn, P. F. Heidrich, and B. A. Scott, *Appl. Phys. Lett.*, vol. 16, p. 523, 1970.

[17] C. V. Shank and R. V. Schmidt, *Appl. Phys. Lett.*, vol. 23, p. 154, 1973.

[18] H. W. Yen, N. Nakamura, E. Garmire, S. Somekh, and A. Yariv, *Opt. Commun.*, vol. 9, p. 35, 1973.

[19] L. F. Johnson and K. A. Ingersoll, *Appl. Phys. Lett.*, vol. 38, p. 532, 1981.

[20] G. J. Sonek, D. K. Wagner, and J. M. Ballantyne, *J. Vac. Sci. Technol.*, vol. 19, p. 921, 1981.

[21] D. C. Flanders, A. M. Hawryluk, and H. I. Smith, *J. Vac. Sci. Technol.*, vol. 16, p. 1949, 1979.
D. C. Flanders and A. E. White, *J. Vac. Sci. Technol.*, vol. 19, p. 892, 1981.

[22] J. Ballantyne and C. L. Tang, "Nonlinear and active optical devices using artificial periodic structures," in *Proc. 1st NSF Grantee-User Meet. on Optical Communication Systems* (Rice University, Houston, TX, Sept. 1972), pp. 3–5.
J. J. Turner, B. Chen, L. Yang, J. M. Ballantyne, and C. L. Tang, *Appl. Phys. Lett.*, vol. 23, p. 333, 1973.

[23] J. L. Yang, "Study of submicron period structures in GaAs–GaAlAs double heterostructures: Fabrication and distributed-feedback injection lasers," Ph.D. dissertation, Cornell University, 1979, Materials Science Center Rep. 4283.
L. Yang and J. Ballantyne, *Appl. Phys. Lett.*, vol. 25, p. 67, 1974.
L. Yang, J. J. Turner, L. B. Rhodes, C. L. Tang, and J. M. Ballantyne, *IEEE J. Quantum Electron.*, vol. QE-10, p. 391, 1974.

[24] A. Basu and J. M. Ballantyne, *Appl. Opt.*, vol. 18, p. 2575, 1979.

[25] J. E. Goell, *Appl. Opt.*, vol. 12, p. 729, 1973.

[26] W.S.C. Chang, S. Zhou, Z. Lin, S. Foroukar, and J. Delavaux, "Fresnel and Chirped grating lenses in optical waveguides," presented at the SPIE Technical Symposium, Los Angeles, CA, 1981.

[27] J. C. Gammel and J. M. Ballantyne, *Appl. Phys. Lett.*, vol. 36, p. 149, 1980.

[28] J. P. Kurmer and C. L. Tang, *Appl. Phys. Lett.*, vol. 42, no. 2, 1983.

[29] D. Ankri, W. Schaff, C.E.C. Wood, L F. Eastman, D. W. Woodard, and L. Rathbun, "GaAlAs-GaAs heterojunction bipolar transistors with abrupt emitter base interface for ballistic operation," presented at the Int. Symp. on GaAs and Related Compounds, Albuquerque, NM, Sept. 1982.

[30] U. Mishra, E. Kohn, and L. F. Eastman, "Submicron GaAs vertical electron transistor," presented at the Int. Electron Device Meet., San Francisco, CA, Dec. 1982.

[31] J. A. Barnard, C.E.C. Wood, and L. F. Eastman, "Majority carrier light detectors with large gain-bandwidth products," presented at the Int. Symp. on GaAs and Related Compounds, Japan, 1981.

[32] D. F. Welch, G. W. Wicks, D. W. Woodard, and L. F. Eastman, "GaInAs-AlInAs heterostructures for optical devices grown by MBE," presented at the 4th MBE Workshop, Urbana, IL, Sept. 1982.

[33] J. P. Krusius, J. Nulman, J. V. Faricelli, and J. Frey, "Two- and three-dimensional analytical solutions to post-anneal implant profiles through arbitrary mask edges," *IEEE Trans. Electron Devices*, vol. ED-29, pp. 435–444, 1982.

[34] J. Nulman and J. P. Krusius, "A novel fine line patterning technique for submicron devices based on selective oxidation of aluminum," *Appl. Phys. Lett.*, vol. 42, p. 442, 1983.

[35] J. Nulman, J. Faricelli, and P. Krusius, "$\frac{1}{2}$ micron Si MESFET logic devices," *IEEE Trans. Electron Devices*, vol. ED-29, p. 1665, 1982.

[36] G. Bischoff and J. P. Krusius, "Technology independent device modeling for simulation of integrated circuits in FET technologies," to be published.

[37] T. Wada and J. Frey, "Physical basis of MESFET operation," *IEEE Trans. Electron Devices*, vol. ED-26, p. 476, 1979.

[38] T. Maloney and J. Frey, "Transient and steady-state electron transport properties of GaAs and InP," *J. Appl. Phys.*, vol. 48, p. 781, 1977.

[39] R. Cook and J. Frey, "Two-dimensional numerical simulation of energy transport effects in Si and GaAs MESFET's," *IEEE Trans. Electron Devices*, vol. ED-29, p. 970, 1982.

[40] F. Buot and J. Frey, "Effects of velocity overshoot on the performance of GaAs devices, with design information," *Solid-State Electron.*, to be published.

[41] J. Faricelli and J. Frey, "PATHFINDER—A CAD tool for analyzing CMOS latchup structures," presented at the 1982 Symp. on VLSI Technology, Oiso, Japan, Sept. 1982.

[42] A. W. Kleinsasser and R. A. Buhrman, *Appl. Phys. Lett.*, vol. 32, p. 841, 1980.

[43] B. D. Hunt and R. A. Buhrman, *J. Vac. Sci. Technol.*, vol. 19, p. 1308, 1981.

[44] B. D. Hunt and R. A. Buhrman, in *Proc. Appl. Supercond. Conf.* (Knoxville, TN, 1982), *IEEE Trans. Magn.* (in press).

Developing a Technology Base for Advanced Devices and Circuits

NICHOLAS P. ECONOMOU

Invited Paper

Abstract—Lincoln Laboratory is engaged in a wide range of research activities aimed toward the development of a technology base for advanced semiconductor electronics. This paper is an overview of that research and discusses work in the areas of submicrometer lithography and processing, materials growth, circuit testing and restructuring, and device research. Specific projects in each of these areas are described in order to depict the overall thrust of the research effort. In addition, some applications which successfully utilize advanced technologies are discussed to illustrate the viability of these techniques and the potential performance advantages they afford.

I. Introduction

THE DEMAND for increasing levels of performance from semiconductor devices and circuits has stimulated large investments in technology development. The realization of higher speeds and more complex circuit functions will require devices with smaller features and higher packing densities along with increased chip sizes. Clearly, no single technological achievement will be sufficient to meet these goals. For example, the ability to produce submicrometer features using advanced lithographic techniques is not, in itself, sufficient to fabricate the types of devices and circuits which will be of interest in the future. New developments in processing techniques, materials growth, device design, and circuit architecture will also be needed. In attempting to meet new challenges, the lack of a single key technological capability can render the whole undertaking unfeasible. Therefore, a wide range of research and development activities is necessary in order to maintain an adequate base of technology with which to work.

This paper is an overview of the Lincoln Laboratory research which is aimed toward the development of a viable technology base for advanced semiconductor electronics. A comprehensive treatment of this work is not possible given the limitations of space. The intent here is to accurately portray the overall thrust of the work by highlighting specific projects in several areas of technology development. As a rule, these technologies are intended for applications which require a modest number of highly specialized, high-performance electronic components. For this reason, the emphasis of the Laboratory's research is somewhat different than in the semiconductor industry in general, although the areas of research are often the same.

This discussion is organized into four sections. The first three deal with broad areas of technology development in submi-

crometer lithography and processing, materials growth, and circuit architecture. The fourth section discusses the permeable base transistor (PBT), a device which utilizes many of the advanced techniques which will be described. It is included to illustrate the viability of these techniques and the potential performance advantages they afford.

II. Submicrometer Fabrication Technology

The work on submicrometer fabrication technology spans a wide range of activities including electron-beam, X-ray, and ion-beam lithography, dry etching, and high-resolution processing techniques. As pointed out above, the work is motivated by the particular needs of Lincoln Laboratory which require, for example, high resolution, accurate overlay, and stringent linewidth and profile control as opposed to high throughput. There is, therefore, a strong emphasis on exploring and attaining the ultimate resolution of fabrication techniques and investigating new areas which may enhance our overall capabilities. Part of this is done before a clear application for the technology exists, and, in some cases, a new capability has led to an application which was not previously envisioned (the PBT is a case in point).

This emphasis on high resolution and exploratory work gives the effort a strong flavor of what is best called "microstructures research," and has led to work on diffractive X-ray optics [1], [2], liquid crystals [3], [4], artificial dielectrics for novel optical components [5], [6], the low-temperature behavior of thin conductors [7], and enhanced Raman scattering from microstructures [8]. Exploratory work, together with work more directed toward identified needs, gives rise to a broad framework of fabrication techniques for advanced electronics. In this section, several areas of research will be described to illustrate the breadth of the activities being pursued.

A. Scanning Electron-Beam Lithography (SEBL)

SEBL is a key element of our microfabrication capability. Lincoln Laboratory is not engaged in the development of electron-beam systems specifically targeted for high-throughput, direct write-on-wafer, or large-volume mask making. Instead, effort has been directed toward establishing a versatile, high-resolution (~ 0.1-μm) capability which can be used in a wide range of research activities.

Starting with a commercially available vector-scan machine,[1]

Manuscript received November 30, 1983. This work was sponsored by the Department of the Air Force and the Defense Advanced Research Projects Agency. The U.S. Government assumes no responsibility for the information presented.
The author is with Lincoln Laboratory, Massachusetts Institute of Technology, Lexington, MA 02173.

[1] LEBES-D SEBL System, ETEC Corp., Hayward, CA.

Reprinted from *Proc. IEEE*, vol. 71, pp. 601–611, May 1983.

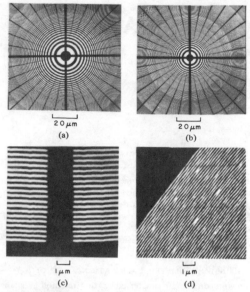

Fig. 1. Scanning-electron micrographs of gold zone-plate absorber patterns on an X-ray mask. The patterns were written by SEBL, followed by a liftoff of 500 Å of gold. In (a) and (b), the inner and outer zones of a zone plate with 0.2-μm minimum feature size is shown. The zone plate shown in (c) and (d) has a minimum feature size of 0.1 μm. (The moire patterns in (a) and (c) are artifacts due to the screen printing process.)

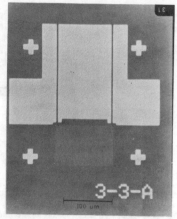

Fig. 2. Optical micrograph of submicrometer gate-length FET pattern defined by SEBL on GaAs. The first pattern level (light areas) consists of four alignment crosses, the drain contact (center), and two source contacts. The second level gate pad (dark square) and gate electrode patterns were defined in a subsequent exposure.

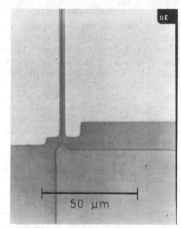

Fig. 3. Higher magnification view of FET pattern showing the gate electrode between the source and drain contacts and the gate pad.

we have made hardware and software modifications and developed processing which makes possible the fabrication of high-quality masks for photolithography and for X-ray and ion-beam lithography. Fig. 1 shows scanning-electron micrographs of an X-ray mask containing Fresnel zone-plate patterns which were generated by the SEBL system. The minimum zone widths are 0.2 and 0.1 μm, respectively. These particular patterns were generated for studying diffractive X-ray optics [1]. However, they serve to demonstrate the ability to generate arbitrary geometries with high resolution. Even for masks with larger dimensions, the SEBL system is invaluable when unusual pattern geometries or large die sizes are required.

In addition to mask making and other single-level applications, a pattern-alignment technique has been developed [9] for use in multilevel, direct-write processes. An example of this capability is shown in Fig. 2, which is an optical micrograph of a submicrometer gate-length FET pattern on a GaAs substrate. The device is shown part way through processing. The first-level pattern of ohmic contacts and alignment marks (light areas) was exposed in the SEBL system. The wafer was subsequently removed from the SEBL system for development of the pattern, metallization, and formation of the ohmic contacts, and then returned to the system for alignment and writing of the gate pattern. The gate pad, defined in resist, is the dark square just above the 100-μm marker. It is connected to two 0.5-μm-long gates which have been precisely aligned in the 1.5-$\times$ 200-μm FET channels. Fig. 3 is a higher magnification view of the bottom of one of the channels showing the gate pattern between the source and drain contacts. These devices are of interest for building low-noise and high-power microwave amplifiers in the 20–40-GHz frequency range [9], [10].

The SEBL system is also used for a variety of other tasks such as resist characterization, mask inspection, and metrology. In addition, the SEBL system is used in applications which are not lithographic in nature. One of these is exploring the feasibility of using an electron beam to test and restructure wafer-scale integrated circuits. This work will be discussed in Section IV.

B. X-Ray Lithography

X-ray lithography was first demonstrated at Lincoln Laboratory [11] in 1972, and has been an active area of research ever since. Currently, work is being carried out in the key technologies of mask fabrication, precision multiple-mask alignment, and source/resist development. The research is divided into moderate resolution (0.1–0.2-μm) proximity exposure with precision alignment ($\sim$200 Å), and high-resolution ($\sim$100-Å) contact exposure without precision alignment. The former

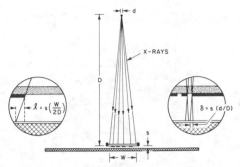

Fig. 5. Transmission-electron micrograph of 50-Å-thick electrically continuous tungsten pattern on an SiO$_2$ substrate. The structure was produced by liftoff from an X-ray-exposed pattern in 400-Å-thick PMMA.

Fig. 4. Schematic representation of the X-ray exposure process. Penumbral blurring δ arises from the finite size d of the source. The amount of blurring depends on mask-to-wafer gap s and source-to-substrate distance D. The shift l of a point at the edge of a field of size W is caused by the divergence of the X-rays. The shift, which is proportional to s/D, causes a magnification of the mask pattern on the wafer. Typical operating parameters would be $d = 3$ mm, $D = 30$ cm, $s = 20$ μm, and $W = 1$ cm. These would result in a penumbral blurring of 0.2 μm and a pattern shift of 0.33 μm at the edge of the field.

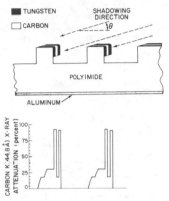

Fig. 6. Schematic diagram of the cross section of an X-ray mask with narrow lines and spaces. Alternate evaporations of W and C produces a modulated attenuation pattern as indicated in the plot.

is of interest as a general lithographic tool having submicrometer resolution and sufficient overlay accuracy to make the resolution useful in a multilevel process. The latter effort is aimed toward exploring the resolution limits of X-ray lithography. However, contact exposure is also an extremely powerful technique for device and circuit fabrication when critical alignment is not needed, or when the process contains a single X-ray level which is defined first, with subsequent optically or electron-beam defined layers aligned to it.

The X-ray exposure process is shown schematically in Fig. 4. A mask consisting of a patterned absorber on a thin, X-ray-transmissive membrane is positioned over a wafer coated with an X-ray-sensitive resist. Resolution is limited by penumbral blurring, due to the finite size of the source and magnification of the mask pattern caused by the divergence of the exposing radiation. In addition to these purely geometrical effects, there is a loss of resolution due to diffraction of the X-rays and the finite range of photoelectrons produced by absorption of the X-rays in the resist. Diffraction effects are minimized by using shorter wavelength X-rays; however, this produces more energetic electrons which have a longer range.

For some applications, extremely high resolution ($\sim$100 Å) is required. The only practical way to achieve this resolution with X-rays is to place the mask and wafer in contact. This virtually eliminates penumbra and pattern magnification. Obtaining optimal resolution then becomes a tradeoff between diffraction and photoelectron range (ignoring any effects due to nonlinear behavior of the resist). An analysis [6] of this tradeoff shows that resolution is limited to about 50 Å with an X-ray wavelength of 45 Å, for the ideal case of zero gap. In practice, the finite thickness of the resist and the X-ray absorber material on the mask limit resolution to slightly larger dimensions. One of the smallest structures which has been successfully replicated was produced at Lincoln Laboratory and is shown in Fig. 5 [12]. Two 200-Å-wide tungsten lines are separated by a 200-Å space. These lines were formed by liftoff[2]

---

[2] Liftoff is a process in which material is evaporated onto a surface containing a soluable surface relief structure. Dissolution of the surface relief structure carries away the material which has been deposited on it, leaving behind a patterned layer of the evaporated material.

from an X-ray-exposed pattern in 400-Å-thick polymethylmethacrylate (PMMA).

Perhaps the most challenging problem in producing features with such high resolution is the fabrication of a mask containing the desired pattern. One approach is oblique evaporation of an X-ray absorber onto a periodic surface-relief structure defined on a thin transmissive membrane [13]. The linewidth produced is a geometric function of the shape of the relief structure, the thickness of the evaporated film, and the angle of evaporation. The mask used to produce the 200-Å lines and spaces was generated by sequential evaporations of tungsten, which is highly absorbing, and carbon, which is relatively transmissive, onto a square-profile structure formed in a polyimide membrane, as shown in Fig. 6. By using variations on this technique, it is possible to produce patterns with linewidths controlled to $\pm$50 Å over areas as large as several centimeters square. The ability to produce these patterns over large areas makes them useful for a number of applications [12], as well as for resolution test patterns.

The second area of research in X-ray lithography at Lincoln Laboratory centers on the design and construction of a precision aligner for proximity (20–40 μm mask-to-wafer gap) X-ray exposure [14]. Precision overlay of multiple mask patterns is one of the most difficult problems to be solved in realizing the full potential of high-resolution lithographic techniques. Although our present emphasis is on an X-ray exposure system, it should be noted that an aligner is a quite general tool and could easily be adapted for use in a system that used exposing radiation other than X-rays. Since mechanical and thermal dis-

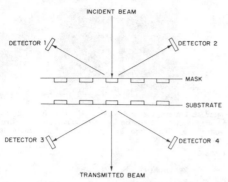

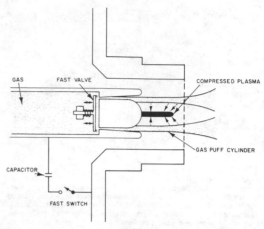

Fig. 7. Schematic illustration of interferometric alignment technique. Either detectors 1 and 2 or detectors 3 and 4 can be used to compare the intensities of the diffracted beams. Alignment is achieved when the intensities are equal.

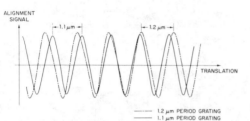

Fig. 8. Measured alignment signals for 1.1- and 1.2-μm period marks in transmission (detectors 3 and 4 in Fig. 7). The use of two grating marks of slightly different periodicities increases the capture range to $\pm(\frac{1}{2})(P_1 P_2)/(P_2 - P_1)$, where P_1 and P_2 are the periodicities.

Fig. 9. Schematic representation of the gas-puff z-pinch apparatus. The fast-acting gas release valve and shaped nozzle form a hollow cylinder of gas. A discharge current through the gas causes the cylinder to collapse, forming the plasma X-ray source.

tortion of the mask and wafer become severe problems as dimensions are reduced, the aligner is designed to be a step-and-repeat rather than a full-wafer exposure system. The design goals for our X-ray system are a minimum feature size of 0.2 μm, with pattern overlay accuracy of ~200 Å over a 1-cm² field.

There are six degrees of freedom which must be controlled in any proximity alignment system: two perpendicular lateral motions and a rotation (X, Y, θ) in a plane parallel to that of the mask and wafer, mask-to-wafer gap, and two rotations which define mask-to-wafer tilt. Our basic alignment scheme, which has been shown to be capable of 200-Å precision [15], is illustrated in Fig. 7. Diffraction of a laser beam from periodic alignment marks on the mask and wafer give rise to four signal beams. The alignment signal is the difference in intensity between detectors 1 and 2 or detectors 3 and 4. When exact overlay is achieved, the intensity difference is zero. This can be understood by noting the symmetry of the system when aligned. A minimum of three such marks is required to obtain alignment in X, Y, and θ.

One limitation of the scheme is that the alignment signals are periodic functions of the relative position of the mask and wafer. To insure correct positioning, the mask and wafer must initially be placed to within a quarter period of correct alignment. The capture range can be extended by using alignment marks which consist of two grating patterns of slightly different periodicity [14]. Fig. 8 shows measured alignment signals from this type of mark with gratings of 1.1- and 1.2-

μm periods. Alignment is achieved when the signals from both sets of gratings are simultaneously nulled.

Another drawback of the alignment technique is that it gives no information about mask-to-wafer gap or tilt. As discussed above, the gap causes a magnification of the mask pattern when it is transferred to the wafer. Variations in gap or tilt from layer to layer will cause misregistration either between layers or from one side of a wafer to the other for the same layer. Measurement of the capacitance between metal pads placed on the mask and wafer can be used to measure gap; a three-point measurement is needed to control tilt. The accuracy of this method is adequate, but to obtain acceptable signal-to-noise ratios, inconveniently large pads must be used. Recently, a precision, wide-range optical gap control technique has been developed [16]. Since the mask and wafer form a Fabry–Perot cavity, the spacing between them can be determined by analyzing the fringe pattern produced by reflected laser light. As in the capacitive technique, a three-point measurement is required.

High throughput, although not a major driving force in the design of our X-ray system, is nevertheless of interest. Projected alignment times are, at most, a few seconds, while the exposure times for high-resolution resists using conventional electron-bombardment X-ray sources range from several minutes to several hours. In addition to the inconvenience of these long exposures, there is the practical problem of maintaining alignment throughout a long exposure cycle. One possible alternative is to use the intense soft X-ray emission of pulsed high-temperature plasmas [12]. Initial feasibility experiments have been successfully completed [18] on one type of plasma source, the gas-puff z-pinch shown schematically in Fig. 9. The challenge is to engineer the source into a reliable lithographic tool.

C. Ion-Beam Lithography

Ion-beam exposure of resists is a promising technique for the replication of patterns having submicrometer features. Work at Lincoln Laboratory [19], [20] on proton exposure of resists

Fig. 10. Schematic illustration of membrane mask structure for ion-beam lithography. The surface relief structure provides contrast for resist exposure since the ion beam is attenuated in the thick areas of the mask. A stencil-type mask can be formed by etching completely through the membrane as indicated by the dotted lines.

Fig. 11. Scanning-electron micrograph of PMMA structure produced by proton exposure using a stencil mask. Spaces of 0.1 μm, reproduced at a mask-to-wafer gap of 0.25 mm, are shown.

was stimulated by the possibility of having a high-resolution lithographic technique that would not require the long exposure times necessary with X-rays. Protons do not diffract significantly, produce low-energy secondary electrons when interacting with matter, and can be formed into highly collimated beams. In addition, simple, commercially available sources can provide sufficient current to expose even the most insensitive resists in a fraction of a second. The main difficulty is in the development of a suitable mask technology which will provide sufficient contrast while causing minimum scattering of the incident beam.

A proton mask, like other masks, has transparent and opaque areas which define the pattern to be replicated. The penetration depth of protons in materials which can be used as the absorber differs by only about a factor of two from that in resist materials such as PMMA. Therefore, the thickness of the absorber must be of the same order as that of the resist, and the production of a high-aspect-ratio structure in resist requires a high-aspect-ratio absorber pattern.

One mask structure currently under investigation at Lincoln Laboratory is shown in Fig. 10. Reactive-ion etching is used to define a high-aspect-ratio surface relief structure in a thin polymer or dielectric membrane. Protons are stopped in the thick areas of the mask but pass through the thin areas to expose the resist. Features as small as 600 Å have been replicated in PMMA using a polyimide membrane mask in contact with the wafer [19]. Scattering of the protons in the thin areas of the mask causes a reduction in resolution when there is a gap between mask and wafer. This problem can be eliminated by continuing to etch the pattern all the way through the membrane, as indicated by the dotted lines in Fig. 10. This stencil-type mask [20] allows the protons to pass unimpeded through the patterned areas and expose the resist. Since diffraction is not a problem, it is possible to expose submicrometer patterns at large gaps. Fig. 11 shows 0.1-μm features exposed in 0.5-μm-thick PMMA using a Si_3N_4 stencil mask at a mask-to-wafer spacing of 0.25 mm. The ability to produce such features at macroscopic gaps is unique to ion-beam lithography, and is a distinct advantage in step-and-repeat exposure systems, since it

readily allows large relative motion between the mask and wafer. At smaller gaps, using our present proton source, it should be possible to replicate features at the resolution limit of the technique (thought to be $\sim$100 Å).

The stencil mask has limitations as to the types of patterns which can be produced; an annulus, for example, cannot be produced with a single mask. This problem can be solved if precision alignment of multiple mask levels can be achieved. As previously mentioned, our step-and-repeat aligner is of a general design and could be easily adapted to an ion-beam exposure system. This would become an attractive alternative if a reliable mask technology can be developed.

D. Processing Techniques

As improving lithographic techniques allow features to be scaled down, other processing steps must continue to be improved. Patterns exposed in resist must be transferred to the substrate as either doping variations or surface relief structures in a metal, dielectric, or semiconductor. There is a strong effort at Lincoln Laboratory devoted to the development and complete characterization of dry-etching techniques, which are based on a combination of physical sputtering by low-energy-ion bombardment and chemical etching by a neutral or ionized reactive species (the sputtering and reactive species may or may not be the same). The role of ion bombardment in activating the chemical reactions varies depending on the particular combination of gases and material to be etched. The aim of these techniques is to achieve anisotropic, vertical etching so that the types of pattern degradation encountered in isotropic wet etchical can be avoided.

Two techniques which have been extensively developed at Lincoln Laboratory are reactive-ion etching (RIE) which utilizes a low-pressure RF plasma, and ion-beam assisted etching (IBAE) which uses an ion beam in conjunction with reactive species introduced separately into the etching chamber through gas jets. Three examples of structures which were etched using these techniques are given in Fig. 12 which shows scanning-electron micrographs of 0.32-μm-period surface relief structures etched in a dielectric (SiO_2) (Fig. 12(a)) [5], a metal (W) (Fig. 12(b)) [21], and a semiconductor (GaAs) (Fig. 12(c)) [22]. The SiO_2 and W were etched by RIE, the former using CHF_3, and the latter using CF_4. The GaAs was etched by IBAE using an Ar^+ beam and Cl_2 as the reactive gas. These results demonstrate that under the appropriate conditions, a high degree of etching anisotropy can be achieved and excellent pattern fidelity maintained. Both of these capabilities are essential for the fabrication of advanced devices and circuits which require closely packed submicrometer features to be defined in relatively thick layers of material. Etching techniques for other materials such as Si [23], Si_3N_4 [20], Al [24], [25], Al–Cu–Si alloys [24], and polymers [26], [27] have been developed or are under study.

An important issue is whether surfaces which are etched using these techniques are damaged so that they are unsuitable for subsequent device fabrication. Damage effects have been observed in both Si [28] and GaAs [29] and an important aspect of any etch is the degree to which damage is introduced (e.g., creation of surface states) and the ease with which it can be removed (e.g., by annealing or brief, wet chemical etch).

Another class of processing techniques which is under study is the use of selected, laser-induced photochemical reactions for localized etching, deposition, and doping [30], [31]. The

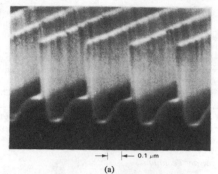

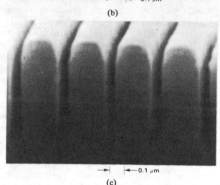

Fig. 12. Scanning-electron micrographs of structures produced by dry etching, showing (a) 300-Å-wide SiO_2 lines produced by reactive-ion etching (RIE) with CHF_3, (b) W lines produced by RIE wtih CF_4, and (c) 500-Å-wide slots in GaAs produced by ion-beam-assisted etching (IBAE) with an Ar^+ beam and Cl_2.

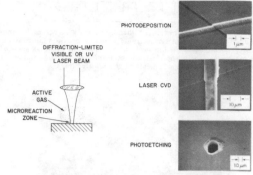

Fig. 13. Schematic illustration of direct, maskless processing using laser-induced photochemical reactions. Patterns are generated by scanning the beam over the sample. Also shown are examples of photodeposition of metal, laser-induced chemical-vapor deposition of polysilicon, and photoetching of Si.

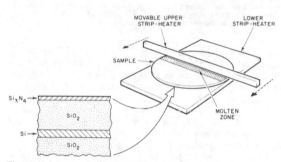

Fig. 14. Schematic diagram of zone-melting recrystallization process showing the sample structure and the oven configuration.

III. Materials Growth

Ultimately, material properties will determine the performance limits of semiconductor electronics. New device structures or scaled-down versions of existing devices often require improvements in the state of the art of materials growth. Most of the advanced materials effort at Lincoln Laboratory is concentrated on the epitaxial growth of III–V semiconductors and the production of semiconductor-on-insulator (SOI) thin films.

The work on III–V compounds encompasses all of the current epitaxial growth technologies: vapor-phase epitaxy (VPE), molecular-beam epitaxy (MBE), liquid-phase epitaxy (LPE), and organometallic chemical vapor deposition (OMCVD). Detailed discussions of this work are given in [32]–[35]. The motivation for the work is the improved device performance available from the superior optical and electronic properties of III–V compounds as compared with Si.

The growth of device-quality semiconducting films on insulators is an area which has long been of interest. Dielectric isolation of devices allows higher packing densities and increased speeds. Heteroepitaxial Si films grown on single-crystal sapphire substrates (SOS) are, at present, the only commercially available SOI structures, and these suffer limitations in terms of film quality. Our SOI research is focussed on the production of thin Si films on amorphous SiO_2 by a process we call zone-melting recrystallization [36], [37]. This process is illustrated schematically in Fig. 14. A thin polycrystalline Si

concept is illustrated in Fig. 13. A focused laser beam is used to initiate chemical reactions in a localized volume of gas above the sample surface. Photodecomposition of some component of the gas generates atoms or free radicals which can either condense on or react with the sample surface. Patterns are written by scanning the focussed laser beam over the sample. Fig. 13 shows examples of photodeposition of metal, laser-induced chemical-vapor deposition of polysilicon, and photoetching of Si. In addition, photodeposition can be combined with heating of the substrate to produce direct doping of semiconductors. The resolution of these techniques is determined primarily by the size of the laser focal spot which can be less than 1 μm in diameter. This type of direct, maskless processing provides unique fabrication capabilities particularly for applications requiring trimming, repair, or customization.

film is deposited on a SiO_2-coated substrate and capped with layers of SiO_2 and Si_3N_4. A graphite strip heater oven is used to recrystallize the Si film. The oven consists of a large-area stationary lower heater and a long, narrow upper heater which can be scanned across the wafer. The motion of the upper heater causes a narrow molten zone to move across the wafer, leaving a high-quality recrystallized film in its wake. Films up to 3 inches in diameter have been produced in this way [38].

Detailed descriptions of the properties of the recrystallized films have been published [39]-[41]. Although they consist of a number of large crystallites, these SOI films are useful for device applications. Depletion-mode n-channel MOSFET's fabricated in the films [37] exhibit typical surface electron mobilities of 650-700 $cm^2/V \cdot s$, values which are comparable to those obtained in bulk single-crystal Si wafers and considerably higher than those in SOS films. Also, the electrical properties of the recrystallized films are uniform throughout their depth, even at the lower Si-SiO_2 interface. For this reason, high-quality layers as thin as 0.2 μm can be produced. Thin layers are of interest for the fabrication of radiation-hard circuits [42] and short gate-length FET's.

In addition to the n-MOS devices, complementary MOS (CMOS) integrated circuits have been fabricated in recrystallized Si films [43]. A 3-$\times$ 4-mm test chip containing ring oscillators, transistor arrays, and inverter chains was designed to evaluate the worthiness of the films for integrated circuit fabrication. Arrays of chips with FET gate lengths of 5 μm were fabricated in films recrystallized on SiO_2-coated, 2-in Si wafers. The ring oscillators gave typical switching delay times of 2 ns and power-delay products of 0.2 pJ/stage for a fan-in and fan-out of 1. These results were obtained with a supply voltage of 5 V.

Results from device and circuit fabrication have thus far been encouraging. To become a viable material for commercial large-scale integrated-circuit fabrication, the recrystallized films will have to be further refined. This work is currently under way.

Other SOI structures are also being studied. A high-quality semiconducting film on a thick dielectric substrate is an ideal material for monolithic microwave circuits. Recrystallized Si films that we have made on thick SiO_2 [44] substrates exhibit enhanced electron mobilities and are useful for low-frequency applications.

IV. TESTING AND RESTRUCTURING OF INTEGRATED CIRCUITS

The performance and cost advantages inherent in highly integrated systems have stimulated the development of increasingly complex chips. Increased levels of integration have been achieved both by reducing feature sizes and by increasing chip sizes. Realizing high yields (or any yield) with such complex structures is a severe problem. The ever-larger systems which will be needed will inevitably exceed our capacity to make them defect-free. The ability to test circuits for defect location and to restructure circuits for defect avoidance would greatly enhance yield and could make possible wafer-scale integrated systems. The use of redundancy, a limited form of restructuring, has already led to dramatic yield improvements in commercial 64K RAM chips. Research at Lincoln Laboratory on testing and restructuring of integrated circuits includes work on fault avoidance, but its scope is more general and includes the study of restructurability for functional specialization.

The overall approach is illustrated in Fig. 15 [45]. Individu-

ally testable and restructable subsystems or cells are fabricated within an interconnection matrix consisting of metal lines and programmable switches or links. Each subsystem is customized for specific functions and tested. Access to the cell might be provided through the interconnection matrix which could be temporarily reconfigured for this purpose. Fault avoidance is accomplished either by the use of redundancy within a cell or by the substitution of a spare cell for a nonfunctioning one. The interconnection matrix is then used to wire together working subsystems to form the final integrated system.

A major effort at Lincoln Laboratory utilizes laser-formed links as programmable interconnects [46], [47]. These links have the advantage of high off-resistance and low on-resistance, and have been shown to be reliable. Fig. 15 shows a photograph of a wafer-scale integrated system which has been successfully built using laser links. The 2-in wafer contains 49 cells of 240 transistors each. The final integrated circuit was formed by interconnecting 16 of these cells to form a digital integrator. A new system has been designed for 3-in wafers [45]. It will consist of 192 cells of 1600 devices each; 64 cells will be interconnected to form a system with approximately 100K devices. One of the limitations of this technique is the low rate at which laser links can be programmed (a few per second). Also, a link can be programmed only once, so that if a connection must be made and broken several times during the testing and restructuring process, several parallel links must be provided along with a method for severing links.

An alternate approach being pursued is the use of an electron beam to perform all the necessary testing and restructuring functions [48]-[50]. Our SEBL system, discussed above, is an ideal instrument for this purpose in several important ways. The electron-beam probe is small, it can be positioned anywhere on a wafer, and it can be turned on and off under computer control. Since the system can store mask-level descriptions, testing can be automated. The beam can be deflected at megahertz rates, so that high-speed testing of circuits and programming of links is possible.

The three essential functions which must be performed by the electron beam are: 1) input injection—application of logical inputs to a subsystem under test; 2) output sensing—detection of the output levels of a subsystem under test; and 3) nonvolatile switching—programming of nonvolatile links for fault avoidance, customization, and interconnection of subsystems.

Initial experiments have concentrated on the development of suitable electron-beam-controllable structures which can be incorporated into a standard process sequence. Test chips of n-MOS structures have been fabricated which successfully perform all three functions. The circuit diagram for one of these structures is shown in Fig. 16. It consists of two cross-coupled inverters, which form a bistable latch for generating input data, and an FET whose gate is connected to the output of the latch. Electron-hole pairs, produced by electron bombardment of the Si, cause current to flow in the diodes formed between the n^+ diffusion and the p-type substrate, pulling these points to ground potential. In this way, the output of the latch can be set to either zero or one by directing the electron beam to the appropriate diode. The latch output is sensed by directing the beam to the source-substrate diode of the sensing FET (far right in Fig. 16) and monitoring the power-supply current. This simple electron-beam-controlled circuit demonstrates how input injection and output sensing can be accomplished with no external wiring except for power and ground. The third function, nonvolatile switching, has been accomplished using electron-beam-programmable floating-gate transistors.

RVLSI DIGITAL INTEGRATOR USING CMOS GATE ARRAYS

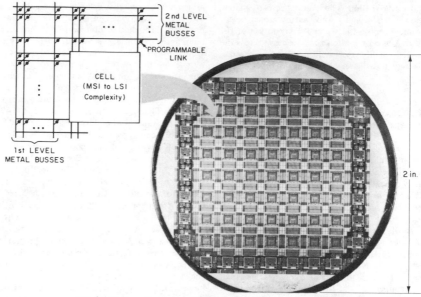

Fig. 15. Wafer-scale array of cells fabricated within an interconnection matrix. After testing of the individual cells, a wafer-scale circuit is produced by interconnecting working cells. The particular array shown was used to produce a digital integrator by interconnecting 16 cells.

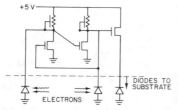

Fig. 16. Circuit diagram of n-MOS, electron-beam-controllable test structure. Electron-beam bombardment causes current to flow in diodes formed between the n^+ diffusion and the p-type substrate. The state of the bistable latch and the sensing FET (far right) can be controlled by directing the electron beam to the appropriate diode.

These have off–on resistance ratios of $\sim 10^4$ and good retention properties (several years at $85°C$). In addition, these links are reversible by exposure to UV light and by other techniques. Such transistors are used in commercially available UV-erasable electrically programmable read-only memories where they are programmed by hot-electron injection.

These initial results have demonstrated the feasibility of using an electron beam for testing and restructuring integrated circuits. Efforts are now being made to use these techniques to construct wafer-scale integrated circuits. Design and fabrication of a wafer-scale 128K electron-beam programmable memory has recently been completed and initial testing is underway [51].

The problem of proper placement and optimal utilization of redundant units as well as overall system architecture are common to both the laser and electron-beam approaches. A con-

siderable effort is being directed toward devising solutions to these problems [52].

V. PERMEABLE BASE TRANSISTOR (PBT)

In Sections II–IV, a cross section of the electronics technology development effort at Lincoln Laboratory has been described and some of the applications of this technology highlighted. In this section, the focus will be on the PBT [53]–[55]. The PBT has been chosen for two reasons: first, the successful fabrication of the PBT has depended upon utilizing several of the advanced techniques described above and integrating them into a real device process; secondly, the measured and projected performance of the PBT demonstrates that new levels of performance can be achieved by the use of advanced fabrication technology.

The development of the PBT differs from the submicrometer gate-length FET, for example, in that it was not an originally foreseen result of the technologies being developed. Well before the device was conceived, exploratory work on X-ray lithography, electron-beam lithography, and dry etching were underway. The resulting ability to produce submicrometer features with ~ 100-Å linewidth control over large areas using contact X-ray lithography made the development of the PBT possible.

The PBT is similar to a metal-base transistor (i.e., a semiconductor sandwich) but has lithographically defined openings in the base to reduce scattering of the carriers. It can also be thought of as a parallel array of vertical field-effect transistors with gate lengths equal to the thickness of the metal layer. Both the size and size uniformity of the openings are important

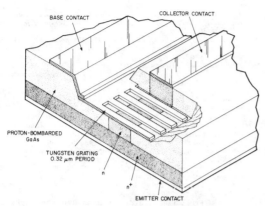

Fig. 17. Schematic illustration of the GaAs PBT. A 0.32-μm-period W base grating is encapsulated in a GaAs crystal. Electron flow from emitter to collector through the finger openings is controlled by means of the Schottky barrier between the W and the GaAs.

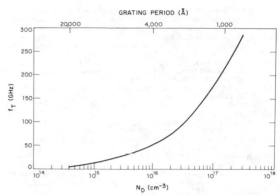

Fig. 18. Plot of the calculated f_T of the GaAs PBT as a function of base-grating periodicity. Also shown is the doping density which must be increased when dimensions are reduced.

since these affect the speed and threshold characteristics of the device. PBT's are being developed in GaAs and Si. Both devices employ a submicrometer-period metal grating structure as the base. The Schottky barrier which is formed between the metal and the semiconductor is used to control the flow of current between the base fingers.

Fabrication of the GaAs device, shown schematically in Fig. 17, depends on several advanced techniques. A thin film of high-purity W (300–500 Å) must be patterned to form the 0.32-μm-period base grating. The dimensions of the lines and spaces must be equal to a tolerance of ~100 Å. This is accomplished using contact X-ray lithography and reactive-ion etching. Next, high-quality crystalline material must be grown to encapsulate the metal base. Although this step has not yet been perfected, excellent device performance has been achieved. Microwave measurements of recently fabricated PBT's [56] have yielded an extrapolated maximum frequency of oscillation f_{max} of 100 GHz. For digital applications, the unity current gain frequency f_T provides a more relevant figure of merit. Devices having small-signal f_T's as high as 38 GHz, corresponding to a switching delay time of ~12 ps, have been fabricated. Both the microwave and digital performance of present GaAs PBT's are a factor of two to three below theoretical predictions. Improvements in crystal growth technology should allow the fabrication of PBT's with the predicted levels of performance.

Recently, PBT's have been successfully fabricated in Si [57]. Although the level of performance expected from these devices is lower than for PBT's in GaAs, simulations [58] indicate that Si PBT's should be considerably faster than present Si bipolar transistors. This performance combined with the advanced state of Si processing and integrated circuit technology, makes the Si PBT an attractive device for high-speed circuit applications. The structure of the Si PBT differs from the GaAs version in that the base fingers are not encapsulated. As in the case of the GaAs PBT, fabrication of the Si device draws on several of the advanced techniques described previously. The 0.32-μm-period base grating pattern is defined on the Si surface using X-ray lithography and reactive-ion etching used to form etched grooves. W is evaporated normal to the surface to form the base and collector contacts simultaneously (the bottoms and tops, respectively, of the grooves). This structure is feasible in Si since the exposed vertical sur-

faces can be passivated to prevent pinchoff of base-to-collector conduction through the Si fingers. The performance achieved on these initial devices is an f_{max} of 10 GHz and an f_T of 3 GHz (switching delay time of 0.16 ns). Planned improvements in the fabrication sequence should yield results closer to the predicted levels of f_{max} = 100 GHz and f_T = 35 GHz.

Much of the interest in the PBT arises from its potential performance as the finger size is scaled down. Fig. 18 shows the calculated f_T of the GaAs PBT as a function of base grating periodicity. As can be seen, significant gains in performance are expected as grating dimensions are reduced. Reduction of the period to 0.1 μm should yield an f_T greater than 200 GHz, and an f_{max} in excess of 600 GHz. The expectations for Si devices are somewhat lower but still of great interest. Reduction of the base grating periodicity to 0.1 μm will be a challenging task. However, the lithographic and etching techniques for producing microstructures are highly advanced and it is likely that, with some refinements, such a base grating could be produced with excellent uniformity over large areas.

VI. SUMMARY

An overview of the research efforts being pursued at Lincoln Laboratory has been presented to illustrate the wide range of activities which is necessary to insure a viable technology base for advanced electronics. In addition to the examples discussed above, Lincoln Laboratory is engaged in other research areas such as charge-coupled devices [59], [60], monolithic microwave circuits [61], [62], surface-acoustic wave devices [63], superconductive analog circuits [64], and optoelectronics [65], [66], which will be significantly impacted by advances in fabrication technology. The new levels of performance which are anticipated from devices with smaller dimensions and from more highly integrated circuits provide strong motivation for the development of advanced technology. The challenge in the future will be to bring together techniques developed in different research areas and to integrate them into reliable circuit-fabrication processes.

ACKNOWLEDGMENT

The author would like to thank Dr. F. J. Bachner for many helpful discussions and suggestions during the preparation of this manuscript.

REFERENCES

[1] D. C. Shaver, D. C. Flanders, N. M. Ceglio, and H. I. Smith, "X-ray zone plates fabricated using electron-beam and x-ray lithography," *J. Vac. Sci. Technol.*, vol. 16, pp. 1626-1630, Nov./Dec. 1979.

[2] N. M. Ceglio, D. C. Shaver, D. C. Flanders, and H. I. Smith, "Microfresnel structures for microscopy of laser generated bright x-ray sources," *Ann. N. Y. Acad. Sci.*, vol. 342, p. 65, 1980.

[3] D. C. Flanders, D. C. Shaver, and H. I. Smith, "Alignment of liquid crystals using submicrometer periodicity gratings," *Appl. Phys. Lett.*, vol. 32, pp. 597-598, May 1978.

[4] D. C. Shaver, "Alignment of liquid crystals by surface gratings," M.S. theses, Massachusetts Institute of Technology, 1978, reprinted as M.I.T. Lincoln Lab. Tech. Rep. 538, Oct. 1979.

[5] D. C. Flanders and A. E. White, "Application of ≈100 Å linewidth structures fabricated by shadowing techniques," *J. Vac. Sci. Technol.*, vol. 19, pp. 892-896, Nov./Dec. 1981.

[6] D. C. Flanders, "Research at the limits of microstructure fabrication," in *Proc. Int. Conf. on Microlithography, Microcircuit Engineering 81*, pp. 22-23, 1981.

[7] A. E. White, M. Tinkham, W. J. Skacpol, and D. C. Flanders, "Evidence for interaction effects in the low temperature resistance rise in ultrathin metallic wires," *Phys. Rev. Lett.*, vol. 48, pp. 1752-1755, June 1982.

[8] P. F. Liao, J. G. Bergman, D. S. Chemla, A. Wokaun, J. Melngailis, A. M. Hawryluk, and N. P. Economou, "Surface-enhanced Raman scattering from microlithographic silver particle surfaces," *Chem. Phys. Lett.*, vol. 82, pp. 355-359, Sept. 1981.

[9] T. M. Lyszczarz, G. A. Lincoln, and C. Smith, "Pattern registration using the scanning electron beam lithography system," Solid State Res. Rep., Lincoln Laboratory, M.I.T., DTIC ASTIA Doc. AD-A110947, pp. 50-53, Feb. 1981.

[10] A. Chu, A. Gopinath, G. L. Durant, G. A. Lincoln, M. Pierce, and C. Smith, "Submicrometer-gate-length GaAs FET,"Solid State Res. Rep., Lincoln Laboratory, M.I.T., DTIC ASTIA Doc. AD-A092724/4, pp. 33-35, Feb. 1980.

[11] D. L. Spears and H. I. Smith, "X-ray lithography—A new high-resolution pattern replication process," *Solid State Technol.*, vol. 15, pp. 21-26, Jul. 1972.

[12] D. C. Flanders, "Replication of 175-Å lines and spaces in polymethylmethacrylate using x-ray lithography," *Appl. Phys. Lett.*, vol. 36, pp. 93--96, Jan. 1980.

[13] D. C. Flanders, "X-ray lithography at ~100 Å linewidth using x-ray masks fabricated by shadowing techniques," *J. Vac. Sci. Technol.*, vol. 16, pp. 1615-1619, Nov./Dec. 1979.

[14] T. M. Lyszczarz, D. C. Flanders, N. P. Economou, and P. D. DeGraff, "Experimental evaluation of interferometric alignment techniques for multiple mask registration," *J. Vac. Sci. Technol.*, vol. 19, pp. 1214-1218, Nov./Dec. 1981.

[15] D. C. Flanders, H. I. Smith, and S. Austin, "A new interferometric alignment technique," *Appl. Phys. Lett.*, vol. 31, pp. 426-428, Oct. 1977.

[16] D. C. Flanders and T. M. Lyszczarz, "A precision wide-range optical gap measurement technique," presented at 1983 Workshop on Micrometer and Submicrometer Lithography, Palm Springs, CA, Jan. 1983.

[17] N. P. Economou and D. C. Flanders, "Prospects for high-brightness x-ray sources for lithography," *J. Vac. Sci. Technol.*, vol. 19, pp. 868-871, Nov./Dec. 1981.

[18] S. M. Mathews, R. Stringfield, I. Roth, R. Cooper, N. P. Economou, and D. C. Flanders, "Pulsed plasma source for x-ray lithography," *Semiconductor Microlithography VI, Proc. SPIE*, vol. 275, pp. 52-54, 1981.

[19] N. P. Economou, D. C. Flanders, and J. P. Donnelly, "High resolution ion beam lithography," *J. Vac. Sci. Technol.*, vol. 19, pp. 1172-1175, Nov./Dec. 1981.

[20] J. N. Randall, D. C. Flanders, N. P. Economou, J. P. Donnelly, and E. I. Bromley, "High resolution ion beam lithography at large gaps using stencil masks," submitted for publication.

[21] N. P. Economou and G. A. Lincoln, unpublished work.

[22] M. W. Geis, G. A. Lincoln, N. N. Efremow, and W. J. Piacentini, "A novel anisotropic etching technique," *J. Vac. Sci. Technol.*, vol. 19, pp. 1390-1393, Nov./Dec. 1981.

[23] D. D. Rathman, S. M. Cabral, J. Melngailis, N. P. Economou, and N. N. Efremow, "High resolution patterning of silicon with SiCl₄ reactive-ion etching," Solid State Res. Rep. Lincoln Laboratory, M.I.T., DTIC ASTIA Doc. AD-A112696, pp. 54-56, Mar. 1981.

[24] T. O. Herndon and R. L. Burke, "Plasma etching of aluminum," in *Proc. Kodak Microelectronics Seminar, Interface '77*, pp. 33-41, Oct. 1977.

[25] S. M. Cabral, D. J. Silversmith, and R. W. Mountain, "Characterization of a BCl₃ parallel-plate plasma system for aluminum," Solid State Res. Rep. Lincoln Laboratory, M.I.T., DTIC ASTIA Doc. AD-A112696, pp. 51-54, Mar. 1981.

[26] T. O. Herndon and R. L. Burke, "Inter-metal polyimide insulation for VLSI," in *Proc. Kodak Microelectronics Seminar, Interface '79*, Oct. 1979.

[27] P. D. DeGraff and D. C. Flanders, "Directional oxygen-ion beam etching of carbonaceous materials," *J. Vac. Sci. Technol.*, vol. 16, pp. 1906-1908, Nov./Dec. 1979.

[28] S. Pang, D. D. Rathman, D. J. Silversmith, R. W. Mountain, and P. D. DeGraff, "Damage induced in Si by ion milling or reactive ion etching," submitted for publication.

[29] G. A. Lincoln, M. W. Geis, L. J. Mahoney, B. A. Vojak, K. B. Nichols, W. J. Piacentini, N. Efremow, and W. T. Lindley, "Ion beam assisted etching for GaAs device applications," *J. Vac. Sci. Technol.*, vol. 20, pp. 786-789, Mar. 1982.

[30] D. J. Ehrlich, R. M. Osgood, Jr., and T. F. Deutsch," Laser microphotochemistry for use in solid-state electronics," *IEEE J. Quantum Electron.*, vol. QE-16, pp. 1233-1243, Nov. 1980.

[31] ——, "Laser microreaction for deposition of doped silicon films," *Appl. Phys. Lett.*, vol. 39, pp. 957-959, Dec. 1981.

[32] G. J. Davies, R. Hekingbottom, H. Ohno, C.E.C. Wood, and A. R. Calawa, "Arsenic stabilization of InP substrates for growth of $Ga_xIn_{1-x}As$ layers by molecular beam epitaxy," *Appl. Phys. Lett.*, vol. 37, pp. 290-292, Aug. 1980.

[33] A. R. Calawa, "On the use of AsH_3 in the molecular beam epitaxial growth of GaAs," *Appl. Phys. Lett.*, vol. 38, pp. 701-703, May 1981.

[34] Z. L. Liau and J. N. Walpole, "A novel technique for GaInAsP/InP buried heterostructure laser fabrication," *Appl. Phys. Lett.*, vol. 40, pp. 568-570, Apr. 1982.

[35] T. S. Low, G. E. Stillman, A. Y. Cho, H. Morboc, and A. R. Calawa, "Spectroscopy of donors in high purity GaAs grown by molecular beam epitaxy," *Appl. Phys. Lett.*, vol. 40, pp. 611-613, Apr. 1982.

[36] E. W. Maby, M. W. Geis, Y. L. LeCoz, D. J. Silversmith, R. W. Mountain, and D. A. Antoniatis, "MOSFET's on silicon prepared by moving melt zone recrystallization of encapsulated polycrystalline silicon on an insulating substrate," *IEEE Electron. Device Lett.*, vol. EDL-2, pp. 241-243, Oct. 1981.

[37] B-Y. Tsaur, M. W. Geis, J.C.C. Fan, D. J. Silversmith, and R. W. Mountain, "N-channel deep-depletion metal-oxide-semiconductor field-effect transistors fabricated in zone-melting-recrystallized polycrystalline Si films on SiO_2," *Appl. Phys. Lett.*, vol. 39, pp. 909-911, Dec. 1981.

[38] J.C.C. Fan, B-Y. Tsaur, R. L. Chapman, and M. W. Geis, "Zone-melting recrystallization of 3-in.-diameter Si films on SiO_2-coated Si substrates," *Appl. Phys. Lett.*, vol. 41, pp. 186-188, Jul. 1982.

[39] M. W. Geis, H. I. Smith, B-Y. Tsaur, and J.C.C. Fan, "Zone-melting recrystallization of encapsulated Si films on SiO_2—Morphology and crystallography," *Appl. Phys. Lett.*, vol. 40, pp. 158-160, Jan. 1982.

[40] B-Y. Tsaur, J.C.C. Fan, M. W. Geis, D. J. Silversmith and R. W. Mountain, "Effects of subgrain boundaries on carrier transport in zone-melting recrystallized Si films on SiO_2-coated Si substrates," *IEEE Electron Device Lett.*, vol. EDL-3, pp. 79-82, Apr. 1982.

[41] B-Y. Tsaur, J.C.C. Fan, and M. W. Geis, "Microsecond carrier lifetimes in Si films prepared on SiO_2-coated Si substrates by zone-melting recrystallization and by subsequent epitaxial growth," *Appl. Phys. Lett.*, vol. 41, pp. 83-85, Jul. 1982.

[42] B-Y. Tsaur, J.C.C. Fan, G. W. Turner, and D. J. Silversmith, "Effects of ionizing radiation on n-channel MOSFET's fabricated in zone-melting-recrystallized Si films on SiO_2," *IEEE Electron. Device Lett.*, vol. EDL-3, pp. 195-197, Jul. 1982.

[43] B-Y. Tsaur, J.C.C. Fan, R. L. Chapman, M. W. Geis, D. J. Silversmith, and R. W. Mountain, "SOI/CMOS circuits fabricated in zone-melting-recrystallized Si films on SiO_2-coated Si substrates," accepted for publication, *IEEE Electron Device Lett.*

[44] B-Y. Tsaur, J.C.C. Fan, and M. W. Geis, "Stress-enhanced carrier mobility in zone-melting recrystallized polycrystalline Si films on SiO_2 coated substrates," *Appl. Phys. Lett.*, vol. 40, pp. 322-324, Feb. 1982.

[45] J. I. Raffel, G. H. Chapman, K. H. Konkle, and A. M. Soares, "A demonstration of very large area integration using laser restructuring," in *Proc. IEEE Int. Symp. on Circuits and Systems*, Newport Beach, CA, May 1983.

[46] J. I. Raffel, M. L. Naiman, R. L. Burke, G. H. Chapman, and P. G. Gottschalk, "Laser programmed vias for restructurable VLSI," in *IEEE Int. Electron Devices Meet. Tech. Dig.*, pp. 132-135, Dec. 1980.

[47] J. A. Yasaitis, G. H. Chapman, and J. I. Raffel, "Low resistance laser formed lateral links," *IEEE Electron. Device Lett.*, vol. EDL-3, pp. 184-186, Jul. 1982.

[48] D. C. Shaver, Electron beam techniques for testing and restructuring of wafer-scale integrated circuits," Ph.D. dissertation, Massachusetts Institute of Technology, 1981.

[49] D. C. Shaver, "Electron beam testing and restructuring of inte-

grated circuits," in *Proc. 2nd Caltech Conf. on Very Large Scale Integration*, to be published.

[50] ——, "Techniques for electron beam testing and restructuring of integrated circuits," *J. Vac. Sci. Technol.*, vol. 19, pp. 1010–1013, Nov./Dec. 1981.

[51] D. C. Shaver, R. W. Mountain, and D. J. Silversmith, "Electron-beam programmable 128K bit wafer-scale EPROM," submitted for publication.

[52] P. E. Blankenship, *Semiannual Technical Summary, Restructurable VLSI Program*, DTIC ASTIA Doc. AD-A120471. Lexington, MA: Lincoln Laboratory, M.I.T., Mar. 1981.

[53] C. O. Bozler, G. D. Alley, R. A. Murphy, D. C. Flanders, and W. T. Lindley, "Fabrication and microwave performance of the permeable base transistor," in *IEEE Int. Electron Device Meet. Tech. Dig.*, pp. 384–387, Dec. 1979.

[54] C. O. Bozler and G. D. Alley, "Fabrication and numerical simulation of the permeable base transistor," *IEEE Trans. Electron Devices*, vol. ED-27, pp. 1128–1141, June 1980.

[55] ——, "The permeable base transistor and its application to logic circuits," *Proc. IEEE*, vol. 70, pp. 46–52, Jan. 1982.

[56] G. D. Alley, C. O. Bozler, A. R. Calawa, N. P. Economou, D. C. Flanders, M. W. Geis, W. T. Lindley, G. A. Lincoln, R. W. McClelland, R. A. Murphy, K. B. Nichols, W. J. Piacentini, S. Rabe, J. P. Salerno, and B. A. Vojak, "Millimeter-wavelength GaAs permeable base transistors," presented at Device Research Conf., Fort Collins, CO., June, 1982.

[57] D. D. Rathman, N. P. Economou, D. J. Silversmith, R. W. Mountain, and S. M. Cabral, "The microwave silicon permeable base transistor," in *IEEE Int. Electron Devices Meet. Tech. Dig.*, Dec. 1982.

[58] B. A. Vojak and G. D. Alley, "Two-dimensional numerical simulations of Si permeable base transistors," submitted for publication.

[59] B. E. Burke, D. L. Smythe, D. J. Silversmith, W. H. McGonagle, R. W. Mountain, and B. J. Felton, "A high-speed CCD time-integrating correlator," in *Proc. IEEE Int. Solid-State Circuits Conf.*, Feb. 1983.

[60] A. M. Chaing, "A new CCD parallel processing architecture," in *VLSI Systems and Computations*, H. T. King, B. Sproull, and G. Steele, Eds. MD: Comput. Sci. Press, Inc., 1981.

[61] B. J. Clifton, G. D. Alley, R. A. Murphy, and I. H. Mroczkowski, "High-preformance quasi-optical GaAs monolithic mixer at 110 GHz," *IEEE Trans. Electron Devices*, vol. ED-28, pp. 155–157, Feb. 1981.

[62] A. Chu, L. J. Mahoney, M. E. Elta, W. E. Courteny, W. J. Piacentini, and J. P. Donnelly, "A two-stage monolithic IF amplifier utilizing a high dielectric constant capacitor," in *Proc. IEEE Microwave and Millimeter-Wave Monolithic Curcuit Symp.*, pp. 61–63, May 1982.

[63] R. W. Ralston, "Acoustoelectronic microcircuits: A new technology for signal processing," in *Proce. IEEE Int. Symp. on Circuits and Systems*, pp. 1–9, 1980.

[64] S. A. Rieble, "Wideband analog signal processing with superconductive circuits," in *Proc. of 1982 Ultrasonics Symp.*, San Diego, CA, to be published.

[65] A. G. Foyt, F. J. Leonberger, and R. C. Williamson, "Picosecond InP optoelectronic switches," *Appl. Phys. Lett.*, vol. 40, pp. 447–449, Mar. 1982.

[66] F. J. Leonberger, C. E. Woodward, and R. A. Becker, "4-bit 828-megasample/s electro-optic guided-wave analog-to-digital converter," *Appl. Phys. Lett.*, vol. 40, pp. 565–568, Apr. 1982.

IC Process Modeling and Topography Design

ANDREW R. NEUREUTHER, MEMBER, IEEE

Invited Paper

Abstract—The device features in the third dimension in VLSI affect packing density and circuit performance. Establishing techniques to characterize and design these nonplanar device features is a major goal of the research on IC process modeling and simulation. Simulation is well accepted as a means of optimizing individual lithography, etching, and deposition processes. It is also well suited for studying the complex tradeoffs between conflicting physical mechanisms in the context of complete multistep process sequences. The success of modeling and simulation has created a demand for more extensive models and new applications. IC process modeling and simulation will not only contribute heavily to technology design but also offers a potential window through the layout rule bottleneck for more complete design insight and optimization.

I. INTRODUCTION

THE FUNDAMENTAL LIMITS of performance and packing density in VLSI circuits are determined at the wafer level. The important issues are the types of physical features that can be built with adequate yield and their corresponding electrical performance. Design aids traditionally simplify the interface to these technology issues through the use of well-established layout rules. Yet CAD tools for IC processing and device analysis are also being used as aids in developing new technologies. The purpose of this article is to give an overview of CAD tools for technology design, particularly in the area of topography effects in lithography, etching, and deposition. The future potential for enlarging the design aids window through the layout rule bottleneck is also discussed.

As IC fabrication technology pushes toward finer linewidths, the topographical features of devices are becoming an increasing concern. Not only is greater linewidth control required for high resolution, but it must be accomplished in a context where features in the third dimension are as large as the linewidth itself. SEM cross sections of wafers are frequently used to examine problems related to topography. While these device cross sections or line edge profiles give true process feedback, they are time consuming to perform and require unusually accurate process control to systematically explore a matrix of experimental parameters. If process models can be established, algorithms can often be used to explore process effects by simulating the time evolution of the line edge profile. Besides the advantages of controllability and observability, simulation can be done much more rapidly and economically.

A good example of the need for careful device topography design occurs in sputter deposition of metal into small contact holes. In shrinking VLSI layout for high density, the size of

Manuscript received July 6, 1982; revised November 23, 1982. This work was supported in part by a National Sciences Foundation under Grant ECS-8106234, and in part by industrial grant in aid.
The author is with the Department of Electrical Engineering and Computer Sciences and Electronics Research Laboratory, University of California, Berkeley, CA 94720.

Reprinted from *Proc. IEEE*, vol. 71, pp. 121–128, Jan. 1983.

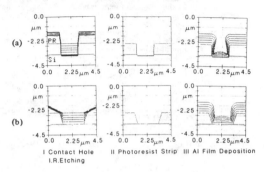

Fig. 1. Simulation of contact hole formation process using infrared baking to reflow the resist prior to plasma etching and deposition. Nominal 1.5-μm opening in 1.0-μm oxide through 1.0-μm resist coated with 1.0-μm sputtered metal after plasma ashing. (a) Without photoresist post-baking. (b) With photoresist post-baking.

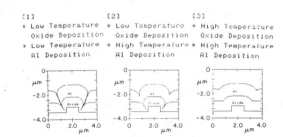

Fig. 2. Simulation of oxide and aluminum deposition in which low-pressure oxidation and high-temperature metallization eliminate the "crack" problem. Rectangular step 0.4 μm high by 1.0 μm wide covered by an 0.8-μm insulator (oxide) prior to 1.0-μm metallization.

the contact holes is one of the limiting factors. Not only must the lithography be capable of resolving these two dimensional features, but the deposition must be capable of adequately coating them. Fig. 1 illustrates how a multistep combination of resist processing, plasma etching of oxide, and aluminum alloy sputter deposition are used to form the contact to the substrate [1]. The thickness in the bottom of the contact and along the sides is greatly influenced by the aspect ratio of the opening and edge profile shape. A tapered process results in much better coverage and reduced sensitivity to electromigration induced by high current densities.

Another common problem in VLSI is that the detailed shape of underlying steps can propagate through overcoating films to affect device parameters and performance. For example, Fig. 2 shows how an aluminum film on oxide is affected by underlying vertical steps in polysilicon [1]. Disastrous "cracks"

IC PROCESS APPLICATION AREAS

LITHOGRAPY	ETCHING
OPTICAL	WET
E-BEAM	ION MILLING
X-RAY	PLASMA ETCHING
ION-BEAM	ION ASSISTED ETCHING

THERMAL PROCESSING	DEPOSITION
OXIDATION	EVAPORATION
DOPING	SPUTTERING
ION IMPLANTATION	CHEMICAL VAPOR DEPOSITION
ANNEALING	ELECTROPLATING
	EPITAXIAL GROWTH

Fig. 3. IC processing areas for which modeling and simulation are potentially applicable. Four major groupings are shown.

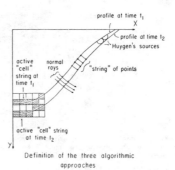

Definition of the three algorithmic approaches

Fig. 4. Three algorithms for implementing surface etching simulation and the analogy to a Huygen's source problem.

occasionally occur at steps, and the materials at these step edges are readily attacked laterally along step edges creating "mouse holes" and a necking down of conductors at steps. Low-pressure oxidation techniques and high-temperature metallization tend to improve the topography. Even with new deposition technologies, the shape of the film layer varies and degrades the electrical parameters of long conductors such as the resistance of the word line in a memory which must cross many steps. The added arc length and reduced width at steps may increase the resistance by as much as a factor of ten. The capacitance is also increased compared to a planar film, especially in the vicinity of steps, and the thinned coating can lead to breakdown voltage problems.

The general problem of device topography affecting circuit performance can be explored with computer simulation. User-oriented lithography, etching, and deposition models have been established which agree well with experiment. Multistep simulation using these processes is also available. Post processors for extracting the electrical parameters from the simulated profiles are also being developed. In the future it is likely that the topography simulation and circuit performance evaluation will be driven directly from the layout system. This includes rapid topography emulation to give designers direct feedback from their layouts.

This paper gives an overview of simulation and modeling of IC processes. It focuses primarily on the areas of lithography, etching, and deposition and their particular embodiment in the user-oriented program SAMPLE [2], [3]. The related thermal process of ion implantation, diffusion, and oxidation and their incorporation into the programs SUPREM and ICECREM have recently been described elsewhere [4], [5] and are recommended for additional reading. Section II gives an overview of the status and uses of simulation. The computer requirements and algorithms for carrying out process simulation are described in Section III. A survey of simulation results and comparisons with experiment are given in Section IV. Finally, the future trends and issues are discussed in Section V.

II. Status of Simulation

It is potentially possible to find both physical models and efficient algorithms to simulate most IC fabrication processes. Fig. 3 lists a variety of examples. They are divided into four major areas: lithography, etching, deposition, and thermal processes. Simulation work has been carried out for most of these processes by a number of authors. The simulation of the time evolution of line edge profiles began about ten years ago, although the models themselves in some cases are related to basic work extending back even further.

Simulation has been used to study key issues in all types of lithography. Optical lithography simulation was made possible by the establishment of an exposure-bleaching development-etching model for positive photoresist [6]. This permitted the modeling of projection printing [7]-[11] and has been useful in the characterization of modern optical lithography tools [12]-[19] and resist materials [14], [20]-[26]. Electron beam lithography simulation has been based on Monte Carlo simulation of the latent energy deposition profile [27], [28] and a solubility-versus-dose model for PMMA resist [29], [30]. Profile simulation has been useful in characterizing effects of machine, wafer, and resist parameters on lithographic performance [31]-[45]. X-ray and ion beam lithography have also been simulated using energy deposition models with the PMMA resist model [46]-[49].

A variety of etching and deposition models have also been developed. Basic etching concepts have evolved from crystal growth models and have been applied to plasma etching, reactive-ion etching, and ion milling [50]-[57]. Sputter deposition and evaporation have also been simulated [62]-[67]. The conditions necessary for metal "lift-off" [66], [67] and step coverage have been explored [65].

Simulation and modeling of processing have been utilized by process and device designers for a number of purposes. A very common use is for education and understanding of new processes or equipment. The ability to investigate individual physical phenomena and interactions of different phenomena through the huge number of process parameters is especially useful. This leads frequently into more quantitative use of simulation in the determination of optimum processing conditions for equipment such as projection printers. A third type of use is in exploration studies of new processes and new process sequences. A good example here is the study of the use of isotropic deposition combined with anisotropic etching to planarize the wafer surface. Another important use is the assessment of the impact of hypothetical and future technology advances, such as new lithography exposure tools or new resist technologies. It is also possible to use simulation in diagnostic and discovery modes in which the physical models are modified to create new effects or establish plausible explanations of experimental observations.

III. Algorithms

Simulation is typically carried out on large computer systems with the aid of graphics terminals. Most source codes are in Fortran and require about 5 to 60 s of execution time ($10^{**}7$–8 machine instructions). If more extensive calculations are required such as in the case of Monte Carlo techniques, a reusable library of data is first generated and then accessed by the program for rapid execution. A file handling system

Segment Motion Algorithm

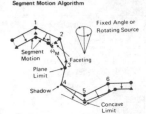

Fig. 5. Improved segment motion algorithm for reactive ion etching and ion milling which incorporates more information about the physical mechanisms and boundary conditions.

and editor are convenient for creating and selectively running data sets. Terminals and support packages for interactive operation and graphics are also desirable.

Many of the processes can to first order be considered as surface reaction rate limited processes. This is true for positive resist development, dry etching, and even deposition (negative etching). Thus the simulation of many of the IC processes can be based on a generalized surface etching algorithm. Fig. 4 graphically depicts the surface etching problem for lithography along with several algorithmic approaches. Each point on the initial surface acts like an infinitesimal Huygen's source, and the advancing contour is the locus of tangents to all the Huygen's spheres of influence. Computationally, this process has been implemented by cell removal, by analogy to optical ray tracing, and by advancing a string of line segments. The string approach has been commonly used for two-dimensional problems, while for three-dimensional problems the ray approach may have inherent advantages.

To make simulation accurate and efficient, the physical mechanisms and boundary conditions of the process being simulated must be incorporated into the algorithms. For this reason, the string advance algorithm is evolving into a variety of algorithms for special purposes. One example is the segment motion algorithm shown in Fig. 5, which is suitable for plasma etching and ion milling [54]. For this algorithm the segments advance to form new segment intersections. Faceting at exterior corners and the preservation of angles at interior corners have also been included. The addition of new segments and deletion of small segments must be made in accordance with these conditions as well. Another example of the need for modifications of the algorithms occurs in deposition. Here a negative etch rate can be used to make the etch front move backward. However, the mechanisms of motion and boundary conditions for evaporation and sputtering differ. Care must also be taken to insure that the etching algorithm which is stable in the forward direction is also stable when advanced in reverse.

IV. SIMULATION RESULTS

The impact which simulation is capable of making on device processing is best illustrated by surveying a few examples from the lithography, etching, and deposition areas. The most extensive use of simulation has been in optical lithography where it has been used to study important aspects of the aerial image, wafer topography, and resist materials. In simulating the aerial image, the illumination, mask, and objective lens must be considered as a total system. For example, the aerial image can be improved by restricting the cone of rays which illuminate the mask to be smaller than the cone of rays accepted by the objective lens. The filling factor or partial coherence parameter "s" is the ratio of the sines (numerical

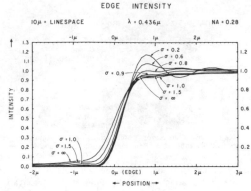

Fig. 6. Projection printed image of a knife edge pattern for a diffraction limited lens as a function of the partial coherence parameter s normalized to a clear field intensity of 1.0.

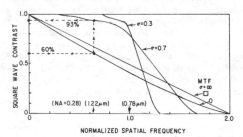

Fig. 7. Square wave contrast and modulation transfer function for a diffraction limited lens.

aperture na) of the illumination and objective lens cone angles. The effect on the aerial image is illustrated in Fig. 6 for a knife edge pattern [11]. Decreasing s allows more coherent phase interactions to occur. This produces an overshoot, an increase in edge slope, and a reduction in the intensity in the masked region. The latter effect is by far the most important.

In practice, it is more convenient to characterize the aerial image by means of the square wave contrast given by (I max − I min)/(I max + I min) where I max and I min are the maximum and minimum intensities for an equal line and space mask pattern. A plot of the square wave contrast of a diffraction limited lens as a function of the spatial frequency of the pattern is given in Fig. 7 [16]. It is normalized by dividing the the period by the wavelength/na where na is the numerical aperture of the objective lens. Note that the square wave contrast for the traditional operating point of 60 percent modulation transfer function is 93 percent for $s = 0.7$. The contrast required for 10 to 20 percent linewidth control is 80 to 90 percent as shown in Fig. 8 [16].

The wafer reflectivity and topography are also important considerations. A 1.0-um resist coating over a 1.0-um step may thin to 0.5 um at the top of the step and may be as thick as 1.5 um at the bottom. In addition to this global change, a local thickness change of a quarter of a wavelength (65 nm) will change the exposure energy coupling from maximum (odd multiples) to minimum (even multiples). Profiles typical of these extreme cases are shown in Fig. 9 [18]. The resulting linewidth can be seen on a plot of linewidth versus thickness in Fig. 10, which shows the local periodic variation as well as a global drift.

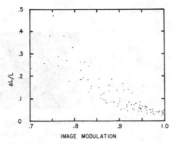

Fig. 8. Fractional resist linewidth change due to a 50-percent exposure increase versus square wave image contrast. Nominal conditions for about 1.0-μm positive resist on quarter wavelength of oxide for a single wavelength direct wafer stepper with 0.28 numerical aperture.

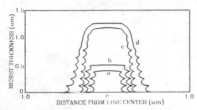

Fig. 9. Resist line edge profiles typically seen at step crossings due to resist thickness change at the top (a, b) and bottom (c, d) for maximum coupling (a, c) and minimum coupling (b, d).

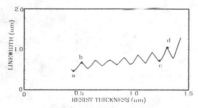

Fig. 10. Resist linewidth versus thickness showing local periodic variation and global increase. A 1.0-μm equal line and space array under conditions similar to Fig. 8.

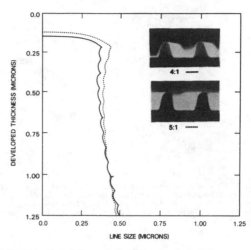

Fig. 11. Use of modeling and simulation to characterize processing conditions such as developer concentration. A 1.25 equal line and space array in AZ2400 exposed at 313 nm on a scanning system with 0.17 numerical aperture.

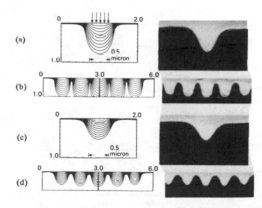

Fig. 12. Comparison of simulated and experimental electron beam exposed PMMA resist profiles. A 0.5-μm isolated line and 5 equal line and space array.

The resist characteristics are chosen to improve the pattern contrast from the relative poor quality of the aerial image. Modeling parameters for positive resist are generally available [20]–[26]. The "induction" effect or delay in development [14] and negatively processed positive diazo resists [25] have also been modeled. An example of modeling the resist behavior as influenced by one of the processing conditions, developer concentration, is shown in Fig. 11 [14].

A comparison of experimental and simulated resist profiles for electron beam lithography is shown in Fig. 12 [36]. Here the ninth or next-to-last profile corresponds to the 90-s experimental development time. The profile depth and size agree well with experiment as a function of dose and proximity of other features. The experimental profile is also slightly more vertical, indicating that an additional physical mechanism may need to be modeled.

Numerous simulation studies have been carried out in electron beam lithography. The magnitude of intraline and interline proximity effects on various substrates has been studied [31]–[45]. Three-dimensional development effects have been explored [45]. The role of scattering by high-energy secondary electrons has been shown to be relatively small [28]. The

optimum bias has been predicted from a pluralistic scattering model [40]. The advantages of multilayer resists [39] and the relative advantages of electron beam compared to optical lithography [43], [44] have been explored. Profile description parameters have been used to show that bias correction for proximity effects gives better linewidth control and profile quality although it may be more difficult to implement in machine design. These profile description parameters [41] are shown in Fig. 13 and are applicable to quantitative profile comparisons in other lithography and etching processes as well.

For X-ray and ion beam lithography the exposure mechanisms for depositing energy into the resist are well understood and can readily be simulated. Generally, it is assumed that the etch rate for development is the same function of deposited energy as used for electron beam lithography. An example of simulation of an X-ray lithography resist profile in multilayer resist from a mask with a tapered edge is shown in Fig. 14 [46]. Photoelectrons can be generated in the substrate which

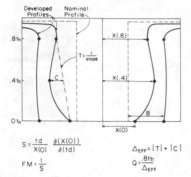

S = \frac{td}{X(O)} \frac{\partial(X(O))}{\partial(td)}

FM = \frac{1}{S}

$\Delta_{EFF} = |T| + |C|$

$Q = \frac{.8th}{\Delta_{EFF}}$

Fig. 13. Line edge profile description parameters convenient for quantitative experimental and simulation studies. The linewidth at three heights is used to calculate the quality Q and the rate of opening at the substrate is used to find the figure of merit FM for development time sensitivity.

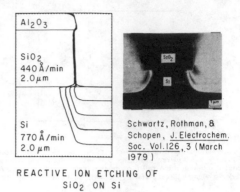

REACTIVE ION ETCHING OF SiO_2 ON Si

Schwartz, Rothman, & Schopen, J. Electrochem. Soc. Vol.126, 3 (March 1979)

Fig. 15. Comparison of simulated and experimental profiles for reactive ion etching.

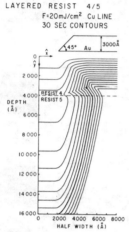

LAYERED RESIST 4/5
$F = 20mJ/cm^2$ Cu LINE
30 SEC CONTOURS

Fig. 14. Multilayered X-ray resist profile after exposure through a mask with a tapered edge.

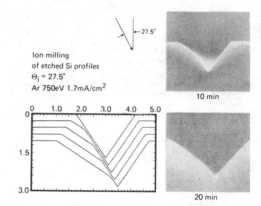

Ion milling of etched Si profiles
$\Theta_i = 27.5°$
Ar 750eV 1.7mA/cm^2

Fig. 16. Comparison of simulated and experimental profiles for ion milling of a v-groove in silicon.

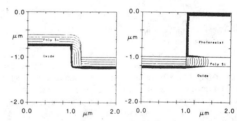

Fig. 17. Polysilicon residue removal at a step and the associated conflicting side effects of underetching of the gate structure and etching of the underlying oxide.

may undercut positive resists [47], [48]. To simulate ion beam lithography profiles, Monte Carlo exposure simulation must include nuclear as well as electronic scattering [49].

An example of simulating plasma etching is shown in Fig. 15. Here isotropic and anisotropic etching components determined from published etch rates have been used to simulate the profile [53]. The simulated profile generally tracks the experimental profiles well as a function of power, pressure, and voltage. The task of determining the etch rate components directly from the physical, electrical, and chemical tool parameters is a much more formidable task [55], [58]–[59]. Ion milling is fairly well characterized by etch rate versus angle of incidence curves for various materials [60]. Ion reflection effects such as trenching and redeposition of materials with low etch rates can greatly complicate the basic process. A comparison of an ion milled v-groove in silicon is shown in Fig. 16 [54]. It is interesting to note that the angle at the bottom of the groove tends to be preserved.

The simulation of plasma etching can be used to optimize tradeoffs between process steps and competing effects as a function of operating conditions. An example of simulating

the residue problem in dry etching [1] is shown in Fig. 17. Here a CVD polysilicon layer (isotropically grown) is being patterned by RIE (anisotropic etching). The residue that results can be removed by overetching at the expense of the underlying oxide thickness due to poor selectivity. A more isotropic removal with good selectivity results in overetching the polysilicon gate. The tradeoff between anisotropy and selectivity in etching is shown in Fig. 18 [61]. Simulation was used to generate the design graph in Fig. 19, which shows

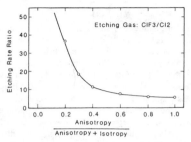

Fig. 18. Tradeoff in etch rate ratio selectivity with anisotropy [61].

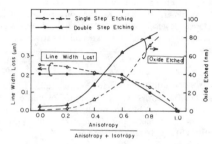

Fig. 19. Design graph for loss in gate linewidth versus etching of the underlying oxide.

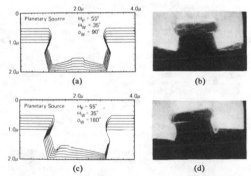

Fig. 20. Comparison of simulation and experimental profiles for vacuum deposition on 2.0-μm equal line and spaces on a 2-in wafer located in the outboard position in a planetary deposition system. Symmetrical (90) and asymmetrical (180) cases.

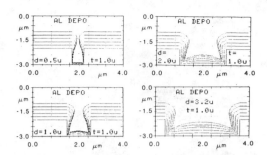

Fig. 21. Illustration of how the width d of a contact influences the amount of material which can be sputtered on the bottom and side-walls.

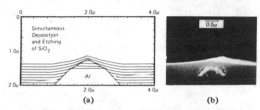

Fig. 22. Simultaneous deposition and etching of SiO_2 to planarize aluminum lines showing the stationary cap which forms on top of the line.

the tradeoff in oxide etching and gate undercut as a function of the anisotropy of the etching.

Many geometrical effects occur in deposition and etching which can be investigated with simulation. Fig. 20 shows an experimental-simulation comparison for a test structure in a planetary evaporator system [65]. This structure illustrates the tradeoff in symmetry which must be made in configuring the tooling for reasonable throughput. The coating process becomes asymmetrical for lines oriented perpendicular to the plane radius on the outboard wafers. This is because the source is located below the intersection of the planet axis with the system axis to achieve good step coverage, and the wafer is not free to rotate independent of the planet rotation. Studies of the effects of orientation angles and profile shapes in evaporation have been carried out [62]–[67].

Even with sputtering, a "crack" tends to form at steps, and the coating of sidewalls is less than that deposited on a planar surface. The effectiveness of adding surface migration such as might occur with heating during deposition was shown in Fig. 2 [1]. Although the "crack" can be removed, the basic problem of achieving sufficient sidewall and bottom coating for high aspect ratio features still remains. Fig. 21 illustrates how the coating becomes more difficult as the aspect ratio increases.

A combination of isotropic deposition and anisotropic etching can be used to planarize the wafer surface. Fig. 22 shows a comparison of experiment and simulation for simultaneous deposition and reactive-ion-etching of SiO_2 [65]. A stationary cap forms on top of the aluminum at the angle at which the deposition and etching rates are equal. The deposition in the planar regions continues and thus catches up to the cap to planarize the surface. A similar planarization effect can be obtained by isotropically depositing a film sufficiently thick to fill laterally across small openings. The film is then aniso-tropically etched so that the residue fills in the small openings as shown in Fig. 23 [1].

V. FUTURE PROGNOSIS

The success of modeling and simulation has created a demand for better models and new simulation capabilities. For example, photolithography engineers view the careful quantitative modeling of resist materials and processing conditions as a hopeful sign of finally being able to understand the complex tradeoff which must be made in process design. Better modeling of modern production tooling, such as sputter deposition systems including three-dimensional effects, is needed. Unusual corner shape effects in low-temperature oxidation of silicon structures must be considered. The algorithms themselves need to be more flexible and robust to handle the ever increasing myriad of physical mechanisms and parameter values. Finally, coupling physical intuition of simulation trend analysis with the multiparameter optimization of experi-

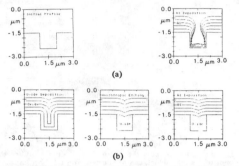

(a)

(b)

Fig. 23. Simulation of oxide deposition and anisotropic etching to planarize prior to metallization with aluminum. (a) Without planarization process. (b) With planarization process.

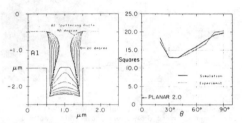

Fig. 24. Topography dependent step coverage resistance in squares showing a large increase over the resistance of a planar film (2 squares). An intermediate sputtering source solid angle is optimum for vertical steps.

mental response surface analysis [68] will allow orders-of-magnitude more complex processes to be systematically designed.

Wafer topography simulation will play an important future role in forming a link from the layout and process design to device and circuit performance. Post processors will be added for extracting the electrical parameters from the simulated topographical features. One example is the determination of the increased resistance and capacitance of deposited films crossing steps shown in Fig. 24 [69], [70]. Layout designers will likely be aided by topography emulators such as a new SAMPLE-related CAD tool SEMPLE, which is being developed to display a pseudo SEM of the device cross section that would result from the current layout. In the future these topography emulators, simulators, and electrical parameter extraction routines will likely be driven directly from the layout system through a hierarchal structure to give the designers feedback on the consequence of their design.

Simulation and modeling of IC fabrication processes have reached an important point where a critical mass of tools can be invoked to address technology problems. The progress and current level of effort on industry-wide programs such as SAMPLE and SUPREM generally exceed that available within any individual company. This is partly because the nature of research on simulation and modeling is well suited to graduate student projects, especially if it can be carried out in collaboration with industry. This mode of program development is currently enjoying considerable interest and support from both industry and government. The problems of careful documentation and software maintenance are, however, difficult to carry out in universities, and alternative support structures are needed. Finally, developing simulation tools on an industry-wide basis raises the issue of maintaining a delicate balance between competition and collaboration.

VI. SUMMARY

IC process modeling and simulation will likely be a leading contributor to future VLSI design. It is well accepted as a means of characterizing individual lithography, etching, and deposition processes. Today process simulation is being applied to the study of the complex tradeoffs between conflicting physical mechanisms in the context of complete multistep process sequences. The success of modeling and simulation has created a demand for better process parameter data, the extensions of the capability to new manufacturing tools, the incorporation of new physical process into models, and more flexible and robust algorithms. In the future topography emulation, simulation, and electrical parameter extraction will likely be driven directly from the layout system to provide the designers feedback on the consequences of their designs. These developments will likely be made on an industry-wide basis at universities through collaborative support with industry.

ACKNOWLEDGMENT

The author would like to thank his colleagues, students, and industrial collaborators whose assistance over the last several years have made possible the results presented here. A special thanks goes to Y. Sakai for his interest in many of the new applications of the SAMPLE program.

REFERENCES

[1] Y. Sakai, J. L. Reynolds, and A. R. Neureuther, "Topography simulation for dry etching process," in *Proc. ECS Spring Meeting* (Montreal, Canada, May 9–14, 1982), Abstract no. 166.
[2] W. G. Oldham, S. Nandgaonkar, A. R. Neureuther, and M. M. O'Toole, "A general simulator for VLSI lithography and etching processes: Part I–Application to projection lithography," *IEEE Trans. Electron Devices*, vol. ED-26, no. 4, pp. 717–722, Apr. 1979.
[3] W. G. Oldham, A. R. Neureuther, C. Sung, J. L. Reynolds, and S. N. Nandgaonkar, "A general simulator for VLSI lithography and etching processes: Part II–Application to deposition and etching," *IEEE Trans. Electron Devices*, vol. ED-27, no. 8, pp. 1455–1459, Aug. 1980.
[4] R. W. Dutton and S. E. Hansen, "Process modeling of integrated circuit device technology," *Proc. IEEE*, vol. 69, no. 10, pp. 1305–1320, Oct. 1981.
[5] H. Ryssel, K. Haberger, K. Hoffmann, G. Prinke, R. Dumcke, and A. Sachs, "Simulation of doping processes," *IEEE Trans. Electron Devices*, vol. ED-27, no. 8, pp. 1484–1492, Aug. 1980.
[6] F. H. Dill, "Optical lithography," *IEEE Trans. Electron Devices*, vol. ED-22, no. 7, pp. 440–444, July 1975.
[7] F. H. Dill, A. R. Neureuther, T. A. Tuttle, and E. J. Walker, "Modeling projection printing of positive photoresist," *IEEE Trans. Electron Devices*, vol. ED-22, no. 7, pp. 456–464, July 1975.
[8] A. Brochet, G. M. Dubreucq, and M. Lacombat, "Modelisation des process d'exposition et de development d'une resine photosensible positive. Application ou masquage par projection," *Revue Technique Thompson-CSF*, vol. 9, no. 2, pp. 287–335, Juin 1977.
[9] S. Fujimori, "Computer simulation of exposure and development of a positive resist," *J. Appl. Phys.*, vol. 50, no. 2, pp. 615–623, Feb. 1979.
[10] J. Bauer and H. Haferkorn, "Berechnung zur Polychromatischen Projektionsfotolithografie," *Feingeratetchnik*, 28, Jg. Heft 4, pp. 166–171, 1979.
[11] M. M. O'Toole and A. R. Neureuther, "The influence of partial coherence on projection printing," *SPIE*, vol. 135, pp. 22–27, 1979.
[12] M. A. Narasimham and J. H. Carter, Jr., "Effects of defocus on photolithographic images made with projection printing systems," *SPIE Proc.*, vol. 135, pp. 2–9, Apr. 1978.
[13] C. N. Ahlquist, P. Schoen, and W. G. Oldham, "A study of a high-performance stepper lens," in *Proc. Kodack Microelectronics Sem.*, 1979, and *Proc. Microcircuit Engineering* (Aachen, Germany, Sept. 25–27, 1979).
[14] D. C. Hofer, C. G. Willson, A. R. Neureuther, and M. Hakey, "Characterization of the 'induction effect' at mid UV exposure: Application to AZ2400 at 313 nm," *SPIE*, vol. 334, "Optical Microlithography," pp 196–205, Mar. 1982.
[15] W. G. Oldham and A. R. Neureuther, "Projection lithography

with high numerical aperture optics," *Solid State Technol.*, vol. 24, no. 5, pp. 106–111, 140, May 1981.

[16] W. G. Oldham, S. Subramanian, and A. R. Neureuther, "Optical requirements for projection lithography," *Solid State Electron.*, vol. 24, no. 10, pp. 975–980, 1981.

[17] P. K. Jain, A. R. Neureuther, and W. G. Oldham, "Influence of axial chromatic aberration in projection printing," *IEEE Trans. Electron Devices*, vol. ED-28, no. 11, pp. 1410–1416, Nov. 1981.

[18] A. R. Neureuther, P. K. Jain, and W. G. Oldham, "Factors affecting linewidth control including multiple wavelength exposure and chromatic aberration," *SPIE*, vol. 275, pp. 110–116, 1981.

[19] P. D. Robertson, F. W. Wise, A. N. Nasr, A. R. Neureuther, and C. H. Ting, "Proximity effects and influences of nonuniform illumination in projection lithography," *SPIE*, vol. 334, "Optical Microlithography," pp. 37–43, Mar. 1982.

[20] F. H. Dill, W. P. Hornberger, P. S. Hauge, and J. M. Shaw, "Characterization of positive photoresist," *IEEE Trans. Electron Devices*, vol. ED-22, no. 7, pp. 445–452, July 1975.

[21] F. H. Dill and J. M. Shaw, "Thermal effects on the photoresist AZ1350J," *IBM J. Res. Develop.*, vol. 21, pp. 210–218, May 1977.

[22] J. M. Shaw and M. Hatzakis, "Performance characteristics of Diazo-type photoresists under e-beam and optical exposure," *IEEE Trans. Electron Devices*, vol. ED-25, no. 4, pp. 425–430, Apr. 1978.

[23] ——, "Developer temperature effects on positive photoresists," in *Proc. Kodak Microelectronics Sem.* (San Diego, Oct. 1978).

[24] M. M. O'Toole and W. J. Grande, "Characterization of positive resist development," *IEEE Electron Device Lett.*, vol. EDL-2, no. 12, Dec. 1981.

[25] T. Matsuzawa, A. Kishimoto, and H. Tomioka, "Profile simulation of negative resist MRS using the SAMPLE photolithography simulator," *IEEE Electron Device Lett.*, vol. EDL-3, no. 3, pp. 58–60, Mar. 1982.

[26] M. Exterkamp, W. Wong, H. Damar, A. R. Neureuther, and W. G. Oldham, "Resist characterization: Procedures, parameters, and profiles," *SPIE*, vol. 334, "Optical Microlithography," pp. 182–187, Mar. 1982.

[27] R. J. Hawryluk, "Exposure and development models used in electron beam lithography," *J. Vac. Sci. Technol.*, vol. 19, pp. 1–17, May/June 1981.

[28] K. Murata, D. F. Kyser, and C. H. Ting, "Monte Carlo simulation of fast secondary electron production in electron beam resists," *J. Appl. Phys.*, vol. 52, no. 7, pp. 4396–4405, July 1981.

[29] M. Hatzakis, C. H. Ting, and N. S. Viswanathan, "Fundamental aspects of polymeric resist systems," in *Electron and Ion Beam Science and Technology, 6th Inter. Conf. Proc.*, R. Bakish, Ed., ECS, p. 542, 1974.

[30] J. S. Greeneich, "Developer characteristics of PMMA electron resist," *J. Electrochem. Soc.*, vol. 122, p. 970, 1975.

[31] ——, "Time evolution of developed contours in PMMA electron resist," *J. Appl. Phys.*, vol. 45, pp. 5264–5268, 1974.

[32] N. S. Viswanathan, R. Pyle, and D. Kyser, "Simulation of lithographic images in electron-beam technology," in *Electron and Ion Beam Science and Technology, 7th Inter. Conf. Proc.*, R. Bakish, ECS, pp. 218–232, 1976.

[33] J. S. Greeneich, "Impact of electron scattering on linewidth control in electron-beam lithography," *J. Vac. Sci. Technol.*, vol. 16, no. 6, pp. 1749–1753, Nov./Dec. 1979.

[34] J.C.H. Phang and Ahmed, "Line profiles in thick electron resist layers and proximity effect correction," *J. Vac. Sci. Technol.*, vol. 16, no. 6, pp. 1759–1763, Nov./Dec. 1979.

[35] K. Murata, E. Nomura, and K. Nogami, "Experimental and theoretical study of cross-sectional profiles of resist patterns in electron-beam lithography," *J. Vac. Sci. Technol.*, vol. 16, no. 6, pp. 1734–1736, Nov./Dec. 1979.

[36] A. R. Neureuther, D. F. Kyser, and C. H. Ting, "Electron beam resist edge profile simulation," *IEEE Trans. Electron Devices*, vol. ED-26, no. 4, pp. 686–692, Apr. 1979.

[37] D. F. Kyser and R. Pyle, "Computer simulation of electron beam resist profiles," *IBM J. Res. and Develop.*, vol. 24, no. 4, pp. 426–437, July 1980.

[38] M.P.C. Watts, P. Rissman, and J. Kahn, "Solubility ratio, sensitivity and line profile control in positive e-beam resists," in *Electron Ion Beam Science and Technology, 9th Inter. Conf. Proc.*, R. Bakish, Ed., ECS, pp. 375–381, 1980.

[39] J. S. Greeneich, in *Electron Ion Beam Science and Technology, 9th Inter. Conf. Proc.*, R. Bakish, Ed., ECS, pp. 282–303, 1980.

[40] J. S. Greeneich, "Electron beam processes," Chap. 2 in *Electron-Beam Technology in Fabrication*. New York: Academic Press, 1980.

[41] M. G. Rosenfield, A. R. Neureuther, and C. H. Ting, "The use of bias in electron-beam lithography for improved linewidth control," *J. Vac. Sci. Technol.*, vol. 19, no. 4, pp. 1242–1247, Nov./Dec. 1981.

[42] M. G. Rosenfield and A. R. Neureuther, "Exploration of electron-beam writing strategies and resist development effects," *IEEE Trans. Electron Devices*, vol. ED-28, no. 11, pp. 1289–1294, Nov. 1981.

[43] T. S. Chang, D. F. Kyser, and C. H. Ting, "Comparison of electron beam and optical projection lithography in the region of one micrometer," *SPIE Proc.*, vol. 275, pp. 117–121, 1981.

[44] ——, "Exploration of electron-beam writing strategies and resist development effects," *IEEE Trans. Electron Devices*, vol. ED-28, no. 11, pp. 1295–1300, Nov. 1981.

[45] F. Jones and J. Paraszczak, "RD3D computer simulation of resist development in three dimensions," *IEEE Trans. Electron Devices*, vol. ED-28, no. 12, pp. 1544–1552, Dec. 1981.

[46] A. R. Neureuther, "Simulation of X-ray resist line edge profiles," *J. Vac. Sci. Technol.*, vol. 15, no. 3, pp. 1004–1008, May/June 1978.

[47] P. Tischer and E. Hundt, "Profiles of structures in PMMA by x-ray lithography," in *Electron and Ion Beam Science and Technology, 8th Inter. Conf. Proc.*, R. Bakish, Ed., ECS, pp. 444–457, 1978.

[48] K. Heinrich, H. Betz, A. Heuberger, and S. Pongraz, "Computer simulations of resist profiles in x-ray lithography," *J. Vac. Sci. Technol.*, vol. 19, no. 4, pp. 1254–1258, Nov./Dec. 1981.

[49] L. Karapiperis, I. Adesida, C. A. Lee, and E. D. Wolf, "Ion beam exposure profiles in PMMA—Computer simulation," *J. Vac. Sci. Technol.*, vol. 19, no. 4, pp. 1259–1263, Nov./Dec. 1981.

[50] J. P. Ducommun, M. Cantagrel, and M. Moulin, "Evolution of well-defined surface contour shapes submitted to ion bombardment: Computer simulation and experimental investigation," *J. Mater. Sci.*, vol. 10, pp. 52–62, 1975.

[51] H. W. Lehmann, L. Krausbauer, and R. Widmer, "Redeposition—A serious problem in rf sputter etching of structures with micrometer dimensions," *J. Vac. Sci. Technol.*, vol. 14, no. 1, pp. 281–284, Jan./Feb. 1977.

[52] N. S. Viswanathan, "Simulation of plasma etched lithographic structures," *J. Vac. Sci. Technol.*, vol. 16, no. 2, pp. 388–390, Mar./Apr. 1979.

[53] J. L. Reynolds and A. R. Neureuther, "Simulation of dry etched line etched profiles," *J. Vac. Sci. Technol.*, vol. 16, no. 6, pp. 1772–1775, Nov./Dec. 1979.

[54] A. R. Neureuther, C. Y. Liu, and C. H. Ting, "Modeling ion milling," *J. Vac. Sci. Technol.*, pp. 1167–1171, 1979.

[55] L. Mei, S. Chen, and R. W. Dutton, "A surface kinetics model for plasma etching," *1980 IEDM Tech. Dig.*, pp. 831–832, Dec. 1980.

[56] R. W. Dutton, L. Mei, D. Chin, and M. Kump, "Two dimensional process modeling for high density (LOCOS) technology," in *1981 Symp. VLSI Technology Tech. Dig.*, pp. 90–91, Aug. 1981.

[57] A. R. Neureuther, "Simulating VLSI wafer topography," *1980 IEDM Tech. Dig.*, pp. 214–218, Dec. 1980.

[58] M. J. Kushner, "A kinetic study of the plasma-etching process. I—A model for the etching of Si and SiO_2 in $CnFm/O_2$ plasmas," *J. Appl. Phys.*, vol. 53, no. 4, pp. 2923–2938, Apr. 1982.

[59] M. J. Kushner, "A kinetic study of the plasma-etching process. II. Probe measurements of electron properties in an rf plasma-etching reactor," *J. Appl. Phys.*, vol. 53, no. 4, pp. 2939–2946, Apr. 1982.

[60] A. B. Jones and G. S. Plonski, "Ion milling of thin films for magnetic bubble circuits," in *ECS Extended Abstracts*, San Francisco, 1974, and L. D. Bollinger, "Ion milling for semiconductor production process," *Solid State Technol.*, pp. 66–70, Nov. 1977.

[61] D. L. Flamm, D.N.K. Wang, and D. Maydan, "Multiple etchant loading effect and silicon etching in ClF_3, NF_3 and related mixtures," presented at the 1981 ESC Fall Meet.

[62] I. A. Blech, "Evaporated film profiles over steps in substrates," *Thin Solid Films*, vol. 6, pp. 113–118, 1970.

[63] I. A. Blech, D. B. Fraser, and S. E. Hasyko, "Optimization of Al step coverage through computer simulation and scanning electron microscopy," *J. Vac. Sci. Technol.*, vol. 15, no. 1, pp. 13–19, 1978.

[64] F. Van de Weile, W. L. Engle, and P. G. Jespers, Eds., *Process and Device Modeling for Integrated Circuit Design*. Leyden, The Netherlands: 1978.

[65] A. R. Neureuther, C. H. Ting, and C. Y. Liu, "Application of line-edge profile simulation to thin-film deposition process," *IEEE Trans. Electron Devices*, vol. ED-27, no. 8, pp. 1449–1455, Aug. 1980.

[66] T. Batchelder, "Simple metal lift-off process for 1 micron AL/5% Cu lines," *SPIE Proc.*, vol. 275, pp. 143–149, 1981, and *Solid State Technol.*, vol. 25, no. 2, pp. 111–114, Feb. 1982.

[67] Y. Homma, A. Yajima, and S. Harada, "Feature size limit analysis of lift-off metalization technology," *1981 IEDM Tech. Dig.*, pp. 570–573, Dec. 1981.

[68] G. Box and J. Hunter, "Experimental designs for the exploration of response surfaces," in *Experimental Designs in Industry*, V. Chew, Ed. New York: Wiley, 1958, p. 138.

[69] K. Lee, Y. Sakai, and A. R. Neureuther, "Topography dependent step coverage resistance simulation for VLSI design," in *Proc. 1982 Symp. VLSI Technology* (Oiso, Japan, Sept. 1–3, 1982).

[70] ——, "Topography dependent electrical parameter simulation," in *IEDM Tech. Dig.*, pp. 298–301, Dec. 1982.

Part IV
Micron and Submicron Circuit Engineering—
Digital and Analog Applications and Results

THE next four papers summarize large-scale engineering efforts which have resulted in the fabrication of state-of-the-art micrometer scale circuits. These efforts involved significant resources allocated to all aspects of the engineering of such circuits including design, process development, advanced lithography, testing, etc. The first of these papers, by G. L. Varnell, P. L. Shah, and R. H. Havemann, shows results of work on highly integrated chips using both MOS and bipolar Si devices. The authors describe the design, processing, and test results for a scaled 4K static RAM with 12–15 ns access time and a chip size of 6000 square mils. In bipolar technology, the authors have fabricated a scaled 16-bit integrated injection logic microprocessor with 1.25 micron minimum feature size and a 10 MHz clock frequency.

Next, a paper by M. P. Lepselter, D. S. Alles, H. J. Levinstein, G. E. Smith, and H. A. Watson relates results of another large effort which explored a variety of lithographic techniques, used advanced two- and three-dimensional modeling, and new submicron processes. The resulting micrometer scale circuits test chips included ring oscillators and a divide-by-16 counter, a 500 MHz clock rate ramp generator for an electron beam lithography system, and a 4K static RAM with 4 ns access time.

The last two papers describe engineering work which uses high-resolution fabrication in the special applications of high-speed radiation hard circuits, and GaAs microwave devices. For military applications, the paper by M. C. Peckerar and R. E. Neidert describes both digital circuits and analog ones. These authors describe the potential impact of 25 MHz clock rate digital circuits with >400 000 gates/cm^2, and of analog transmitters and receivers operating at frequencies up to 150 GHz. Technology support work in these types of systems at the Naval Research Laboratory is reviewed, with special emphasis on fabrication processes and radiation hardness.

Finally, the important field of GaAs circuits at submicron dimensions is reviewed in a paper by W. R. Wisseman, H. M. Macksey, G. E. Brehm, and P. Saunier, which describes GaAs FET's used both as discrete microwave devices and as components in monolithic microwave integrated circuits, covering the frequency range from 3 to 25 GHz. The high-speed performance of these devices and circuits is achieved by fabricating submicron gates by electron-beam lithography and subsequent high-resolution processing. The chapter reviews the modeling of such circuits, in which the fabrication of FET's on a semi-insulating substrate permits microfabrication of passive impedance matching elements which couple the active devices into high-density integrated circuits. Along with the modeling, detailed process descriptions are given, and also a discussion of the significance for circuit performance of various process alternatives. Descriptions of operating results are also given for a variety of finished circuits, some of which have been produced in large numbers and with relatively high yield. This last statement shows that for GaAs as well as for silicon, high-performance submicron circuit engineering is a successful discipline which currently is used to provide significant numbers of useful functioning circuits. Such results were unachievable a few years ago. This success then makes large-scale design automation and circuit modeling, as described in the remainder of this book, a pragmatic discipline capable of hardware realization, rather than merely an academic exercise.

MOS and Bipolar VLSI Technologies Using Electron-Beam Lithography

GILBERT L. VARNELL, PRADEEP L. SHAH, MEMBER, IEEE,
AND ROBERT H. HAVEMANN, MEMBER, IEEE

Invited Paper

Abstract—Key issues for micrometer and submicrometer MOS and bipolar device fabrication are discussed, including lithography, device and circuit scaling limitations, and process considerations. Lithographic requirements are presented in terms of an overall technology—machine, resist and pattern transfer methods—and an electron-beam slice writing technology is described which satisfies those needs. Viable micrometer and submicrometer MOS and bipolar process technologies are demonstrated by scaling complex LSI circuits to VLSI density using electron lithography. For the MOS case, scaling of static memories is discussed in detail, including fabrication of a 4K SRAM with 1.5-μm minimum feature sizes, 12-15-ns access times, and a chip size of only 6K mil^2. A discussion of bipolar device and process scaling issues is highlighted by the successful fabrication of a scaled 16-bit integrated injection logic (I^{2}L) microprocessor with 1.25-μm minimum feature sizes and a clock frequency of 10 MHz with a chip current of only 250 mA.

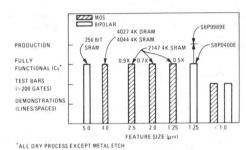

Fig. 1. Electron-beam device fabrication.

I. OVERVIEW

IN THE EARLY 1970's, it became clear that new lithography techniques must be developed since UV optical lithography would become limited somewhere between the exposing wavelengths (4047 and 4358 Å) and 1 μm (10 000 Å) due to diffraction effects. It was also recognized that as wafer sizes tended to grow and designers required tighter overlay, some type of step-and-repeat system with automatic alignment would be required. Electron-beam direct writing had the potential to satisfy all these requirements. Texas Instruments began a program to develop this technology for cost-effective submicrometer IC device fabrication. The approach differed substantially from an equipment vendor approach of developing only the lithography equipment necessary for this task. The program involved development of the total system, including machines, resists, etching techniques, device scaling, and the fabrication of micrometer and submicrometer MOS and bipolar devices. The program's progress in terms of device scaling is charted in Fig. 1, from MSI circuit fabrication at 5-μm design rules in the late 1970's to demonstrations of complex MOS and bipolar LSI circuits with VLSI density and ~1-μm design rules in 1981.

This paper discusses the lithographic, design, and process issues involved in the scaling of MOS and bipolar circuits to VLSI density, with particular emphasis on electron-beam direct-slice-write fabrication methods. By combining electron-beam's superior resolution and registration capability with advanced process techniques, a new generation of complex MOS and bipolar circuits has been demonstrated with packing densities and performance that serve as harbingers for VLSI. The next challenge will be the cost-effective implementation of these technologies; other lithography techniques are being developed for this same purpose and ultimately the cost-effectiveness (yield, throughput, etc.) or uniqueness for a particular application will determine the method of choice.

II. LITHOGRAPHY

A. Introduction

Micrometer and submicrometer lithography for VLSI devices (>100 000 AEG's[1]) has been largely in the development stage during the last decade. The early 1980's will require these micrometer lithographic techniques for such devices as the 256K MOS DRAM, the 64K MOS SRAM, and VHSIC processors and gate arrays. The mid to late 1980's will demand submicrometer ($\geqslant$0.5-μm) techniques for devices with packing densities of a 1M MOS DRAM and 256K MOS SRAM, and for higher speed, higher density, VHSIC processors and gate arrays.

This submicrometer lithography demand is governed primarily by competitive forces to reduce the cost/AEG. The projected and demonstrated device performance improvements with micrometer and submicrometer geometry design rules lead to another demand as evidenced by the VHSIC program. In cases where device performance is the main thrust, the cost/AEG can be significantly larger; and thus can utilize more expensive lithography techniques. Several types of lithographic systems have been explored in the 1970's and will subsequently be discussed, but ultimately the key factors are resolution, accuracy (Design Registration Accuracy—defined later in text),

Manuscript received November 22, 1982.
The authors are with Texas Instruments Incorporated, Dallas, TX 75265.

[1] AEG = Active Electronic Group.

Reprinted from *Proc. IEEE*, vol. 71, pp. 612–639, May 1983.

TABLE I
IMAGING ALTERNATIVES

IC Pattern Computer Data Input	Reticle (5X–10X)	Master Mask	Slice Printing	Potential Usable Resolution (μm)
			E-Beam Slice Writing	≤ 0.5
			• Projection print	
			Optical 1:1	1.0
Tape		E-Beam Mask Printer	E-Beam 1:1	≤ 0.5
			Deep UV 1:1	≤ 1.0
			• Proximity print	
			X-ray	≤ 0.5
			Optical	2.0
Disk	Optical or E-Beam Pattern Generator	Optical Step and-Repeat Camera	Ion Beam	≤ 0.5
			• Contact print	
			Optical	1.0
			Deep UV	≤ 0.5
			Optical	
Cards	Optical or E-Beam Pattern Generator		Step-and-repeat camera (5X–10X)	≤ 1.0
			Ion beam Slice writing	≤ 0.5
		E-beam Mask Printer	Step-and repeat X-ray	≤ 0.5

defect density, device yield, and throughput. The large research effort in lithography during the last decade has been an attempt to achieve high performance in all five factors simultaneously.

B. Key Factors for Lithographic Techniques

1) Resolution: Resolution limits are easily determined in the case of diffraction-limited refracting or reflecting optical systems since the modulation transfer function can be calculated from the numerical aperture and the wavelength of the exposing radiation. The image modulation required for good geometry control for IC production using standard photoresists is generally accepted to be 0.6 [1]. These resolution limits assume perfect focus on the wafer surface and this is not necessarily realized in practice, especially for high numerical apertures with their corresponding short depths of focus. Contact printing and off-contact printing limits can be determined by Fresnel diffraction theory. The key factors are the wavelength and the distance separating the mask and the wafer.

Resolution in an electron-beam imaging system is normally limited by the electron scattering effects in the resist and by backscattered electrons from the substrate and not by diffraction effects, since the wavelength is <1 Å. Compensation for scattering is called "proximity effect correction" and can effectively improve geometry control, especially for geometry spacings of 1 μm and below [2]. X-ray resolution is limited ultimately by Fresnel diffraction ($\lambda = 4$–50 Å) and by the range of the photoelectrons formed when the X-ray photon energy is absorbed in the resist, but practically by the penumbral blurring due to the finite source size and image contrast due to X-ray transmission through the masking material. The use of a storage ring source effectively eliminates the penumbral blurring effect. High-energy ion beams can be used to expose resist layers and should have less image blurring than electron-beam systems due to less lateral scattering than electrons.

A comparison of the resolution capability of the possible imaging techniques for IC fabrication is shown in Table I. In addition to several assumptions, most of the techniques have been downgraded slightly to reflect the projected capability of a production line as opposed to a research laboratory.

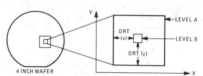

• <u>DESIGN REGISTRATION TOLERANCE</u> – MAXIMUM DESIGN REGISTRATION TOLERANCE (A:B; x,y) ALLOWABLE BETWEEN LEVEL A AND LEVEL B SO THAT THE FINISHED DEVICE WILL STILL MEET ALL PERFORMANCE SPECIFICATIONS. THE DIMENSIONS ON LEVEL A AND LEVEL B ARE MEASURED IN THE ETCHED MATERIAL SO THAT IN DETERMINING THE DESIGN REGISTRATION ACCURACY OF A GIVEN LITHOGRAPHIC TECHNIQUE, THE RESIST AND ETCHING FACTORS MUST BE CONSIDERED, AS WELL AS THE LITHOGRAPHY MACHINE AND MASK FACTORS.

Fig. 2. Design registration tolerance ($A:B; X, Y$).

All of the lithographic techniques listed except for optical proximity printing can achieve at least 1-μm resolution. Electron-beam direct-wiring, electron-beam projection, X-ray proximity, X-ray step-and-repeat, deep UV contact printing, ion-beam projection, and ion-beam writing can all achieve at least 0.5-μm resolution. Thus the real issue involved in micrometer and submicrometer lithography is not whether the resolution can be achieved, but whether a given imaging technique can achieve the resolution, alignment accuracy, and dimensional control with an acceptable defect density, device yield, and throughput.

2) Design Registration Accuracy: A more discerning factor for lithographic systems in the fabrication of high-volume micrometer and submicrometer VLSI devices is the AEG packing density achievable. Let us define new terms to aid in the discussion of AEG packing density. The "Design Registration Tolerance" (DRT) of a device is defined to be the registration tolerance required of one etched device pattern level to another so that the device still meets all performance specifications. "Design Registration Accuracy" (DRA) refers to the capability of a technology to achieve a certain DRT. Thus if the designer wishes to place geometries of level A inside geometries of level B (Fig. 2) so that the geometries do not coincide or overlap an entire wafer, the design registration accuracy ($\pm x, y$) of the

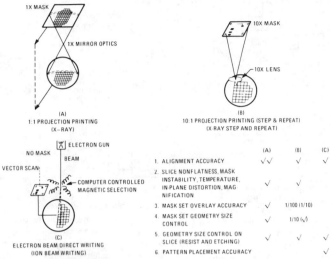

Fig. 3. Lithography techniques, design registration accuracy.

technology required is the minimum distance $(+x, y)$ of any geometry from level A to level B measured along the x and y axes, respectively. This is normally defined so that 99 percent of the $\pm 3\sigma$ statistical distribution of the chips are within the required accuracy. Some of the lithographic factors that can affect the design registration accuracy are 1) alignment accuracy (machine and operator); 2) mask set overlay accuracy; 3) slice nonflatness, mask instability, temperature, slice in-plane distortion, vibration, etc.; 4) mask set geometry size control; and 5) geometry size control on the slice (resist and etching). This definition allows us to compare the entire patterning process and not just the lithography machine as has been done in the past.

The factors that are common to all technologies are the level-to-level registration and the linewidth control in the imaged resist and in the etched oxide, silicon, nitride, or metal (Fig. 3). Several other factors such as mask set overlay accuracy, slice flatness, temperature effects, and in-plane distortion affect some lithographic techniques, but not others. For example, electron-beam direct slice writing is a maskless technology, so master mask accuracy is not a factor. Electron-beam direct writing with every chip alignment is also not affected by temperature effects, slice flatness, and in-plane distortion. With so few factors that affect dimensional and placement control and an excellent automatic alignment system, the root sum square (rss) value of the various errors will generally be lower in the case of electron-beam direct writing than with any other lithography technique developed to date. Optical direct step-on-wafer (DSW) is the second best technique because it eliminates the need for precise 1X master masks. In the future, an X-ray stepper could be developed with design registration accuracy almost equivalent to an optical stepper. The trends and conclusions are obvious, the fewer factors that are involved in dimensional and placement control (design registration accuracy), the more likely a lithographic technique can be implemented for fabrication of micrometer and submicrometer design-rule devices. One can also conclude from this type of analysis that micrometer and submicrometer device fabrication will be based on a step-and-repeat system of some type.

TABLE II
Design Registration Accuracy for Projection Print and Electron-Beam Writing

	Mask Based Optical, UV, and E-Beam Projection Print		Maskless E-Beam Writing	
	Status (μm)	Future (μm)	Status (μm)	Future (μm)
1. Registration accuracy (3 σ)	±1	±0.3	±0.25	±0.1
2. Mask set overlay accuracy	±0.5	±0.3		
3. E-Beam placement accuracy			±0.2	±0.1
4. Slice nonflatness, mask instability, temperature effects, in-plane distortion	±0.1−0.2	±0.1−0.2		
5. Mask set critical dimension	±0.2	±0.2		
6. Line-width control on slice (resist and etching)	±0.5	±0.3	±0.3	±0.1
RMS = $\sqrt{1^2 + 2^2 + \ldots 6^2}$	±1.2	±0.6	±0.4	±0.17

Table II shows the design registration accuracy achievable with a projection printer and a Texas Instruments electron-beam system with electron-beam resists and oxide etching processes. The projected accuracy for advanced electron-beam systems and advanced electron-beam resist etching processes is also given. To show the impact of design registration accuracy, Fig. 4 shows a simplistic model of what would happen with improved DRA in the production of 4K static RAM's. In reality, the peripheral circuitry will not scale in the same manner and thus the real impact should be obtained on higher density parts such as 64K and 256K SRAM's. The financial impact is also given, assuming the same machine and resist costs and the same yields for all lithographic techniques. Note that the cost scales linearly with area in this case. Changes in throughput and machine costs are second-order effects since the machine/mask lithography cost is now only about 2–10 percent of the total IC front-end cost and thus a 5–10X increase in lithography cost/wafer can be justified with only a 0.7X linear shrink (2X area) at the same device yield.

It is also interesting to note that even with a lithography

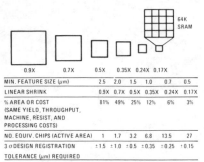

	0.9X	0.7X	0.5X	0.35X	0.24X	0.17X
MIN. FEATURE SIZE (μm)	2.5	2.0	1.5	1.0	0.7	0.5
LINEAR SHRINK	0.9X	0.7X	0.5X	0.35X	0.24X	0.17X
% AREA OR COST (SAME YIELD, THROUGHPUT, MACHINE, RESIST, AND PROCESSING COSTS)	81%	49%	25%	12%	6%	3%
NO. EQUIV. CHIPS (ACTIVE AREA)	1	1.7	3.2	6.8	13.5	27
3σ DESIGN REGISTRATION TOLERANCE (μm) REQUIRED	±1.5	±1.0	±0.5	±0.35	±0.25	±0.15

Fig. 4. 4K static MOS RAM.

cost half the processing cost less lithography (machine/mask) or 33 percent of the total IC front-end cost, a 2X improvement in throughput only lowers the cost to 83.3 percent of the original cost and a 4X improvement only lowers the cost to 75 percent of the original cost. A 0.5X linear shrink in both x and y decreases the area by a factor of four and thus the cost by a factor of four (25 percent of the original cost) assuming the same yield. Increases in yield also scale the cost in a linear fashion. Thus chip size improvement (AEG packing density or Design Registration Accuracy) and yield improvement are far more impactive than thoughput improvements.

3) Defect Density: The lithographic yield Y_{LD} is defined with a very simplistic model as

$$Y_{LD} = 1/(1 + DA)^n$$

where

D defect density
A chip area
n number of mask levels.

In general, the fewer the lithographic processing steps, the fewer the lithographic defects. This was evident in changing from contact printing to projection printing. Master masks were used instead of contact masks, thereby eliminating one lithographic step as well as contact with the wafer and the defect density of the processed wafer improved significantly. Defect density data in the fabrication of micrometer and submicrometer VLSI devices are still largely unknown for the various lithography techniques, but this will be a key factor in final determination of cost/AEG for the various technologies. Defect density can only be determined experimentally on a production line with large amounts of data. One significant point is that if the defect density remains constant for smaller geometry devices, then significant gains in yield can be obtained by shrinking devices. It is also interesting to note that if micrometer VLSI device yields of 40–50 percent or better can be obtained for 50K mil^2 chip sizes and throughputs of 20 wafer levels/h on fully automated systems, further increases in throughput have very little impact on the cost of the tested and packaged VLSI chip.

The overall yield, Y, is a product of the defect lithographic yield, Y_{LD}, the yield due to DRA limitations, Y_{DRA}, and the yield due to other factors, Y_0; that is $Y = Y_{LD} \cdot Y_{DRA} \cdot Y_0$. Data for Y_{LD} and Y_{DRA} on micrometer and submicrometer VLSI devices for each lithographic technique will allow determination of the most cost-effective technology for fabrication of these VLSI devices.

TABLE III
OVERVIEW OF RECENT ELECTRON-BEAM SYSTEMS

	Gaussian Beam	Shaped Beam		
		Fixed Shape	Variable Line Beam	Variable Shape Beam
Vector Scan	JBX-5A (JEOL) EBMF-11 (Cambridge) VS-1 (IBM) EB-52 (NTT) VL-F1 (VLSI Lab) EBPG-3 (Phillips)	EBMII–III (TI) EBSP (TI)	V/E	VL-S2 (VLSI Lab) JBX-6A (JEOL) 2BA-10 (Carl Zeiss) EL3 GCA PE/Hughes
Raster Scan – Continuous Table	EBES (Bell Labs) MEBES (ETEC) EE–BES-40 (Varian) VL-RI (VLSI Lab) EBM-105 (Toshiba)	Electro-Composer (Thompson-CSF)	VL-R2 (VLSI Lab)	
Raster Scan – Step-and-Repeat		EL-1 (IBM)		EL-2 (IBM)

C. Electron-Beam Lithography

In the late 1960's and early 1970's, several companies began exploring the use of computer-controlled Scanning Electron Microscopes (SEM) for application to microcircuit fabrication of submicrometer geometry microwave transistors and surface wave devices. Using relatively slow resists (PMMA and polystyrene) and ±0.25-μm automatic alignment, microwave transistors were fabricated at Texas Instruments Incorporated. This alignment was far superior to the accuracy that could be achieved by any otpical system. These early accomplishments at TI and other laboratories led several companies (TI, IBM, Bell Labs, Phillips, Thompson-CSF, JEOL) to develop electron-beam systems for IC patterning and direct slice writing. In most cases, the development centered on mask and reticle fabrication equipment. The mask fabrication systems are in widespread use today.

More recently, several companies have begun developing electron-beam direct writing systems. The primary advantages of electron-beam over contact-printing and projection-printing techniques for direct slice writing are 1) the elimination of masks and mask defects, 2) the alignment accuracy achieveable, 3) the fast turnaround of computer-controlled imaging, 4) the superior resolution capability, and 5) geometry size compensation.

The major disadvantage to date has been the low throughput and the requirement for different resists and processes. In addition, the electron scattering in the resist necessitates proximity compensation by software techniques at or below 1-μm geometries unless bilevel or trilevel techniques are used.

Table III lists the electron-beam systems that have been developed for various applications. These electron-beam systems can be divided into vector and raster, Gaussian beam and shaped beam, and continuous stage motion or step-and-repeat systems.

1) Factors Limiting Throughput on EBSP: The electron-beam direct writing system approach taken at Texas Instruments was to use dynamic focusing and a computer-aided design deflection system to achieve large field coverage (6.5 mm by 6.5 mm) to minimize the step-and-repeat time required. A vector scan system was chosen because it is inherently 3 to 4 times faster than a raster scan system, but the full advantage is only realizable with the elimination of eddy currents. This has been accomplished on the TI EBSP (Electron Beam Slice Printer) with the use of ferrite liners and ferrite pole pieces.

A vector scan system is limited in throughput by the writing rate, the exposure rate, and several overhead factors (pattern overhead, step-and-repeat time, load/unload, automatic alignment). The writing rate is a function of the pattern generator, deflection amplifier, and electron optics. The exposure rate is a function of the gun brightness and electron-resist sensitivity. The writing rate and the exposure rate must be equal, and thus the slower of these two rates will dominate. This relationship is given by

$$E \cdot D = S/I \cdot 10^4$$

where E is the inverse scan speed (ns/μm), D is the line density (lines/μm), S is the resist sensitivity (μC/cm^2), and I is the beam current (nA).

The exposure time (seconds) is then given by

$$T_E = E \cdot D \cdot A_G \cdot 10^1 = S/I \cdot A_G \cdot 10^3$$

where A_G is the area of exposed geometries (cm^2).

As can be seen by the equation above, the exposure time can vary significantly in a vector scan system depending on the particular pattern to be exposed. Using both a positive and negative resist, the average area for a typical static or dynamic MOS RAM is approximately 25 percent of the total chip area.

The EBMII–EBMIII type system was designed as a balanced system so that to significantly increase the throughput, improvements in every one of the rate limiting factors had to be accomplished. For EBSP, new pattern generator electronics (interface), electron optics, and a deflection amplifier were developed to increase the system bandwidth from 2 to 10 MHz, allowing beam scan speeds of 25 μm/μs. This is an equivalent data rate of 100 MHz for 0.25-μm beam spacing. This new EBSP optics system allows a resolution of 1.25 μm over a 6.5 mm by 6.5 mm field and submicrometer features over a smaller field size ($\sim$2 mm by 2 mm). Large-chip submicrometer devices are fabricated using the laser interferometer capability of the system to "stitch" fields together (the mosaic approach). The system is capable of automatically handling 3-, 4-, and 5-in slices. The EBSP electron-optical column and X–Y table assembly is shown in Fig. 5, the computer and electronics for the EBSP system are shown in Fig. 6, and a block diagram of the system is shown in Fig. 7.

The impact of the new optics and other development on EBSP can be seen in Table IV. The total overhead for a 3-in wafer with 60 000 geometries per level and 150 chips per wafer is approximately 1.7 min. Examples of the exposure time required for 3-in slices are shown in Table IV for both $E = 40$ and 80 ns/μm depending upon the resist sensitivity available.

In addition to throughput and resolution, the other key factor of any imaging system is the pattern registration capability. Texas Instruments has developed and used for several years a fully computer-controlled automatic alignment system on the electron-beam machines. Pattern registration for slice printing is accomplished by scanning the electron beam across reference marks in the scribe lines of each chip on the silicon wafer, detecting and amplifying the secondary and back-scattered electrons, and processing this video signal to determine the correct position for the subsequently exposed pattern. This method allows a 3σ alignment accuracy of ±0.25 μm and 0.1-s alignment time per chip. A three-chip automatic alignment system is also available using the laser interferometer capability of the electron-beam machine, but for submicrometer devices the every-chip alignment mode would be used since it is two times more accurate.

Fig. 5. Electron-beam slice printer (EBSP).

Fig. 6. Computer and electronics of EBSP.

Table V lists the pattern writing time for TI and other electron-beam systems. The upper practical limit for resist sensitivity for negative resists for device fabrication (nonmulti-level approach) appears to be about 1 μC/cm^2 and about 2–4X that for positive resists. Beam current densities are shown for tungsten and LaB$_6$, but field emission guns can achieve much higher current densities for beam sizes smaller than 0.5 μm. The upper limit of magnetic deflection systems appears to be about 100 MHz, but electrostatic systems can be even faster. For micrometer and submicrometer geometries, one possible way to achieve chip writing times of less than 0.5 s is to use a variable-shaped-beam approach as IBM has done with the development of EL-3. This system allows throughputs of 20–30 4-in wafers/h.

2) Electron-Beam Resists: To meet the demands of resist performance for VLSI and VHSIC technology, the positive and negative electron-beam resists need $\leqslant$1-μm resolution capability, compatibility with device processing techniques, and 1–4-μC/cm^2 sensitivity. The resists must not only provide the image, but retain the proper linewidth during processing, which usually requires nearly vertical resist walls. To be used in direct slice writing, the electron-beam resists must stand up to dry etch processes and serve as ion implant masks. The sensitivity is dictated by the electron-beam machine through-put rate necessary for electron-beam lithography to be economically feasible.

TI's present production electron-beam resists meet most, but not all, of the requirements. TI-323 (Fig. 8(a)), the positive resist for direct slice writing, has 1-μm resolution capability

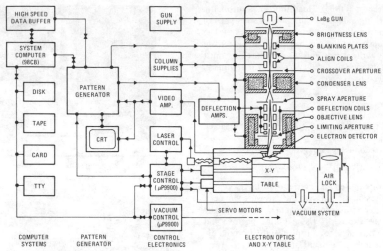

Fig. 7. Block diagram of EBSP.

TABLE IV
EBSP THROUGHPUT

Minimum Geometry (μm)	E (ns/μm) D (lines/μm)	Write time (minutes/3-inch slice)	Throughput* (3-inch slice/hr.)	I (nA)	Required Resist Sensitivity S (μC/cm²)
2.5	E 80 D 2	2.7	14	125	2.0
1.25	E 80 D 4	5.4	8.5	50	1.6
2.5	E 40 D 2	1.3	20	125	1.0
1.25	E 40 D 4	2.7	14	50	0.8

* Overhead = 1.7 minutes, 25-percent area coverage

TABLE V
PATTERN WRITING TIME/CHIP
(Chip size = 200×200 mil²; pattern area 25 percent.)

System	Type Scan	Beam Stepping Rate (MHz)	Resist Sensitivity (coul/cm²)	Beam Current Density (A/cm²)	Beam Addresses/ Chip	Minimum Geometry (μm)	Pattern Writing Time (Sec)/Chip
EBES	Raster	20	10^{-6}	20	64×10^6	2.5 (5 Passes)	3.2
EBES	Raster	20	10^{-6}	20	256×10^6	1.25 (5 Passes)	12.8
VSI	Vector	10	2.5×10^{-5}	300	16×10^6	2.5 (5 Passes)	1.6
VSI	Vector	10	2.5×10^{-5}	300	64×10^6	1.25 (5 Passes)	6.4
EBM III	Vector	20[†]	5×10^{-5}	120[†]	64×10^6	1.25 (5 Passes)	3.2
EBM III	Vector	10[†]	5×10^{-5}	60[†]	16×10^6	2.5 (5 Passes)	1.6
EBM VB	Vector	100[†]	10^{-6}	120[†]	64×10^6	1.25 (5 Passes)	0.6
EBM VB	Vector	50[†]	10^{-6}	60[†]	16×10^6	2.5 (5 Passes)	0.3
EL1	Raster	5	10^{-5}	50	4×10^6	2.5 (1 Pass)	0.8
EL1	Raster	5	10^{-5}	50	16×10^6	1.25 (1 Pass)	3.2
EL2	Raster	5	10^{-5}	50	4×10^6	1.25 (1 Pass)	0.8
EL3	Vector	5	10^{-5}	50	1×10^6	1.25 (1 Pass)	0.2

Variable[††]
Shaped Beam

[†]Equivalent

[††]Projected

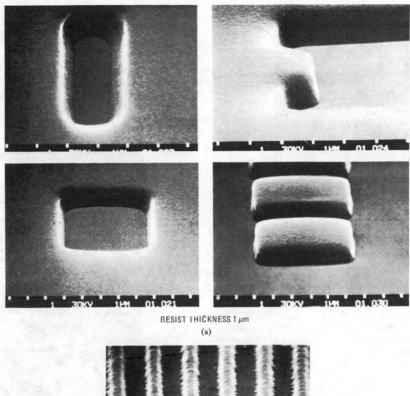

RESIST THICKNESS 1 μm

(a)

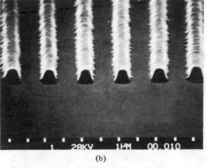

(b)

Fig. 8. Positive (TI-323) and negative (TI-309) electron-beam resists.

in thicknesses of 1 μm and is dry process compatible. The sensitivity is 12–14 $\mu C/cm^2$, which is slower than desired. The fact that TI-323 has been used successfully for device fabrication attests to its performance. Sensitivity is being addressed in the next generation of positive resists. TI-309 (Fig. 8(b)), the negative resist for direct slice writing, has 1.25-μm resolution capability in resist thicknesses of 6400 Å after developing and is excellent for dry processing. The sensitivity is $3\ \mu C/cm^2$. The resolution of TI-309 is of primary concern as it is necessary for high-throughput submicrometer devices. Multilevel resist development is aimed at addressing this problem by using a thin top layer to achieve better resolution.

The basic problems in extending the present 1.25-μm resist technology to 0.5 μm are resolution, sensitivity, linewidth control, defect density, and device fabrication process compatibility. Resolution and sensitivity of various resists have been reviewed in several articles [3]. At present, the usefulness of resists is better gauged by process compatibility. Fig. 9

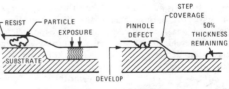

- PROCESS CONDITIONS
  REQUIRING THICKER RESIST
  STEP COVERAGE
  DEFECT DENSITY
  PLASMA ETCH EROSION
  COATING UNIFORMITY
  DEVELOPER REMOVAL
  IMPLANT MASKING

- PROCESS CONDITIONS
  REQUIRING THINNER RESIST
  RESOLUTION
  SWELLING

- CURRENTLY FEASIBLE FEATURE/THICKNESS ASPECT RATIOS
  1/1 FOR MOST POSITIVE RESISTS
  2.4/1 FOR MOST NEGATIVE RESISTS DUE TO SWELLING

Fig. 9. Typical resist processing constraints.

99

Fig. 10. Tri-level for submicrometer.

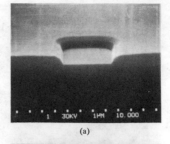

(a)

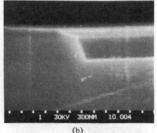

(b)

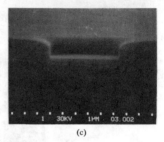

(c)

Fig. 11. Etch profiles with TE-323 electron-beam resist and KTI-17 photoresist.

shows the typical processing constraints and the tradeoffs between thicker and thinner resists. These requirements are generally applicable to all lithographic techniques. Resolution of 0.5 μm can easily be obtained in thin resist films ($<$0.5 μm), but the defect density in these films is generally too large for VLSI device fabrication. In addition, thicker resists are required for step coverage, plasma etch erosion, and ion implant masking. There are basically two possibilities to achieve 0.5-μm resist processes with 0.05-μm linewidth control compatible with device fabrication processes. First, an all-positive resist process may be achievable if resist thickness requirements due to processing constraints can be reduced to $\sim$5000 Å. The reduced thickness requirements may occur because, in general, 0.5-μm devices will have thinner films to be etched.

A second method for patterning 0.5-μm geometries can be achieved by the lamination of a thin film of resist (positive or negative) imaged over one or more underlying layers, which (when patterned sequentially by appropriate techniques) serves as a composite masking film providing high resolution and effective resistance to etch and implant processes [4]. One such system employs a thick polymer layer covered by a thin layer of plasma-deposited silicon dioxide upon which a thin layer of resist is applied. The thin resist is patterned to achieve high resolution. This layer is adequate to allow protection for plasma etching of the thin oxide layer which, in turn, masks the plasma etching of the thick polymer. Highly directional plasma techniques such as reactive-ion etch may be used for this etching with essentially vertical edges resulting. This has been demonstrated in several laboratories [5] and Fig. 10 shows the work accomplished at Texas Instruments. Resist patterns 0.4 μm wide and 1.6 μm thick can be seen in these scanning electron micrographs.

Further advantages of this multilevel resist system include excellent step coverage, a planar surface for resist imaging, and less backscattering from the substrate, resulting in more constant linewidths across all topographies and materials. For reverse deposition metal patterning ("liftoff"), the thick polymer may be undercut during etching to favor that technique.

An obvious disadvantage of multilayer patterning is increased processing time and cost. However, superior results in patterning submicrometer devices will probably justify this increased cost. The key to both the all-positive process and the multi-

layer resist technique is the reduction of resist defects so that a thinner layer of resist can be used.

3) Dry-Etch Pattern Transfer: The etching requirements for delineating 1.25 μm and smaller VLSI device geometries demand control of the following parameters: 1) directionality, 2) uniformity, 3) selectivity, 4) end-point detection, and 5) cleanliness. The transition from wet etching to not only dry etching, but anisotropic dry etching has presented both advantages and new problems. In the case of linewidth control, undercutting is no longer a source of linewidth loss, but there is resist erosion which generally increases with the degree of anisotropy. This typically results from the higher energy and orthogonality of the ions striking the slice surface for more anisotropic etch processes. However, the use of nonerodable or vertical-walled masks leads to very vertical etch profiles. These sharp steps can cause problems with subsequent processing such as deposition coverage over the step, reflections from the step during resist exposure, and etching of the filaments along the base of the step. Fig. 11 illustrates the use of erodable and nonerodable resist masks for anisotropic oxide etching. Fig. 11(a) and (b) shows the etching of 6000 Å of thermal SiO_2 using TI-323 electron resist as a mask resulting in a 60–70° slope in the etched oxide profile, while Fig. 11(c) indicates the 90° etch profile in 9000 Å of PSG patterned with noneroding KTI-17 photoresist.

Fig. 12. Post-etch profile of nitride, oxide, and silicon epi-layer.

Since sloped etch profiles are generally preferred, processes which provide well-controlled mask profiles in erodable resists need to be developed. Also, in order to provide linewidth control, the etch rate across the slice and throughout the reactor for a batch process must be very uniform. When the need for anisotropic etching of a layer over steps arises, the overall process becomes very complicated. Due to the extra vertical thickness of the material to be etched at the step, considerable overetch (typically 50–100 percent) using an anisotropic etch process is required to clear the material without leaving a filament along the base of the step. This requires appropriate mask sizing to allow for the resist/linewidth erosion during the overetch plus very high selectivity between the etched material and underlayer as needed. Unfortunately, higher anisotropy typically means lower selectivity.

Fig. 12 shows the post-etch profile for the sequential anisotropic etching of a nitride layer, oxide, and silicon epi-layer. The etch mask used in this instance was TI-323 electron resist. The nitride and oxide layers were etched in a parallel-plate plasma reactor using a fluorocarbon etchant gas mixture; the silicon was then etched in a similar reactor using a chloro-fluorocarbon plasma. No undercutting can be detected; there is some slope on the nitride layer due to the resist eroding back from the edge. Slope can also be observed on the silicon etch profile; the reason for this has not been determined, but would likely not occur with an etch process that involved more directional higher energy ion bombardment of the silicon surface during etching. In general, RIE and high-field plasma etch processes will be required to clear material in small spaces on VLSI devices.

It is clear that the patterning and etching processes must be closely coupled in order to meet the critical dimension requirements of micrometer and submicrometer VLSI.

D. Conclusions

Lithography is in a period of transition from optical projection printing to other types of printing systems. There is no sure way at present to determine the ultimate lithographic solution for fabrication of micrometer and submicrometer devices, but some trends are obvious. Step-and-repeat techniques will become mandatory for high-density micrometer and submicrometer VLSI device fabrication because of the design registration accuracy required. Multilevel resist techniques will become highly desirable for resolution and linewidth accuracy control. Intermix of lithographic techniques will be used as demanded by device densities and economic factors. Because of the many factors involved in device fabrication and

the fact that the lithography machine/mask cost is, at present, less than 10 percent of the device fabrication cost, a valid cost comparison of different patterning technologies can be made only after obtaining statistically meaningful yield data on micrometer and submicrometer VLSI devices. Device yield, and not throughput, will ultimately be the deciding factor among the various lithographic technologies for micrometer and submicrometer devices. The following MOS and bipolar sections demonstrate why electron-beam lithography will be a key factor for submicrometer VLSI device fabrication.

III. MOS SCALING AND TECHNOLOGY IMPLEMENTATION

A. Introduction

Over the past decade, MOS integrated circuit technology has shown exponential growth in on-chip component density, with memories leading the way. The growth in the early days of the medium-scale integration (MSI) and large-scale integration (LSI) era was attributed mainly to innovations in circuit design such as the 1-T dynamic random-access memory (RAM) cell and advances in process technology from metal-gate PMOS to self-aligned, double-level polysilicon-gate technology. The continued exponential growth in the past few years of the LSI era and projections of device densities in the forthcoming very-large-scale-integration (VLSI) era are, however, attributed mainly to the advances in lithographic and patterning capabilities. To realize devices at VLSI densities (above 100 000 components on a chip), not only the lithographic resolution capabilities must improve, but also the associated level-to-level registration and patterning tolerances must scale down.

Among the various lithographic tools mature enough for fabrication of VLSI devices, direct electron-beam lithography has shown the most evolution in terms of MOS and bipolar circuits. Although conventional lithographic tools are expected to approach the limits of optical resolution and associated electromechanical system capabilities, the direct use of electron beam as a lithographic tool will continue to demonstrate higher circuit densities at a VLSI level owing to its unique level-to-level alignment schemes and overall tighter design registration tolerances.

This section describes the evolution of MOS device process technology development and its ultimate demonstration on 1-μm VLSI densities using direct electron beam as a lithographic tool. The development program, spanning the years 1979–1981, not only required development of an electron-beam lithographic technique compatible to the MOS devices, but also simultaneous device design and process development aspects of a generic nature required for a 1-μm MOS structure such as memory cell optimization, thin gate dielectrics, anisotropic dry patterning of oxide, nitride, polysilicon, and metal layers, low-resistivity interconnects, and low-temperature processing. Since no VLSI chip designs were available in this exploratory stage, existing LSI products such as static memory were modified and scaled down to VLSI densities for use as vehicles for VLSI demonstration.

The evolution of the scaled 4K static memory SRAM described in detail in the following is shown schematically in Fig. 13 and is compared with the currently manufactured TMS 2147 static memory at 2- to 3-μm features. Also plotted on the chart are higher density devices such as 16K and 64K SRAM's, based on the comparable VLSI technologies already demonstrated on the 4K level. Typical chip sizes for these memories, using evolution of optical and direct electron-beam

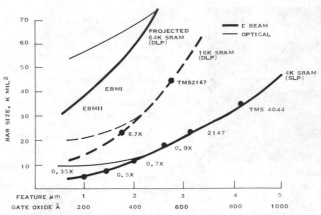

Fig. 13. Evolution of static memory chip size at 4K, 16K, and 64K, projected as a function of design rules using optical and electron-beam lithography.

lithographies, are shown. The chip size advantage using electron-beam lithography is clearly visible in overall circuit scaling.

The choice of a static memory as the LSI vehicle for scaled MOS technology demonstration was based on the fact that the device density and chip area of a static memory are stronger functions of the lithographic capabilities such as resolution and level-to-level registration in comparison to other vehicles such as dynamic or read-only memories. Such overall circuit scaling is a true and more realistic evaluation of high-density, high-performance technology for VLSI applications rather than fabrication of an isolated device or a ring oscillator at a projected resolution limit. In addition to demonstrating the lithographic and patterning capability, scaled static memory also provides a more realistic LSI measure of improvement in electrical performance achieved through reduction of both the channel length of an active MOS transistor and the parasitic elements.

Traditional MOS scaling for improved performance is described with its current limitations in the 1980's followed by the needs of MOS circuit scaling for improvement in component density. The latter being the major thrust, driven by cost-reduction aspects of VLSI chips, is discussed in detail with a static memory cell as a test case in Section III-B. Single- and double-level polysilicon MOS processes developed for static memory fabrication of 4K and 16K complexities are described in Section III-C. Also described are the critical generic processes such as low defect gate dielectric and anisotropic patterning and their implementation in complex static memories. Characterization of results for scaled active, as well as isolated, MOS devices and overall LSI circuits is described in Sections III-D and III-E, respectively.

B. Scaling MOS for VLSI

Two primary reasons for scaling MOS structures in the LSI/VLSI technology are scaling for improvement in performance and scaling for increase in component density and reduction in cost of overall electronic function on a chip.

1) Scaling for Performance: Basic laws of MOS device scaling [7] developed in the early 1970's have been extensively used in the past decade to obtain improved performance at individual device levels and at LSI circuit levels as demonstrated by the HMOSI and HMOSII experience [8], [9]. The improved performance was primarily due to scaling of the individual transistor channel length without substantially altering the overall component density [10]. Most noteworthy of the consequences of scaling are the decrease in the gate insulator thickness and junction depth and increase in doping in the active-channel region. Scaling merely for performance at IC levels, however, becomes difficult when other associated parasitic elements, such as signal line resistances [11], capacitances, and contact resistances do not scale. This limits the overall performance improvements in spite of higher performance transistors.

Continued application of the scaling theory to MOS transistors below 1-μm channel lengths is even harder from the standpoint of basic device physics. Device gain has been shown [12] to peak at a channel length of 1 μm due to electron-velocity saturation in a channel, finite inversion-layer thickness, and parasitic series resistance. Basic reliability of MOS transistors will also degrade due to hot carrier, impact ionization—especially at higher operating temperatures.

2) Scaling for Density: The second and probably more important reason for scaling is to increase the component density and thereby reduce the cost of AEG's and overall function on a chip—a feature unique to semiconductor IC manufacturing technology. As described earlier, the majority of advances in lithography and etching as well as related equipment technology are driven by this thrust. The leverage in terms of cost reduction offered by the increase in component density has already been illustrated schematically in the lithography section using static memory as an example. The concept of scaling for higher component density has evolved over the past decade. This evolution and the relative impact of contributing factors, such as circuit innovation, process technology, and lithographic and patterning advances can be illustrated using static memory as a test case. The static memory cell probably is one of the best MOS AEG models to illustrate the concept since in the six-transistor cell configuration (or four-transistor and two-resistor load cell) it consists of a pair of inverters with transfer gates—a unit widely used in other static MOS logic circuits. The area of the static memory cell is plotted in Fig. 14 as a function of average design features for 5-T and 6-T configurations designed

TABLE VI
MOS Scaling for LSI and VLSI

Parameter	LSI (1970–1980)	VLSI 1980–
1. Feature	λ	• Limited by lithography, etching technologies
2. Density	$1/\lambda^2$	• Limited by design, registration, interconnect
3. Channel Length	λ	• Limited by short channel effect, system voltage, reliability requirements
4. Gate Delay	λ	• Intrinsic device delay limited by velocity saturation, gate dielectric, parasitic resistance
	λ	• In circuit delay limited by interconnect resistance, line capacitance, current drive capability
5. Supply Voltage	λ	• Lower system supply voltages mandatory from dielectric breakdown, hot electron injection reliability considerations
6. Power Dissipation	λ^2	• Sub-threshold leakage does not scale. Larger leakage due to barrier lowering, drain modulation
7. Power Delay Product	λ^3	• Speed power product enhancements limited by parasitics, interconnect limitations
8. Gate Oxide	λ	• Gate thickness 100Å required with significantly severe process control, defect constraints
9. Parasitic Elements		• Do not scale, contact resistance increases with area reduction with reliability hazard

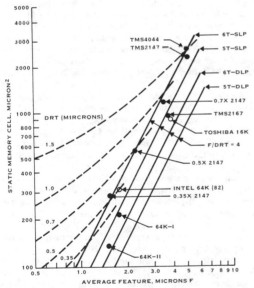

Fig. 14. Static memory cell as function of feature, process, and design registration.

number a designer uses regardless of its origin—lithography, etch bias, mask tolerance, depth of focus variations, etc. The DRT's chosen include 1.0, 0.5, and 0.35 μm representative of the 1:1 projection, 10:1 stepper, and electron-beam equipment in a mature equipment and etching technology time frame. The relative cell areas for full-size currently manufactured TMS4044, TMS1247 static memories and their 0.7X, 0.5X, and 0.35X linearly scaled versions are plotted on the chart for reference. Also plotted are 16K and projected 64K SRAM cell sizes.

Through the decade of the 1970's, the improvement in density progressed either in an evolutionary fashion along one of the straight lines or in revolutionary fashion, from one line to another at a comparable design rule and lithographic capability, through either circuit innovation or process complexity enhancement. In the coming decade of the 1980's, however, LSI/VLSI technology with 2–3-μm average feature design registration is playing an important part in determining overall density. The overall rate of density improvement is saturating along the lines of constant DRT for given lithographic equipment capability in a manufacturing environment. Further reduction in only the channel length with shorter wavelength exposure or multilayer resists will have marginal or no effect on overall density. The limitations in performance improvement due to mere feature reduction were discussed earlier. It is, therefore, clear that further reduction in density and performance is feasible only with DRT's ⩽0.35 which are achievable using advanced lithographic tools such as electron-beam slice writers.

Additional considerations and limitations in realizing high-density, high-performance VLSI, such as overall circuit interconnect, leakage, and packaging have been discussed in the literature and only an overall summary of the scaling laws of the 1970's and their status for the MOS technology of the 1980's is described in Table VI.

3) Layout Considerations: Other considerations unique to electron-beam direct slice writing are related to the actual exposure of individual geometries in the resist and the optimi-

in single- and double-level polysilicon gate processes, all plotted for an ideal lithographic process which provides design registration tolerance as a fraction (0.25 in this analysis) of average feature. Each of the cells scale in straightforward geometric fashion along the straight line with a slope of 2. It may be noted that no device-related scaling limitations and nonlinearities, such as isolation, are included. The effect of level-to-level registration is illustrated by a family of curves for a 6-T, single-level poly-SRAM cell for fixed DRT's. The design registration tolerance as defined earlier is a cumulative

2.9 MIL²	1.76 MIL²	0.88 MIL²	0.44 MIL²
4K = 21K MIL²	4K = 12K MIL²	4K = 6K MIL²	4K = 3K MIL²
0.9X	0.7X	0.5X	0.35X

Fig. 15. Layout of scaled static memory at 0.9X, 0.7X, 0.5X, 0.35X linear scale factors.

zation necessary at layout to minimize the total exposure area, total exposure count, and overall resist definition to improve slice writing throughput. The case of a 4K static memory cell, drawn for conventional optical lithography at full scale and optimized for linear 0.7X, 0.5X, and 0.35X scale factors, is shown in Fig. 15. Note the restructuring of the active area in the scaled versions to minimize exposure count and improve scalability, even at 0.125X the original area. Additional improvements in terms of increased W/L ratios and contact structures were implemented and can be seen in Fig. 30 described in Section III-E.

C. Scaled MOS Technology Development

The overall evolution of MOS technology, highlighted by reductions in transistor channel length and gate oxide thickness as demonstrated on scaled LSI static memory, was illustrated earlier in Fig. 13. Over this period of development, the overall MOS technology progressed from an original state-of-the-art 4–5-µm channel to the present 1-µm channel as evidenced by the respective 1X and 0.5X linear scale factors applied to the TMS4044-2147 4K SRAM. The lithographic and associated registration requirements were also demonstrated on 0.35X linearly scaled versions with submicrometer dimensions; however, no full LSI parts were built at this scale of reduction.

The LSI fabrication at each of the scaling stages required not only the lithographic and pattern transfer processes such as resists and dry anisotropic etching, but also other generic MOS technologies such as thinner gate dielectrics [13] optimized isolation processes, shallow junctions, high sheet poly resistive loads, buried contacts, and overall MOS transistor optimization in conventional, natural (unadjusted), and depletion modes. Additional VLSI enhancements addressed some of the performance and density-related scaling considerations such as low-resistivity interconnects [14], planarization, and low-temperature processing. The overall process development and device optimization was performed in coordinated fashion by

use of a test vehicle which addressed device, process, and circuit-related aspects as described in detail elsewhere [15].

The single-level polysilicon process with buried poly contacts which was applied to 4K static memory was extended to a double-level polysilicon process with a shared contact and high-resistance poly loads. This process, when applied to 16K memory [16] offers a twofold increase in the density for same design rules.

1) Single-Level Polysilicon (SLP) Process for 4K SRAM: The basic process used to fabricate this scaled memory is based on the standard selective oxidation process shown schematically in Fig. 16. The process is a single-level polysilicon-gate NMOS process with 250-, 400-, and 600-Å gate oxides, self-aligned arsenic-implanted source, drains, and submerged substrate contacts with ten overall patterning steps that include electron-beam alignment markers and the final protective overcoat pattern. The film thickness and doping distributions were optimized for a 1-µm channel transistor through appropriate scaling and are listed in Table VII. The process forms conventional enhancement, depletion, and natural transistors, all with appropriate channel-doping implants before gate oxidation, as described in the paragraph below.

The patterning of the various films was done using dry-plasma etch as described below. The shallow source drains were formed using implanted arsenic and were contacted with a sputter-deposited, silicon-doped aluminum layer.

2) Double-Level Polysilicon (DLP) SRAM Process for 16K SRAM: A factor-of-2 improvement in the memory density is achieved by configuring the static memory cell in four first-level polysilicon active transistors with two resistive loads in a second level of polysilicon stacked on top of the active transistors.

A cost-effective DLP process was developed, using "shared" contacts in the cell instead of relying on the classic first, or "buried," contacts as normally used for the first polysilicon-to-diffusion connections. These shared contacts use second level and moat as shown in Fig. 17, thereby reducing the number of contacts per cell from seven to four. The smaller

104

TABLE VII
ELECTRON-BEAM MOS PROCESS PARAMETERS FOR STATIC MEMORIES
SCALED AT 0.9×, 0.7×, AND 0.5×

PARAMETER DEVICE	0.9X	0.7X	0.5X
Gate Oxide	600 Å	400 Å	250 Å
Field Oxide	12,000 Å	9000 Å	7000 Å
Interlevel Oxide	10,000 Å	10,000 Å	10,000 Å
Polysilicon	4500 Å	4000 Å	3000 Å
Metal	9000 Å	8000 Å	6500 Å
Junction Depth	4000 Å	3000 Å	2500 Å
Substrate Resistivity	50 ohm-cm	35 ohm-cm	12 ohm-cm
Source Drain Resistance	18 ohm/Sq	28 ohm/Sq	35 ohm/Sq
Gate Resistance	18 ohm/Sq	20 ohm/Sq	39 ohm/Sq

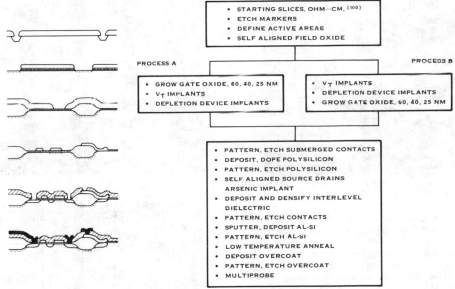

Fig. 16. Static memory process flow, using single-level poly gates.

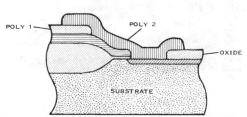

Fig. 17. Shared contact configuration in 16K memory.

number of contacts in the array can enhance the manufacturability of the 16K-by-1 SRAM with more than 100K device elements in the chip as a VLSI product. Furthermore, this DLP structure is used only where it improves density and when looser metal layout rules can be used. However, a single-level polysilicon (SLP) is used in the peripheral circuit areas to ensure a planar structure for better metal-step coverage and to allow a tighter metal pitch.

Second-level polysilicon resistors having a resistance typically in the 20–200-MΩ range are used as cell-load devices. This second-level polysilicon is highly doped only where contacts or low-resistance connections are to be formed. Four NMOS transistors, using first polysilicon, form the drivers and transfer gates of the flip-flop cell.

3) Electron-Beam Resist and Lithographic Processes: All the patterns necessary to fabricate the scaled memories were defined on the Texas Instruments electron-beam slice writer, using positive or negative electron-beam resists to optimize the writing time. The process used to fabricate the scaled memory is described in Table VIII. The process is negative-resist intensive; dense levels, such as active area, gate, and metal interconnect, were patterned in TI-309 high-speed negative electron-beam resist. The contacts, implant

TABLE VIII
ELECTRON-BEAM NMOS MEMORY RESIST/ETCH PROCESS FOR
SCALED 2147 4K SRAM

Step	Resist	Etch/Implant	Critical Geometry (Space/Feature)		
			0.9 × Linear (μm)	0.7 × Linear (μm)	0.5 × Linear (μm)
Alignment Markers	TI-323 *	Silicon etch	>5.0	>5.0	>5.0
Inverse Moat	TI-309*	Nitride/oxide plasma etch and channel stop implant mask	2.5	2.0	1.5
Enhancement	TI-309	Implant mask	>3.0	>3.0	>3.0
Depletion	TI-323	Implant mask	>3.0	>3.0	>3.0
First Contact	TI-323	Plasma etch oxide	>3.0	3.0	2.1
Gate	TI-309	Plasma etch polysilicon, MoSi₂Mo, W	2.5	1.8	1.5
Second Contact	TI-323	Plasma etch >10 kA PSG	4.0	3.0	2.1
Metal	TI-309	Wet etch aluminum-Si	3.0	2.0	1.5
PO	TI-323	Plasma etch nitride	>3.0	>3.0	>3.0

*TI-323   –Positive resist
**TI-309   -Negative resists

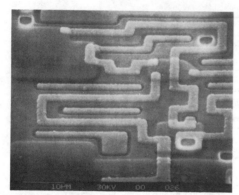

Fig. 18. Photomicrograph of 0.5X-2147 with metal removed showing
dry-etched 1-μm poly, buried and n⁺ contacts.

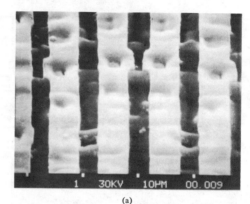

(a)

(b)

Fig. 19. Photomicrographs of dry-etch aluminum in scaled 16K SRAM
using electron-beam lithography.

masks, and protective overcoat levels were patterned using TI-323, a high-resolution, high-speed positive electron-beam resist. Each level needed optimization in terms of resist thickness, exposure level, and development to achieve the feature size and compatibility for subsequent processing listed in the table. The auto-align feature for chip-by-chip alignment with on accuracy of ±0.25 μm over the field of 250 mil × 250 mil was used with markers defined in the scribe lines as described earlier [17].

4) Pattern Transfer Technology: The patterning of the various films for this 1.0-μm scaled MOS process was done using dry-plasma etch processes in a parallel-plate batch reactor. Special anisotropic etch-process considerations were necessary to achieve desired 1- to 1.25-μm features with adequate line definition uniformity and selectivities to other films such as electron-beam resists and underlying films. Selectivity of the oxide etch over the electron-beam resists was of particular importance in controlling the size of the contacts in thick phosphorus-doped interlevel oxide. A typical pattern with 1.0- to 1.2-μm polysilicon features and oxide openings is shown in Fig. 18.

Etching of the silicon-doped aluminum leads on the 4K memories was an aqueous alkaline etch process which was compatible with the negative electron-beam resist. The metal design rules on the scaled 16K static memories required oversized geometries in the resist to allow for undercut and etch

nonuniformity. The difficult 2- to 3-μm step heights topography of two-level polysilicon process with a requirement of 1.0- to 1.5-μm resist space over these undulations make above-metal patterning marginal. More recent results of dry aluminum etching of the scaled 16K SRAM pattern in a parallel-plate plasma reactor are shown in Fig. 19. Note the vertical etch profile on the unfavorable topography of the double-level polysilicon process. The linewidth loss observed was less than 0.3 μm. Excellent linewidth control over the topography was possible owing to the large effective depth of focus of the electron-beam slice writing.

5) High-Integrity Thin-Gate Dielectric Process:

a) Thin-gate dielectric processes: The scaled MOS process at 1 to 1.5 μm requires a 200- to 250-Å gate dielectric. Process development was directed toward studying the growth kinetics in conventional wet and dry ambient, as well as at pressures as high as 10 atm. These gate oxides were characterized in detail for uniformity, intrinsic process reliability, interface charge (Q_{SS}), fast surface states (N_{st}), and flat-band voltage compatibility with conventional polysilicon as well as refractory silicide and polycide gate electrodes.

A serious reliability/yield-related gate oxide problem was observed during early development of the 1-μm SRAM process. The SRAM uses submerged contacts with patterning of the active gate oxide required before polysilicon gate deposition. The first fabricated 0.5X TMS2147As showed a number of wafers with excellent pattern quality and good electrical device characteristics, but with low yields. Test devices fabricated with varied contact structures on 250-Å gate oxides were found to have seriously degraded oxide integrity with defect densities in excess of 200/cm². Further tests revealed that the simple coating and subsequent removal of the resist on the 250-Å oxide caused a tenfold increase in the defect density. A process change to protect the gate oxide during the various contact patterning and etching processes was made and demonstrated on scaled memory [13].

Process modifications were introduced to alter the sequence of gate oxidation and threshold-adjust implants, thereby minimizing the process steps following gate oxidation to increase the integrity of the thin-gate dielectric. In the standard process, as many as three device threshold adjust implants are done through the thin-gate oxide before gate deposition (process A). The modified sequence used on the scaled memory utilized an initial pad oxide as a mask for these implants, which were done before gate oxidation (process B in Fig. 16).

Another approach to increase the integrity of the thin-gate dielectric is the use of dual-layer dielectric such as thermal oxide and LPCVD-deposited nitride. Improved device performance and gate integrity are expected since the added nitride layer exhibits a higher dielectric constant and breakdown field strength. In an experiment to evaluate gate oxide integrity as a function of dielectric thickness and process effects, the processes were split in two different sequences, A and B, as described above. Each of these processes was then further split for oxide and oxide–nitride gates. Fig. 20(a) and (b) shows the breakdown voltage of capacitors plotted as a function of the percent of capacitors breaking down at a given voltage. The breakdown of thin-oxide test capacitors shows ideal distributions with two intercepting straight lines, corresponding to a normal and a defective distribution. Other distributions show more complex structures, each component associated with a probable defect mechanism. Defect density is computed using the relationship $D = -\ln Y/A$ where D is the defect density (cm⁻²), Y is the fractional yield, and A is the area of the test capacitor. Comparison of the two dielectrics immediately after gate definition shows that the intrinsic single-oxide-gate dielectric has a lower defect density, owed to minimum processing. After the entire SRAM process, the nitride–oxide dual layers have fewer defects and exhibit a distribution which is more ideal than the case of a single-gate oxide. Although there is no significant difference between process A and B from the standpoint of capacitor breakdown after the gate

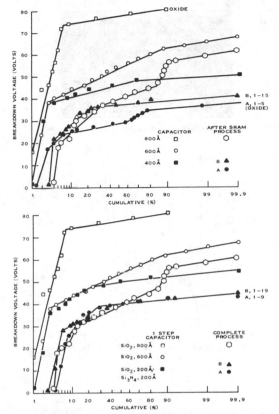

Fig. 20. Statistical breakdown voltage distribution for MOS capacitors with simple and complete static RAM process at 800-, 600-, and 400-Å gate dielectrics with conventional and modified process sequences.

deposition, final LSI yields of the complete static memory demonstrated a considerably higher percentage of functional memories (or memories with a higher fraction of functional bits) for parts fabricated with process B.

D. Device Process Characterization

Successful fabrication of high-speed, 1-μm 4K static memories at reasonable yields was accomplished using the modified LOCOS and associated VLSI enhancements. Optimization of not only the active transistors at these geometries, but also the optimization of isolation devices was essential to realize integration of a large number of devices with reasonable active and standby powers. The characterization results of the scaled isolation devices, subthreshold leakage, and moat encroachment are described below. Typical parameters for 1-μm transistors fabricated with this process are listed in Table IX with I_D–V_D characteristics shown in Fig. 21.

1) Scaled Isolation Device: Moat encroachment and the lateral diffusion of channel-stop implants determine the effectiveness of thick-field isolation transistors with polysilicon or metal electrodes. Fig. 22 shows the I–V characteristic of the thick-field isolation transistor with 2-μm source-to-drain spacing. Leakage currents less than 10⁻⁹ A were observed for gate voltages as high as 15 V. A channel-stop implant of 5×10^{12}/cm² and a 7000-Å-thick field oxide were used. The knee of the drain current characteristic is a sensitive function

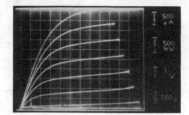

Fig. 21. I_D-V_D characteristics of 1.2-μm transistor.

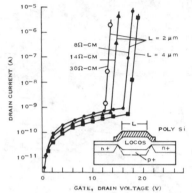

Fig. 22. Thick oxide parasitic MOSFET leakage current.

TABLE IX
SUMMARY OF 1.2-μm TRANSISTOR

Parameter	Value
Threshold voltage at $V_{BS} = -2$ V	0.7 V
K'	42.5 μA/V²
Body effect coefficient	0.21 V^{1/2}
BV_{DSS}	13 V
Thick-field threshold voltage	16 V
Depletion pinchoff voltage	-3.8 V
Channnel mobility	630 cm²/V·s
n⁺ sheet resistance	35 Ω/□
Polysilicon sheet resistance	38 Ω/□

of the substrate resistivity for a given channel-stop implant. Hence, selection of the starting resistivity was not only determined by the scaled transistor, but the overall standby power considerations.

2) Moat Encroachment in Active Devices: To determine the moat encroachment in our high-density LOCOS process, transistors of varying nominal widths (2, 1.75, and 1.5 μm) were fabricated. The current through the transistor should be proportional to the width of the transistor and, if the data through these three nominal widths are extrapolated to zero drain current, the moat encroachment can be estimated. For the depletion and enhancement transistors, straight lines are obtained, and a moat encroachment of 0.92 and 1.5 μm are calculated, respectively. For the natural transistor, a straight line is not obtained, indicating that the threshold throughout the transistor is modulated by the moat encroachment. Drain currents for enhancement, natural, and depletion transistors with varying widths are shown in Fig. 23.

3) Scaled MOSFET's: MOSFET's with channel lengths scaled to submicrometer and micrometer dimensions, which were fabricated using the scaled process, were characterized in detail for threshold-voltage control and subthreshold

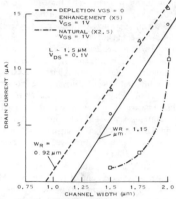

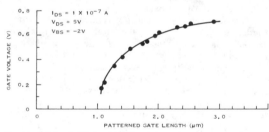

Fig. 23. Moat encroachment projected for depletion, enhancement, and natural transistors for electron-beam LOCOS process.

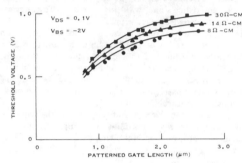

Fig. 24. Effect of gate length on threshold voltage.

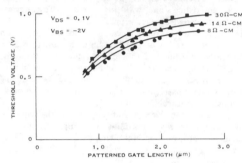

Fig. 25. Subthreshold characteristic of short-channel transistors plotted as gate voltage required for 10^{-7}-A drain current.

leakage—parameters critical for circuit scaling. Fig. 24 shows the variation of the threshold voltage as a function of patterned gate length for the 250-Å gate-oxide process. Effective scaling was demonstrated by substantial reduction in the sensitivity of V_T to the channel-length reduction as compared to devices with thicker gate oxide processes [13]. Another measure of effective scaling is the subthreshold leakage. This is plotted in Fig. 25 as the gate voltage required for 10^{-7}-Å drain current for a 5-V drain voltage and as a function of the channel length. Although the overall shape of the curve is similar to that of Fig. 24, the steeper slope at small feature dimensions confirms the concern that the subthreshold leakage does not scale with channel length. Desired threshold voltages for the device were obtained through modeling of the electron potential as a function of the depth of inversion. Calculated potentials and

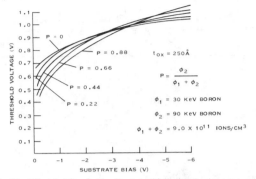

Fig. 26. Calculated threshold voltage sensitivity (12-$\Omega \cdot$ cm substrate).

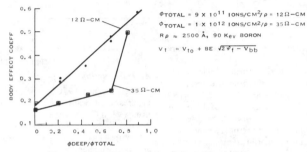

Fig. 27. Body effect versus punchthrough implant dose.

threshold voltage sensitivity are shown in Fig. 26. Scaling the devices at micrometer and submicrometer dimensions increases the sensitivity of the surface potential to the drain voltage. The reduction in punchthrough voltage is minimized through a deeper implant in the channel region at the expense of increased sensitivity of threshold voltage to the substrate potential (body effect). The body effect modeled for the two substrate resistivities is shown in Fig. 27.

Fig. 21 shows the I_D-V_D characteristic of a typical 1.2-μm patterned polysilicon transistor shown in the linear, saturation, and punchthrough regions. The transistor shows a BV_{DSS} of 13 V and excellent characteristics through voltages as high as 7 to 8 V.

A number of ring oscillators were fabricated to evaluate the process sensitivity of electron mobility in the enhancement transistor at these channel lengths since velocity saturation and mobility degradation are two of the chief concerns for device scaling in the submicrometer region. Ring oscillators were built with 3-, 2-, and 1-μm patterned gate lengths on substrates with varying doping concentration. Electron mobility was found to be sensitive to the substrate concentration. The effect, although understood on the device level, was measured on the circuit level using oscillation frequency as a sensitive measure. Speed/power characteristics for the ring oscillators are shown in Fig. 28.

E. LSI Fabrication and Characterization

4K static memories based on the currently manufactured TMS2147 at 0.9X, 0.7X, and 0.5X linear scale factors and 16K static memories based on the TMS2167 were fabricated using the single-level and double-level poly processes described in detail earlier. Memories were characterized for dc and ac

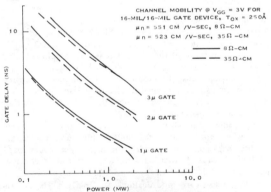

Fig. 28. Enhancement load ring oscillator, with a fan-out of 3.

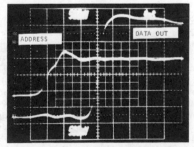

Fig. 29. Oscillograph of address select data out signal for 0.5X-2147, at 100°C with V_{CC} at 4.5 V.

TABLE X
SUMMARY OF SCALED STATIC MEMORY PERFORMANCE

	0.9X TMS2147	0.7X TMS2147	0.5X TMS2147
Organization	4K x 1	4K x 1	4K x 1
Cell Size	2.9 mil^2	1.76 mil^2	0.88 mil^2
Chip Size	20.2K mil^2	12.1K mil^2	6.0 mil^2
Address Access Time	35 nsec	22 nsec	15 nsec
Power Active	500 mw	520 mw	500 mw
Power Standby	50 mw	50 mw	80 mw
Minimum Feature	2.5μm	1.8μm	1.2μm
Channel length	2.0μm	1.3μm	0.9μm
Alignment	1.5μm	1.0μm	0.7μm
Gate Oxide	600 Å	400 Å	250 Å

performance over the temperature range of room temperature to 100°C. The functionality, access time, and elevated temperature measurements were made in slice form. Devices were packaged for further reliability and operating life tests. A typical address and data signal oscillograph for a 0.5X–4157 4K memory is shown in Fig. 29. Access times of 12–15 ns were observed for memories with 0.9–1.2-μm channel length transistors—with access time standby power strongly dependent on the channel length. All memories were functional over the elevated temperature of up to 100°C. The 0.9X and 0.7X scaled memories were also successfully built using the dual dielectric gates. Substantial improvement, both in yield and its distribution on wafer and wafer-to-wafer, was obtained using the dual dielectric process.

Relative performance of the 4K SRAM's at various scale factors is shown in Table X. Significant improvement in the performance in terms of the access time was accomplished—not only due to transistor scaling, but also due to reduction of the parasitic capacitances. In addition, overall component density improvement can be seen in the relative cell and overall chip distribution on wafer shown in Fig. 30, the latter accounting for the cost leverage.

The bonding pad size and configuration at a 0.5X scale factor were not suitable for multiprobing and packaging. To allow packaging and probing, the memory was fabricated on a larger area chip, with pads connected to a 0.7X configuration of the TSM2147. In the prototype phase, this was done with simple software modifications on EBMIII. The results are shown in Fig. 31.

F. Conclusion

The development of MOS device process technologies and the demonstration of 1-μm LSI and VLSI density using direct electron-beam lithography has been summarized. Traditional scaling concepts and present limitations in improving circuit performance and reducing overall cost through an increase in component density have been discussed. Improvements in both performance and component density have been successfully demonstrated by fabricating full 4K X 1 static memories which have 12–15-ns access times and a chip size of only 6K mil^2. The requirements for extending this evolution to true VLSI products such as the 64K/256K SRAM's have also been described in terms of process, device, and lithographic capability.

IV. BIPOLAR SCALING AND TECHNOLOGY IMPLEMENTATION

A. Introduction

Since the early 1970's, bipolar technology has shown a steady progression toward the realization of very-large-scale integration (VLSI), a scaling threshold which has generally been defined as 5K bipolar logic gates or 64K memory bits per chip [18]. Dramatic improvements in packing density and performance have been achieved primarily through evolutionary, and in some cases revolutionary, changes in lithographic systems and generic process techniques.

The improved bipolar production technologies of the late 1970's and early 1980's can be attributed to the advent of ion implantation and projection imaging tools as well as improvement in device isolation and epitaxy processes. Ion implantation and improved epitaxy allowed considerable reduction in junction depth and lateral diffusion while providing precise doping control. Oxide isolation methods offered increased packing density and reduced sidewall capacitance. Projection printing and direct-step-on-wafer (DSW) systems enabled imaging technologies to fully leverage the available process innovations, as evidenced by the significant decrease in minimum feature size from 4 μm in 1979 production to 2 μm today. By 1985, 1.25-μm minimum design rules are expected to be the new production standard for complex bipolar parts.

Such evolutionary improvements in lithographic capability have, when coupled with process scaling enhancements, provided significant reductions in active gate area and led to dramatic increases in performance. Table XI illustrates how one bipolar technology, integrated injection logic (I^2L), has evolved to higher levels of sophistication as evidenced by the evolution of the I^2L microprocessor. The SBP0400 serves a typical example of bipolar microprocessor technology in the early 1970's. Design complexity is limited to 4-bit words and approximately 1600 gates. This is due, in part, to process-determined packing density and chip size, both of which are strong functions of yield concerns. The diffused-junction and contact-print technology of this era limited not only packing density, but performance as well, primarily due to parasitic capacitance effects. The 1-MHz clock frequency is typical of the I^2L performance which could be achieved in 1974 using the available production tools and processes.

With the advent of projection-print lithography, ion implantation, and oxide isolation methods in the mid-1970's, complex

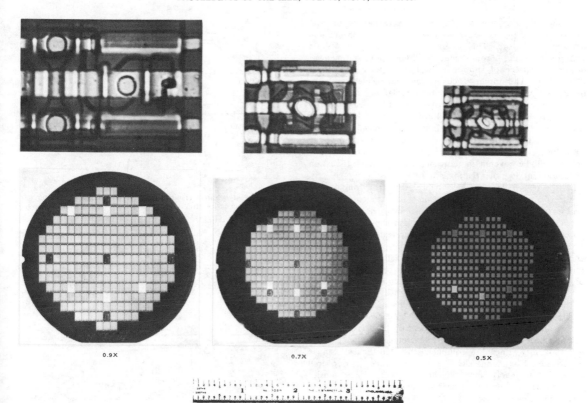

Fig. 30. Static memory cell and chip layout at 0.9X, 0.7X, and 0.5X.

Fig. 31. Photomicrograph of 0.5X-2147 with extended bond pads and alignment markers.

16-bit designs such as the SBP9900 and SBP9989 were made possible, and chip size as well as gate densities were effectively doubled. In comparing the SBP9900 and SBP9989, which used similar processes and design rules, a performance improve-

TABLE XI
EVOLUTION OF THE I²L MICROPROCESSOR IN BIPOLAR PRODUCTION

Year	1974	1976	1980	1982
Part	SBP0400	SBP9900	SBP9989	SBP9990*
Word Size (bits)	4	16	16	16
Chip Size (mm²)	20	48	36	16
Number of Gates	1616	6034	4788	4788
Chip Gate Density (gates/mm²)	81	126	133	300
Clock Frequency (MHz)	1	3	4.4	10

* Prototype Production

ment is noted for the SBP9989 that can primarily be attributed to differences in design. This is an important factor which is often overshadowed by scaling concerns; namely, both device scaling and design ingenuity must evolve together to optimize overall circuit performance.

The SBP9990 provides an example of how effective scaling can be in improving performance. The SBP9990 is fundamentally a 0.5X shrink of the SBP9989, with design enhancements which will be discussed later. Packing density is increased dramatically from 133 gates/mm² for the SBP9989 to 300 gates/mm² for the SBP9990, but the most noteworthy improvement is in performance—clock frequency is more than doubled for the scaled part. The SBP9990 gate density (300 gates/mm^2) and complexity ($\sim$5K logic gates) are representative of a VLSI bipolar technology which required considerable development effort. This program covered a number of years and involved the development of lithography and generic processes capable of supporting a 1-μm bipolar technology [19]–[22]. The primary focus was on utilizing electron-beam direct-slice writing to scale complex bipolar parts for use as process development vehicles, starting with the scaled SBP0400, which was designated the SBP0400E [20] and culminating in the scaled SBP9989, which was first designated the SBP9989E [21] and later, with some design enhancements, renamed the SBP9990. Details of the past, present, and future scaling efforts will be covered in more detail later after a discussion of fundamental bipolar scaling issues.

In this regard, one can reasonably ask: How long density and performance can scale in unison before tradeoffs become necessary? This question addresses not only the fundamental barriers to bipolar device scaling, but also the limitations imposed upon the device by external considerations as it is embedded into a VLSI circuit configuration. Factors such as chip heat dissipation and interconnect reliability and delay must be considered; scaling LSI circuits to VLSI density is one method of exploring these concerns and examining tradeoffs between performance and packing density.

Electron-beam direct-slice-write systems continue to serve as ideal scaling and prototyping tools by providing not only the resolution and registration required in the micrometer and submicrometer regime, but also an extremely flexible patterning capability, since the computer-generated "mask" can be easily altered to change either individual geometries or overall design. The steady improvements in bipolar circuit density and performance that have been demonstrated using electron-beam direct slice writing [19]–[22] have necessarily required considerable process evolution and innovation. Stringent pattern transfer demands have thus far been met by refining isotropic wet-etch techniques or utilizing anisotropic plasma and reactive-ion etching. Ion implantation has provided the means to accurately scale doping levels and junction depths while low-temperature processes have been employed to limit subsequent dopant diffusion. Double-level-metal (DLM) processes have also been developed which accommodate 1-μm device interconnect density and reliability requirements without undue sacrifices in performance.

With generic processes in place to support a 1-μm bipolar technology, the stage is set to explore the next generation of device structures and processes. Additional process evolution and device structure innovation will no doubt be required to meet the submicrometer challenge. Shrinking linewidths and registration tolerance to achieve tighter packing density will severely test lithographic tools and fuel alternative lithographic techniques. Section II of this paper discussed some of the basic lithographic issues and briefly surveyed current imaging techniques. Electron-beam direct-slice writing was concluded to be a submicrometer imaging technology mature enough to satisfy VLSI circuit prototyping needs. The intent of this section is to examine the issues involved in applying electron-beam direct-slice writing to the scaling of complex bipolar circuits. Bipolar scaling fundamentals are first addressed within the contexts of both the device and overall circuit. Then, as a case study, the scaling of an LSI integrated injection logic (I^{2}L) microprocessor to VLSI density is described with particular emphasis on electron-beam lithographic techniques and process scaling. Finally, the performance advantages afforded

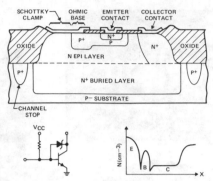

Fig. 32. Typical Schottky-clamped n-p-n transistor: including a cross section of the device structure, an equivalent circuit, and the n-p-n doping profile.

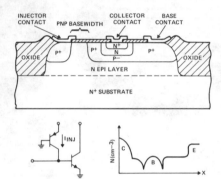

Fig. 33. Typical inverted n-p-n transistor with a p-n-p current injector: including a cross section of the device structure, an equivalent circuit, and the n-p-n doping profile.

by scaling are highlighted and future goals are discussed within the framework of a submicrometer bipolar technology.

B. Bipolar Scaling Issues

1) Device Structure: Figs. 32 and 33 illustrate two basic types of transistor structures used to build bipolar logic gates. There are many forms of bipolar logic and only a few will be briefly described here to preface a discussion of bipolar scaling issues. Lohstroh has presented a more detailed comparison of the bipolar logic forms and processes which appear to be viable candidates for VLSI implementation [18]. Each logic form involves a unique set of tradeoffs between speed, power dissipation, noise immunity, and packing density. Differences in device switching speed are primarily due to differences in logic voltage swing, operating current, and the degree of transistor saturation allowed. Transistor f_T, junction capacitance, and series resistance are also of obvious importance in determining overall performance and are key parameters for scaling.

Transistor saturation is typical of most implementations (ECL, or emitter-coupled logic, is one notable exception), and some means of clamping the transistor for minimal saturation is normally required to improve switching speed. The configuration shown in Fig. 32 utilizes a Schottky diode to clamp the n-p-n transistor out of saturation and is typical of Schottky TTL and STL (Schottky transistor logic). ISL, or integrated Schottky logic, uses a p-n-p base–collector clamp rather than a Schottky. In all of these logic forms, the n-p-n transistor is operating in the normal mode with a doping profile similar to that shown in Fig. 32. Typical logic voltage swings range from 1.2 V for low-power Schottky (LS) TTL to ~200 mV for STL and ISL, with ECL covering the entire range of 200–700 mV. Although larger voltage swings lead to somewhat slower switching speeds, they do provide better circuit noise immunity.

Logic gates are normally fabricated in n-type epi on p-type substrates. Oxide separation is achieved by a recessed LOCOS (ROX) technique which produces an approximately planar surface and consumes the epitaxial layer [23] as shown in Fig. 32. Isolation is provided underneath the epitaxial layer by a back-biased collector-to-substrate diode; buried n^+ layers separated by p^+ channel stops enhance collector conductivity along the gate. The collector–base clamp minimizes the accumulation of stored charge in the base region; junction capacitances as well as base and collector series resistance are then the major factors limiting device performance. For configurations with Schottky outputs, such as ISL and STL, Schottky-to-collector series resistance in the epi region is also a concern since it leads to inefficient clamping and excess stored charge.

The gate configuration shown in Fig. 33 utilizes current injection into the base of an inverted n-p-n to form a saturating logic with a rather large voltage swing (~700 mV) which is accordingly slower than nonsaturating or clamped logic forms. This structure is typical of $I^2 L$ which, in its simplest form, uses an n^+ substrate as the circuit's common ground. Since only oxide separation of the gates is required, the packing density is greater than can be achieved with present fully oxide-isolated device technology. A lateral p-n-p is normally used as the current source since it provides greater latitude in choosing operating conditions and also requires less space than the bulk resistors which are used for sources and pullups in other bipolar logic forms. For the inverted mode of operation, the substrate now serves as the emitter and is much larger than the collector; a thin, lightly doped intrinsic base assures adequate n-p-n gain. Typical doping profiles for an inverted n-p-n are also shown in Fig. 33. Scaling $I^2 L$ for performance has focused primarily upon improving transistor f_T and thinning the epitaxial layer to reduce the volume of inactive device regions (which store excess charge in the absence of a clamping device). Base-to-emitter (substrate) capacitance is also a major contributor to slower device performance and several $I^2 L$ poly base-on-insulator structures have been explored as a means of reducing this parasitic capacitance for improved performance [24], [25].

2) Fundamental Barriers: Principal bipolar scaling thrusts have been directed toward minimizing junction capacitance, base transit time, internal series resistance, and interconnect RC time constants. Scaling resistor components is also a major concern, especially for logic forms requiring several resistors per gate (such as ECL). Current-density limitations for junctions, Schottkys, and interconnects must also be closely examined. What are some of the barriers to bipolar scaling? This question can only be addressed within the context of overall circuit parameters. Some elements of the puzzle are more clear than others, but prototyping remains the only sure way of answering the scaling challenge. However, first consider some of the fundamental barriers and problems associated with understanding and predicting bipolar device behavior.

Forecasting bipolar device evolution has always proven to be a difficult task since no simple set of scaling rules can be applied as in the MOS case. Bipolar scaling requires both resistive and capacitive elements to model active device behavior, and as devices continue to shrink, more fundamental intrinsic effects such as bandgap narrowing and Auger recombination become important. Sidewall capacitances also begin to make significant contributions to device behavior which can only be understood through two- or pseudo three-dimensional modeling techniques. As scaled device performance continues to improve, delays associated with interconnect must also be pared by clever design or improved interconnect techniques. Scaling strategies must comprehend, through modeling and prototyping, how three-dimensional effects (including interconnect capacitance) impact overall circuit performance.

Efforts to improve device performance have focused on three-dimensional scaling to reduce junction capacitance and series resistance. Using advanced lithographic techniques, considerable reductions in emitter (or collector for the inverted transistor mode) and base area have been achieved in conjunction with the vertical scaling of epitaxial-layer thickness and junction depths. Intrinsic base width has also been scaled to reduce transit time while extrinsic base doping levels have been increased to lower base series resistance. As base widths shrink, n-p-n doping levels must increase to provide narrow junction depletion regions and prevent "punchthrough," which occurs when the collector and emitter regions reach through the base. Doping concentrations are, in turn, limited by a voltage-dependent junction field emission "breakdown." In the scaling limit, breakdown and punchthrough voltages are equal, and 1.2-V minimum-size transistors have a calculated base width of ~70 nm with a base doping concentration of 2.3×10^{18} cm^3 [26]. For more practical cases, doping profiles must be tailored to meet each specific set of operating conditions and junction breakdown requirements.

An additional scaling constraint is placed upon operating voltage, which is limited to a minimum of approximately 1 V by noise margin considerations and the transistor turn-on requirement $V_{BE} > ~0.6$ V. Power density is also likely to remain fixed in a typical scaling scenario due to chip heat dissipation limitations and reliability problems which are associated with electromigration and ohmic/Schottky-contact current-density restrictions. Therefore, if gate area is scaled with fixed power density and minimum operating voltage, gate-drive current must be reduced with the scale factor, or in other words, junction current density must be held constant. Although scaling with constant current density presents fewer interconnect-related reliability problems, improvements in performance are less dramatic since less current is available to drive circuit RC time constants. This point is illustrated in Fig. 34 where current versus propagation delay is plotted for $I^2 L$ ring oscillators fabricated using 4.5- and 1.25-μm design rules. The top curve represents the performance of a typical second-generation $I^2 L$ production design utilizing 4.5-μm minimum design rules. The lower curve represents the performance of a 0.5X linear shrink which required 1.25-μm minimum design rules to allow extra margin for adequate design registration tolerance. If both gates are driven at 200 μA, then the scaled device holds a speed advantage of approximately $3:1$. However, since the original device has been linearly scaled by a factor of 0.5X, the area has been scaled by a factor of 0.25X. Holding current density constant would require dropping the operating current of the scaled

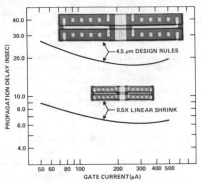

Fig. 34. I²L ring-oscillator performance data for worst case near base-far collector layout using 4.5-μm design rules as compared with similar data for a 0.5× linearly scaled design.

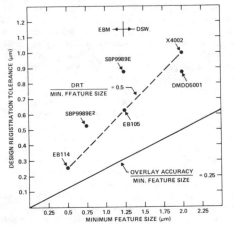

Fig. 35. Minimum feature size versus design registration tolerance for several I²L, ISL, and STL designs.

device to only 50 μA, and under these circumstances, the speed advantage of the scaled device is only 2:1. Process enhancements or design alterations which allowed the scaled devices to operate at higher current densities would obviously provide much greater scaling leverage.

3) Lithography and Process Limitations: Superior lithographic resolution is a key requirement for scaling and has been adequately covered in Section II. The impact of design registration tolerance (DRT), also discussed in Section II, will now be viewed from the perspective of actual bipolar circuit scaling. Fig. 35 illustrates how scaling places increasing demands on lithography and process. As a general rule of thumb, efficient designs require that the ratio of overlay accuracy to minimum feature size be better than one to four as plotted in Fig. 35. Process allowances are than added to determine an overall DRT for a particular process and device structure.

Scaling dramatically reduces DRT as shown in Fig. 35 for several advanced I²L, ISL, and STL designs. In general, for designs with minimum feature sizes greater than or equal to 1.25 μm, DSW was the lithographic tool of choice to maximize throughput; circuits with minimum feature sizes less than 1.25

μm required electron-beam direct-slice writing. The circuits shown with 1.25-μm minimum feature size (SBP9989E and EB105) have been fabricated using exclusively electron-beam or DSW lithography.

I²L technology is represented in Fig. 35 by the DMDD5001 (a 4K gate array), the SBP9989E (a 16-bit microprocessor), and the SBP9989E² (a 60-percent linear shrink of the SBP9989E). STL and ISL are represented by the X4002 and EB105 test chips; EB114 addresses 0.5-μm STL technology. Although design rules vary from the aggressive DRT's used on test chips to more conservative DRT's for production designs such as the SBP9989E, the obvious trend is toward tighter overall registration tolerance. Note also that the apparent slope of the DRT versus minimum feature size is steeper (~0.5 for the STL designs) than the slope assumed for overlay accuracy versus minimum feature size (~0.25). This implies that dramatic process improvements (such as self-aligned structures) will be required to carry bipolar production into the submicrometer regime.

For example, in the case of SBP9989E, which will be discussed in more detail later, a DRT of approximately +/- 0.9 μm allows for process-induced linewidth variations of +/- 0.6 μm where the overlay accuracy is assumed to be +/- 0.3 μm. Scaling this design by 60 percent to a 0.75-μm minimum feature size forces a DRT of only +/- 0.5 μm, assuming an improved overlay accuracy of less than +/- 0.2 μm for the lithographic tool. If the lithographic tool is not capable of achieving the required overlay accuracy, then either the process engineer must improve process control or the design engineer must relax the DRT. The latter course leads to inefficient designs and less improvement in packing density.

One can speculate on the fundamental limitation to design registration tolerance for submicrometer bipolar devices. If bipolar processes can be developed which are totally self-aligned between critical patterning levels, then linewidth control becomes the dominant issue. A bipolar device, and in particular, its minimum-sized emitter width, is less sensitive to linewidth variations than the MOS device counterpart of channel length. For this reason, linewidth tolerances in bipolar devices will probably be less stringent than in MOS devices as minimum feature size shrinks. A reasonable estimate of the degree of linewidth control achievable for 0.5-μm devices is approximately +/- 0.1 μm, including measurement error. Therefore, critical levels which are self-aligned will have a total DRT of approximately +/- 0.1 μm, independent of overlay accuracy. Other, less critical levels which are not self-aligned will still require stringent overlay accuracy to assure efficient designs and maximize packing density. Ultimate overlay accuracy will be determined not only by the capability of the lithographic tool itself, but also by the alignment marker integrity after each process step. At present, overlay accuracies of less than +/- 0.1 μm appear feasible in bipolar processes using electron-beam direct-slice writing with automatic chip-by-chip alignment as described in Section II.

Clearly, dramatic improvements in both process and lithographic techniques are required to meet the challenge of diminishing design registration tolerance. Self-aligned structures and improved lithographic tools will obviously play key roles in meeting this challenge. This point is emphasized in Fig. 36, where cross sections of n-p-n transistor structures are depicted for the SBP9989 microprocessor and its 50- and 30-percent linearly scaled versions, the SBP9989E and SBP9989E², respectively, which were discussed earlier. Note that for the

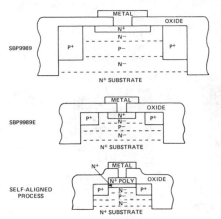

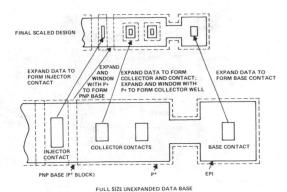

Fig. 38. A flexible data expansion technique for I^2L design.

Fig. 36. Cross sections of n-p-n transistor structures for I^2L implementations.

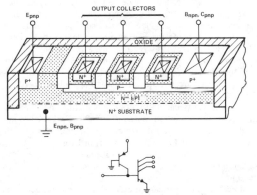

Fig. 37. Integrated-injection logic (I^2L) gate and equivalent circuit.

SBP9989E^2, the extrinsic base is self-aligned to a poly collector diffusion source to eliminate n$^+$ to p$^+$ lithographic tolerance and thereby enhance scalability. Similar processes have been demonstrated elsewhere [27]–[29] and are currently under development at Texas Instruments for use on VLSI circuits such as the SBP9989E^2.

To consider how design registration tolerance affects device performance, one needs to examine the I^2L gate structure in more detail. A typical I^2L gate and equivalent circuit are shown in Fig. 37. The gate structure reflects an oxide-separated second-generation production process with n$^+$ collectors nested inside of a p$^+$ extrinsic base. The lateral p-n-p is particularly important from the standpoint of optimizing current injection efficiency and device speed. Switching speed can be improved by decreasing the p-n-p base width to increase the p-n-p recollection current gain (along with forward current gain). This, in turn, reduces stored charge in the n-p-n by lowering the effective n-p-n upward gain. The n-p-n upward gain cannot, however, be allowed to degrade below unity or the gate will not function properly. Therefore, p-n-p base width must be carefully controlled to assure a safe compromise

between functionality and maximum speed–power product. Misalignment of the n$^+$ and p$^+$ levels would also degrade n-p-n gain and collector–base breakdown voltage. Utilizing the self-aligned collector–base structures discussed above would avoid this particular limitation.

C. Scaling Complex Circuits

1) The Scaling Vehicle: As individual devices shrink, circuit performance tends to be dominated by associated interconnect capacitance, and for this reason, scaling issues need to be addressed within the framework of complex circuits. Choosing an appropriate scaling vehicle is not an easy task. For complex circuits, two key considerations are design flexibility and process simplicity. Whenever possible, the design database should be configured for discriminatory scaling since not all aspects of a given design can be scaled equally. For example, I/O transistors cannot usually scale by the same factor used for internal logic gates since interface requirements such as sink current and minimum breakdown voltages remain fixed. Bonding-pad dimensions and separations are also constrained by bonding requirements and may, in fact, determine chip size independent of active area for aggressively scaled designs. Custom designs based on scaled processes which have been demonstrated on the scaling vehicle prototype would presumably utilize as many gates as chip area allowed and bonding-pad overhead would be less of a factor. A final, but most important point is that the design registration tolerance of the scaling vehicle must, after the appropriate scale factor is applied, provide a reasonable match for the available lithography and generic process capabilities.

2) Design Considerations: As mentioned previously, a discriminatory scaling capability is extremely important from the standpoint of facilitating design refinements and necessary sizing adjusts. This flexibility can be achieved by utilizing a design database which allows scaling of selected critical geometries in the gate or unit cell independent of the overall scaling factor. For example, in the case study described below, a design database was used which allowed injector, collector, and base contacts to be sized independently in accordance with the scaling requirements, and p-n-p base width could be varied without changing the collector well sizing (which would affect n$^+$ to p$^+$ spacing). This method is illustrated in Fig. 38 for a typical I^2L gate. Entire mask levels can be generated

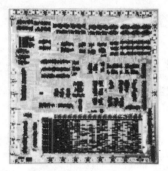
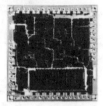

FULL SIZE SBP9989
BAR AREA: 57.5K MIL^2
CLOCK FREQUENCY. 4–5 MHz

50% LINEAR SHRINK SBP9989E
ACTIVE BAR AREA: 17.3K MIL^2
CLOCK FREQUENCY: 10–12 MHz

30% LINEAR SHRINK SBP9989E^2
ACTIVE BAR AREA: 6.2K MIL^2
CLOCK FREQUENCY: 20 MHz (EST.)

Fig. 39. Photomicrograph comparisons of full-size, 0.5X, and 0.3X
linearly scaled SBP9989's.

from a few key geometries. This is a particular advantage where electron-beam lithography is employed since the convenient computer-generated "mask" can be leveraged to provide rapid, in-process design alterations.

D. A Bipolar Case Study

1) Circuit and Design: As a case study in scaling complex circuits, consider the scaling of the SBP9989, a ~5K gate, 16-bit, I^{2}L microprocessor. The initial goal was to linearly scale the LSI chip by 50 percent to achieve VLSI density. The minimum designed feature size for the scaled version (designated the SBP9989E) was 1.25 μm, which required a 0.85-μm feature size in resist to allow for resist erosion during subsequent plasma etching. Overall design registration tolerance was a rather conservative +/- 0.875 μm, which included level-to-level registration, linewidth control, and process allowances. A conservative DRT was chosen to allow additional scaling to a 30-percent shrink with minimal design changes.

Electron beam was chosen as the most conservative lithographic approach, since EBMIII [30] could easily satisfy the submicrometer patterning and registration requirements with its 0.5-μm nominal beam size and +/- 0.25-μm level-to-level registration tolerance. Electron beam also offered sufficient lithographic latitude to eventually explore more agressively scaled designs such as 40- and 30-percent SBP9989's.

Although basic design changes were kept to a minimum, the scaled part did require some alterations, particularly in the input and output circuits where extensive redesign was required to assure adequate breakdown voltages and optimum performance. For internal logic gates, extrinsic base and collector levels were sized to improve design registration tolerance and optimize the collector-to-base area ratio for performance [19]. Contact and via levels also required sizing adjusts to assure adequate DRT's after scaling; consequently, the minimum feature size required for both contacts and vias was 1.25 μm after the 0.5X shrink (from 4.5 to 2.25 μm) plus additional sizing adjusts. Fortunately, by enlarging selected contacts, it was possible to avoid the restriction of scaling with constant current density. For the SBP9989E, operating current was reduced by a factor of 0.5X instead of the factor of 0.25X

that would have been required to keep the current density constant with a 0.5X linear scale factor. Other circuit alterations included the addition of clamp diodes to improve static discharge protection, and bonding-pad size/spacing limitations also necessitated some rearrangement and required extra area. Although active area was reduced by a factor of ~0.3X to 11.2 mm^2, the total original chip area of 37.1 mm^2 was reduced by a factor of only ~0.4X to 14.4 mm^2. The difference between the two areas is the excess bonding pad overhead.

Fig. 39 offers a size comparison of full-size, 50-percent, and 30-percent linearly scaled SBP9989's. Note that the 30-percent shrink is bond pad limited to a chip size of 128 mils X 128 mils. Transistor pitch for the full-size chip is 30 μm, corresponding to a gate density of 129 gates/mm^2. Transistor pitches for the 50- and 30-percent versions are 15 and 9 μm, respectively, corresponding to respective gate densities of 428 and 1168 gates/mm^2.

Scaling in the vertical direction included reducing the epitaxial-layer thickness from the 1.5 μm used in the original process to 1.2 μm for the SBP9989E. The resistivity of the epitaxial layer was 1 Ω · cm for both devices. Normally, epi doping would be increased in the scaled device to reduce stored charge and to narrow depletion regions. However, this is not necessary because the scaled process formed the extrinsic base by ion implantation and low-temperature anneal, whereas the original production process employed boron deposition and deep diffusion which required considerable oversizing of the p-n-p base width pattern. Using the 50-percent scale pattern with the improved process, an active p-n-p base width was obtained which was comparable to the full-sized active base width. For this reason, the epi doping was kept constant in order to preserve the p-n-p gain characteristics. The scaled process is discussed in more detail in the next section.

2) Electron-Beam Lithography and Process: All patterns were delineated in TI-323 positive or TI-309 negative electron resists using EBMIII [30]. Each chip was aligned automatically using the alignment technique discussed in Section II. Scan density, writing speed, and beam size varied depending upon resist type and pattern resolution requirements, but were typically optimized to minimize patterning time. A nominal 0.5-μm beam size with a scan line spacing of 0.1 μm was

TABLE XII
SBP9989E Electron-Beam Lithography and Process Flow

LEVEL	MIN. GEOM. μm (mil)	RESIST THICKNESS/±/TYPE	PROCESS STEP
ALIGNMENT MARKERS	10.0 (0.4)	1.2 μm/+/TI-323	ISOTROPIC PLASMA ETCH – SILICON
ISOLATION	2.0 (0.08)	1.2 μm/+/TI-323	ANISOTROPIC PLASMA ETCH – NITRIDE, OXIDE AND SILICON
COLLECTOR	3.5 (0.14)	1.0 μm/+/TI-323	ANISOTROPIC PLASMA ETCH – OXIDE, IMPLANT As USING OXIDE MASK ONLY
RESISTOR	5.0 (0.2)	1.0 μm/+/TI-323	ANISOTROPIC PLASMA ETCH – OXIDE: IMPLANT As
P+ EXTRINSIC BASE	2.25 (0.09)	1.6 μm/+/TI-323	IMPLANT B
P– INTRINSIC BASE	11.25 (0.45)	1.8 μm/+/TI-323	IMPLANT B
CONTACTS	1.25 (0.05)	1.0 μm/+/TI-323	ANISOTROPIC PLASMA ETCH – OXIDE
1ST METAL	3.0 (0.12)	0.8 μm/–/TI-309	WET ETCH – Al/Cu, TiW
VIAS	1.25 (0.05)	1.2 μm/+/TI-323	ANISOTROPIC PLASMA ETCH – OXIDE
2ND METAL	5.0 (0.2)	1.1 μm/–/TI-309	WET ETCH – Al/Cu, TiW

utilized for patterns with minimum 0.85-μm features; a beam size of ∼2 μm with a scan line spacing of 0.25 μm was used for patterns requiring the least resolution. Although no systematic corrections were made for electron-beam proximity effects, some levels were sized for additional process allowance.

A summary of the SBP9989E electron-beam process flow is given in Table XII. All levels except metal leads were patterned in a positive electron resist (TI-323) capable of 1-μm resolution in 1 μm of resist. Metal patterns were delineated in a negative electron resist (TI-309) capable of 1.25-μm resolution in 0.6 μm of resist. The process made extensive use of high energy and heavy dose ion implants, dry etching, and multilevel interconnect. These process requirements placed stringent demands upon the resists in terms of achieving the required pattern resolution and contrast, minimizing resist ablation during ion implantation or dry etching, and maintaining resist step coverage over difficult topography. A brief discussion of key process steps follows; details of a similar first generation of 1-μm process have been presented elsewhere [20].

Initially, a 1.2-μm thick, 1-Ω · cm As-doped epitaxial layer was grown on a 0.02–0.008-Ω · cm Sb-doped (100) silicon substrate. Electron-beam alignment markers were then patterned and isotropically etched ∼4 μm deep into the silicon substrate using a CF_4/O_2 plasma. Next, active device regions were oxide-separated with a standard recessed oxidation (ROX) technique [23] which was enhanced by anisotropic plasma etches to limit epi-pattern linewidth loss. The 120-nm nitride and 110-nm oxide layers were anisotropically plasma etched in a parallel-plate reactor using a fluorocarbon gas mixture; approximately one-half of the epi-layer was then anisotropically plasma etched in a chlorofluorocarbon gas mixture. The non-undercutting nature of this process was illustrated in Section II. Subsequent field oxidation provided a reasonably planar recessed oxide 1.2 μm thick, as shown in Fig. 40 (oxide regions appear dark in the electronmicrograph). Note that although anisotropic plasma etches can minimize linewidth loss in the original pattern, oxide encroachment or "bird's beak" still limits the available epi-width. As epi-widths continue to shrink, new isolation schemes will be required which eliminate or reduce "bird's beak" and provide a more planar surface for subsequent patterning by eliminating the "bird's crest" as well.

After oxide separation, transistors were formed through a series of implant steps. Collector and resistor were implanted first since the required high-temperature (1000°C) anneals would have driven the extrinsic base too deep and reduced the lateral p-n-p base width as discussed earlier. The arsenic dose of 1.5×10^{15} ions/cm² was too heavy to allow resist masking during collector implant. An oxide mask was formed

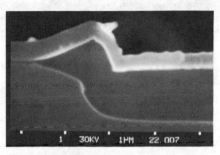

Fig. 40. Electronmicrograph of recessed oxide isolation region in cross section.

by depositing an additional 100-nm-thick plasma oxide onto the original 110-nm-thick thermal oxide buffer layer and anisotropically plasma etching the sandwiched oxides. Afterwards, the plasma oxide was removed by a selective etchback in 1-percent buffered HF and the resistor pattern was anisotropically plasma-etched in the remaining 110 nm of thermal oxide. A dose of 2.3×10^{13} arsenic ions/cm² was implanted and annealed at 1000°C for 10 min to form the required 1-kΩ/□ resistor regions.

A final etchback to silicon and regrowth of a thin 30-nm chlorinated oxide was performed prior to base implantation. All base implants utilized resist masking only, and thick positive TI-323 resist layers were required to effectively mask the high-energy intrinsic base implant and allow for resist ablation during the heavy-dose extrinsic base implant. The high contrast of TI-323 resist was key to forming vertical walls in the thick resist to obtain sharp implant boundaries. The electronmicrograph in Fig. 41 shows a typical TI-323 resist mask for the p⁺ extrinsic base implant. The minimum feature size is 3.5 μm and the resist thickness after develop is ∼1.4 μm.

A double boron implant (1.5×10^{15} ions/cm² at 50 and 70 keV) provided a uniformly doped extrinsic base with a sheet resistance of ∼50 Ω/□. Low base sheets are extremely important since base resistance, along with base–emitter capacitance, play a dominant role in determining the device switching speed. Doubly charged boron was used for the high-energy intrinsic base implant (effectively 1.5×10^{12} ions/cm² at 300 keV) to obtain a sheet resistance of ∼15 kΩ/□. Both base implants were annealed at low temperature to minimize diffusion and control doping profiles. The extrinsic base was initially annealed for 15 min at 900°C;

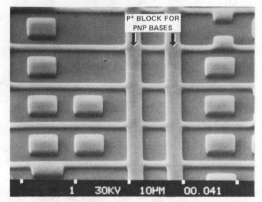

Fig. 41. Electronmicrograph of SBP9989E extrinsic base pattern in TI-323 positive electron resist.

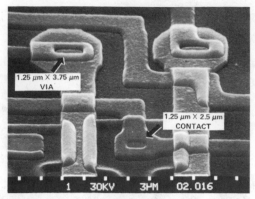

Fig. 43. Electronmicrograph showing typical SBP9989E double-level-metal interconnect structures.

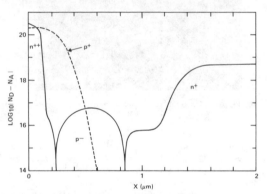

Fig. 42. Calculated vertical n-p-n diffusion profiles for the SBP9989E process (the dashed line indicates the p^+ extrinsic base profile).

low temperatures were also used for the subsequent intrinsic base anneal (30 min at 850°C) and phosphorus stabilization (25 min at 900°C). Calculated vertical diffusion profiles for the scaled n-p-n and extrinsic base are plotted in Fig. 42. Doping levels and implant energies were chosen to optimize the performance of I^2L devices fabricated in 1.2-μm-thick, 1-Ω · cm n-type epitaxial silicon.

Contact and via patterns required the finest pattern resolution. Design rules called for 1.25 μm × 2.5 μm minimum contacts and 1.25 μm × 3.75 μm minimum vias after process. However, these levels were generally undersized by ~0.2 μm per side in the resist pattern to allow for resist edge loss during plasma etching. Both contact and via resist patterns were sloped at approximately 60° to enhance metal-step coverage into the contact, since this slope is replicated in the underlying oxide during plasma etch, as discussed in Section II. Contacts were etched in ~0.25 μm of densified plasma oxide; vias were etched in ~0.6 μm of plasma oxide which was used as the interlevel dielectric between first- and second-metal levels.

Ohmic contacts were formed by Pt deposition and sintering. The unalloyed Pt was removed in aqua regia prior to deposition of the first-metal level which consisted of 175 nm of TiW as a barrier metal and 400 nm of Al 2 percent Cu. Con-

tact resistance was less than 5×10^{-7} Ω · cm², which translates to a specific resistance of 15 Ω for the minimum 1.25 μm × 2.5 μm contacts. The first leads pattern required minimum spaces of approximately 2 μm in 0.6 μm of negative electron resist. After wet etching, final metal widths of 3 μm were achieved with 3.25-μm spaces for a 6.25-μm total first-metal pitch. A 600-nm plasma oxide interlevel dielectric was then deposited and vias were patterned and etched as noted above. The second-metal level consisted of 175 nm of TiW underneath 600 nm of Al 2 percent Cu, and second-metal pitch was a conservative 10 μm, with 5-μm lead width and 5-μm spaces. A typical sample of the SBP9989E double-level-metal (DLM) interconnect is shown in Fig. 43 where minimum 1.25-μm contacts and vias are highlighted.

The isotropic nature of the wet metal etch naturally leads to sloped metal walls which enhance step coverage of subsequent metal levels. However, reducing metal pitch further will require a nonundercutting (dry) metal etch. Anisotropic metal etches lead to vertical walls and require a planarized interlevel dielectric to assure adequate step coverage of subsequent metal levels. Anisotropic etches also require planarized surfaces to limit the amount of overetch required to clear steps, since the vertical etch depth at a step is the material thickness plus the step height, as discussed in Section II. Additional scaling to a 30-percent SBP9989 results in a 3.75-μm first-metal pitch which will no doubt require planarized dielectrics and anisotropic metal etching. An example of how one planarizing technique, bias-sputtered quartz, improves metal-step coverage is illustrated by comparing the standard technique used on the SBP9989E (Fig. 44) with the bias-sputtered quartz interlevel technique shown in Fig. 45.[2]

3) Performance: Scaled SBP9989E's typically operated at twice the speed and half the power of their full-size counterparts. Table XIII summarizes key performance parameters for the SBP9989E and SBP9989. Projected performance parameters are also presented for a 30-percent SBP9989 with self-aligned polysilicon collectors. Using self-aligned structures, I^2L has the potential to rival the speed of present nonsaturating bipolar logic such as STL and ISL [29]. Self-aligned polysilicon

[2] Courtesy of C. R. Fuller and R. L. Love, Advanced Technology Development, Texas Instruments Incorporated.

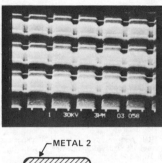

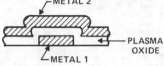

Fig. 44. Electronmicrograph and illustration of second-level metal step coverage over first metal using a plasma oxide interlevel.

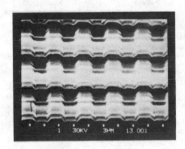

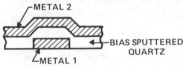

Fig. 45. Electronmicrograph and illustration of second-level metal step coverage over first metal using a bias-sputtered quartz interlevel.

TABLE XIII
PERFORMANCE COMPARISON FOR THE SBP9989, SBP9989E, AND SBP9989E[2]

ITEM	SBP9989	SBP9989E	SELF-ALIGNED
NUMBER OF LEVELS	10	10	9
MINIMUM PATTERN SIZE μm (mil)	4.5 (0.18)	1.25 (0.05)	1 (0.04)
ACTIVE AREA mm^2 (Kmil^2)	37.1 (57.6)	11.2 (17.4)	4.1 (6.4)
GATES PER mm^2 (Kmil^2)	129 (83)	428 (275)	1168 (748)
INTERNAL GATE DELAY @ 100 μA (nsec)	18–20	6–10	2–4*
TYPICAL MAX CLOCK FREQ (MHz)	5.2	10.6	20*
CURRENT (mA) @ 5 MHz CLOCK FREQUENCY	400	67	–
OPEN COLLECTOR OUTPUT SINK CURRENT (mA)	16	5	–
I/O BREAKDOWN (VOLTS)	7.0	6.5	–

*ESTIMATED

collector structures are currently being explored using the 30-percent SBP9989 as a VLSI demonstration vehicle.

Fabricated 50-percent SBP9989's were fully functional over the standard military temperature range of −55°C to +125°C and operated at maximum clock frequencies in excess of 10 MHz. Fig. 46 shows a data bus output and its corresponding address output at a clock frequency of 11 MHz. All outputs required an external pullup resistor to the supply

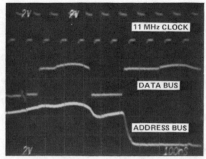

Fig. 46. SBP9989E microprocessor address and data bus outputs at an 11-MHz clock frequency.

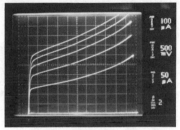

Fig. 47. I–V characteristic for SBP9989E multicollector n-p-n with a fan-out of 4.

voltage. Typically, the scaled chip operated at ∼10 MHz with 250 mA of current as compared to a nominal 5-MHz operation with 500 mA of current for the full-sized chip. At 5 MHz, the SBP9989E required only one-sixth the power of SBP9989. The scaled design was also fully TTL compatible with an open-collector sink current of 5 mA and V_{CEO} breakdowns of greater than 5.5 V at 10 μA. The I–V characteristic of a typical multicollector n-p-n (gate fan-out = 4) is shown in Fig. 47. Ring-oscillator data were previously shown in Fig. 34 for a worst case near base–far collector design; the speed × power product is approximately 0.9 pJ with 50 μA of injection current.

E. Conclusion

Some of the basic scaling issues for bipolar technology have been discussed, followed by a detailed case study in the scaling of complex LSI circuits to VLSI density. The scaling vehicle was a ∼5K gate, 16-bit I^{2}L microprocessor which was linearly scaled by 0.5X using direct electron-beam lithography and generic processes which were developed to support ∼1-μm bipolar circuit fabrication. The lithographic latitude afforded by the electron beam easily coped with submicrometer linewidths and design registration required by the scaled part, thereby demonstrating the technological leverage provided by electron-beam direct-slice writing. The 1-μm bipolar process made extensive use of anisotropic plasma etching, ion implantation, low-temperature processing, and double-level-metal interconnect techniques.

Scaling produced dramatic improvements in performance and reduced active chip area by 70 percent. The SBP9989E microprocessor typically operated at a 10-MHz clock frequency with 250 mA of total current, which corresponds to over twice the nominal frequency and half the power of its full-sized counterpart, the SBP9989. For a chip of the SBP9989E's complexity, the demonstrated improvements in performance and packing density provide a significant step toward the realization of bipolar VLSI circuits.

However, several areas of concern were also noted. Scaling into the submicrometer regime will require additional refinements of the generic 1-μm bipolar process discussed here. Isolation and interconnect processes in particular need considerable improvement to fully leverage a submicrometer patterning capability. Self-aligned structures will ease registration requirements for some levels, but the scaling trend will continue towards tighter design registration tolerances. Future designs will also have to comprehend the limitations of circuits, as contrasted to device, scaling as interconnect time constants become the dominant scaling parameter. In this regard, using advanced lithographic tools such as electron-beam direct writing systems provides valuable insight into future design and process needs for bipolar VLSI.

ACKNOWLEDGMENT

The lithographic, MOS, and bipolar technology developments discussed in this paper involved several groups, each addressing different aspects of the overall VLSI implementation problem. The authors would like to thank

M. Abbott	J. Hebley	G. Pollack
L. Arledge, Jr.	G. Henry	R. Robbins
G. Brown	W. Lee	J. Shu
C. Carpenter	R. Love	R. Smith
R. Chamblee	M. Malone	D. Spicer
J. Covington	G. Merritt	J. Stidham
S. Evans	R. Miller	V. Sutcliffe
C. Fuller	H. Pearce-Percy	C. Winborn

for making key contributions to this effort, and would also like to acknowledge the invaluable technical assistance of all Semiconductor and Research Development Laboratory personnel and management who were involved in this program.

REFERENCES

[1] A. N. Broers, "Resolution, overlay and field-size for lithography systems," in *IEEE IEDM Tech. Dig.*, pp. 2–6, Dec. 1980.

[2] M. Parikh, "Self-consistent proximity-effect correction technique for resist exposure (SPECTRE)," *J. Vac. Sci. Technol.*, vol. 15, no. 3, pp. 931–933, May/June 1979.

[3] M. Hatzakis, "Lithographic processes in VLSI circuit fabrication," *Scanning Electron Microsc.*, vol. I, pp. 275–284, 1979.

[4] ——, "Multilayer resist systems for lithography," *Solid-State Technol.*, vol. 24, no. 8, pp. 74–80, Aug. 1981.

[5] J. M. Moran and D. Maydan, "High resolution, steep profile resist patterns," *J. Vac. Sci. Technol.*, vol. 16, no. 6, pp. 1620–1624, Nov./Dec. 1979.

[6] G. Moore, VLSI "Some fundamental challenges," *IEEE Spectrum*, vol. 6, pp. 30–37, Apr. 1979.

[7] R. H. Dennard, F. H. Gaenselen, H. N. Yu, and V. L. Rideout, "Design of ion implanted MOSFETs with very small physical dimensions," *IEEE J. Solid-State Circuits*, vol. SC-9, pp. 256–268, 1974.

[8] R. D. Pashley et al., "A high performance 4K static RAM fabricated with an advanced MOS technology," in *ISSCC Dig.*, pp. 22–23, Feb. 1977.

[9] R. Jaceman et al., "A 25ns 4K static RAM," in *ISSCC Dig.*, pp. 100–101, Feb. 1979.

[10] P. K. Chatterjee and A. H. Shah, "Enhanced performance of 4 × 1 high speed SRAM," *IEEE J. Solid-State Circuits*, vol. SC-17, p. 330, Apr. 1982.

[11] P. Shah, "Refractory-metal gate processes for VLSI applications," *IEEE Trans. Electron Devices*, vol. ED-26, pp. 361–640, 1979.

[12] Y. A. El Mansy, "On scaling MOS devices for VLSI," in *Proc. IEEE Int. Conf. on Circuits and Computers* (ICCC80), vol. 1, p. 457.

[13] P. Shah, "High performance scaled MOS processes suitable for micron channel VLSI devices," Device Res. Cent., Cornel. Univ., Ithaca, NY, June 1980.

[14] P. Shah, D. Laks, and A. Wilson, "High performance MOS process using polymide interlevel insulation," in *IEEE IEDM Tech. Dig.* (Paper 20.4), p. 465, Dec. 1979.

[15] P. Shah, "Unified device design optimization key to VLSI," *Proc. IEEE Int. Conf. on Circuits and Computer* (ICCC80), vol. 1, p. 446.

[16] S. D. Kang, J. Allen, B. Ashmore, T. H. Herndon, S. Wolpert, and W. Bruncke, "30 nsec, 16KX1, fully static RAM," *IEEE J. Solid-State Circuits*, vol. SC-16, no. 5, p. 444, Oct. 1981.

[17] P. Shah, G. Pollack, G. Varnell, G. Rhodes, D. Kang and W. Bruncke, "A 22 nsec 4K SRAM fabricated with direct electron beam lithography," in *IEEE IEDM Tech. Dig.*, Paper 29.7, p. 776, Dec. 1980.

[18] J. Lohstroh, "Devices and circuits for bipolar (V)LSI," *Proc. IEEE*, vol. 69, pp. 812–826, July 1981.

[19] S. A. Evans, J. L. Bartelt, B. J. Sloan, and G. L. Varnell, "Fabrication of integrated injection logic with electron-beam lithography and ion implantation," *IEEE Trans. Electron Devices*, vol. ED-25, pp. 402–407, Apr. 1978.

[20] S. A. Evans, S. A. Morris, L. A. Arledge, Jr., J. O. Englade, and C. R. Fuller, "A 1-μm bipolar VLSI technology," *IEEE Trans. Electron Devices*, vol. ED-27, pp. 1373–1379, Aug. 1980.

[21] R. H. Havemann, R. L. Smith, S. A. Evans, L. A. Arledge, Jr., R. L. Love, and G. L. Varnell, "Electron-beam fabrication of a 1.25 μm, 16-bit I^2L microprocessor," in *Proc. 16th Symp. on Electron, Ion, and Photon Beam Tech.*, D. R. Herriott and J. H. Bruning, Eds. See also: *J. Vac. Sci. Technol.*, vol. 19, pp. 901–904, Nov./Dec. 1981.

[22] R. H. Havemann, L. A. Arledge, Jr., R. L. Smith, and S. A. Evans, "E-beam fabrication of bipolar VLSI logic, including a ~ 5K gate 16-bit I^2L microprocessor," in *IEEE IEDM Tech. Dig.*, pp. 528–531, Dec. 1981.

[23] E. Bassous, H. N. Yu, and V. Maniscalco, "Topology of silicon structures with recessed SiO_2," *J. Electrochem. Soc.*, vol. 123, pp. 1729–1737, Nov. 1976.

[24] T. Nakamura et al., "Self-aligned transistor with sidewall base electrode," *IEEE Trans. Electron Devices*, vol. ED-29, pp. 596–600, Apr. 1982.

[25] D. D. Tang, V. J. Silvestri, H. N. Yu, and A. Reisman, "A symmetrical bipolar structure," in *IEEE IEDM Tech. Dig.*, pp. 58–60, Dec. 1980.

[26] B. Hoeneisen and C. A. Mead, "Limitations in microelectronics II. Bipolar technology," *Solid-State Electron.*, vol. 15, pp. 891–897, 1972.

[27] K. Okada et al., "PSA—A new approach for bipolar LSI," *IEEE J. Solid-State Circuits*, vol. SC-13, pp. 693–698, Oct. 1978.

[28] T. Sakai et al., "Elevated electrode integrated circuits," *IEEE Trans. Electron Devices*, vol. ED-26, pp. 379–385, Apr. 1979.

[29] D. D. Tang et al., "Subnanosecond self-aligned I^2L/MTL circuits," *IEEE Trans. Electron Devices*, vol. ED-27, pp. 1379–1384, Aug. 1980.

[30] G. L. Varnell, "Electron beam fabrication of high density integrated circuits," presented at the SPE Conf. on Photopolymers—Principles, Processes and Materials, New York, NY, Oct. 1976.

A Systems Approach to 1-μm NMOS

MARTIN P. LEPSELTER, FELLOW, IEEE, DAVID S. ALLES, MEMBER, IEEE,
HYMAN J. LEVINSTEIN, GEORGE ELWOOD SMITH, FELLOW, IEEE, AND
HUGH A. WATSON, SENIOR MEMBER, IEEE

Invited Paper

Abstract—In 1977, groups from diverse disciplines at Bell Labs were brought together for the first time, with the goal of applying a systems approach to high-performance NMOS technology. These groups, namely, solid-state physics, device design, materials, processing, and lithography found a symbiotic relationship that has produced not only NMOS devices with unparalleled performance, but also improved materials, processes, and tools—many of which are in production today.

I. INTRODUCTION

FIVE YEARS AGO, Bell Labs formed the Advanced LSI Development Laboratory, because it was realized that without a major research effort, a production-worthy 1-μm NMOS technology would not evolve from 1977's technology. The new laboratory was staffed with researchers from a wide variety of disciplines so that they could apply a systems approach to the development of a high-performance NMOS intergrated-circuit technology. The new organization combined groups having expertise in solid-state physics; device modeling; device design; materials; chemistry; device processing; electron-beam (E-beam), X-ray, and optical lithography; lithographic equipment development; and analytical techniques.

Although each of these groups existed individually, the new organization represented the first time they were integrated systematically with a common cause and leadership. Initially, each group attacked problems that had to be solved in order to build the next generation of NMOS devices [1].

Starting from first principles, the solid-state physicists and device modelers developed two- and three-dimensional models of NMOS devices and models of the corresponding fabrication processes for these devices.

The device designers developed layout styles to minimize interdevice capacitance and to maximize output current; they also developed device test structures.

The lithographers fine tuned their current E-beam and optical techniques, and developed new E-beam, X-ray, and optical equipment to meet the eventual production requirements of the new devices.

The processing groups developed both the low-temperature device fabrication processes and the high-accuracy pattern transfer techniques needed to fabricate 1-μm devices.

The materials groups developed high-reliability, high-conductivity interconnection materials, while also studying the semiconductor-device failure modes.

Establishing an experimental device-processing line insured

Manuscript received January 31, 1983.
The authors are with Bell Laboratories, Murray Hill, NJ 07974.

that the new device designs, new materials, and new processes actually worked.

The analytical group worked with the just mentioned groups to improve their own understanding of the new materials and processes using Auger electron spectroscopy (AES), scanning-electron microscopy (SEM), transmission-electron microscopy (TEM), etc., techniques.

The solutions to these problems from the various groups were combined and tested on real devices. From these tests, new goals were established to increase device performance and the groups' understanding of the overall device fabrication process.

The synergy that developed among the various groups led to the rapid development of worthwhile ideas and prevented poor ones from being carried too far. In addition, having designers who had to serve real customers present at an experimental processing line kept the activities focused on the development of a manufacturable technology.

The procedure resulted in unexpected payoffs in high-performance NMOS technology. For instance, the development of the three-level resist process for X-ray lithography led to improvements in both optical and E-beam lithography. High-speed NMOS devices made a new approach to high-speed E-beam lithography practical; this approach, in turn, promises to improve device lithography.

The following sections discuss in more detail a few of the developments that resulted from and were made necessary by a "systems" design methodology.

II. MODELING AND DESIGN

To develop an NMOS technology using 1-μm lithography, it was necessary to devise a processing sequence that would produce devices with optimal electrical characteristics. Varying processing steps and making empirical measurements until satisfactory results are achieved is both costly and time consuming. It is far more efficient to explore various process combinations by having accurate numerical simulation models that can be run on a modern computer reasonably quickly. These models also allow a detailed study of the effect of process variations on device behavior.

With large devices, one-dimensional calculations can produce the desired accuracy, and many models are readily available to demonstrate this. At dimensions below about 3 μm, however, edge effects become important [2] and a two-dimensional calculation must be used. Because the complexity of the equations precludes analytical solutions, numerical simulations are required. Existing two-dimensional programs were costly to

Reprinted from *Proc. IEEE*, vol. 71, pp. 640–656, May 1983.

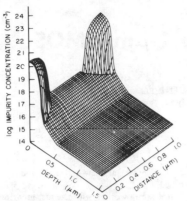

Fig. 1. Net impurity concentration versus dimension for an enhancement-mode device. The gate length is 1 μm.

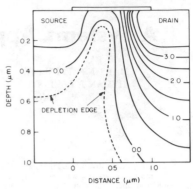

Fig. 2. Potential distribution for an enhancement-mode device. The bias conditions are: $V_{gs} = 0.6$ V (threshold), $V_{ds} = 3$ V (V_{dd}), and $V_{bs} = 0$. The impurity profile in Fig. 1 is used in the simulation.

run and their results were inaccurate; therefore, new ones were developed. These were a two-dimensional process model and two- and three-dimensional electrical models.

A. Process Modeling

The device fabrication sequence involves more than 100 processing steps, and although every step is necessary, only a few directly influence the transistor's performance. These are the ones that the process-modeling computer program simulates to determine the oxide thicknesses and impurity distributions within the NMOS transistor. These quantities are calculated using a mathematical model of the device-fabrication process in which the times, temperatures, and ambients of furnace steps; the energies and doses of ion implantations; substrate doping; and device geometry are all considered. The device structure predicted by the modeling program is then used as input for the electrical characterization program. Several problems arose when adapting the then existing diffusion models in SUPREM to the two-dimensional diffusion program. As a result, new physical models for both boron and arsenic diffusion had to be devised to fit the experimental data [3]. Also, the existing computational method for two-dimensional diffusion at a mask edge was replaced by one with greater accuracy and lower cost [4]. Fig. 1 shows the impurity concentration plotted as a function of dimension for a typical depletion-mode device having been modeled with nominal processing conditions. The gate length is 1 μm, resulting in a channel length of 0.6 μm.

B. Electrical Modeling

The structure resulting from the process-modeling program is now used as input to the electrical-modeling program [5] in which voltages are applied to source, gate, drain, and substrate, and the resulting current is calculated. The equations necessary to describe the devices are sets of nonlinear elliptic partial-differential equations. A finite-difference method was chosen using a nonuniform mesh [6]. The modeling programs were implemented using a CRAY-1 computer that incorporates such features as a first-principles (electron) mobility model in which velocity saturation and perpendicular-field dependence are included as well as avalanche effects. These high-field effects be-

come increasingly important as devices shrink, because the device's operating voltages cannot be reduced in direct proportion to the device dimensions without incurring serious signal-to-noise problems. Fig. 2 shows the potential distribution in a device made with a 1-μm gate when a gate voltage ($V_g = 0.6$ V) and drain voltage ($V_d = 3$ V) are then applied. The resulting electron current density and lateral electric field are shown in Figs. 3 and 4. Fig. 5 shows a comparison of the calculated current–voltage curves and the corresponding experimental results. The subthreshold[1] region is chosen for comparison since this is the region most sensitive to short-channel effects. To assure the correctness of the physical models, we made many comparisons between the results of actual process steps and the results of the simulations. The level of agreement between the model and experimental results allowed the computer-aided design of the total process to be a viable and economical approach to the design of a device. In addition to improving the accuracy of the device modeling, the new computer program [7] reduced the cost of calculating the current (I) versus voltage (V) characteristics for a transistor from several hundred dollars to about two dollars per "IV" point. This cost reduction was made possible by the use of advanced numerical analysis techniques and the parallel-processing capabilities of the CRAY-1 computer.

C. Scaling Law

Many processing variations were investigated as a function of gate length in order to make the best compromise between electrical characteristics and processing difficulty. In the course of this investigation, a generalized scaling law was discovered [8] and is plotted in Fig. 6. In this plot, $L_{\min}$ is the minimum channel length for which long-channel behavior will be observed. X_j is the junction depth, t_{ox} is the oxide thickness, and W_s and W_d are the source and drain depletion depths.

---

[1] In this subthreshold region, the drain current I_d for a long-channel NMOS transistor varies exponentially with gate-to-source voltage and shows no dependence on drain voltage V_d. Short-channel effects occur when the electric field in the channel is no longer dominated by the gate-to-source voltage but is also influenced by the drain bias voltage. In this case, the drain current is increased for a given gate voltage, and in the limiting case the transistor cannot be turned off.

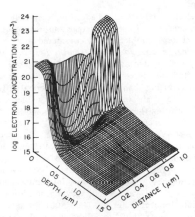

Fig. 3. Electron density distribution for the same bias conditions as in Fig. 2.

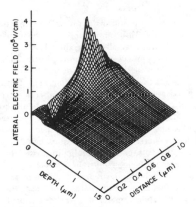

Fig. 4. Lateral electric field distribution for the same bias conditions. The lateral field reaches the maximum value near the drain contact below the interface. ($E_{max} = 2.7 \times 10^5$ V/cm.)

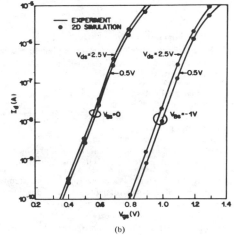

(a)

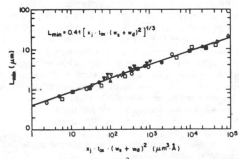

(b)

Fig. 5. Comparison of simulated and experimental current–voltage curves for an enhancement device with a gate length of 1 μm. The saturation region is shown in (a) and the subthreshold region in (b).

Long-channel behavior is taken to mean a sharp cutoff in the subthreshold region with no punchthrough at high-drain voltages. This scaling law is less restrictive than others that scale physical quantities by constant factors; this means that there is a wider range of processing choices.

Although the two-dimensional model is accurate for wide transistors (in NMOS transistor terminology the term channel length refers to the distance the electrons must flow under the gate region and wide/narrow refers to the dimension of the device perpendicular to the current-flow direction), for narrow ones a three-dimensional model is required. A three-dimensional model is particularly important for minimum-geometry CMOS and depletion-load devices. Three-dimensional simulation is an inherently costly calculation, so that care was taken to use the most efficient numerical methods. Even so, the resulting cost for one current-voltage point was approximately 200 dollars.

The major conclusion drawn from this study [9] is that minimum-geometry devices cannot be described by a two-deminsional calculation below about 2 μm. This is illustrated in Fig. 7 where two- and three-dimensional calculations are com-

pared against experimental results. The three-dimensional calculation continues to fit the data accurately after the two-dimensional calculation shows significant departures from the data (note that the current axis is a log scale).

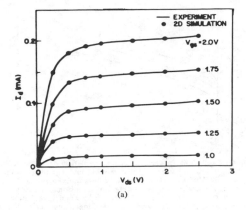

Fig. 6. L_{min} versus $[X_j t_{ox}(W_s + W_d)^2]$. Points are values obtained from two-dimensional computer calculations. The straight line of slope (1/3) is the predicted value using the equation in the figure. The open symbols are simulations and the closed ones are experimental.

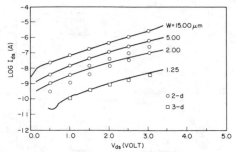

Fig. 7. Drain current I_d versus V_{ds} for a depletion device with a gate length of 1 μm and four different gate widths. The bias conditions are $V_{gs} = -2$ V, $V_{bs} = -1$ V. The solid lines are experimental curves and the circles are the corresponding two-dimensional calculations. It is seen that the two lower plots for 2 and 1.25 μm depart significantly from experiment. The squares are three-dimensional calculations for the 1.25-μm gate width.

III. MATERIALS AND PROCESSING

The results of the electrical- and process-modeling studies lead to a materials and processing "wish list" that included the following characteristics:

High-conductivity silicides
Electromigration-resistant metals
An understanding of device failure mechanisms
Low-temperature processing
High-fidelity pattern-transfer techniques
Equipment that makes the new materials and processes compatible with the integrated circuit (IC) production line.

This phase of the fine-line NMOS development program was carried out by several groups working together to develop new materials and processes. By continually sharing information, discoveries by one group were quickly utilized by all the others. Our small experimental device-processing line [10] became an integral part of this activity. (It was capable of starting one twenty-wafer-lot per week with a minimum turnaround time of five weeks.) This processing line provided the groups with an opportunity to test the equipment, materials, and fabrication processes that they developed on real circuits. Without this line, the development process would have gone on as though in a vacuum, and processes and materials might have been developed to solve nonexistent problems.

The value of a systems approach to developing materials and processes for the manufacture of IC's will be demonstrated by the following discussion. By systems approach we mean that all aspects of the circuit's design, manufacture, testing, and eventual use must be considered when a new material is developed, or when a fabrication process is changed. The complications that can arise from apparently simple requests to increase packing density, maintain shallow junctions, or reduce the interconnection resistance will be discussed in the following paragraphs.

Maximizing the Device Packing Density: To maximize packing density means that every level of the device will contain minimum-sized features. It also means that the pattern transfer process must transfer the mask's features into all the underlying semiconductor materials reliably and without altering the feature size. These constraints require vertical feature edges, thus prohibiting the tapering of windows and oxide walls. Without this tapering, the field oxide cannot be gener-

ated by selective oxidation. In addition, steep-walled features create problems in both step coverage and in subsequent pattern transfer steps—problems to be considered later.

Maintaining Shallow Junctions (Depths Less than 0.3 μm): These very shallow depths limit the maximum processing temperature after the source and drain implantation to $\leqslant 950°C$. Temperatures higher than this will cause thermal diffusion of the source and drain impurities, thereby reducing channel lengths and causing the devices to be short circuited or to exhibit short-channel characteristics [8].

Reducing the Interconnection Resistance: The decrease in the gate width to 1 μm and requirement of shallow junctions (dictating a change from phosphorus- to arsenic-doped polysilicon for the polycon contacts) results in excessive interconnection resistances. Therefore, a new interconnect metallization at the gate level was needed, as was a new low-resistance top-level interconnect material. The resulting top-level aluminum metallization exhibited two deficiencies: electromigration as the linewidth was reduced to 1 μm, and poor step coverage as the contact windows were reduced to 1 μm.

A. Pattern-Transfer Processes

The goal of the pattern-transfer-process development effort was to achieve the faithful reproduction of the mask's pattern on the wafer's surface at all lithographic levels. In the past, the pattern-transfer processes frequently resulted in linewidths on the wafer that were either larger or smaller (depending on the process used) than the corresponding mask feature. This inaccuracy was corrected by making a compensatory change in the linewidths on the mask. However, on circuits containing 1-μm-wide lines, it is no longer practical to alter the mask's linewidths because either the lines or the spaces between them will disappear. Therefore, the masks must be fabricated with the desired linewidths, and the etching processes that transfer these lines into the silicon must be completely anisotropic. They must also etch the desired material more rapidly than either the masking layer on the wafer's surface or the stopping layer below the etched material. Any deviation from pure anisotropy results in a change in linewidth, particularly where the depth of the etched layer is not uniform.

However, even with an anisotropic etching process, there are other problems. Erosion of the top masking layer results in a change in linewidth even if the etching process is totally anisotropic. Thus the relative etch rates must be very different for the etched layer and the resist layer, and for the etched layer and the underlying (or stopping) layer. The latter is important because over-etching is frequently necessary to assure that the etched layer is completely removed in areas where it may be thicker, for example along the edges of steps.

This relative etch ratio is referred to as selectivity and is defined as the ratio of the etch rate of the desired material to the etch rate of the other material. The selectivity requirement of the etching process to the stopping or underlying layer depends on the specific process. As an example, etching a thick polysilicon layer (5000 Å) over a thin gate oxide (250 Å) requires an etch rate ratio of polysilicon to SiO_2 of greater than 25:1, while etching thin polysilicon (3000 Å) over the intermediate dielectric oxide (1 μm) requires a selectivity of about 1. Because there were no commercially available processes or equipment that fulfilled our requirements, we developed the reactive sputter etching process.

1) Reactive Sputter Etching: The pattern transfer development program started by studying and evaluating plasma etch-

Fig. 8. Prototype of the multifacet RSE reactor. The wafers are held on vertical trays that form the RF excited electrode.

ing (the best dry-etching process available at the time), and then by developing the reactive sputter etching (RSE) process. Plasma-etching processes are performed in parallel-plate reactors in which the wafers rest horizontally on the lower, grounded electrode, and the similarly sized upper electrode is excited at radio frequencies (RF). The gas, at between 0.1 and 1.0 torr, is ionized at the RF-excited electrode and the chemical (as opposed to mechanical) action of the positive ions and neutrals etches the wafer.

Our initial plasma-etching processes produced anisotropic etching profiles, but these processes lacked the necessary selectivity to the underlying layer. As a result, parametric etching studies were initiated in parallel-plate reactors in which the pressure, power, RF, reactor geometry, and so on, were varied. Optimal etching results were obtained when the wafers were held on the driven electrode (which was smaller in area than the grounded electrode), and when the pressure in the reactor was 0.005 to 0.05 torr. We now refer to this process as reactive sputter etching (RSE) [11]. In this etching process, the positive ions are accelerated by the RF field against the wafer's surface. Both chemical and mechanical actions contribute to the etching process.

Efficient, highly selective RSE processes were developed in a parallel-plate reactor for etching SiO_2, doped and undoped polysilicon, aluminum, and tantalum silicide ($TaSi_2$). However, the parallel-plate reactor configuration was not amenable to large batch processing because the wafers were arrayed over the surface of the smaller, horizontal electrode. As a result, when this design was enlarged to accept production quantities of large-diameter wafers it occupied too much expensive VLSI clean room floor space.

2) The Multifacet Reactor: An equipment-development project was initiated to design a production RSE etcher [12], called a multifacet reactor, that would take advantage of the new processes, while minimizing the power and floor space requirements. The new system has a central RF-driven electrode and a concentric bell jar that serves as the grounded electrode. The prototype of this system is shown in Fig. 8. Because the wafers are arrayed vertically, rather than horizontally, the floor space requirements are minimized. To begin processing, the wafers are automatically loaded into the trays from cassettes. The trays are then transferred to the etcher and attached to the central electrodes by an operator. The multi-

facet system has a number of other attributes including:

A large throughput of wafers per unit of floor space

A symmetrical arrangement of wafers in the electrical field results in excellent wafer-to-wafer uniformity

A more efficient use of power

Automated wafer handling

The ability either to increase the number of wafers per run, or to etch larger wafers by minor mechanical modifications

Wafers in the reactor oriented vertically to minimize particulate contamination on the wafer

Wafers that face radially outward visible through quartz windows in the bell jar; this makes optical end-point detection practical.

The results of this system on the production line have been so favorable that it has been licensed to a number of commercial equipment manufacturers [13].

B. Low-Temperature Processing

The electrical modeling results indicated that in gates with 0.5-μm channel lengths, the junctions must be no deeper than 0.25 μm in order to maintain long-channel behavior. This requirement had profound effects on the entire processing sequence. For instance, it limited the maximum processing temperature after the source and drain implantation to 950°C because the higher temperatures resulted in the thermal diffusion of the source and drain regions, thereby obliterating the 1-μm channel.

Eliminating high temperatures, in turn, prevented the common practice of flowing the P-glass to reduce the steep-edged topography on the device's surface. Without this high-temperature flow step, subsequent depositions might not cover these steps completely or reliably, resulting in open circuits. The problem was made more serious by the extremely steep profiles that result from the reactive sputter etching process described above. Therefore, it was necessary to develop both new conformal deposition techniques and new planarizing techniques.

1) P-Glass Planarization: The integrated circuit fabrication process is a sequence of material depositions followed by the etching of selected areas. The result is a bumpy surface topography that succeeding depositions must cover uniformly. Because this has not been easy, various approaches have been developed to reduce the steepness of (planarize) the surface features. In the conventional process, the intermediate dielectric is a phosphorus-doped SiO_2 (P-glass) deposited at low temperature (300–400°C). It is then heated to temperatures as high as 1100°C to cause the glass to flow. The purpose of this flow step is to eliminate the reentrant steps that occur on the surface during the P-glass deposition process. A cross section through a P-glass layer as it crosses a step is shown in Fig. 9(a). The subsequent metallization layers cannot cover this structure and the result will be open circuits. Therefore, a process had to be developed to achieve structures that were flatter than could be obtained by flowing the glass as shown in Fig. 9(b), and that did not involve high-temperature processing.

The solution involved two components: the development of a more conformal[2] P-glass coating and a new method of planarizing the coating. The improved conformal coating technique used a higher temperature chemical vapor deposition

[2] Conformal coatings have a uniform thickness over all of the wafer's surface topography including the sides of steps and the bottoms of trenches.

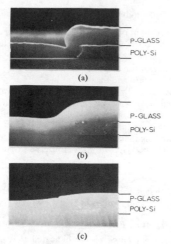

Fig. 9. (a) P-glass as-deposited at low temperatures. (b) Surface resulting from 1100°C flow process. (c) Surface after plasma planarization.

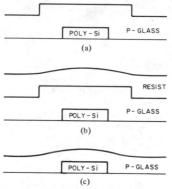

Fig. 10. (a) The plasma planarization process: as-deposited conformal P-glass layer. (b) The thick resist layer planarizes the surface. (c) The resulting planarized surface after plasma etching the resist and P-glass.

(CVD) process for P-glass deposition. The rationale was that most high-temperature deposition processes tend to give conformal coatings because of the increased surface mobility that comes with an increase in temperature.

A low-pressure CVD process using tetraethylortho-silicate (TEOS) as the source material and phosphine as the dopant solved the problem. The deposition temperature here was 700°C and the process produced conformal coatings. However, the conformal coating alone was not enough. All the steps in the structure generated prior to the deposition of the P-glass had vertical walls and thus the structure after P-glass depostion contained steep profiles that made step coverage of the subsequent metal layer difficult (see Fig. 10(a)).

2) Plasma Planarization: In order to smooth the structure further, a process called plasma planarization was developed [14]. First, the wafer to be planarized is coated with a polymer layer that is thick enough to result in a smooth surface, as shown in Fig. 10(b). The sample wafer is then etched in a plasma which has an equal etch rate for the resist and the P-glass, thus transferring the planarized surface into the P-glass layer. The surfaces obtained by this process are much flatter than those achieved by glass flow (as shown in Fig. 9(c)) thereby simplifying both the window and metal-level lithographies.

3) Conformal Conductors: The next step in the wafer-fabrication process that is changed by the low-temperature requirement is the formation of the contact after window etching. In our process, the windows have vertical walls resulting from the RSE process. In the conventional NMOS process, these steep profiles would be removed by flowing the P-glass at a high temperature to assure continuity of the window conductor across the steep step.

However, the proscription against high-temperature processes (above 950°C) again prevented the use of the reflow process. The solution involved a dual metallization consisting first of doped polysilicon followed by aluminum. The polysilicon deposition has the additional advantage of being conformal and of assuring electrical continuity in the structure. It also satisfies the solubility limit for silicon in aluminum everywhere, thereby preventing the spiking in shallow junctions normally associated with aluminum window contacts.

C. Low-Resistivity Interconnections

The device-modeling studies that we have discussed thus far demonstrate that as device geometries shrink, the interconnection resistance and capacitance increase. This is a consequence of the conductors becoming smaller and more closely spaced. The edges of these conductors, now no longer thin when compared to their width, also contribute significantly to the overall capacitance. Any increase in the resistance–capacitance (RC) time constant will limit the ultimate circuit performance. This places a premium not only on careful design layouts that reduce capacitance, but also on reliable low-resistivity interconnection material systems. The materials chosen must be compatible with existing device materials and processing; they must also be reliable under high current densities, even after years of service at high temperatures.

In addition, device reliability played a major role in the selection of interconnection materials both at the window level and at the second (interconnection) level. For instance, silicon is soluble in aluminum at elevated temperatures. To satisfy this solubility requirement, the aluminum conductors on large-geometry devices were, in the past, either codeposited with silicon or were allowed to dissolve the silicon from the deep junction. In fine-line devices, the windows are small (1 μm^2) and the junctions are shallow (0.25 μm). The resulting volume of silicon is insufficient to reliably satisfy the solubility requirement for either pure aluminum or for the aluminum codeposited with silicon. For the second-level interconnection, the materials have been predominantly metals. However, metals have suffered from reliability problems resulting from the electromigration of the materials (notably aluminum) when they are subjected to high current densities at elevated temperatures [15].

1) Interconnection at the Gate Level: The various groups recognized early in the program that fine-line, high-speed devices will require lower resistivity interconnects at the gate level than can be obtained with polysilicon alone. Therefore, we initiated a program to develop a replacement for the poly gate. Circuit modeling dictated a gate structure having a resistivity of 2 Ω/sq (which could be manufactured with little or no change in the production line's post-gate-formation processes).

These requirements led to the use of a two-layer gate structure. The lower (first) layer is polysilicon and the second layer is a metal silicide. This structure enables us to take advantage of the excellent MOS stability of the polysilicon gate, and to achieve a high-conductivity interconnection through the use of a metal silicide.

A number of metal silicides were made and their properties evaluated. The criteria used to evaluate them include the following:

Resistivity
Stress in the as-deposited and sintered film
The ability to be etched in plasma
Crystal structure
High-temperature stability in oxidizing and reducing ambients.

Two silicides, tantalum silicide ($TaSi_2$) having a resistivity of $\leqslant 50$ $\mu\Omega \cdot$ cm and titanium silicide ($TiSi_2$) having a resistivity of $\leqslant 20$ $\mu\Omega \cdot$ cm, were selected from this initial survey as the most promising materials. These two silicides were then evaluated for their compatibility with NMOS processing steps that follow gate formation. Both films were found to retain their structural integrity and their low resistivity throughout the processing sequence; however, $TiSi_2$ was unstable in the presence of any solution containing HF (hydrofluoric acid). Eliminating HF would have required major changes in the processing; as a result, $TaSi_2$ was chosen as the interconnection material.

Silicides can be formed by depositing a metal on silicon and then heating the structure. At a temperature specific to the particular silicide involved, the metal disilicide MSi_2 will form. A second available process is to codeposit the metal (M) and silicon in the ratio of MSi_2. Because the as-deposited material has the right composition but not the desired silicide crystal structure, it must be sintered at a high temperature.

What we have learned from this study has been published in a series of papers describing the use of $TaSi_2$ as a gate material for CMOS [15], as well as its oxidation characterization [16], MOS compatibility, and kinetics of formation [17]. Murarka [18] has written a book on the properties of these metal silicides that will soon be published.

2) Second-Level Interconnection: Very-Large-Scale Integration (VLSI) entails the integration of an increasing number of functions on a single chip. Because the chip's surface area is frequently dominated by the area required for interconnection metallization, it is quite important to reduce conductor linewidths and spacings. When reduced chip size is combined with an increased number of circuit functions, the maximum allowable chip temperature will limit the maximum clock rate because power dissipation increases with clock rate.

The pressures to reduce linewidth and to increase clock rates make the interconnection metallization an important reliability issue. Both the increased current density in the smaller conductors and the increased chip temperature promote electromigration-induced open circuits in the aluminum runners and contacts. Moreover, shallow junctions together with smaller contact geometries increase the susceptibility to junction leakage due to the dissolution of the silicon into the aluminum and the electromigration of the aluminum into the resulting void. This is called "aluminum spiking." In view of these concerns, a research program was set up to evaluate different aluminum metallization schemes, and to produce a metallization system that results in a failure rate of less than 100 FITS (device failures per 10^9 device hours) for devices designed with 1-μm conductors.

To prevent junction shorts caused by the preferential dissolution of silicon into aluminum, it was necessary to use either an aluminum–silicon (Al–Si) alloy metallization, or a sacrificial

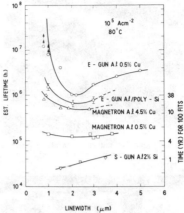

Fig. 11. Electromigration lifetimes of aluminum conductors.

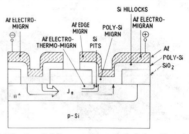

Fig. 12. Schematic of failure modes and their locations in Al/poly-Si interconnect/contact structure.

diffusion barrier of CVD polysilicon between the aluminum and the diffused silicon substrate. The former approach was investigated [15] by using sputter-deposited Al–Si alloy because this process offers the advantage of precise composition control. However, the electromigration resistance of sputtered aluminum/silicon alloy (S-gun Al 2 percent Si) films proved to be inadequate, as illustrated in Fig. 11. The second approach used a diffusion barrier of polysilicon; it was evaluated and met the electromigration requirements. These results are shown in Fig. 11 on the curve "E-gun Al/poly-Si." Although this n^+ polysilicon layer lowers the electromigration lifetime of the E-gun-evaporated aluminum/copper alloy (Al 0.5 percent Cu) by a factor of 2, this composite was chosen for our fine-line NMOS process because of its superior step coverage and diffusion barrier properties.

Our generic reliability studies of aluminum/polysilicon contact and interconnects indicate that this composite is susceptible to several failure modes as identified in Fig. 12:

Conventional electromigration of aluminum in runners as well as at contacts
Electromigration of silicon from the polysilicon into aluminum at positively biased windows
Electromigration of silicon from diffused regions under the contact, resulting in junction leakage the growth of silicon dissolution pits
Catastrophic junction breakdown by Al–Si eutectic electrothermomigration.

These failure modes are illustrated in Figs. 13 and 14.

Fig. 13. SEM micrograph of failure in Al/poly-Si interconnect due to electromigration.

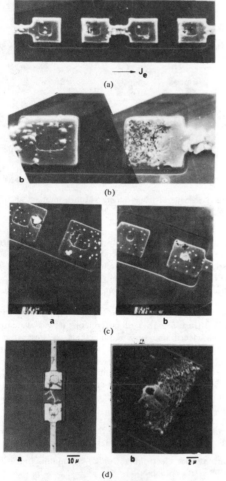

(a)

(b)

(c)

(d)

Fig. 14. (a) Contact electromigration at alternating "+" windows. (b) Void formation in aluminum at "+" window. (c) Poly-Si depletion at large "+" and window, uniform silicon precipitation at 1-μm window. (d) Electrothermomigration of aluminum starting from junction starting at "+" windows.

Electromigration in aluminum runners and contacts is activated both by current density and temperature. For aluminum runners, the median lifetime t_{50} follows the relationship

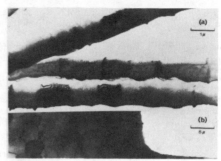

Fig. 15. Bamboo-like arrangement of (111) oriented grains in 1-μm-wide aluminum conductor.

$$t_{50} = AJ^{-2} \exp(E_a/k_T) \tag{1}$$

where E_a is the thermal activation energy for grain boundary diffusion (in aluminum, $E_a = 0.55$ eV), J is the current density, and A is a structural parameter that depends on conductor geometry and film microstructure. For films of the same composition, this parameter can be quantitatively correlated to both the grain size and its variance, as well as to the degree of (111) crystal orientation within the film.

Because electromigration failures nucleate at points of flux divergence, conductor lifetimes are expected to decrease linearly with linewidth as a result of the conductor's increased microstructural inhomogeneity across its width. While such a correlation is valid for widths >1 μm, 1-μm-wide (E-gun Al 0.5 percent Cu) lines have been fabricated having lifetimes longer than the 5-μm lines of the same material (Fig. 11). This increase in lifetime at narrow linewidths can be attributed to a bamboo arrangement of (111) oriented grains along the entire length, as illustrated in Fig. 15.

3) Contact Electromigration: For contact electromigration, the current activation is proportional to I^{-10}, where I is the current. This is indicative of steep temperature gradients in the vicinity of the contacts. Our studies indicate that the thermal-activation energy associated with this failure mode is 0.9 eV, corresponding to the diffusion of silicon along aluminum grain boundaries. The process is therefore a function of interconnect aluminum grain size and film thickness.

A decrease in contact size or an increase in junction depth x_j increases the uniformity in the current-density profile across the window, and in turn, the uniformity of the polysilicon depletion from the positively biased window. Lifetimes are found to scale as the square of s_j in the range of 0.1 to 1.5 μm, where s_j is the sum of the polysilicon thickness and the junction depth at the contact. An aluminum head surrounding the window serves to back-fill the electromigrated aluminum over the positive contact, thus preventing the windows from becoming discontinuous along the sidewalls.

Despite these failure modes, it has been confirmed that for the composite Al/poly-Si interconnect–contact system, conductor failures will be open circuits in the runners, unless current densities are increased well beyond the present design rules of 10^5 A/cm² as shown in Fig. 16.

IV. X-RAY LITHOGRAPHY

In 1977, our lithographic activities centered around the use of E-beam and X-ray lithography. The former is a pattern-generation technology and the latter a pattern-transfer technology. Although E-beam lithography can be used for direct

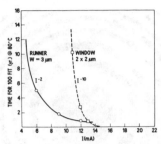

Fig. 16. The relative electromigration lifetimes for Al/poly-Si runners and contacts.

wafer pattern writing, it is relatively slow; therefore, we have considered E-beam and X-ray to be complementary rather than competitive methods.

In 1975, the E-beam pattern-generator development groups began licensing the Electron Beam Exposure System (EBES) [19] pattern generators through Western Electric. These machines produce all of the Bell Labs and Western Electric photo and X-ray masks and are used worldwide for mask making. Following EBES, this group embarked on the development of a more sophisticated pattern generator to support an anticipated need for a patterning system with higher resolution and throughput.

X-ray lithography appeared to have promise as a submicron pattern-transfer technology; however, there were many questions that had to be answered before X-ray wafer printing could be put into production. These questions concerned mask distortion, defect density, mask level to mask level re-registration capability, and throughput. Even in its early stages of development, X-ray lithography demonstrated that it could print the 1-μm patterns needed for the device characterization and process development phases of the fine-line NMOS program.

Therefore, a program to develop an X-ray printing capability was initiated. Its short-term goal was to provide high-quality 1-μm lithography for small test circuits; its long-term goal was to develop the components required for a production lithography tool [20] capable of accurately aligning and printing VLSI devices with micron or submicron features. X-ray lithography was expected to have advantages over both the industry-standard optical lithography and the high-resolution E-beam pattern generators in the following areas;

Increased throughput by parallel exposure: Since X-ray lithography uses masks, all of the patterns on the mask are transferred to the wafer at the same time, as opposed to the serial approach of E-beam pattern generation where each feature is written sequentially. This gives X-ray printers a throughput of many wafers per hour.

Improved control of diffraction effects: The X-ray wavelength is short (about 4 Å) when compared with the normal ultraviolet light (about 4000 Å) used for optical printing. Therefore, the diffraction effects that plague fine-line optical lithography are not applicable in X-ray lithography.

Minimized feature broadening due to electron scattering: When X-rays interact with resist molecules, the X-rays generate low-energy electrons; it is these electrons that actually cause the exposure. Because the electron energies are relatively low (0 to 2.5 keV), their scattering range is small, and the exposed feature size is nearly equal to the mask feature. In contrast,

E-beam pattern generators use relatively high-energy electrons (about 20 kV); and these electrons have a scattering range in resist of several micrometers. The scattering of these electrons into the unexposed area surrounding the pattern degrades the feature edge definition and is referred to as the proximity effect.

Relative simplicity of X-ray equipment: X-ray printing equipment is comparable in complexity to an optical near-contact printer, but is capable of much better resolution. X-ray printing equipment is also relatively simple and inexpensive when compared to an E-beam pattern generator with similar resolution.

Our approach was to develop an X-ray near-contact printer in which the mask-to-wafer spacing is no more than 40 μm, with the mask illuminated by a point source of X-rays from a palladium target. Those X-rays that pass through "transparent" areas on the mask expose the X-ray-sensitive resist on the wafer's surface. The following criteria guided the development of this lithography system:

Source wavelength and brightness: The X-ray-source wavelength must be long enough to be absorbed by the resist and short enough to pass through the "clear" areas of the mask. In addition, the source must be bright enough to expose an entire wafer in several minutes and require little maintenance.

Automated wafer handling: The exposure tool must provide automated wafer handling, mask-to-wafer alignment, and protection for the operator from X-ray exposure.

High-quality mask characteristics: The mask must have good contrast (the ratio of X-ray transmission through the "clear" to the transmission through the absorber) and be dimensionally stable. That is, nonhomogeneous in-plane distortions must be less than 0.1 μm over a 75-mm diameter. Optical transparency is valuable (if not essential) to the printing process to allow for mask-to-wafer optical alignment.

High-quality resist characteristics: The resist used in the X-ray printing process must have good resolution, a low defect density, be sensitive to the exposing X-ray wavelength, have good adhesion, and have good dry-etching resistance.

A. The Exposure Tool

X-ray exposure tools [21] similar to the one shown in Fig. 17 have been in daily use since 1980 for the patterning of 1-μm devices. These computer-controlled tools were designed to provide both a fine-line device patterning capability and a test bed for further development of the X-ray sources, masks, and resists. The relative locations of the X-ray source, the mask, and the silicon wafer during exposure and mask-to-wafer alignment are shown schematically in Fig. 18.

The space between the beryllium window of the source and the mask is filled with helium at room pressure, since air is a great absorber of X-rays. The 40-μm space between the mask and the silicon wafer is filled with a mixture of nitrogen and 0.3 percent oxygen [22]. The latter mixture is injected between mask and wafer during X-ray exposure to improve the resolution of the X-ray resist.

The mask and wafer are mounted on a platform or stage which, in turn, is mounted on a horizontal track. Loading and unloading the mask and wafer as well as aligning the mask to the wafer are done with the stage at the specified alignment position (see Fig. 18); exposure then takes place with the stage beneath the X-ray source.

The wafer is held on a pin chuck [23] that reliably flattens the back of the wafer to within 1 μm. This is important be-

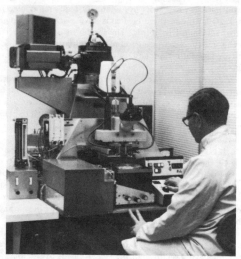

Fig. 17. X-ray exposure machine.

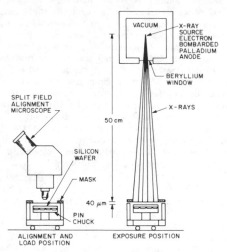

Fig. 18. X-ray system schematic.

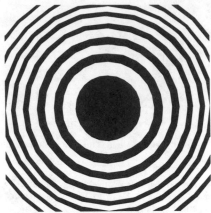

Fig. 19. Zone plate etched in polysilicon.

cause it minimizes the in-plane distortion of the wafer due to warping, and assures that the wafer will be clamped flat at every lithography step. During exposure, the area surrounding the mask, wafer, and source is enclosed in an X-ray shield.

A new alignment system had to be devised for the X-ray printer since the mask and wafer planes are separated by 40 μm, and the depth of focus of suitable microscopes is only 1 to 2 μm. Without an imaging system that produces clear, well-focused images at high magnification simultaneously in both the mask and wafer planes, the submicron registration necessary for fine-line device patterning is impossible.

Our approach [24] uses a conventional Zeiss split-field alignment microscope modified to focus simultaneously in both the mask and wafer planes. This is accomplished by a birefringent (refractive index dependent on polarization) lens element in each objective that is in focus in the wafer plane, for light of

one polarization, and in the mask plane, for light of the opposite polarization. Although this system has allowed us to fabricate well-aligned devices, it is difficult for the operator to resolve 0.25-μm registration errors. As a result, other approaches are being developed to satisfy our long-term need for a fully automatic, 0.1-μm X-ray mask-to-wafer alignment.

B. Zone-Plate Registration System

Recent studies into ways to improve alignment accuracy in X-ray printing have involved the use of zone plates [25] on the mask and wafer. A zone plate (shown in Fig. 19) is a series of concentric rings that act as a lens through the diffraction of light. When a zone plate is placed on the mask or wafer and illuminated by a parallel light beam, it will produce both a real and a virtual image of the illuminating source. This has several processing advantages which are described as follows:

Resistance to defects: Because the device image is formed by the diffraction of light from the entire area of the zone plate, small defects in the zone plate only reduce the contrast of the focused spot, but do not alter its location.

Correction for mask-to-wafer separation: Because the zone plate is a lens, its focal length can be adjusted to compensate for the 40-μm separation between the mask and wafer. Our approach is to make the focal length of the wafer zone plate 340 μm and the mask zone plate 300 μm. As a result, both plates focus the incident light at the same elevation.

In our system, the mask and wafer zone plates are illuminated by a collimated laser beam; each zone plate focuses the laser beam to a small spot, as shown in Fig. 20(a). The zone plate on the mask has a focal length 40 μm less than the corresponding zone plate on the wafer; thus the images produced are in focus at the same elevation. In addition, the angle of illumination is chosen so that the chief (central) ray points toward the X-ray source. As a result of this inclination, uniform magnification errors (such as those resulting from changes in the temperature of the wafer) can be detected, and the error can be corrected by altering the separation of mask and wafer until the focused spots from both sides of the mask and wafer align. This process is illustrated in Fig. 20(a) and (b). This alignment can be done automatically by an image-processing system that determines the relative positions of the focused spots from the mask and wafer. This system brings the mask and wafer into alignment in the X, Y, θ, and Z directions by

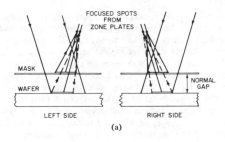

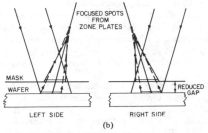

Fig. 20. The mask and wafer zone plates focus at the same elevation. By adjusting the mask relative to the wafer in X, Y, θ, and Z the focused spots from mask and wafer can be superimposed. (a) Mask and wafer misaligned. The wafer is small relative to the mask (possibly the result of thermal effects). (b) Mask and wafer properly aligned by correcting the mask-to-wafer spacing.

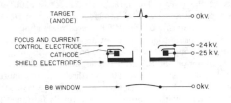

Fig. 21. The stationary anode X-ray source.

moving the mask or wafer to superimpose the mask and wafer spots on both the right and left sides of the mask/wafer.

C. The X-Ray Source

A new X-ray source was developed for this system to minimize its cost and to maximize its performance. Conventional X-ray sources use a rotating anode in which the water-cooled rotating drum is bombarded with high-energy electrons; this bombardment produces X-rays with wavelengths characteristic of the drum material and the electron energy. Our design uses a stationary source [26] in which electrons bombard a water-cooled palladium cone to produce X-rays. This source (shown in cross section in Fig. 21) is small, light, inexpensive, and has a life expectancy of several thousand hours at full power. Because it is stationary, the vibration associated with rotating sources is also eliminated.

The X-ray wavelength chosen was the 4.36-Å palladium line because a new resist [27] material was developed that has enhanced sensitivity to X-rays of this wavelength. In addition, this wavelength was short enough to allow the exposures to be made in helium at atmospheric pressures and to allow the use of high-strength mask substrates. Longer X-ray wavelengths require exposures to be made in a vacuum. Although a vacuum does eliminate the absorption of the X-rays between the source and the mask, it greatly complicates the design of the wafer-handling system.

In order to produce X-rays, the palladium anode is bombarded with 25-keV electrons from an annular dispenser-type tungsten cathode. The electrons are accelerated from the cathode and focused into an annular spot on the inner surface of the anode; this anode is shaped like a hollow cone about 1 cm long and 6 mm across at the open end. In normal operation, the axis of the cone is vertical and the open end of the cone faces downward. The electrons strike only the upper part of the cone so that the X-ray source appears to be a "spot" 3 mm in diameter when viewed from below.

The E-beam current is 160 mA, and reliability of the source depends on its being cooled properly. This is accomplished by nucleate boiling of water as it passes at a velocity of 40 m/s over the back of the cone. Experiments indicate that the power can be increased without a loss in reliability. The characteristics of the source are summarized as follows:

accelerating voltage	25 keV
apparent source diameter	3 mm
beam current	160 mA
anode power dissipation	4 kW
cooled surface power density	12 kW/cm^2.

The cone of X-rays emitted from the palladium anode passes through a 50-μm beryllium window at the lower side of the source. The beryllium window separates the vacuum inside the source from ambient pressure outside the source; vacuum within the source is maintained by a titanium ion pump.

The X-ray spectrum consists of two parts, a broad band of wavelengths with photon (X-ray) energies up to 25 keV that is usually called "continuum" radiation, and a sharp X-ray emission peak at 4.36 Å (2850 eV). The latter is the result of the palladium Lα atomic transition and is referred to as "characteristic" radiation. The characteristic radiation is responsible for about 80 percent of the exposure of the X-ray resist. The absorption distribution of the characteristic X-rays is as follows:

Materials	Percent of Characteristics X-Rays Absorbed
Beryllium window	25
Helium column	5
Mask (clear area)	15
Resist	9
Substrate	46

D. The Mask

Following development of X-ray lithographic equipment, the next priority was the development of a manufacturable mask structure that had good long-term stability, low defect density, and good X-ray contrast. Initial experiments with Kapton® and Mylar® demonstrated the difficulty of making masks with organic materials. Both Kapton and Mylar had high coefficients of thermal and humidity expansion and low stiffness. In addition, mask substrates containing silicon (SiN, or SiC) were unsuitable because the silicon absorption edge blocks the 4.4-

®Registered trademarks of E. I. du Pont

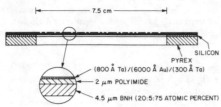

Fig. 22. X-ray mask structure.

Å palladium X-rays. Therefore, boron nitride was chosen because of its good mechanical stability, stiffness, minimal absorption of palladium X-rays, and ease of deposition.

1) Mask Structure: The X-ray mask structure [28], as shown in Fig. 22, consists of a 4-μm-thick membrane of boron, nitrogen, and hydrogen (BNH) in the atomic percent ratio of 20:5:75; this membrane is then overcoated with polyimide 2 μm thick. The membrane is supported by an annular ring of silicon. That, in turn, is epoxy-bonded to a rigid annular ring of pyrex. The metal absorber (300 Å of tantalum overcoated with 6000 Å of gold and 800 Å of tantalum) is deposited on the membrane and patterned using an E-beam exposure system.

2) Mask Fabrication: The fabrication process begins by depositing BNH onto both sides of silicon wafers, 11.2 cm in diameter, using a chemical vapor disposition (LPCVD) process. B_2H_6 and NH_3 are the reagents, and low-pressure N_2 is the carrier gas. After deposition, the BNH is removed from one side of the wafer by reactive sputter etching; the BNH film on the other side of the wafer is overcoated with polyimide 2 μm thick and the tantalum/gold metallization. The side of the wafer from which the BNH has been removed is then epoxy-bonded to a rigid pyrex ring. The part of the silicon wafer that is not covered with the pyrex ring is then removed using a fountain etch. The final product is called a mask blank.

The mask blank is coated with either poly(butene-1 sulphone) PBS, or GMC I (glycidyl methoacrylate co-chlorostyrene) negative electron resists. EBES I then writes the desired pattern on the mask with a 20-kV, 0.25-μm-diameter E-beam. Plasma-etch and sputter-etch processes are used to transfer the patterns from the developed electron resist to the tantalum and gold metallizations.

3) Mask Results: Newly fabricated masks have an average density of 0.5 to 1 defects ($\geqslant$ 1 μm) per square centimeter. Standard deviation of linewidths over the area of the mask is ≤0.06 μm. The root-mean-square pattern placement errors over a 4.5 cm × 4.5 cm area of the mask are less than 0.1 μm; these errors include the substrate distortion resulting from all effects (temperature, warping, etc.). There is no evidence of long-term distortion changes in the substrates.

In all cases, the distortion measurements have been made with the EBES "MARKET" program [29]. This system uses the laser interferometer-controlled EBES pattern generator as an inspection system that scans a substrate like an electron microscope and measures the appropriate alignment-mark coordinates using the laser interferometer.

E. The Resist

Many organic materials are sensitive to X-ray radiation, and several have been used as lithographic resists for years, most notably PMMA (polymethyl methacrylate). Unfortunately, the high X-ray doses required by most of these materials require exposure times of tens of minutes to hours with our

4-kW source. In order to make a production X-ray lithography system, new resists had to be developed. These not only had to be sensitive, but they also had to have good resolution, good adhesion to the substrate, and good etching resistance. The search for such a resist was made in cooperation with Bell Laboratories Chemical Research Laboratory, which provided numerous candidates; they were evaluated, modified, and retested. The current resist of choice is DCOPA [30] (dichloro propyl acrylate and glycidyl methacrylate-co-ethyl acrylate), a negative resist. (This resist was used to fabricate the majority of devices described in this paper.) The high sensitivity of this resist can be traced to the strong absorption of the 4.36-Å X-rays by the chlorine contained in the resist.

1) Multilayer Resist: The three-layer resist system [31] is used for all levels of lithography in silicon-wafer processing. This system uses a thick, radiation-insensitive polymer layer overcoating the wafer to planarize its topography. An SiO_2 layer is deposited on top of this, followed by the X-ray-sensitive top layer.

After the X-ray resist has been exposed and developed, the resulting pattern is etched into the intermediate layer. It is this oxygen-resistant layer that serves as a reactive-sputter-etch mask to transfer the mask pattern into the planarizing layer anisotropically. This approach allows the material of the *top* layer to be optimized for resolution and sensitivity (at the expense of etch resistance), and the *lower* layer to be optimized for adhesion and dry-etch resistance.

In our process, the bottom layer is a 1.8-μm-thick layer of a novolac-based positive photoresist that is baked to remove the solvents in the resist. The intermediate layer is 1200 Å of plasma-deposited SiO_2, and the top layer is 7000 Å of DCOPA X-ray resist. Exposure of the DCOPA resist takes about 4 min using the exposure-tool configuration described previously, and in Figs. 17 and 18. This X-ray exposure results in a resist thickness of about 3500 Å after development. The pattern in the developed resist is transferred in three reactive-sputter-etching steps. First, it is transferred into the $SiO_{(2)}$ layer, then into the 1.8-μm layer of photoresist, and finally into the thin-film layer on the surface of the silicon wafer. Because each of the etching steps is anisotropic, the features etched into the silicon are dimensionally identical to the mask features.

New resist systems that are 2–4 times more sensitive than DCOPA resist are being experimentally evaluated [32].

F. X-Ray Lithography Results

The performance criteria used to evaluate IC lithography systems that we have discussed so far include: linewidth control, defect density, and pattern overlay accuracy. Our X-ray lithography development program has now achieved an acceptable level of performance in all three areas, making it useful for patterning devices containing several thousand transistors with 0.75-μm features.

1) Linewidth Control: Linewidth measurements on mask features greater than 0.75 μm show a 3-sigma variation of 0.18 μm. When these masks are used to print wafers, resist features on the wafers show a linewidth variation of 0.33 μm (3-sigma). In addition, there is little or no change in the feature size from mask to wafer either in the X-ray exposure process or in the three-level pattern-transfer process; therefore, mask linewidth compensations are not necessary to achieve the correct feature sizes on the wafer.

2) Defect Density: A defect is defined as either an unwanted opaque spot or an unwanted clear spot (called a pinhole) larger than approximately 0.75 μm in the printed pattern. Unlike optical masks, X-ray masks cannot be inspected optically because many optically opaque defects (like dust) are X-ray transparent and do not print. Similarly, thin areas in the gold absorber may be X-ray transparent and optically opaque. Thus rather than direct inspection of the masks, the wafers printed from the mask are used to determine the mask defect density. Defect densities of 2 or 3 defects per square centimeter are common. Although this is still too high for VSLI circuits, it is acceptable for 1-μm devices containing up to several thousand transistors. Because of the system's insensitivity to dust, the mask defect density does not increase with use.

3) Overlay Accuracy: Pattern-overlay accuracy for successive levels of mask and wafer lithography is determined by several factors. These include the optical alignment system, the mechanical system for holding the mask and wafer parallel during exposure, mask in-plane distortion, and the accuracy of placing patterns on the mask during E-beam exposure. Registration data from electrical test patterns [33] on completed devices show that the level-to-level registration has a 1-sigma variation of about 0.25 μm from all causes. We expect this tolerance to improve when the zone-plate registration system is implemented on our exposure tools.

V. EXPERIMENTAL DEVICE TEST RESULTS

While the new materials, processes, and lithographic techniques were being developed, a series of test chips containing individual transistors, several simple circuits to measure speed, and a variety of structures to measure process and lithographic parameters were also developed. (A representative list of test structures used is given in Table I.) A minicomputer-controlled test system was constructed for automatic testing of these structures and subsequent reduction of the data. As an example, one very important parameter in fine-line device fabrication is the reregistration capability; therefore, structures were devised to allow electrical measurement of the magnitude and direction of the misalignment [34] on all relevant levels. A typical wafer map of misalignment between levels is shown in Fig. 23. This plot is the result of mask-to-wafer reregistrations using the birefringent-lens alignment microscope, not the zone-plate registration system.

The transistors manufactured this way exhibited the predicted long-channel behavior shown in Fig. 24 where the drain current is plotted versus drain voltage for various values of gate voltage. This device has a coded channel length of 1.0 μm, an effective channel length of 0.4 μm, and width of 500 μm. The device has a transconductance (the transconductance g_m is the partial derivative of the drain current I_d with respect to the gate voltage V_g) of 70 mS/mm and a cutoff frequency of 11 GHz. From the linear increase of current with gate voltage, it can be seen that the carrier velocity is in saturation.

Among the circuits on the test chips were ring oscillators and a divide-by-sixteen counter [35]. The ring-oscillator structure is shown in Fig. 25; the best speeds and power–delay products are shown in Table II. The room-temperature results are for two different load devices. One had the depletion implant optimized for high speed and the other for low power. The divide-by-sixteen counter was run at a maximum clock speed of 2.5 GHz. The gate delay was 130 ps with a fan-out of 3 and a power dissipation of 3 mW.

The first attempt to use the results of this advanced NMOS development effort for a real application arose when the E-beam pattern generator development group requested a programmable ramp generator that would operate at a clock rate

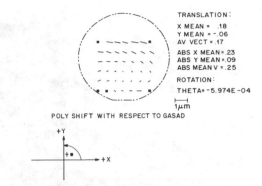

Fig. 23. A typical wafer map of misalignment between two levels and the accompanying statistical data. The pattern shows a rotation about a point close to the center of the slice. The squares are bad data points.

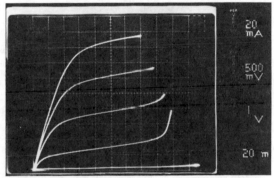

Fig. 24. Current–voltage curves for a transistor having an effective channel length of 0.4 μm and a width of 500 μm.

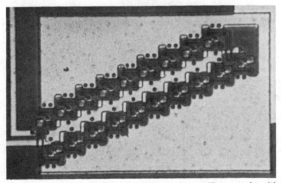

Fig. 25. A photomicrograph of a 19-stage ring oscillator made with 1-μm X-ray lithography.

of 500 MHz. It was not possible to do this using available emitter coupled logic (ECL) technology so a chip was designed in NMOS using 1.25-μm design rules [36] and is shown in Fig. 26.

The chip is a 5-bit digital-to-analog converter which produces a 500-MHz differential output current staircase across 25-Ω balanced loads with a programmable offset. Synchronized to this staircase is a 4-V pulse of programmable width which

Fig. 26. A photomicrograph of an A to D converter used to drive the E-beam deflection plates in an E-beam pattern generator.

TABLE I

1) Set of eight different length fixed width gate enhancement and depletion MOS transistors which give: V_t, beta, electrical channel length, g_m, g_d, and beta match.
2) Set of six different-width fixed-length gate enhancement and MOS transistors to give V_t, beta, g_m, and g_d.
3) Set of six field and composite oxide transistors to give V_t, beta, and punchthrough voltage.
4) Contact window resistance tester to polysilicon and diffusion.
5) Set of four different width diffusion lines.
   Set of four different width polysilicon lines which give sheet resistance and change from coded linewidth.
6) Large-area p-n junction for both capacitance and leakage measurements.
7) Large perimeter diffusion comb feature to determine sidewall capacitance and sidewall p-n junction leakage.
8) Capacitors:
   Gate oxide
   Field oxide
   Composite oxide
   Deposited oxide.
9) Set of four different-width metal lines used to determine sheet and change from coded linewidth.
10) X and Y level-to-level alignment testers for
    Poly diffusion
    Window poly
    Window diffusion
    Metal window.
11) Same MOS transistors as under 1) or 2), but depletion-mode devices.
12) Minimum contact window and spacing tester
    a) window to diffusion
    b) window to polysilicon
    c) polycon
    d) polycon–polycon spacing
    e) through level contact.
13) Set of three different square $L = W$ enhancement MOS transistors.
14) Set of three different square $L = W$ depletion MOS transistors.
15) Large square MOS device.
16) Polycon misalignment tester for both x and y directions.
17) Contact over thin oxide with slot and square holes.

TABLE II

Temperature (K)	Delay/Stage (ps)	Power–Delay Product (fJ)
300	28	40
300	75	5
77	22	50
4	18	40

TABLE III

Microns		Volts		Angstroms
L_G	X_J	V_{DD}	V_T	X_0
1	0.25	5	0.6	250
0.5	0.15	2.5	0.4	180
0.25	0.1	1.5	0.3	120
0.1	0.05	1	0.2	75

drives a 25-Ω load. The staircase has less than 0.2-percent nonlinearity and the beam-blanking pulse less than a 500-ps rise time. The experimental results are shown in Fig. 27.

A 4-kbit, random-access memory chip has also been fabricated and has a measured access time of 4 ns. The chip (shown in Fig. 28) uses 1-μm design rules and has dimensions of 1.4 mm × 1.4 mm. By 1-μm design rules, we mean that 1-μm lines and spaces are used on all levels, and no feature size compensation is allowed in the mask, resist, or etching steps.

VI. FUNDAMENTAL LIMITS OF FINE-LINE TECHNOLOGY

One micron is certainly not the limit in fine-line technology. The modeling programs have been used to design process sequences that will produce transistors using gate lengths below 1 μm which still exhibit long-channel behavior. A list of representative gate lengths and the major associated device parameters are shown in Table III. From this study, it has been concluded that the conventional MOSFET structure can be made with gate lengths down to 0.1 μm without exhibiting severe short-channel effects. To support this conclusion, a device with a 0.25-μm gate length (0.14-μm effective channel length) has been fabricated and is shown in Fig. 29. The measured current/voltage characteristics are as expected and are shown in Fig. 30. The transconductance of this device is seen to be 200 mS/mm [37].

It is doubtful that one can scale the device dimensions to below 0.1 μm and gain any advantage in circuit performance because of several basic limitations. A major limitation is that the series resistances of the source and drain do not scale linearly with linewidths, and their resistances eventually become comparable to the device resistance in the fully on-state. Another is that as linewidths are reduced, ever thinner gate oxides are required but tunneling limits the thinnest oxides to

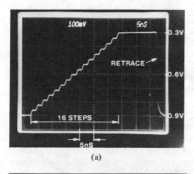

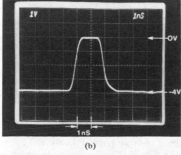

Fig. 27. (a) Single ended staircase output operating at 500 MHz. (b) Beam-blanking pulse corresponding to one staircase step.

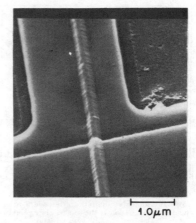

Fig. 29. SEM micrograph of 0.25-μm gate (0.14-μm effective channel length) NMOS transistor.

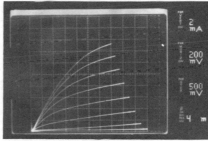

Fig. 30. Current–voltage characteristics of the transistor pictured in Fig. 29.

Fig. 28. A photomicrograph of a 4-kbit static RAM made with 1-μm lithographic rules for lines and spaces on all levels.

about 50 Å. Also, doping densities under the gate region must stay below the degeneracy limit which is about $10^{19}/cm^3$ and the supply voltage must be larger than 0.5 V in order to maintain adequate signal-to-noise margins.

Aside from these basic device physics considerations, there are two other basic areas to consider when scaling device dimensions down: wiring parasitics and thermal considerations.

It must be kept in mind that these affect not only the chip architecture but also chip packaging.

A. Wiring Limitations

There are three major fundamental limitations when shrinking the conductors on an IC: electromigration limits, edge capacitance, and wire resistance.

1) Electromigration: The electromigration problem becomes worse as the lithographic dimension decreases. The current (per unit width) from a transistor increases and the area of the minimum width conductor decreases causing an increase in current density. As an example, a typical 1-μm MOSFET gate can output 1 mA, and thus a 1-μm^2 aluminum conductor carrying this current will have a current density 10^5 A/cm^2 which is the electromigration limit. This can, of course, be circumvented by widening the conductors and reducing the circuit packing density.

2) Edge Capacitance: The capacitance between a conductor and the substrate consists of parallel-plate and edge capacitances. The parallel-plate part varies directly with linewidth but the edge component stays constant, causing a saturation in line capacitance. At 1-μm linewidths, these two components are approximately equal, and for practical field oxide thicknesses, the edge capacitance starts to be significant at about 2 μm. A plot of capacitance versus the ratio of linewidth to oxide thickness is shown in Fig. 31. The dot–dash line shows

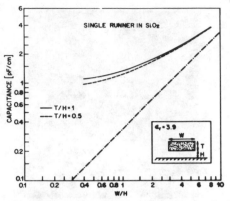

Fig. 31. Plot of capacitance versus ratio of linewidth to oxide thickness. The dot–dash line shows the parallel-plate component.

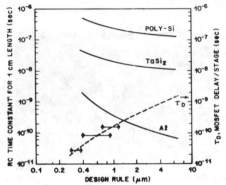

Fig. 32. MOSFET delays and conductor *RC* time constants versus design-rule dimensions.

the parallel-plate component. The field oxide thickness is normally chosen as large as possible to keep total capacitance down. A related problem is that line-to-line capacitances dominate line-to-substrate capacitances as dimensions shrink, causing a crosstalk problem. This can be eliminated by routing ground wires next to signal wires at the expense of an increase in area.

3) Wire Resistance: Since resistivity remains constant, the resistance of wires increases as dimensions shrink and this increased resistance coupled with the above-mentioned capacitance problem makes the *RC* time constant of a 1-cm-long conductor equal to the gate delay of a typical 1.5-μm gate. A graph showing MOSFET delays and conductor *RC* time constants versus design rule dimensions is shown in Fig. 32.

All of the above can be viewed as design constraints, but they are fundamental ones, and they detract from the advantages of reducing device dimensions.

B. Power Limitations

The power required to drive an IC is proportional to the number of gates and the frequency at which they are switched (clock frequency). The temperature rise caused by this power dissipation in an IC package is limited by the thermal conductivity of the package material. Since the maximum allowable

temperature rise is limited by the bandgap of silicon, the resulting maximum power dissipation of an air-cooled package is about 10 W. As a result, we must limit either the maximum clock rate or the number of gates on a chip. As an example, an integrated circuit containing all 1-μm devices, running at a 2-GHz clock rate, will be limited to 80 000 gates if a 10-percent duty cycle is assumed. Again, this can be looked at as a design constraint fixed by basic material parameters.

C. Ultimate Device Limits

If new device structures are allowed, the limiting dimension drops to about 200 Å for several basic reasons. One is that our ability to define a line by any imaginable lithographic means is limited by basic particle scattering considerations to 200 Å. Another is that any electron at an interface requires an area of about 100 Å on a side. Any smaller area will cause breakdown in any known material. 100 Å is also the spacing between dopant atoms at the degeneracy limit. Certainly, statistical considerations of both geometry and electron scattering events will prohibit any reduction beyond this point. Even to enter the regime below 0.1 μm will undoubtedly require the use of quantum theory rather than Boltzmann statistics and radically new device structures must be devised. Chip architectures with error correction will be mandatory.

VII. Conclusions

By combining and coordinating the efforts of diverse groups, Bell Labs has developed the capability to design, model, and manufacture NMOS IC's with submicrometer design rules. In fact, several chip designs have already been produced, and one is destined to boost the speed and accuracy of a new E-beam pattern generator.

A number of challenges were met by these groups as they worked together and in parallel. These challenges were:

The need for more sophisticated computer programs to model both the device-fabrication process and the electrical characteristics of very small devices: Bell Labs developed a new device-fabrication modeling program that models the ion implantation, diffusion, oxide growth, and so on, for 1-μm devices more accurately than previous programs. In addition, two- and three-dimensional electrical-modeling programs were used both to design the devices and to optimize the fabrication processes.

The need for better precision in transferring patterns from the resist to the silicon: Anisotropic reactive-sputter-etching techniques were developed for a variety of materials, and a new multifacet reactor was developed to implement the etching process. The resulting etching system, now widely used throughout the semiconductor industry, has improved the precision of the pattern transfer process and increased device yields.

A low-temperature device-fabrication process: Fine-line devices require low-temperature processing to minimize unwanted diffusion of the source and drain impurities into the channel region. These low-temperature techniques required further developments in materials technology—such as new methods of planarizing the wafer's topography, new conformal conductors, and a new P-glass deposition process.

Low-resistivity interconnections: As the dimensions of circuit elements become smaller, the reliability and conductivity of the conductors that interconnect the circuit elements becomes critical. To meet the need for improved interconnections, Bell Labs developed a two-level gate conductor using polysilicon and a metal silicide, and a second-level interconnection of high-reliability aluminum.

A lithography system with submicron resolution: X-ray lithography was developed as a production tool to allow the fabrication of the new 1-μm devices. The development of the X-ray tools and processes led to inventions that have benefited other lithographic technologies—namely, the zone-plate registration system and the multilayer resist system.

High-performance device designs: The Bell Labs device designers used the results of their modeling programs to design test devices that, in turn, assisted in developing the fabrication processes and the X-ray lithographic tools. In addition, they developed high-speed devices for specific customers, such as the 4-ns-access 4-kbit static RAM, and a 500-MHz digital-to-analog converter.

Further, these groups at Bell Labs have defined the fundamental limits of fine-line NMOS devices. However, there is much work to be done to develop and extend our current 1-μm technology into the submicron region before we must contend with the fundamental 0.1-μm limit.

ACKNOWLEDGMENT

The authors wish to acknowledge the contributions of all the members of the Advanced LSI Development Laboratory, and the many others at Bell Labs who have collaborated with us. As authors, we are merely speaking for these people because it has been their enthusiasm, ideas, experiments, and late-night efforts that have made our fine-line high-performance NMOS circuits a reality.

REFERENCES

[1] M. P. Lepselter, "Silicon picocircuits," presented at GaAs Integrated Circuit Symp., San Diego, CA, Oct. 1981.

[2] F. H. Gaensslen, "Geometry effects of small MOSFET devices," presented at IEDM, Washington, DC, Dec. 1977, Paper 24.1.

[3] W. Fichtner, E. Kinsbron, and N. Lifshitz, "Ion implantation and low temperature diffusion of arsenic in silicon," presented at Electrochem. Soc. Fall Meet., Denver, CO, Oct. 11–16, 1981; Abstract Number 383.

[4] W. Fichtner, R. M. Levin, T. T. Sheng, and R. B. Marcus, "Residual lattice damage in B and BF$_2$ implanted and annealed p-channel MOSFET structures," presented at Electrochem. Soc. Spring Meet., Montreal, Canada, May 9–14, 1982; Abstract Number 182.

[5] W. Fichtner, "Physics and simulation of small MOS devices," presented at 1982 IEDM, San Francisco, CA, Dec. 13–15, 1982; Paper 27.1.

[6] W. Fichtner and D. J. Rose, "On the numerical solution of nonlinear elliptic partial differential equations arising from semiconductor device modeling," in *Elliptic Problem Solvers*, M. H. Shultz, Ed. New York: Academic Press, 1981.

[7] R. Bank and D. J. Rose, "Parameters selection for Newton-like methods applicable to nonlinear partial differential equations," *SIAM J. Numer. Anal.*, vol. 17, p. 806, 1980.

[8] J. R. Brews, W. Fichtner, E. H. Nicollian, and S. M. Sze, "Generalized guide for MOSFET miniaturization," *IEEE Electron Device Lett.*, vol. EDL-1, p. 2, 1980.

[9] W. Fichtner, R. L. Johnson, and D. J. Rose, "Three-dimensional modeling of small-size MOSFET's," *IEEE Trans. Electron Devices*, vol. ED-28, p. 1215, 1981.

[10] E. N. Fuls, "X-ray lithography applied to the fabrication of 1 μm n-channel metal oxide semiconductor (NMOS) circuits," *SPIE* (Submicron Lithography), vol. 333, p. 113, 1982.

[11] D.N.K. Wang, D. Maydan, and H. J. Levinstein, "Reactive sputter etching and its applications," *Solid State Technol.*, vol. 23, no. 8, p. 122, Aug. 1980.

[12] D. Maydan, "High capacity etching apparatus and method," U.S. Patent 4 298 443, Nov. 3, 1981.

[13] A. Weiss, "Plasma etching of aluminum: Review of process and equipment technology," *Semicond. Int.*, vol. 5, no. 10, p. 69, Oct. 1982.

[14] A. C. Adams, "Plasma planarization," *Solid State Technol.*, vol. 24, no. 4, p. 178, Apr. 1981.

[15] D. B. Fraser, S. P. Murarka, A. R. Tretola, and A. K. Sinha, *J. Vac. Soc. and Tech.*, vol. 18, no. 2, pp. 345–348, Mar. 1981.

[16] S. P. Murarka, D. B. Fraser, W. S. Lindenberger, and A. K. Sinha, *J. Appl. Phys.*, vol. 51, p. 3241, 1980.

[17] A. K. Sinha, W. S. Lindenberger, D. B. Fraser, S. P. Murarka, and E. N. Fuls, *IEEE Trans. Electron Devices*, vol. ED-27, p. 1425, Aug. 1980.

[18] S. P. Murarka, *Silicides for VLSI Applications.* New York: Academic Press, Feb. 1983.

[19] D. R. Herriott, R. J. Collier, D. S. Alles, and J. W. Stafford, "EBES: A practical electron lithographic system," *IEEE Trans. Electron Devices*, vol. ED-22, p. 385, July 1975.

[20] M. P. Lepselter, "X-ray lithography breaks the submicron barrier," *IEEE Spectrum*, vol. 18, no. 5, p. 26, May 1981.

[21] A. Zacharias, "X-ray lithography for integrated circuit development and manufacturing," *IEEE Trans. Components, Hybrids, Manuf. Technol.*, vol. CHMT-5, no. 1, Mar. 1982.

[22] J. M. Moran and G. N. Taylor, "Improved resolution for DCOPA negative x-ray resist by exposure under a controlled atmosphere of nitrogen and oxygen," *J. Vac. Sci. Technol.*, vol. 16, p. 2020, Nov./Dec. 1979.

[23] T. E. Saunders, "Wafer flatness utilizing the pin-recess chuck," *Solid State Technol.*, vol. 25, no. 5, p. 73, May 1982.

[24] A. D. White, "Simple bifocus element for microscopy objectives," *Appl. Opt.*, vol. 16, p. 549, Mar. 1977.

[25] M. Feldman, A. D. White, and D. L. White, "Application of zoneplates to alignment in microlithography," *J. Vac. Sci. Technol.*, vol. 9, no. 4, p. 1229, Nov./Dec. 1979.

[26] J. R. Maldonado, M. E. Poulsen, T. E. Saunders, F. Vratny, and A. Zacharias, "X-ray lithography source using a stationary solid Pd target," *J. Vac. Sci. Technol.*, vol. 16, p. 1942, Nov./Dec. 1979.

[27] D. Maydan, G. A. Coquin, J. R. Maldonado, S. Somekh, D. Y. Lou, and G. N. Taylor, "High-speed replication of submicron features on large areas by X-ray lithography," *IEEE Trans. Electron Devices*, vol. ED-22, p. 427, July 1975.

[28] D. Maydan, G. A. Coquin, H. J. Levinstein, A. K. Sinha, and D. K. Wang, "Boron nitride mask structure for x-ray lithography," *J. Vac. Sci. Technol.*, vol. 16, p. 1959, Nov./Dec. 1979.

[29] T. E. Zavecz, "A comprehensive test sequence for the electron beam exposure system," *Solid State Technol.*, vol. 25, no. 2, p. 106, Feb. 1982.

[30] G. N. Taylor, G. A. Coquin, and S. Somekh, "Sensitive chlorine-containing resists for x-ray lithography," *Polym. Eng. Sci.*, vol. 17, no. 6, p. 420, 1977.

[31] J. M. Moran and D. Maydan, "High resolution, step profile resist patterns," *J. Vac. Sci. Technol.*, vol. 16, no. 6, p. 1620, Nov./Dec. 1979.

[32] G. N. Taylor, T. M. Wolf, and J. M. Moran, "Organosilicon monomers for plasma-developed x-ray resists," *J. Vac. Sci. Technol.*, vol. 19, no. 4, p. 872, Nov./Dec. 1981.

[33] J. H. Bruning, "Performance limits in 1:1 UV projection lithography," *J. Vac. Sci. Technol.*, vol. 16, no. 6, Nov./Dec. 1979.

[34] Cover, *IEEE Spectrum*, vol. 18, no. 5, May 1981.

[35] P. I. Suciu, E. N. Fuls, and H. J. Boll, "High speed NMOS circuits made with x-ray lithography and reactive sputter etching," *IEEE Electron. Device Lett.*, vol. EDL-1, pp. 10–11, Jan. 1980.

[36] R. J. Bayruns, P. I. Suciu, N. C. Wittwer, D. L. Fraser, Jr., E. N. Fuls, R. A. Kushner, F. R. Ashley, and E. A. Gere, "A fine line NMOS IC for raster-scan control of a 500-MHz electron-beam deflection system," *IEEE Trans. Electron Devices*, vol. ED-29, pp. 737–744, Apr. 1982.

[37] W. Fichtner, R. K. Watts, D. B. Fraser, R. L. Johnston, and S. M. Sze, "0.15 micron channel-length MOSFETs fabricated using e-beam lithography," in *IEEE IEDM 1982 Tech. Dig.*, p. 722.

High-Speed Microelectronics for Military Applications

MARTIN C. PECKERAR, MEMBER, IEEE, AND ROBERT E. NEIDERT, MEMBER, IEEE

Invited Paper

Abstract—Future defense systems will require high-speed microcircuits for analog and digital applications. This includes digital devices which will operate with 25-MHz system clock, and contain in excess of 4×10^5 gates/cm^2. Analog devices operating as transmitters and receivers of signals up to 150 GHz will also be needed. A fundamental requirement for military systems is that they operate in hostile environments. In particular, they must survive after receiving large doses or dose transients of ionizing radiation. Micron and submicron engineering technology impacts each of these requirements. This paper describes the nature of this impact. Research and development in these technology areas at the Naval Research Laboratory is reviewed in this article.

I. INTRODUCTION

AN IMPORTANT GOAL of submicron feature size microcircuit engineering is high-speed circuitry. Typically, one thinks of silicon digital devices in this context. To press development of this technology through the 1980's, the Department of Defense (DOD) has set up a special-focus program in silicon very-high-speed integrated circuits (VHSIC) working with a 25-MHz clock [1]. The gate density in specific chips will equal or exceed 4×10^5 gates/cm^2. The ability to resolve submicron features (with attendant improvement in level-to-level alignment capability) aids in the realization of this goal in a number of ways. Reduced transistor channel transit time, while important, is just one way in which the ability to produce fine lines helps produce high-speed digital circuits. More compact devices usually employ shorter runs of interconnect line. In some instances, lower total line resistances are obtained. Smaller diffusion tubs lead to smaller diffusion capacitances. But there are negative aspects as well. More tightly packed runs of interconnect yield larger parasitic capacitances. Narrower runs of metallization mean higher interconnect resistance per unit length. The ultimate speed of digital devices is, at present, an active topic of discussion in government and the private sector. Detailed discussions of these problems can be found in other articles of this issue.

In this paper, we focus on unique military requirements for high-speed microelectronics. This means that, in addition to the high-speed digital requirement mentioned previously, we must address analog applications. Radar, electronic warfare, and communication systems require devices capable of generating and receiving signals up to 150 GHz. It might be argued that the need for micron and submicron gate-length field-effect transistor devices was most clearly realized first in this area of technology. Descriptions of submicron gate-length transis-

tors for microwave applications can be found in the literature of the early and middle 1970's [2]. For many years, the Naval Research Laboratory has conducted research in RF applications of hybrid and monolithic integrated circuits. Materials employed include silicon, GaAs, and InP (for both milimeterwave and electrooptical applications). Microwave engineers have long realized the importance of parameter scaling in their circuits. Submicron gate-length metal–semiconductor field-effect transistors (MESFET's) and junction field-effect transistors (JFET's) in GaAs are becoming commercially available today as off-the-shelf items. Some specific examples of circuit techniques employed in this area are given in the following. Questions concerning the impact of reducing channel length below 1 μm are addressed.

Another aspect of microelectronics development which the military values very highly is reliability. While reliability is also a concern in the commercial sector, the military's requirements for reliable parts are usually more demanding. The reliability of VHSIC devices is a matter of concern and debate in industry and government. Appropriate tests for debugging and for reliability projection in complicated integrated systems are just now being hammered out. One area of reliability in which DOD must play a key role is that of reliability in adverse environments. This includes exposure to ionizing radiation. There is some interest in radiation-hard devices (i.e., devices which are capable of withstanding large total dose and dose transients of ionizing radiation) for satellite and reactor applications. However, industry is largely unconcerned as to whether or not digital devices will withstand radiation from nuclear bursts. A considerable amount of work is going on in DOD in general and at NRL in particular directed at radiation hardening of microelectronics devices. How reduced device dimensions influences radiation hardness is discussed later in this paper.

DOD maintains an in-house microelectronics fabrication capability [3]. There are a number of reasons for this. Test structures for evaluation of the problems mentioned previously are designed and developed in these facilities. Hands-on experience is gained by government personnel. This enables them to be "intelligent consumers" in procuring systems. These facilities have provided the basis for many significant research programs in submicron engineering. At NRL, much work has been done on hot-plasma X-ray generators for X-ray lithography. This work is also reviewed later in this paper.

To summarize, the military has unique needs in the area of high-speed microelectronics. These needs include development of very-high-speed digital structures capable of functioning in adverse environments. Adverse environments include exposure

Manuscript received November 18, 1982.

The authors are with the U.S. Naval Research Laboratory, Washington, DC 20375.

Reprinted from *Proc. IEEE*, vol. 71, pp. 657–666, May 1983.

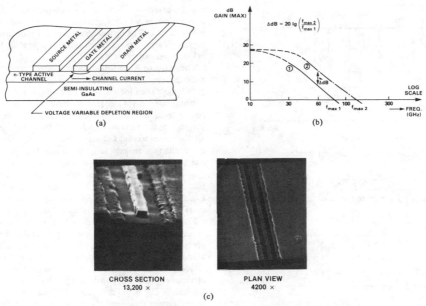

Fig. 1. MESFET layout and performance. (a) MESFET cross section.
(b) Gain versus frequency curves. (c) 0.8-μm-gate-length InP FET.

to large total doses or to rapid dose transients of ionizing radiation. Analog devices are required for systems operating up to 150 GHz. Micron and submicron processing affects both the analog and the digital military needs. How this occurs is the subject of this paper. In addition, some of the Navy internal effort in submicron process engineering and development is reviewed.

II. ANALOG APPLICATIONS

Oscillators, amplifiers, mixers, and detectors capable of operating at microwave and millimeter wavelengths are of critical importance to DOD radar, electronic warfare, and communications systems. Oscillators may be fabricated in a microelectronics context using transistors or transferred-electron devices. Schottky and junction diodes may be used as mixers and detectors. At the heart of the amplifier is the transistor. Here, large improvements in operating frequency range and power gain can be achieved by reducing gate lengths. But the question arises: Is there a minimum length at which further reduction in length no longer improves performance? That is, at what gate lengths do parasitic circuit elements dominate in determining performance? In the following paragraphs, the GaAs MESFET is used as an example of the effects of parasitics in microwave device performance. Semi-empirical modeling, based on codes developed at NRL, which employ measured transistor data, is used to address these questions. This section concludes with a summary of some of the problems in FET fabrication technology and reliability addressed at NRL.

In the short span of about eight years, gallium arsenide MESFET's have risen from "laboratory" status to become the workhorse of the microwave spectrum. The basic MESFET structure is shown in Fig. 1(a). The "gate" forms a Schottky-barrier diode with the underlying semiconductor. Electrons can flow freely from "source" to "drain" in the undepleted region between the barrier space charge and the semi-insulating substrate. Reverse biasing the Schottky diode extends the depletion region into the semiconductor bulk from the gate. This "pinches off" the channel. No charge flows when bias is applied between source and drain under these conditions. A p-type heavily doped region may be made under the gate. In this case, an ohmic-contact metal gate is used and a junction diode, rather than a Schottky diode, is formed. The device functions in basically the same way, only now it is called a JFET (junction FET). Isolation may be accomplished by etching around active devices down to the semi-insulating substrate, or by implanting appropriate doses of hydrogen, helium, or neon outside the active regions. Selective implantation may also be used to provide active device areas surrounded by semi-insulating material. One of the prime MESFET research areas is submicron technology for the fabrication of FET gates.

The performance of FET's generally improves as the gate length is reduced. Operation extends to higher frequencies and to faster switching speeds. As micron and submicron gate lengths have become feasible, it has been observed that halving the gate length does not usually produce as much high frequency improvement as was achieved by halving longer gates. That is, the region of diminishing returns appears to have been reached. The following analysis may provide a qualitative explanation for this behavior. The capacity for a device to amplify the power of an incoming signal is referred to as gain. The frequency at which the matched power gain of an FET drops to unity is called f_{max}. In the high-frequency regime of an FET, as f_{max} is approached, the matched power gain is usually experimentally observed to decrease at the rate of about 6 dB per frequency octave. Therefore, an increase in power gain of 6 dB in this region (perhaps by some device improvement) is equivalent to extending f_{max} by a factor of

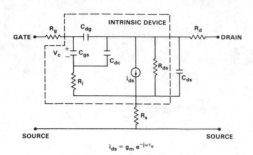

$$i_{ds} = g_m e^{-j\omega\tau_0}$$

Fig. 2. MESFET equivalent circuit.

TABLE I

Gate Length lg (μm)	$A = \dfrac{g_m R_g C_{dg}}{C_{gs}}$	$B = \dfrac{R_g + R_i + R_s}{R_{ds}}$	$\dfrac{A}{B}$
1.2	1.32×10^{-4}	4.79×10^{-2}	.003
0.6	4.81×10^{-4}	4.91×10^{-2}	.010
0.3	20.6×10^{-4}	5.07×10^{-2}	.041

two. Similarly, a gain improvement of 3 dB is equivalent to extending f_{max} by a $\sqrt{2}$ factor. This is graphically illustrated in Fig. 1(b). The curves in this figure show the typical relative performance of short-gate GaAs MESFET's. Thus power gain versus frequency curves give immediate information on f_{max}. This observation leads us to extend Liechti's analysis [2] to estimate f_{max} variation with gate length. Using the equivalent circuit of Liechti, given here in Fig. 2, the following approximate expression can be deduced:

$$f_{max} \approx \frac{g_m/2\pi C_{gs}}{2\sqrt{[(R_g + R_i + R_s)/R_{ds}] + R_g C_{dg}(g_m/C_{gs})}}. \quad (1)$$

The terms in this expression are illustrated in Fig. 2. The numerator of (1) would show a limiting increase of two in f_{max} as the gate length is halved (because C_{gs} is approximately proportional to gate length while g_m remains approximately constant) *provided* the ratio $A/B \ll 1$, where

$$A = \frac{g_m R_g C_{dg}}{C_{gs}} \quad (2a)$$

and

$$B = \frac{R_g + R_i + R_s}{R_{ds}}. \quad (2b)$$

Numerical values for the above circuit elements are given in Table I for a state-of-the-art MESFET of gate width 75 μm. These values were obtained using the NRL developed program FETREN [4]. In the simulation, the gate length was the only variable. The bias point was: drain voltage = +2.5 V and gate voltage = −1.0 V. The external pinchoff voltage for the device was 2 V.

The FETREN program will take device configuration data (i.e., gate length, gate width, depth of the active layer, doping profiles in the active layer, source–drain spacing, etc.) as well as bias information and evaluate the equivalent circuit model parameters. Velocity-saturation effects are accounted for, as

are the effects of Gunn-domain formation. The Gunn domain is a region in which carriers are excited into a low-mobility valley of the GaAs band structure; a dipole layer forms in this region. Various capacitance terms (C_{gs} and C_{dg}) are affected as is the input resistance R_i.

The ratio of A to B is obtained by referring to Table I. This ratio is seen to be an order of magnitude larger for a 0.3-μm gate length than for a 1.2-μm gate length and rises rapidly. The denominator of (1) begins to have an impact as gate length becomes submicron. In fact, if $A/B \gg 1$, then f_{max} becomes proportional to the square root of the gate length (noting that all the terms except C_{gs} are approximately constant with moderate changes in gate length). From the earlier discussion of the shape of the gain curve near f_{max}, the proportionality of f_{max} to the square root of the gate length implies a limit to the gain improvement of 3 dB for halving the gate length. Equation (1) does not actually predict f_{max} accurately, but is merely used to show the qualitative trends of its terms.

Fitting actual transistor data to the FETREN model reveals an equivalent circuit more complex than Fig. 2 suggests. There are parasitic capacitances, more or less shunting C_{gs} and C_{dg}, which do not vary with gate length. They are described by Neidert and Scott in [4] under the following names: inter-electrode, sidewall, pad-to-source, and pad-to-ground capacitances. If C_{gs} in (1) is taken to include these invariant parasitic terms rather than just the intrinsic term, then f_{max} becomes much less a function of gate length as the gate length becomes very small. Also, there may be additional complexity arising from external circuitry, especially the source-to-ground impedance. Therefore, it is unlikely that either of the limiting-case improvements is fully achieved—increasing f_{max} by 2 when halving long gates, or increasing f_{max} by $\sqrt{2}$ when halving short gates. Indeed, as the limit of zero gate length is approached, the incremental improvement may approach zero. The implication here is that even in the "near-ideal" case (just taking the parasitics of the Liechti model into account), f_{max} does not scale exactly linearly with gate length in the micron and submicron region. Furthermore, added parasitics may even prevent realization of the $\sqrt{2} f_{max}$ variation projected by the Liechti model. Added emphasis must be given to minimization of these parasitics if submicron FET's are to realize maximum advantage. Certainly, in going from 1 to 0.5 μm, some increase in f_{max} (almost $\sqrt{2}$) is observed experimentally. Modeling indicates that before much further reduction in gate length is warranted, more work in understanding and reducing parasitics would be useful.

In light of these considerations, FET fabrication work at NRL has focused on the 1–0.5-μm gate length region. Ongoing programs aim at improving device reliability and performance. In the area of reliability, a major thrust in the development of amorphous gate and contact metallization is taking place [5], [6]. Silicides of tungsten, titanium–tungsten, and nickel were formed by overlaying layers of W, TiW, or Ni with 300 Å of silicon by sputtering. The films were heated below the glass transition temperature (~500°C) and rapidly cooled. Electron channeling studies indicate all films produced were the desired amorphous silicides. Accelerated life test data have been taken on gold refractory-gate materials used in GaAs FET's. These data indicated that the primary failure mechanism encountered in this system is formation of a diffusion couple between the gate metal and the GaAs substrate [7], [8]. The use of amorphous layers seems to prevent this. NRL studies have been performed on micron GaAs FET's fabricated with amorphous

TiW–Si gates and AuGeNi contacts [9]. Accelerated life tests indicate that 10^7 h of operation at $100°C$ should be obtainable before interdiffusion becomes significant.

Recently, a comparison of InP FET's and GaAs MESFET's with $0.8-1.5$-μm gates was done at NRL [10]. The InP FET's were fabricated using a gate oxide barrier between the gate and the substrate to minimize leakage. This leakage prohibits low-noise performance at high power levels in MESFET's. Typical structures produced are shown in Fig. 1(c). Higher associated gain was observed in the InP structure, probably due to the higher effective saturated channel drift velocity (≈ 20 percent higher than GaAs). For InP on Cr-doped semi-insulating substrates, the noise figure was just slightly higher than that of GaAs. For InP on Fe-doped substrates, the noise figure was unacceptably high. More recently, a fully implanted 1-μm gate InP JFET technology was demonstrated [11].

All of the above-mentioned structures were realized with contact lithography and liftoff metallization [12]. In liftoff, resist is put down and patterned first. Metal is evaporated over the resist. The metal-coated resist is soaked in organic solvent, the resist washes away, and the metal on top of it "lifts off." Only metal which contacts the workpiece directly remains. Chlorobenzene soaks are usually applied to the resist after pattern development and prior to metallization. It has been found that this creates a "lip" which juts out slightly over the resist openings. Evaporated metals tend to break over this lip. This makes for more efficient liftoff. GaAs FET gates as wide as 300 μm were achieved this way. Typical yields for 100-μm gates are greater than 50 percent. For the thick metal (7000 Å) used, a liftoff assistance technique is required. After the liftoff process is initiated, a quick acid dip [12] is done. This breaks some thin remaining metal bridges and allows clean lifting of undesired metal.

To conclude, the analog applications area of near-micron and submicron engineering is being actively investigated by DOD. In this section, we have focused on FET development. Reasons for developing submicron feature size FET geometries were discussed. Specifically, improvement of f_{max} was analyzed. At present, pressing geometries down to at least 0.5 μm appears to be a fruitful path of technological development. Problems associated with parasitics must be investigated before much finer geometries should be considered. Reliability enhancement by amorphous gate technology was discussed, as was a comparison of 1-μm-gate GaAs FET and InP FET technology. High-frequency operation of GaAs FET's leads one to the conclusion that GaAs would be a good substrate material for logic devices. In fact, there is a large amount of development in the area of GaAs integrated logic circuits. This work is of great interest to the DOD community. High-speed memory applications are envisioned, as are interfaces to optical signal processing systems. Such circuits are discussed in a paper by Wisseman et al. in this issue.

III. DIGITAL CIRCUITRY AND RADIATION EFFECTS

DOD carries on a large amount of work which is of relevance to problems associated with micron and submicron engineering of digital devices. At NRL, this work is mainly related to radiation effects in digital structures. As mentioned above, military applications impose requirements beyond those of speed and density. Specifically, the capacity to function after a high total dose or a rapid transient exposure to ionizing radiation is a military necessity. The nuclear threat can provide just such exposure. Early work done at NRL by Hughes [13] indicates

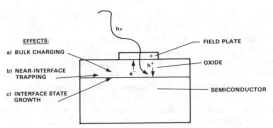

Fig. 3. Ionizing radiation effects on MOS structure. Ionizing radiation incident on the sample creates electron–hole pairs. Mobile electrons leave the oxide relatively quickly. Holes move slowly and leave a positive charge distributed through the insulator. Positive bias forces holes to the oxide/semiconductor interface where some fraction are trapped.

how damaging such exposure can be to sensitive MOS-gate insulators. Basically, what happens is illustrated in Fig. 3. The ionizing radiation causes electron–hole pairs to form in the insulator. The electron is mobile and is quickly transported out of the insulator under the bias of the field plate. This leaves a uniform background of relatively immobile positive charge (holes) in the insulator. The MOS turn-on voltage V_t is shifted in a negative direction. If enough positive charge is present, n-channel enhancement-mode devices will turn on, even without the normally required gate bias. Over time, under positive gate bias, the situation gets worse as positive charge is forced to the interface. At the interface, this charge exercises more control over the silicon surface potential. Eventually, the charge is forced out of the oxide. However, a fractional amount may be trapped at the oxide–semiconductor interface. The trapped charge remains for long periods of time. In addition, charges forced to the interface may cause an increase in the fast interface state density [14]. Strategies to minimize this effect include the use of ultraclean oxides grown in silicon tubes prescrubbed with HCl gas. This minimizes the presence of extrinsic bulk and interface trapping centers (ionic impurities). Oxides are dry grown at a temperature designed to minimize interface states which can later act as hole traps.

The question then arises: Do micron and submicron engineering techniques enhance the severity of the total dose radiation effects problem? The answer is, unfortunately, that they do. They do so in a number of ways. As MOS device channel lengths are reduced, there is a tendency for fields in MOSFET channels to increase. High fields force positive charge to the interface more rapidly and efficiently. This causes larger V_t shifts. Proper scaling and attendant reduction of internal fields alleviate these problems somewhat. However, the lithographic techniques used to realize micron and submicron structures also bring about radiation softening and other deleterious effects. This is because devices are exposed to ionizing radiation in the course of X-ray and electron-beam lithographic procedures. The effects of this lithography on device performance are discussed below.

Ionizing radiation incident on MOS oxides breaks bonds and introduces trapping centers in these oxides. This occurs whether or not bias is present on the MOS gate. Work done at IBM has examined the effect of such traps introduced during electron-beam lithography on transistor performance [15], [16]. These studies have shown that electron-beam lithography creates threshold shifting which is not annealed away in N_2 at temperatures lower than $550°C$. In addition, the electron-beam-irradiated oxides are more susceptible to "hot-electron" effects.

That is, electrons can acquire energies from accelerating fields far in excess of their thermal energies. These "hot" electrons can surmount the normally impenetrable oxide injection barriers and enter radiation-induced trapping sites. Electron charge generally accumulates near the high-field drain end of the transistor. The threshold near the drain is effectively increased. This, in turn, reduces the transconductance of the device. The transistor cannot supply current as effectively. While these effects are not severe enough to destroy device operation, they must be included in device modeling to assure full performance.

Efforts at NRL build on this early work. Hughes [17] has shown that lithography-induced trapping sites increase the trapping fraction for subsequent radiation-induced charging. This may lead to a marked radiation "softening" of MOS devices. In addition, it was shown that X-ray and electron-beam lithography can increase the mobile charge currents and lead to positive charge instability in MOS capacitors [18].

Recent NRL work [19] on ultraclean dry-grown oxides used in an n-MOS polysilicon gate self-aligned transistor process has indicated that the primary lithographic exposure causes the formation of many trapping sites throughout the gate oxide. These sites interact with the silicon bulk charge and create "slow-trapping" instability [20], [21]. That is, under negative gate bias, holes are drawn up into the insulator. Under positive bias, these trapped charges are neutralized. After low-temperature anneal (N_2, 450°C, one-half hour), the slow-trapping instability disappears. What remains is a significant increase in interface charge (5×10^{10} states/cm^2) after a single exposure of COP[1] resist material. This charge decreases mobility and degrades transconductance somewhat. The most significant degradation is on subthreshold leakage current. This is seen in Fig. 4. As much as a 35-percent increase in subthreshold swing (the gate voltage increase required to reduce the leakage current one order of magnitude) was noted. Subthreshold currents are important since, in many IC's, logic device inputs do not tend to bias gates below threshold by very much in the off state. Many devices are really operating in the weak inversion mode. An increase in subthreshold currents means more power dissipated by the circuits. This effect must be included in device modeling to assure that excessive power is not drawn during operation.

There is no apparent channel length dependence to the effects described above for n-MOS polygate transistors, down to 1 μm (see Fig. 5). There does appear to be some width dependence, as channel widths reach 5 μm and below. The reasons for the width dependence are unclear as of yet, and are being investigated [19], [22].

Using techniques described above, considerable progress has been made in radiation hardening gate oxides and in determining the nature and extent of the lithography-induced radiation damage. However, the problem of hardening oxides outside the gate region has proved less tractable. Oxides in the field region (field oxides) are used for device isolation. In addition, they prevent inversion of the surface under interconnects by lifting these further off the semiconductor surface. These oxides are more susceptible to radiation damage than conventional gate insulators because they are usually an order of magnitude thicker than the gate oxides. Thus they intercept more ionizing radiation during exposure. Furthermore, the

[1] COP is a commercially available medium-speed X-ray resist. Approximately 5 Mrad of X-ray energy is deposited in typical MOS gate oxides during a single COP exposure.

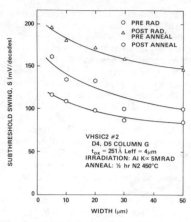

Fig. 4. Subthreshold behavior of various gate-width polysilicon gate MOSFET's. Subthreshold swing is the voltage on the gate needed to reduce source–drain current one order of magnitude. Radiation exposure was that required to expose COP [22].

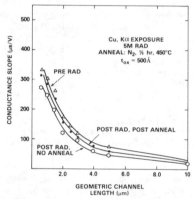

Fig. 5. Change in source–drain conductance with gate voltage for various channel-length polysilicon gate MOSFET's. To first approximation this is: oxide capacitance × width-to-length ratio × carrier mobility. Radiation lowers the conductance slope by degrading the carrier mobility. There is no observed channel length dependence to this effect. The radiation exposure level was that used to expose COP.

processes used to grow these thicker oxides are sometimes different than those used to grow gate oxides for optimum radiation hardness. Increasing the integration density on chip, as is done in high-speed circuits, makes this problem worse. Leakage paths are shortened. This makes the demand for effective isolation more stringent. But the radiation-soft field oxide tends to charge positively during irradiation. This establishes electron leakage "channels" under these field oxides. High-density structures rely on local oxidation techniques to "self-align" the fields to the transistor cuts [23]. In this process, a nitride oxidation mask is used to define the transistor gate region. A thick field oxide is grown around this nitride. The oxide encroaches under the nitride during oxidation, giving rise to "birds-beak" structures. These regions may be highly stressed during growth and would also tend to be radiation soft.

Total dose hardness requirements are only a part of the radiation requirement imposed on many devices targeted for mili-

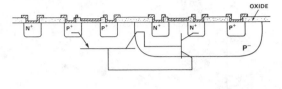

Fig. 6. CMOS inverter cross section. Parasitic transistors are shown.

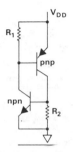

Fig. 7. Redrawn circuit diagram of parasitic transistors shown in Fig. 6, indicating shunting resistor placement.

tary systems. Ionizing radiation transients, as one would encounter in a nuclear burst, are also important. In the following paragraphs, two types of transient-induced problems are discussed. They are latch-up and soft error. Latch-up is of particular concern in the complimentary metal–oxide–semiconductor (CMOS) device family. CMOS is an extremely popular low-power technology frequently used in high-density integration. The soft-error problem is present in high-speed n-MOS technology. It is particularly important in dynamic random-access memories (d-RAM's).

Consider the cross section of a typical CMOS inverter, Fig. 6. We see the complimentary n- and p-channel devices which give CMOS its name. When the input node is activated by a positive voltage, the p-channel device turns off and the n-channel device turns on. The output voltage drops to the negative supply voltage V_{SS}. When the input node is activated by a negative voltage, the n-channel device turns off and the p-channel device turns on. The output rises to the positive supply V_{DD}. Thus a positive input yields negative output and vice versa. This describes the fundamental operation of the inverter.

Inspection of Fig. 6 also indicates the presence of a second complimentary bipolar transistor pair which is parasitic in the fabrication of the MOS structure. The parasitic lateral p-n-p transistor collector acts as a source of base current for the parasitic vertical n-p-n transistor. Currents generated in the substrate by noise spikes on V_{DD} or by ionizing radiation pulses will tend to flow in a direction to forward bias the emitter–base junction of the lateral p-n-p. If sufficient current flows, the emitter–base junction of the external n-p-n will be forward biased. This will create a regenerative current path from V_{DD} to V_{SS}. The current will not turn off until the whole system is shut off. If the current flow is not limited by internal or external resistances, the CMOS device could be permanently damaged.

The equivalent circuit of the parasitic transistors is shown in Fig. 7. Note that this is the equivalent circuit of the three-

terminal thyristor. The criteria for regenerative turn-on in this device are as follows:

1) The product of the current gains in the p-n-p and n-p-n devices ($\beta_{pnp} \cdot \beta_{npn}$) must be greater than unity.

2) The power supplies (V_{DD} and V_{SS}) must be capable of supplying current sufficient to keep both transistors in their active states.

Recent modeling [24] has more adequately accounted for parasitic resistances. Criteria 1) and 2) are to be used as "rules-of-thumb."

It is easy to see how reducing the device-to-device spacing enhances the possibility of latch-up. Scaling reduces the base width of the lateral p-n-p transistor. This sharply increases p-n-p beta, which *enhances* the probability for latch-up.

Initial attempts at eliminating latch-up included the use of gold doping of the substrate to kill minority-carrier lifetime [25]. This destroys the parasitic transistor current gain. The use of thick-field oxides extending below the substrate surface (isoplanar processing) also reduces the severity of this problem by increasing the current path length of the lateral p-n-p. Other design techniques are currently available to lessen the problems [25]. These include improving the grounding of p-wells so the current flows to ground rather than into the base region of the parasitic transistor. In addition, the use of "guard bands" (p-plus diffusions hooked to ground surrounding p-MOS devices and n-plus diffusions tied to V_{DD} surrounding n-MOS devices) is frequently encountered. These rings collect minority carriers and thus reduce the β product of the parasitic transistors. A more recent development is the use of n-well CMOS structures. The high-β parasitic vertical transistor is now a p-n-p device with a lower β. However, complete removal of the silicon substrate eliminates the latch-up problem. This is the case in silicon-on-sapphire (SOS) devices. This underlies the reasoning behind military interest in SOS. In SOS technology, devices are fabricated on silicon islands epitaxially grown on sapphire. This automatically provides dielectric isolation and obviates latch-up. These islands are hooked together by interconnect lines.

An innovation in circuits on insulating substrates is the silicon-on-insulator (SOI) configuration. One popular method for obtaining device-quality SOI is zone recrystallization. The success of this technology rests on the ability of various heating sources to enhance grain size in polycrystalline layers or to create crystal growth from "seeds." In the seed technique, the polycrystalline films on oxide insulators overlap windows cut in these insulators. The windows open to crystalline substrate material. When the substrate is heated, crystal growth proceeds outward from the open window. Lasers [26], electron beams [27], graphite strip heaters [28], and arc lamps [29] have been used to accomplish the heating.

Davis *et al.* have recently reviewed SOI technology from the military perspective [30]. Their collaborators at Hewlett-Packard fabricated n- and p-channel devices on polysilicon layers recrystallized using an argon CW laser. The laser achieved recrystallized areas several microns in size. Device islands were formed by oxidizing the regions surrounding the silicon device islands down to the underlying insulator (see Fig. 8). Devices fabricated in the recrystallized layer were examined for total-dose hardness to Co^{60} gamma rays at NRL. Back-channel leakage was also measured. This study demonstrates that total dose hardness was equivalent to MOS devices fabricated using the same oxidation techniques in crystalline silicon substrates. Back-channel leakages were equivalent to SOS devices and a deep boron implant was helpful in reducing this leakage.

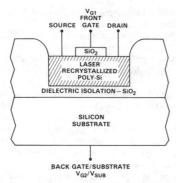

Fig. 8. Laser recrystallized MOSFET [31].

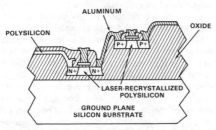

Fig. 9. Proposed vertically integrated CMOS structure designed for radiation hardness through ground-plane/substrate biasing [31].

A dramatic increase in back-channel leakage was observed after irradiation. However, supplying negative bias to the crystalline substrate prevented radiation-induced charge buildup near the back channel and allowed back-channel leakage to remain below 1 μA after 100-krad Co^{60} exposure.

Thus while performance of the SOI devices was similar to SOS devices, the SOI structure could be configured to improve total dose hardness. Specifically, the use of negative substrate bias could reduce radiation-induced leakage. The use of SOI is in its infancy, and one may anticipate more refinement of device processes yielding characteristics surpassing SOS. In addition, multilayer structures become possible (see Fig. 9).

Another radiation-induced failure is called soft error [31]. This failure mode is of interest both to the military and the private sector. High-energy particles from cosmic rays *and* from nuclear decay of packaging ceramics create mobile charge tracks in silicon. These charges can move to switching nodes. If a critical charge Q_{crit} is deposited at the node, the circuit will switch states. This is a particularly severe situation in dynamic RAM's. Here, information is stored as a charge on a capacitor. The particle radiation mentioned above can charge or discharge this capacitor and create a memory error. Cosmic-ray induced pulses can also upset the CMOS and bipolar static RAM cells which are of greater military interest. No permanent damage is done to the device, but critical programs may be destroyed.

How device scaling affects this failure mode is, at present, uncertain. For example, as the capacitor geometry in a dynamic RAM is shrunk, the critical charge threshold Q_{crit} lowers. However, the amount of radiation-induced charge "caught" by the capacitor is less. This situation is complicated by an effect known as funneling [32]. Workers at IBM have shown that in

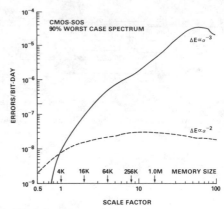

Fig. 10. Effect of scaling scenario on soft-error rate for a CMOS static RAM [34].

a highly ionized particle track, the depletion layer associated with the point of particle entry extends down the length of the track. This creates a "funnel" along which charge is channeled to the surface of the device under electric field assist. In the absence of the funnel, charge can be transferred to the surface of the device only by random diffusion. The funnel concentrates the amount of charge delivered to the surface into a smaller area. It also reduces the path length traveled to the surface for many carriers. This decreases bulk recombination loss. There is also the potential for enhancement of the soft-error rate (SER) since the charge delivered is not spread over 4π sr as it would be if transport was by diffusion only.

Simulation of SER is complicated. The energy deposition and electron–hole pair production density along a particle track must be known. The proximity of the track to critical nodes must also be known, as well as number, type, energy, and angle of incident particles. Whether or not the funnel effect prediction is correct must also be known. Work at NRL has concentrated on verifying the existence of the funnel effect and on modeling the SER.

Recent simulations by Petersen *et al.* [33] have modeled the cosmic ray induced SER for a number of static and dynamic RAM devices. For simple Mead–Conway [34] design scaling, we may anticipate

$$Q_{crit} \propto \alpha^{-2} \qquad (3)$$

where α is a scale factor by which all critical dimensions are reduced. The reasoning behind (3) is as follows. In Mead–Conway scaling, electric fields are kept constant in oxides by reducing oxide thicknesses by the factor α^{-1} and by reducing field plate voltages by the factor α^{-1}. Thus the critical charge necessary to achieve a voltage shift ΔV on a storage capacitor plate scales by α^{-2} (as does the area of the plate). This scaling is, possibly, an oversimplification of what actually occurs in chip design. Thus Petersen *et al.* also performed the study for a "worst case" α^{-3} scaling law. Results are shown in Fig. 10 for an n-MOS dynamic RAM. We see that as the scale factor 1 increases from 10, there is a moderate increase in SER, expressed in errors per bit-day. For the α^{-3} case, a larger increase is observed. In the scaling interval from 10–100, there is a "flattening" effect and the SER does not increase indefinitely. This model does not include funneling. The model is currently being modified to correct for this.

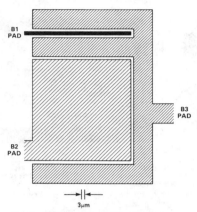

B1
PAD

B3
PAD

B2
PAD

3μm

Fig. 11. NRL charge collection test structure.

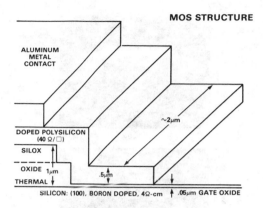

MOS STRUCTURE

ALUMINUM
METAL
CONTACT

~2μm

DOPED POLYSILICON
(40 Ω/□)

SILOX

OXIDE 1μm   .5μm

THERMAL

SILICON: (100), BORON DOPED, 4Ω-cm   .05μm GATE OXIDE

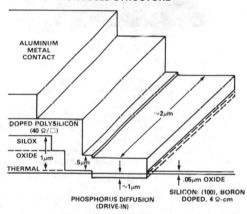

DIFFUSED STRUCTURE

ALUMINUM
METAL
CONTACT

~2μm

DOPED POLYSILICON
(40 Ω/□)

SILOX

OXIDE 1μm   .5μm

THERMAL

~1μm

.05μm OXIDE

PHOSPHORUS DIFFUSION
(DRIVE-IN)

SILICON: (100), BORON
DOPED, 4 Ω-cm

Fig. 12. Cross-sectional views of MOS and diffused versions of the charge collection test structures.

Test structures developed and fabricated at NRL are designed to verify the funnel concept [35]. A typical structure is shown in Fig. 11. A charged-particle beam 2.5 μm in diameter is passed across the electrodes in a direction perpendicular to the long dimension of pad $B1$. The fraction of charge collected by the pads for given biases is recorded and compared to various charge collector theories (including funneling). The structure was fabricated using two cross sections (see Fig. 12). One was a polysilicon-to-diffused junction contact; the other was a polysilicon-over oxide contact. Direct evidence for funneling was observed in the diode diffused structure, but not in the thick (1000-Å) oxide structure. This difference was explained by modeling done by McLean [36]. His model requires minority carriers drawn from a supply through a diffusion to maintain the funnel. In the oxide case, the supply is isolated from the particle track by the oxide, and the funnel collapses quickly. NRL's data do indicate though, that for oxides thinner than 500 Å, enough current may be passing *through* the insulator to sustain the funnel [35]. More work is necessary to support this possibility.

The bulk of this section deals with radiation effects in silicon MOS circuitry. It must not be inferred that GaAs IC's are immune from radiation effects. Recent work at NRL has shown that this is not the case [37]. Exposure to transient bursts (flash X-rays or electron pulses) has been shown to lead to long periods (i.e., up to 100 s) in which GaAs devices will not function improperly. This is due to charge-trapping effects in GaAs substrate material. NRL researchers have found that a deep implanted buried p-layer placed below the active n-layer shielded the devices from substrate charge effects. Once again, as devices scale, smaller currents and voltages are sensed in logic circuitry. Thus the observed radiation effects will increase in importance. However, the buried p-layer significantly improves device performance under these adverse conditions.

To conclude, it can be seen that ionizing radiation affects digital devices in many ways. Large total doses absorbed in MOS oxides cause threshold shifts, interface state growth, and an increase in subthreshold leakage currents. Transient doses can cause "latch-up" or shorting of power supplies. More recently, it has been found that single-particle events can cause logic upset. Reducing device dimensions generally makes each of these effects worse. When devices are scaled, fields may increase causing increased radiation sensitivity and sus-

ceptibility to hot-electron injection. Ionizing radiation lithographies (electon-beam and X-ray) used to produce micron and submicron devices enhance total dose sensitivity, degrade interface quality, and increase subthreshold leakage. While these effects are usually not so severe as to prevent device operation, they must be recognized and accounted for in various applications. The same can be said of latch-up and soft error. Moving to higher density integration usually increases the β product of parasitic bipolar complimentary transistor pairs. Specific design techniques must be developed to prevent latch-up in military parts applications. The threat of soft-error problems also necessitates development of new design techniques. In addition, error-correcting codes must be employed when using scaled devices with very small Q_{crit}. A considerable amount of difficulty associated with transient doses can be eliminated if a good SOI system could be developed. For this reason DOD still pursues work in this area.

IV. SUBMICRON PROCESS ENGINEERING

Despite the difficulties outlined above, there is a clear and present need for submicron structures in military systems. Take, for example, the power FET's whose gate levels are

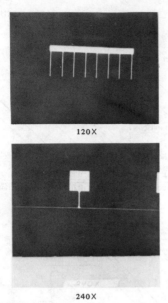

120X

240X

Fig. 13. GaAs power FET. The linear FET (bottom) is 0.6 μm long and 600 μm wide.

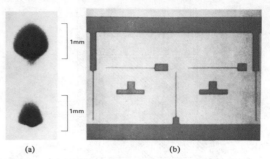

(a)   (b)

Fig. 14. X-ray lithography with a repetitively pulsed laser. (a) Pinhole pictures of soft X-ray output from target plasmas. The repetition rate was 10 Hz. An Nd:glass laser was used. Yb (top) and Al (bottom) plasmas are shown. (b) 4-μm gate pattern exposed in COP with the above X-ray plasma.

shown in Fig. 13. To achieve the described power levels at the frequency of operation required a 0.6-μm gate length. The gate width in the long linear FET gate is 6600 μm. This pattern was produced at the NRL submicron processing facility using a vector scan electron-beam machine. The beam diameter was 1000 Å, the write field was 3 mm × 3 mm, and the writing clock speed was 6 MHz.

The electron-beam generated pattern consists of 99 individual chip patterns (i.e., a nine by eleven matrix) on a 10 cm × 10 cm field. 98 of the chips are comprised of the MOSFET gate pattern and 1 chip is a drop-in gate test array. Each chip requires approximately 45 s to write after initial system calibration and setup which requires approximately 20 min. Total throughput time is, therefore, approximately 1.5 h. This pattern was originally written on a quartz mask blank for replication by deep UV or X-ray lithography. Thus no level-to-level reregistration time was required. Level-to-level reregistration takes even more time. The total increase in time depends on the alignment scheme used. In any event, each time the pattern is written a machine costing over $1 000 000 is occupied for *at least* 1.5 h.

And so, despite continued advances in optical and electron-beam lithography, pattern replication with X-rays may be necessary for the submicron line widths in VLSI chips. The status of optical and X-ray lithography was reviewed recently [38]. Three types of sources are contenders for commercial use in X-ray lithography. They are: electron-impact sources, multi-million-degree dense plasmas, and electron storage rings which emit synchrotron radiation. NRL is performing X-ray lithography research on each of these source types.

Electron impact on solids produces X-rays conveniently, but with low intensity. Such sources, with either stationary or rotating anodes, are being employed for first-generation X-ray exposure stations which were recently announced and are soon to be available. Workers at NRL have formulated codes to

compute the absolute line and continuum output of electron-impact X-ray sources of arbitrary geometry, electron energy, and filtration. Criss *et al.* [39] have produced a code which runs cheaply and yields spectra of useful accuracy. Brown and coworkers have used a numerical solution of the Boltzmann transport equation to follow electron interactions and X-ray production within the solids [40]–[43]. These codes have proven highly useful in computing the output of X-ray sources employed for photoresist exposures, or for studying radiation effects in microelectronics. The codes, and related work, were recently reviewed [43].

Denser plasmas, heated either by laser beams or by electrical discharges, are bright sources of X-rays. While electron-impact sources require exposure times greater than about 1 min, even for sensitive resists, laser-heated plasmas can expose a photoresist in less than 1 μs [44], [45]. Variations in X-ray intensity with laser and target parameters have been studied [46]. While single-shot laser systems can produce adequate exposures, the associated high thermal loading may be deleterious to masks. In order to prolong mask life and to improve exposure control, repetitively pulsed laser–plasma sources are now being studied for X-ray lithography [47]. Neodymium (Nd) lasers with 10-J pulses operating at 10 Hz and excimer lasers with 1-J pulses at 100 Hz are attractive candidates for X-ray lithography sources. Discharge-heated gaseous plasmas, called PUFF's (because the working gas, e.g., argon gas, is blown between the electrodes immediately prior to the discharge) are also being studied for X-ray lithography. They were found to be bright X-ray sources [48]. Recent work with a relatively low-power, repetitively pulsed Nd laser source is shown in Fig. 14. PUFF X-ray sources are being developed commercially [49], [50]. Such sources operable at 10 Hz will be available soon [51]. In light of on-going efforts to produce plasma X-ray sources they may be used in second-generation commercial lithography sources later in this decade.

Synchrotron radiation is both intense and collimated. This translates into short resist exposure times with good edge definition. Despite the high cost of storage rings, many groups are active in assessing the value of synchrotron radiation for X-ray lithography [52]. In one study, NRL collaborated with NBS to build a lithography beam line and to make test exposures at the SURF II facility [53]. That work will soon resume with the goal of making operating microcircuits by synchrotron X-radiation lithography.

DOD looks to these high-speed submicron lithographic techniques for a number of reasons. First, the absolute number of complex parts required by a military system may not be small. For complex VHSIC parts, wafer yields will probably be exceptionally low (1 percent). Thus while "prototype" devices may be produced in small numbers, we may never get sufficient quantities for systems. These high-brightness lithographic sources will increase wafer throughput and increase output. Second, higher throughput usually means lower cost. Finally, with "tuneable wavelength" X-ray sources such as the storage rings, it may be possible to maximize energy deposition in resist and minimize deposition in radiation-sensitive oxides [54]. This will minimize radiation-induced degradation of part performance.

V. CONCLUSIONS

Military applications require high-speed digital circuitry and high-frequency wide-bandwidth analog circuitry. To achieve high speeds, micron and submicron engineering techniques must be employed. Many problems associated with this new area of engineering technology are common to both commercial and military applications. Development of high-resolution lithography, dry etching for faithful pattern transfer, and accurate level-to-level alignment methods are viewed as critical by both sectors. Questions addressing the amount of improvement achieved by dimensional scaling are also common to both sectors. Reliability and testability are common areas of growing interest, as are manufacturability and yield.

Many areas of high-speed microcircuitry are, primarily, of defense interest. Broad-band systems capable of functioning at millimeter-wave frequencies are largely objects of DOD scrutiny. Susceptibility to radiation damage, while of critical military importance, is not of paramount interest in the commercial sector. Furthermore, it appears that scaling down feature sizes enhances many forms of radiation sensitivity. This has been discussed in depth. While modeling and improved circuit design lessens these problems, a considerable amount of development is required in these areas for effective military utilization of submicron engineering.

ACKNOWLEDGMENT

The authors would like to thank the following individuals for substantial contributions to this article: J. Bass, A. Christou, J. Davey, G. Davis, H. Hughes, D. Nagel, D. Patterson, and K. Sleger. Special thanks must be given to J. Davey and D. Nagel. Over the years, Dr. Davey has nurtured and maintained an environment in which the research and development highlighted above could be accomplished. Ongoing collaboration with Dr. Nagel had resulted in much of the lithography progress cited in this review.

REFERENCES

[1] D. Barbe, in IEDM Tech. Dig., p. 20, 1980.
[2] C. A. Liechti, IEEE Trans. Microwave Theory Tech., vol. MTT-24, p. 279, 1976.
[3] M. C. Peckerar and K. F. Galloway, in Proc. University Government Industry Microelectronics Symp., IEEE publ. 81CH1620-4, III, p. 24, 1981.
[4] R. E. Neidert and C. J. Scott, NRL Rep. 8561, 1982.
[5] A. Christou, W. T. Anderson, M. L. Bark, and J. E. Davey, in Proc. Rel. Phys. Symp., p. 180, 1982.
[6] N. A. Papanicolaou, W. T. Anderson, and A. Christou, in Proc. 10th Int. Symp. on GaAs and Related Materials (British Inst. of Phys. Conf. Ser.), to be published.
[7] I. Drukier and J. F. Silcox, in Proc. IRPS, San Francisco, CA, 1979.
[8] E. D. Cohen and A. C. MacPherson, in Proc. IRPS, p. 156, 1979.
[9] A. Christou, J. Appl. Phys, vol. 47, p. 5464, 1976.
[10] K. J. Sleger, H. B. Dietrich, M. L. Bark, and E. M. Swiggard, IEEE Trans. Electron Devices, vol. ED-28, p. 1031, 1981.
[11] J. B. Boos, H. B. Dietrich, T. H. Weng, K. J. Sleger, S. C. Binari, and R. L. Henry, IEEE Electron Device Lett., vol. EDL-3, p. 256, 1982.
[12] J. M. Frary and P. Seese, Semicond. Int., p. 72, Dec. 1981.
[13] H. L. Hughes and R. R. Giroux, Electronics, vol. 37, p. 58, 1964.
[14] F. B. McLean, IEEE Trans. Nucl. Sci., vol. NS-27, p. 1651, 1980.
[15] J. Aiken, IEEE J. Solid-State Circuits, vol. SC-14, p. 294, 1979.
[16] T. H. Ning, P. W. Cook, C. M. Osburn, S. E. Schuster, and H. Yu, IEEE J. Solid-State Circuits, vol. SC-14, p. 283, 1979.
[17] H. L. Hughes, IEEE Trans. Nucl. Sci., vol. NS-26, p. 50, 1979.
[18] M. C. Peckerar, R. Fulton, P. Blaise, D. Brown, and R. Whitlock, J. Vac. Sci. Technol., vol. 16, p. 1658, 1979.
[19] M. C. Peckerar, C. M. Dozier, D. B. Brown, D. Patterson, D. McCarthy, and D. Ma, IEEE Trans. Nucl. Sci., vol. NS-29, p. 1697, Dec. 1982.
[20] K. O. Jeppson and C. M. Svensson, J. Appl. Phys., vol. 48, p. 204, 1977.
[21] S. P. Hofstein, Solid-State Electron., vol. 10, p. 657, 1967.
[22] J. Y. Chen, R. C. Henderson, D. O. Patterson, and R. Martin, IEEE Electron Device Lett., vol. EDL-3, p. 13, 1982.
[23] F. Z. Custode and M. Tam, in IEDM Tech Dig., p. 760, 1980.
[24] D. B. Estrich, Tech. Rep. G-201-9, Stanford Univ., Stanford, CA, Nov. 1980.
[25] J. Lipman, VLSI Des., vol. 3, p. 30, May/June 1982.
[26] A. F. Tasch, T. C. Holloway, K. F. Lee, and J. F. Gibbons, Electron. Lett., vol. 15, p. 435, 1979.
[27] N. M. Johnson, D. J. Bartelink, J. F. Gibbons, K. N. Rathnakumar, and J. L. Regolina, Appl. Phys. Lett., vol. 36, p. 425, 1980.
[28] B. Y. Tsaur, M. W. Geis, J.C.C. Fan, D. J. Silversmith, and R. W. Mountain, Appl Phys. Lett., vol. 39, p. 909, 1981.
[29] M. Haond and D. P. Vu, Electron. Lett., vol. 18, p. 727, 1982.
[30] G. E. Davis, H. L. Hughes, T. I. Kamins, IEEE Trans. Nucl. Sci., vol. NS-29, p. 1685, Dec. 1982.
[31] T. C. May and M. H. Woods, IEEE Trans. Electron Devices, vol. ED-26, p. 2, 1979.
[32] C. M. Hsieh, P. C. Murley, and R. S. O'Brien, IEEE Electron Device Lett., vol. EDL-2, p. 103, 1981.
[33] E. L. Petersen, P. Shapiro, J. H. Adams, and E. A. Burke, IEEE Trans. Nucl. Sci., vol. NS-29, p. 2055, Dec. 1982.
[34] C. A. Mead and L. Conway, Introduction to VLSI Systems. Reading, MA: Addison-Wesley, 1980, p. 33.
[35] A. R. Campbell and A. R. Knudson, IEEE Trans. Nucl. Sci., vol. NS-29, p. 2067, Dec. 1982.
[36] F. B. McLean, IEEE Electron Device Lett., to be published.
[37] W. T. Anderson, M. Simons, E. E. King, H. B. Dietrich, and R. J. Lambert, IEEE Trans. Nucl. Sci., vol. NS-29, p. 1533, Dec. 1982.
[38] D. J. Nagel, SPIE, vol. 279, p. 98, 1981.
[39] J. W. Criss, L. S. Birks, and J. V. Gilfrich, Anal. Chem., vol. 50, p. 33, 1978.
[40] D. B. Brown and J. V. Gilfrich, J. Appl. Phys., vol. 42, p. 4044, 1971.
[41] L. S. Birks, Anal. Chem. Ann. Rev., vol. 44, p. 557R, 1972.
[42] D. B. Brown, J. V. Gilfrich, and M. C. Peckerar, J. Appl. Phys., vol. 46, p. 4537, 1975.
[43] D. B. Brown and D. J. Nagel, in Proc. Topical Conf. on Low Energy X-ray Diagnostics, D. T. Attwood and B. L. Henke, Eds. New York: Amer. Inst. Phys., 1981, p. 253.
[44] D. J. Nagel and M. C. Peckerar, Electron. Lett., vol. 14, p. 781, 1979.
[45] M. C. Peckerar, J. R. Greig, D. J. Nagel, R. E. Pechacek, and R. R. Whitlock, in Proc. Symp. Electron and Ion Beam Sci. Tech., Electro Chem. Soc. Proc., vol. 78-5, p. 432, 1970.
[46] D. J. Nagel, R. R. Whitlock, J. R. Greig, R. E. Pechacek, and M. C. Peckerar, SPIE, vol. 135, p. 46, 1978.
[47] D. J. Nagel, C. M. Brown, M. C. Peckerar, M. L. Ginter, J. A. Robinson, T. McIlrath, and P. K. Carroll, Appl. Opt., to be published.
[48] P. G. Burkhalter, J. Shiloh, A. Fisher, and R. D. Cowan, J. Appl. Phys., vol. 50, p. 4532, 1979.
[49] S. M. Mathews, R. Stringfield, I. Roth, R. Copper, N. P. Economou, and D. C. Flanders, to be published.
[50] J. S. Pearlman and J. C. Riordan, in Proc. 16th Symp. on Electron, Ion and Photron Beam Tech., vol. 26-9, May 1981.
[51] C. Gilman, Maxwell Labs, private communication.
[52] W. P. Grobman, in Handbook on Synchrotron Radiation, E. E. Koch et al. Eds., vol. 1. Amsterdam: North-Holland, 1981.
[53] L. R. Hughey, R. T. Williams, J. C. Rife, D. J. Nagel, and M. C. Peckerar, Nucl. Inst. Meth., vol. 195, p. 267, 1982.
[54] M. C. Peckerar, R. Fulton, and D. J. Nagel, Stanford Synchrotron Radiation Lab. Rep. 79/02, p. 110, 1979.

GaAs Microwave Devices and Circuits with Submicron Electron-Beam Defined Features

WILLIAM R. WISSEMAN, SENIOR MEMBER, IEEE, H. MICHAEL MACKSEY, SENIOR MEMBER, IEEE,
GAILON E. BREHM, SENIOR MEMBER, IEEE, AND PAUL SAUNIER, MEMBER, IEEE

Invited Paper

*Abstract—*This paper describes the fabrication and application of GaAs FET's, both as discrete microwave devices and as the key active components in monolithic microwave integrated circuits. The performance of these devices and circuits is discussed for frequencies ranging from 3 to 25 GHz. The crucial fabrication step is the formation of the submicron gate by electron-beam lithography.

I. INTRODUCTION

HISTORICALLY, microwave devices have been one of the primary driving forces of micron and submicron lithography. The initial work on solid-state microwave sources in the 1960's centered on the silicon bipolar transistor [1]. Since the high-frequency performance of solid-state devices is limited by transit time effects, there was a need for small device geometries. With the advent of the Gunn diode in the middle 1960's and IMPATT diodes a few years later, two-terminal devices played a dominant role [2], [3]. In these devices, the carrier transit time is determined by material parameters rather than the lithographic definition of patterns on the semiconductor surface. Consequently, the rapid progress in the development of GaAs Gunn diodes and silicon, and later, GaAs IMPATT diodes that operated at microwave and millimeter-wave frequencies was not related to lithography improvements. Work also continued on microwave silicon bipolar transistors, and with the development of electron-beam lithography in the late 1960's, culminated in the demonstration of a 10-GHz transistor that delivered 1 W [4]. The effort to develop microwave bipolar transistors was a primary motivation for the development of electron-beam lithography at Texas Instruments.

Beginning in the early 1970's, the GaAs FET became the focus of microwave solid-state device development, and improved lithography was again critical [5]. The GaAs FET is important both as a low-noise amplifier of microwave signals and as a source of microwave power. It is being used in a variety of circuit applications in communications, radar, and electronic warfare. Unlike microwave Gunn and IMPATT diodes, GaAs FET's are planar devices that are fabricated on semi-insulating substrates. This makes it relatively easy to fabricate both active devices and passive impedance-matching elements on the same substrate, and has led to the development of a variety of GaAs monolithic microwave integrated circuits (MMIC's) over the past several years [6]. Complex

Manuscript received November 18, 1982. This work was supported in part by AFWAL, NRL, and NASA Lewis Research Center.
The authors are with Central Research Laboratories, Texas Instruments, Dallas, TX 75265.

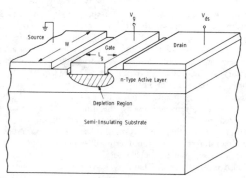

Fig. 1. Basic GaAs FET device structure.

MMIC's are now under development at a number of companies. They offer improved performance and/or reduced cost in comparison with conventional hybrid microwave circuits, and they are expected to result in a variety of systems applications. These include active-element phased-array radars, low-cost expendable jammers for electronic warfare, and receivers for direct satellite television broadcasting.

The development of GaAs FET's paralleled and benefitted from rapid advances in lithography, both optical and electron beam. While the primary motivation for most of these advances was the development of silicon IC's, much of the work on micron and submicron structures carried out to date has involved GaAs. The development of GaAs FET's at Texas Instruments will be described in this paper and their application as discrete devices in hybrid microwave circuits and as the key elements in MMIC's will be discussed. The need for submicron geometries and the means for fabricating structures with these geometries using electron-beam lithography will be covered.

II. REQUIREMENT FOR SMALL DEVICE GEOMETRIES

The basic structure of the GaAs FET is shown in Fig. 1. The structure is formed on a semi-insulating GaAs substrate with a resistivity of about $10^7\,\Omega\cdot\text{cm}$. The conducting layer is formed by epitaxial growth or by direct ion implantation into the substrate. The doping of the conducting layer is n-type since electron mobilities in GaAs are more than an order of magnitude higher than hole mobilities. Current flow between the ohmic source and drain contacts is modulated by changing the voltage on the Schottky-barrier gate metal of length

Reprinted from *Proc. IEEE*, vol. 71, pp. 667–675, May 1983.

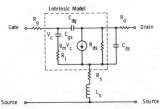

Fig. 2. Equivalent circuit of a GaAs FET.

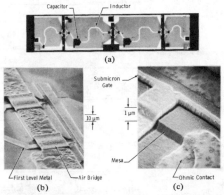

Fig. 3. GaAs monolithic low-noise amplifier. (a) Three-stage amplifier chip. (b) SEM of monolithic FET showing thick metal layers used for inductors and air bridges. (c) SEM showing submicron details of channel region.

L_g. The current handling capability of the FET is determined by the gate width W. Power FET's commonly have multiple-gate fingers in order to provide high current capability without the excessive gate resistance associated with a single-gate finger.

The velocity of electrons in GaAs depends strongly on the electric field. The velocity peaks at about 2×10^7 cm/s and saturates at about 8×10^6 cm/s at high fields. For gate lengths of 1 μm or less, the electron velocity is saturated during most of the transit period. Therefore, the transit time and maximum frequency of operation are determined by the ratio of the gate length to the saturated velocity. For microwave frequency operation, the transit time for the electrons to move through the region under the gate must be minimized. The most obvious way to do this is to reduce the gate length. However, in the limit of very-short gate lengths (<0.25 μm), it has been predicted that the electron transport will be ballistic in nature and that velocities several times the saturation velocity can be achieved [7]. The impact of ballistic transport on microwave FET's is uncertain at this point and is the subject of some controversy [8]. Ballistic transport does not apply to the devices considered in this paper since gate lengths are greater than 0.4 μm for the applications that are described.

In order to explicitly show the effect of gate length on device performance, the FET can be modeled by the lumped-element equivalent circuit shown in Fig. 2 [9], [10]. This equivalent circuit applies to both low-noise and power FET's operated at small-signal levels. The maximum available small-signal gain (MAG) calculated for this circuit is given by

$$MAG = \left(\frac{f_T}{f}\right)^2 \cdot \frac{1}{4g_{ds}(R_g + R_i + R_s + \pi f_T L_s) + 4\pi f_T C_{dg}(2R_g + R_i + R_s + 2\pi f_T L_s)} \tag{1}$$

and the cutoff frequency f_T is given by

$$f_T \approx \frac{g_m}{2\pi C_{gs}} \tag{2}$$

where

f	operating frequency
g_{ds}	drain conductance
R_g	gate series resistance
R_i	channel resistance between source and gate
R_s	source series resistance
L_S	common-source lead inductance
C_{dg}	drain–gate capacitance
C_{gs}	gate–source capacitance
g_m	transconductance.

When component values determined from measurement of device S-parameters at microwave frequencies are inserted into these equations, the agreement with experimentally measured

gain is very good at small-signal levels [11, pp. 13–60]. This approach must be modified to account for the performance of power FET's operated at large-signal levels [11, pp. 61–97]. For given device parameters, the MAG in (1) falls off 6 dB per octave increase in frequency (i.e., as $1/f^2$). The cutoff frequency varies approximately as $1/L_g$ since $C_{gs} \propto L_g$ so that short gate length structures are required to achieve usable gain at high frequencies.

Short gate lengths also are required for low noise figures. An approximate expression for the minimum noise figure in terms of device geometry and material parameters is given by

$$F_{min} = 1 + K_1 L_g f \sqrt{g_m (R_g + R_S)} \tag{3}$$

where K_1 is a fitting factor [12]. The noise figure depends strongly on gate length, although the dependence is not quite linear because some of the device geometry and material parameters also depend on gate length. In summary, minimizing FET gate length maximizes the frequency of operation and the performance at any given frequency.

III. DEVICE FABRICATION

Fabrication of GaAs devices capable of operating at microwave frequencies involves the formation of submicron and micron features, as well as much larger structures, on and in the surface of a single-crystalline GaAs chip. A description of a typical process for fabrication of GaAs MMIC's is given in this section with special emphasis on the techniques used to form the submicron FET gates. The procedure used to fabricate discrete microwave GaAs FET's is a subset of the MMIC process.

Fig. 3 shows a three-stage low-noise amplifier that is representative of GaAs MMIC technology. The chip size is 1 mm $\times$ 4 mm. The overall layout and larger features of this circuit are shown in Fig. 3(a). Submicron features of the circuit are shown in the scanning electron micrographs (SEM) of Fig. 3(b) and (c). The arrows point out features that are formed during processing as described in the following. Several

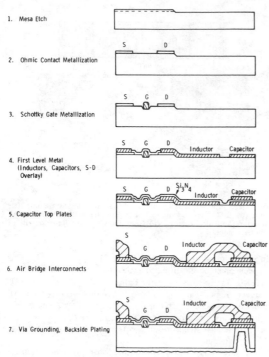

Fig. 4. GaAs MMIC process flow diagram.

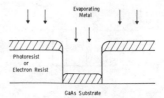

Fig. 5. Schematic diagram of liftoff process.

hundred MMIC's of this type or several thousand discrete devices are fabricated on a single wafer, and several wafers can be processed as a group so that low cost and uniformity of characteristics are obtained.

Two key processes have been used together in the development of submicron GaAs devices: electron-beam lithography for resist patterning and metal definition by resist liftoff. The combination of these two processes produces high-resolution lines with a high aspect ratio (the ratio of metal thickness to line width). Line widths of 0.5 μm with aspect ratios greater than 1 are achieved.

GaAs single-crystal wafers are used as substrates for fabrication of these devices and circuits. Preparation of these substrates involves the synthesis and growth from the purified elements gallium and arsenic of a single crystal of gallium arsenide. The boule is then sawed into wafers that are typically 50 mm in diameter and polished to a mirror finish free of mechanical damage or chemical contamination. The wafers are generally undoped or lightly doped with a compensating impurity such that they are semi-insulating (10^7 $\Omega \cdot$ cm or greater). High crystalline quality and surface finish are required so that submicron features can be formed in and on the substrate in large quantities with high yield. Fig. 4 is a flow diagram for the steps used in wafer processing.

A. Active Layer Formation and Mesa Etch

Using either ion implantation or epitaxial deposition, a continuous n-type layer is formed over the entire wafer surface. This layer is approximately 0.25 μm thick and is the first submicron feature of the circuit. Micron and submicron features will be patterned in the other two dimensions to form

the active channels of the microwave FET's on the surface of this layer. To provide isolation, the n-type active layer is mesa etched to remove it from all areas of the wafer except where the active FET's or diodes will be formed. This is done using conventional contact photolithography to pattern a photoresist layer that protects those areas of the surface where the active layer is to remain during wet chemical etching. Alternative approaches for accomplishing this process step include selective ion implantation of the active area using a photoresist mask or ion bombardment of the area surrounding the active region to destroy the conductivity.

B. Source/Drain Ohmic Contact Metallization

An AuGe/Ni layer is evaporated and defined by photoresist liftoff. Liftoff is a technique used extensively to pattern metals on GaAs. The reasons for using liftoff rather than etching are that the GaAs surface is readily damaged by many of the chemicals commonly employed to etch metal patterns and that liftoff produces much steeper metal edges. Fig. 5 illustrates the liftoff technique. A cross section of a typical pattern defined in a photoresist or electron-resist layer is shown. The pattern is the negative image of the desired metal pattern. Metal atoms evaporated from a distant heated source condense on the substrate. If the resist sidewall is vertical or undercut, the metal deposited on the substrate is not connected to that deposited on the resist. When the resist is dissolved away, the unwanted metal is removed. A technique called dielectric-assisted liftoff can be used to improve liftoff of very thick metal layers. In this case, a dielectric layer such as silicon nitride is deposited prior to the resist. The dielectric layer is undercut during the etching process so that a resist overhang is formed. This procedure helps to prevent a connection between metal deposited on the GaAs substrate and that on the resist surface.

After deposition and liftoff of the source/drain metal layer, alloying at 430°C for 3 min forms ohmic contacts to the GaAs. The contact layers are 0.2 μm thick and they have minimum features of 3 μm. Edge smoothness of 0.25 μm is required since alignment of the gate metal to within 0.5 μm of the edge is sometimes required. This ohmic contact metal layer is also used to form alignment marks used by the electron-beam exposure system to precisely locate the critical submicron gate pattern.

C. Schottky-Gate Metallization

Electron-beam lithography is employed for the submicron gates. This technique allows high uniformity of submicron lines on large wafers. The wafer is divided into many fields having alignment marks at each corner. These alignment marks are deposited during the source/drain contact evaporation. A 2 mm × 2 mm maximum field size is usually used at Texas Instruments. The field size is limited by the maximum amount the electron beam can be deflected without distortion. The wafer is coated with an appropriate electron-sensitive material such as PMMA (polymethylmethacrylate) and loaded on a computer-controlled x–y stage in the vacuum chamber beneath the electron column. The controlling computer is programmed to step the stage from field to field within the array, align to each field, and direct the electron beam to expose the proper patterns. Alignment is accomplished by scanning across the alignment marks located at the four corners of the electron-beam field while detecting the backscattered electrons from the edges of these marks. Once these four marks are located, the computer corrects for x and y positional and rotational errors. It also corrects for magnification errors resulting from earlier operations, from variations in wafer temperature, or from the electron-beam machine itself. Special care must be taken in electron-beam patterning of GaAs to provide a ground connection to all patterns on the wafer surface to avoid charging effects caused by the semi-insulating substrate. After stepping, aligning, and exposing each field, the wafer is removed from the vacuum chamber and the pattern is developed. A tradeoff between the electron-beam exposure dose and the development time is made to optimize the resist contrast and the resist edge profile.

After electron-beam exposure and development, the gate area is recessed using a wet etch to achieve the desired device current, and Ti/Pt/Au is evaporated and defined by a liftoff process similar to that used for ohmic contacts. Fig. 3(b) shows the smooth edges and high aspect ratio that are achieved. This gate metal stripe is 0.6 μm thick and 0.5 μm wide.

D. First-Level Metal (Inductors, Capacitor Bottom Plates, Source/Drain Overlay)

Sequential layers of titanium and gold are deposited and patterned by liftoff to simultaneously form the inductors, the bottom plates of the metal–insulator–metal (MIM) capacitors, and to overlay the alloyed source and drain regions to reduce the spreading resistance. This metal can be almost 2 μm thick to reduce microwave losses in the various components. It is patterned using the dielectric-assisted liftoff procedure described previously.

E. Capacitor Top Plates

High-quality silicon nitride is deposited by a plasma-assisted reaction of silane and ammonia to form the capacitor dielectric. Ti/Au is again vacuum deposited and patterned by liftoff to form the capacitor top plates. For discrete devices, the silicon nitride is used only as a protective layer.

F. Air-Bridge Interconnects

Gold-plated air bridges are used to form low conductor loss, low parasitic capacitance interconnects between source regions of multiple-gate-finger FET's; this is a convenient way, as well, to connect capacitor top plates and first-level metal inductors without step coverage problems. A thick layer of photoresist supports the gold bridge during plating and another layer of resist confines the plating to the desired area. Approximately 5 μm of plated gold is used to form a strong low-loss structure. Elements of the circuit requiring additional conductivity are plated at the same time, as are the pads for wire bonding and dc probing.

G. Thinning, Backside Metallization, and Dicing

After completion of the preceding steps, topside wafer processing is complete and all the micron and submicron features of the device have been formed. The wafer must then be thinned to the proper thickness and metallized on the backside to form an RF ground plane and a strong metallurgical bond for packaging. In some cases, vias are etched through to the topside and backfilled with plated gold where grounding is required in the interior of the circuit. Finally, the individual MMIC chips are separated from each other by a high-speed saw or by a scribe and break technique.

IV. DISCRETE FET'S

A number of discrete GaAs power FET's have been developed at Texas Instruments for use at frequencies from 3 to 25 GHz. The design guideline typically used is that at least 4-dB gain is required at the operating power level for a useful device. The small-signal gain is at least 4 dB higher. The gain drops off as $1/(\text{frequency})^2$ as shown in (1), so that special care must be taken in the design of FET's that are operated at the higher end of this frequency range. In order to obtain the necessary gain, the gate length is reduced in accordance with (1) and (2), but changes in device design are also required. Two of the most effective changes are to reduce the gate-finger widths [13] and the source lead inductance [10].

It has been shown that small devices can produce up to 1-W output power per millimeter gate width almost independent of frequency over most of the frequency range under discussion [15]. However, the maximum output power that has been obtained from GaAs FET's described in the literature decreases from about 30 W at 3 GHz to 1 W at 20 GHz. This decrease in output power with frequency is partially due to the inability to either match the impedance or uniformly feed large transistors as frequency increases, since the chip size is an increasing fraction of a wavelength. Also contributing to reduced output power at higher frequencies is the fact that the design changes to increase gain mentioned in the previous paragraph generally reduce the total gate width that can fit on a given size chip. In this section, three Texas Instruments devices are described in detail in order to illustrate the different design and lithography requirements for different frequency ranges. The devices are an X-band FET (8–12 GHz), a K-band FET (18–26 GHz), and an S-band FET (2–4 GHz). They are described in the order of their development. These devices can, of course, be operated at less than the design frequency at a higher gain level.

A. X-Band FET

The X-band FET has 4.8-mm total gate width in four cells. The large gate width is obtained by the conventional method of paralleling a number of gate fingers—each of the four cells has eight 150-μm fingers. Fig. 6 shows SEM photographs of a bonded device. The gate pad is located at the bottom of Fig. 6(a) and the drain pad at the top. The sources are interconnected by a plated-gold air bridge. In Fig. 6(b) it is seen that the sources are grounded by bond wires at the ends of the 2 mm × 0.5 mm × 0.1-mm-thick chip and also by wires going across the chip. If the wires going across the chip were left off, the source lead inductance would be excessive and the gain would be reduced by several decibels. The gain would

(a)

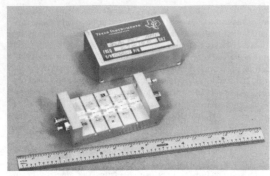

Fig. 7. Four-stage *X*-band GaAs FET hybrid power amplifier.

(b)

Fig. 6. SEM photographs of bonded *X*-band GaAs power FET. (a) Details of a single cell. (b) 4.8-mm gate-width chip.

also be degraded if the wires interconnecting the gate and drain pads were left off. These wires help equalize the amplitude and phase of the microwave signal at each cell.

The devices are fabricated by the process described in Section III with gates defined by electron-beam lithography. Each electron-beam field is 2 mm X 2 mm and contains three 4.8-mm gate-width devices plus several material and processing test patterns. The gate length is typically 0.75 μm and the gates are fabricated by the liftoff of 0.15 μm Ti/0.05 μm Pt/0.4 μm Au with about 0.7 μm of PMMA. The exposure time per field is about 10 s including about 3 s to move the stage between fields and acquire the alignment marks. The total exposure time for a 2.5 cm X 2.5 cm slice is about 25 min. This time could be reduced significantly by changing several photomasks slightly so that the electron-beam machine would not be used to write any part of the gate pad. This improvement has been made on devices developed more recently. Device gain is not significantly improved by reducing the gate length to 0.5 μm, because the increased gain due to the shorter gate length is canceled by gain reduction caused by increased signal attenuation along the more resistive 150-μm gate fingers. In order to take advantage of the higher gain accompanying 0.5-μm gates, it is necessary to reduce the finger width to 75 μm or less. This would cut the device total gate width, and hence the power capability in half. The present gate–gate spacing of the device in Fig. 6 is 30 μm across the drains and 55 μm across the sources. It is not desirable to reduce this

spacing significantly to increase device total gate width, because chip heating would become excessive.

The 4.8-mm gate-width devices typically have 2.5- to 3-W output power with 4- to 6-dB gain at 10 GHz, with the best devices having up to 3.9-W output power with 6-dB gain and 39-percent power-added efficiency. The highest gain devices can be operated into *Ku*-band, producing up to 2-W output power with 4-dB gain at 15 GHz. These devices were developed for use in the transmitter–amplifier of a phased-array radar module which also contains a low-noise receiver and a phase shifter. A large number of identical modules are required in a phased-array radar. The transmitters are typically capable of amplifying a transmitted signal with 25-dB gain and 2-W output power over a 1-GHz bandwidth at *X*-band. This gain requires four stages of amplification and the 4.8-mm device is used in the fourth stage. Fig. 7 is a photograph of a 2-W *X*-band amplifier with four stages of amplification. The input, output, and interstage impedances are matched by the microstrip circuits that take up most of the amplifier area in Fig. 7.

B. K-Band FET

The *K*-band FET has been designed especially for high-frequency (20-GHz) operation. The main feature of this device type is the single straight-line gate with two or more feeds (hence the name π-gate). Devices with 0.3-, 0.6-, 0.9-, 1.35-, and 1.8-mm gate widths have been developed at Texas Instruments.

Fig. 8 is a photograph of a 1.35-mm device. Nine gate pads connect the gate stripe; each gate pad feeds two individual 75-μm-wide gate fingers. This unit gate width is optimum for high-frequency operation and permits the use of 0.5-μm gate lengths to obtain higher gain. Since it is necessary to interconnect the gate pads in order to feed all gates equally, air bridges are needed to connect the individual sources to the grounding bar that extends the length of the chip.

At high frequencies, it is difficult to achieve adequate gain (>4 dB). Therefore, the attainment of small gate lengths is critical. By carefully controlling the exposure of the electron-beam resist and its development time, it is possible to define 0.4- to 0.5-μm-wide stripes and liftoff 0.6-μm-thick metal. For minimum distortion and maximum resolution, a reduced field size of 1.5 mm X 1.5 mm is used. It contains three 1.35-mm, two 0.6-mm, and one 0.3-mm gate-width devices

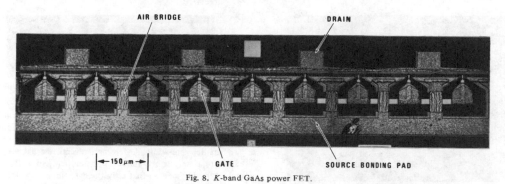

Fig. 8. *K*-band GaAs power FET.

plus several material and processing test patterns. Since the electron-beam machine is not used to write any part of the gate pads, the writing time per field is about 3 s.

The π-gate structure has several advantages over the conventional parallel-finger design. The parasitic reactances, which become increasingly important influences on performance as the frequency of operation increases, are smaller. Equivalent circuit calculations from the *S*-parameters demonstrate that the π-gate structure reduces the gate-to-drain capacitance by about 30 percent. The large-area source-grounding bar connected to ground by a low-inductance mesh or a sheet of solder insures a very low source lead inductance per unit gate width. Another advantage of this structure is that, with a large number of widely spaced gate and drain pads, the effective inductance of the bond wires used to contact the device can be made very low so that the FET input and output capacitances can be resonated at very high frequencies. Finally, the very symmetrical feeding of the gates improves the performance.

A 1.35-mm FET typically has 700- to 800-mW output power with 6-dB gain at 15 GHz. The available gain decreases as the frequency goes up: at 20 GHz the best devices have 675 mW with 5.8-dB gain; at 22 GHz, 355 mW with 4.5-dB gain; and at 23 GHz, 200 mW with 4.0-dB gain. Up to 200 mW at 25 GHz was obtained from a device operated as an oscillator [15].

These devices were used extensively in an amplifier developed for NASA operating in the 17.7–20.2-GHz communication band [16]. Fig. 9(a) is a photograph of the overall amplifier which combines 16 identical modules. Fig. 9(b) is a detailed picture of one module showing the six stages necessary to achieve the goal of 0.5 W with 30-dB gain. The first five stages use, respectively, 150-, 150-, 300-, 600-, and 1350-μm gate-width FET's. In the output stage, two 1350-μm devices are paralleled by using a Wilkinson combiner. The overall amplifier has a power of 8 W with 30-dB gain.

C. S-Band FET

The *S*-band FET was developed recently [17] with a goal of fabricating a device capable of producing 25-W pulsed output power with 6-dB gain across the 3- to 3.5-GHz band. These devices will be used in phased-array radar systems in a transmitter–amplifier application similar to that of the *X*-band device described earlier, but at a lower frequency and con-

(a)

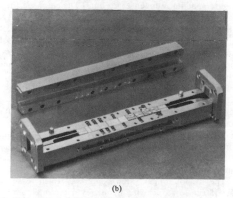

(b)

Fig. 9. *K*-band GaAs FET hybrid power amplifier. (a) 16-module amplifier having 8-W output power with 30-dB gain over the 17.7–20.2-GHz band. (b) Six-stage amplifier module having 30-dB gain and 0.5-W output power.

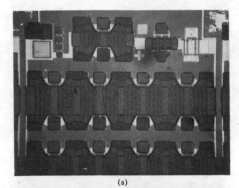

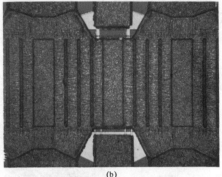

(a)

(b)

Fig. 10. *S*-band GaAs power FET slice during fabrication. (a) 19.2-mm gate-width device. (b) Details of a single cell.

Fig. 11. Four-stage *X*-band GaAs FET monolithic power amplifier chip.

siderably higher yield. There is no mask–slice abrasion, mask runout, or variation in mask contact. A 2 mm × 2 mm electron-beam field contains two 19.2-mm gate-width chips plus two smaller gate-width devices and several test patterns. The exposure time is only about 10 s per field, since the photomasks are designed so that only the gate fingers are defined by the electron beam. Owing to the larger gate length, relatively thick gate metal can be lifted off, resulting in higher gain due to the reduced signal attenuation on the gate fingers. 0.7 μm of PMMA is used to lift off the 0.15 μm Ti/0.05 μm Pt/0.8 μm Au gates.

The best 38.4-mm gate-width devices fabricated to date have had 20-W CW output power with 7-dB gain and 34-percent power-added efficiency at 3 GHz. Pulsed devices have had more than 30-W output power at 3 GHz and 25 W across the 3.0- to 3.5-GHz band.

V. MONOLITHIC CIRCUITS

A number of MMIC's have been developed for a variety of purposes at Texas Instruments. These circuits are generally designed using well-characterized submicron-gate GaAs FET types in a chip layout that makes use of MIM capacitors and high-impedance microstrip lines as inductive elements. This semi-lumped-element approach minimizes the amount of chip area consumed by the passive circuit elements.

These element values are optimized using computer-aided design and are then precisely and repeatably realized during the MMIC fabrication process. On some circuits, plated-through vias are used to ground points within the circuit. The circuits described in this section are typical of power amplifiers, low-noise amplifiers, and oscillators being developed for phased-array radar, electronic warfare, and satellite communications applications from 7 to 20 GHz.

A. X-Band Power Amplifier

A four-stage power amplifier utilizing discrete GaAs FET's was shown in Fig. 7. A similar amplifier which has been integrated onto a single chip of GaAs is shown in Fig. 11 [18]. This amplifier is 5.75 mm × 1.63 mm × 0.15 mm, and GaAs FET's with gate widths of 0.3, 0.3, 0.6, and 1.5 mm are used in the first through fourth stages. Networks of inductors and MIM capacitors are used to provide 50-Ω input and output impedances and the appropriate impedances for interstage matching. The drain bias is brought to the FET's through the line running along the upper side of the chip and the gate bias through the line along the lower side. In Fig. 11, the FET's are the multifinger structures along the center of the chip and the capacitors are the large squares and rectangles. The eight very large pads are ~30-pF shunt capacitors to ground. The ground plane is brought to the capacitor bottom plates through etched vias to the back of the chip which also ground the FET sources. Only four bonds are required

siderably higher power level. The 25-W device has 38.4-mm total gate width in eight cells. Two 19.2-mm gate-width chips are used instead of a single chip in order to increase yield and reduce thermal stresses during bonding. The chips are mounted adjacent to each other and treated as a single 38.4-mm gate-width device. In order to fit this large gate width on a chip, the gate-finger width is increased to 300 μm and the gate-to-gate spacing reduced to 20 μm. The chips are thinned to 0.05 mm to reduce the resulting high operating temperature. Fig. 10 shows photographs of a slice during processing. A 19.2-mm gate-width device is shown in the center of Fig. 10(a) and a single cell is shown in Fig. 10(b). The sources are interconnected by a plated-gold air bridge which also connects to the bonding areas along both sides of the chip.

The major problem with the *K*-band FET described previously is obtaining enough gain at that high a frequency. The gain requirement for the *X*-band device is not as severe, but the yield is more of a concern since large numbers of fairly large devices are required. With this *S*-band device, gain is not a problem due to the low frequency (see (1)). However, it is difficult to obtain high process yields with such a large device (38.4-mm total gate width distributed among 128 gate fingers). The use of longer gates is one way to increase yield. Because of the low operating frequency, adequate gain is obtained with a gate length of 1.5 μm. Although the 1.5-μm gates can be defined either with photolithography or electron-beam lithography, the latter has been found to give a con-

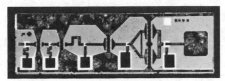

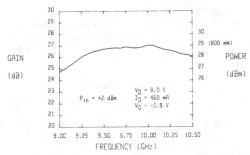

Fig. 12. Gain–frequency response of the power amplifier of Fig. 11.

Fig. 13. Four-stage K-band GaAs FET monolithic power amplifier.

to operate this chip: drain bias, gate bias, RF input, and RF output.

The fabrication process was described in Section III. The gates are approximately 0.75 μm long and are defined by electron-beam lithography. The chip is divided into two electron-beam fields, one with the two 0.3-mm gate-width devices and one with the two larger devices. Fig. 12 shows the gain–frequency response of one of these amplifiers. This chip, with less than 10-mm^2 area, has the performance of a much larger hybrid amplifier employing discrete devices. The monolithic amplifier eliminates numerous bond wires and is potentially much more reliable than an equivalent hybrid amplifier.

A similar four-stage amplifier (without the on-chip bias network) has been developed that produces 1.25-W output power with 30-dB gain over the 7.25- to 7.75-GHz band [19]. Several hundred of these amplifiers have been fabricated for use in a satellite active-array antenna. The slice yields have averaged about 20 percent with some as high as 40 percent.

B. K-Band Power Amplifier

The amplifier discussed in this section makes full use of GaAs monolithic technology to replace the module of Fig. 9(b) with the single 1.4 mm × 4.4 mm chip shown in Fig. 13. The performance goal is 0.5-W output power with 20-dB gain across the 17.7–20.2-GHz bandwidth. This four-stage amplifier now under development at Texas Instruments uses 0.3-, 0.3-, and 0.6-mm FET's in the first through third stages. The output stage is a combination of two 0.75-mm FET's in parallel. The concept of the matching network is the same as for the X-band amplifier described in Section V-A, but the size of the inductors and capacitors are smaller since the circuit is designed for a higher operating frequency. Etched vias are used to ground the FET sources and the capacitor bottom plates.

As stated previously, the FET gate length is particularly critical to the performance of high-frequency FET's. In this case, 0.5-μm-long gates are needed to insure a sufficient gain,

and gate-finger widths of 75 μm are required to minimize losses. The chip is divided into two electron-beam fields, one with the two 0.3-mm devices and one with the 0.6- and 1.5-mm devices.

The advantage of the monolithic approach over the conventional hybrid amplifier employing discrete FET's is particularly obvious if one considers the size difference between this chip and the module of Fig. 9(b). Also of prime consideration, if one were to use monolithic circuits in the 16-module amplifier of Fig. 9(a), would be the saving of most of the 700 bonding steps that are required to assemble and tune the 112 discrete FET's.

C. X-Band Low-Noise Amplifier

An X-band monolithic low-noise amplifier employing three 300-μm gate-width FET's in a three-stage common-source cascade was shown in Fig. 3 [20]. This chip is 4 mm × 1 mm × 0.15 mm in size, which is roughly one-fifth the length and width of an equivalent low-noise amplifier using conventional hybrid techniques. The input-matching circuit presents the optimum source impedance, or noise match, to the first FET of the amplifier, minimizing the noise figure. Succeeding stages incorporate matching circuits to maximize gain over the desired bandwidth. The output stage is matched to 50 Ω. Wire bonds are used only to connect the input and output terminals and to provide gate and drain bias to each FET.

The fabrication process for this amplifier chip was described in Section III. The metallurgical FET gate length (width of the gate stripe) is 0.5 μm. The gates are defined in 0.6-μm-thick Ti/Pt/Au using electron-beam lithography and metal liftoff. To satisfy the special requirements for low capacitance in low-noise devices, a thin layer of silicon nitride is used under the electron resist. This nitride layer is removed after electron-beam exposure and development by plasma etching in a reactor, which allows precise control of the undercut of the nitride layer beneath the resist overhang. This small undercut allows the edge of the gate recess, which is to be etched into the GaAs, to be moved back from the gate metal edge. The gate is then defined by the overhanging resist edge during the evaporation and liftoff process. By enlarging this excess gate recess to slightly more than the gate depletion depth, the depletion-layer capacitance is greatly reduced with only a minimal increase in parasitic resistance. Electron-beam exposure of this circuit, like most large MMIC's, must be accomplished using multiple fields. Actually, a pair of these chips, which are located side by side on the wafer, are exposed together in two electron-beam steps. The gates of the first two stages of the two amplifiers are exposed in one pass followed by the gates of the last stages. Since there is a relatively small amount of exposed area in each field, exposure times are minimal even for relatively insensitive electron resists.

This amplifier will have application in the receiver sections of phased-array radar and communications systems. Fig. 14 is a plot of typical gain and noise figure as a function of frequency. At 10.5 GHz, the noise figure is 3.1 dB and the gain is 26 dB.

D. Voltage-Controlled Oscillator

Fig. 15 shows an MMIC voltage-controlled oscillator (VCO) containing a 300-μm gate-width FET, two varactor diodes, and appropriate passive matching circuitry for achieving wide tuning bandwidths at X- and Ku-bands [21]. The looped trans-

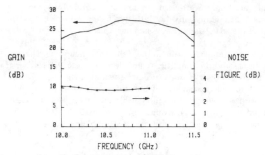

Fig. 14. Gain and noise figure as a function of frequency for the low-noise amplifier of Fig. 3.

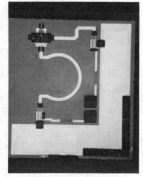

Fig. 15. *Ku*-band monolithic voltage-controlled oscillator chip.

mission line, which has approximately 1-nH inductance, resonates with the sum of the capacitances of the FET and the varactor-diode cathode.

The fabrication process used for these VCO chips is similar to that used for the monolithic power and low-noise amplifiers. The submicron (0.5-μm) gates are defined by electron-beam direct-slice writing as before. This chip is small enough that a complete circuit and surrounding test devices can be included in a single electron-beam field. The varactor-diode anodes, which are the same metallization as the FET gates but are 3 to 6 μm wide, are defined by electron beam for convenience and for precise control of their dimensions. Their size, and therefore their capacitance, can then be changed as needed from run to run by simply changing the electron-beam pattern-control program.

These monolithic VCO's have shown tuning bandwidths over 6 GHz in the 12- to 22-GHz frequency range. They will find application in electronic warfare systems. Other versions of this basic design can be used in microwave receivers with phase-lock-loop frequency control.

VI. CONCLUSION

We have shown why micron and submicron geometries are needed for microwave transistors and how electron-beam lithography is applied to the fabrication of submicron-gate GaAs FET's. Descriptions were given of discrete GaAs FET's and

GaAs MMIC's that operate in the frequency range from 3 to 25 GHz. In the future it is expected that advances in techniques for achieving submicron geometries, such as electron-beam lithography, will continue to be applied first to microwave devices.

ACKNOWLEDGMENT

The authors wish to thank the members of the GaAs Microwave and Digital Technology Branch for their many contributions to the work described in this paper. They are especially grateful to K. Bradshaw and P. Tackett for their efforts in the area of electron-beam lithography.

REFERENCES

[1] H. F. Cooke, "Microwave transistors: Theory and design," *Proc. IEEE*, vol. 59, pp. 1163–1181, Aug. 1971.
[2] J. B. Gunn, "Instabilities of current in III–V semiconductors," *IBM J. Res. Develop.*, vol. 8, pp. 141–159, Apr. 1964.
[3] R. L. Johnston, B. C. DeLoach, and B. G. Cohen, "A silicon diode microwave oscillator," *Bell Syst. Tech. J.*, vol. 44, pp. 369–372, Feb. 1965.
[4] H. T. Yuan, J. B. Kruger, and Y. S. Wu, "X-band silicon power transistor," in *1975 Int. Microwave Symp. Dig. Tech. Papers*, pp. 73–75.
[5] C. A. Liechti, "Microwave field-effect transistors—1976." *IEEE Trans. Microwave Theory Tech.*, vol. MTT-24, pp. 279–300, June 1976.
[6] R. A. Pucel, "Design considerations for monolithic microwave circuits," *IEEE Trans. Microwave Theory Tech.*, vol. MTT-29, pp. 513–534, June 1981.
[7] M. S. Shur and L. F. Eastman, "Ballistic transport in semiconductor at low temperatures for low-power high-speed logic," *IEEE Trans. Electron Devices*, vol. ED-26, pp. 1677–1683, Nov. 1979.
[8] J. Frey, "Ballistic transport in semiconductor devices," in *1980 IEDM Tech. Dig.*, pp. 613–617.
[9] P. Wolf, "Microwave properties of Schottky-barrier field-effect transistors," *IBM J. Res. Develop.*, vol. 14, pp. 125–141, Mar. 1970.
[10] M. Fukuta, K. Syama, H. Suzuki, and H. Ishikawa, "GaAs microwave power FET," *IEEE Trans. Electron Devices*, vol. ED-23, pp. 388–397, Apr. 1976.
[11] R. S. Pengelly, *Microwave Field-Effect Transistors—Theory, Design and Applications*. Chichester: Research Studies Press, 1982.
[12] H. Fukui, "Optimal noise figure of microwave GaAs MESFET's," *IEEE Trans. Electron Devices*, vol. ED-26, pp. 1032–1037, July 1979.
[13] W. R. Frensley and H. M. Macksey, "Effect of gate stripe width on the gain of GaAs MESFETs," in *1979 Cornell Electrical Engineering Conf. Proc.*, pp. 445–452.
[14] J. V. DiLorenzo and W. R. Wisseman, "GaAs power MESFET's: Design, fabrication, and performance," *IEEE Trans. Microwave Theory Tech.*, vol. MTT-27, pp. 367–378, May 1979.
[15] H. M. Macksey, H. Q. Tserng, and S. R. Nelson, "GaAs power FET for K-band operation," in *1981 ISSCC Dig. Tech. Papers*, pp. 70–71.
[16] R. C. Bennett, P. Saunier, R. P. Lindsley, C. H. Moore, and R. E. Lehmann, "20 GHz GaAs FET transmitter," presented at the Int. Conf. on Communications, Philadelphia, PA, June 1982.
[17] H. M. Macksey, H. Q. Tserng, and G. H. Westphal, "S-Band GaAs power FET," in *1982 Int. Microwave Symp. Dig. Tech. Papers*, pp. 150–152.
[18] H. Q. Tserng, H. M. Macksey, and S. R. Nelson, "A four stage monolithic X-band GaAs FET power amplifier with integrated bias network," in *1982 GaAs IC Symp. Tech. Dig.*, pp. 132–135.
[19] H. Q. Tserng and H. M. Macksey, "A monolithic GaAs power FET amplifier for satellite communications," in *1982 ISSCC Dig. Tech. Papers*, pp. 136–137.
[20] R. E. Lehmann, G. E. Brehm, and G. H. Westphal, "10 GHz 3-stage monolithic low-noise amplifier," in *1982 ISSCC Dig. Tech. Papers*, pp. 140–141.
[21] B. N. Scott and G. E. Brehm, "Monolithic voltage-controlled oscillator for X- and Ku- bands," in *1982 Int. Microwave Symp. Dig. Tech. Papers*, pp. 482–485.

Part V
Modeling and Simulation of Devices and Circuits

AS the complexity of the technology grew, optimization of devices through "trial and error" became more and more inefficient. Gradually, this crude method was replaced and complemented by device modeling in order to predict the properties of the devices in advance of the production of expensive hardware. The paper by W. L. Engl, H. K. Dirks, and B. Meinerzhagen deals in detail with the various aspects of device modeling and its significance for the device designer and the circuit engineer, stressing especially the importance of numerical approaches.

With the next paper we proceed to larger units, namely circuits and digital network. The contribution by A. E. Ruehli and G. S. Ditlow is a review of circuit analysis, logic simulation, and design verification, including time analysis. The most significant current problem is to find algorithms and implementations which yield acceptable running times at the VLSI level.

Device Modeling

WALTER L. ENGL, FELLOW, IEEE, HEINZ K. DIRKS, AND BERND MEINERZHAGEN

Invited Paper

Abstract—This paper reviews the progress in device modeling with emphasis on numerical modeling approaches. The reason for this is its ever-increasing importance for the design of small-scale devices suited for VLSI applications. First, the basic field equations with their respective boundary conditions are given. Followed by a description of empirical models for the physical device mechanisms, i.e., mobility, avalanche generation, band-gap narrowing. Subsequently, different numerical models, mainly developed in the past decade, are outlined briefly and discretization as well as solution methods are being discussed. Some remarks are given concerning the relations between finite-difference and finite-element methods. Simplified numerical models are also mentioned and their usefulness for certain type of applications is stressed. In order to clearly demonstrate the power of numerical device modeling, a number of representative examples is given.

The last sections deal with analytical device modeling. Bipolar transistor models are only briefly reviewed since the evolution has led to some kind of standardization, but the development of MOS transistor models, where the same is not true, is described in more detail. Cross references to numerical results should clarify that with decreasing device dimensions the model parameters of analytical MOST models tend to loose their physical significance and change increasingly into fitting parameters.

I. INTRODUCTION

A SEMICONDUCTOR DEVICE is characterized by a set of physical parameters, e.g., mobility, lifetime, as well as technological parameters like geometry, impurity profile, and so on. The aim of device modeling is then to derive from this set a field of electrostatic potential and quasi-Fermi potential for electrons and holes in space and time. These three quantities yield, in turn, the vector fields of the electric-field strength and electric current density. Finally, integration of the first vector along a contour between respective contacts and the second over respective contact areas results in the terminal characteristics of a device.

The reason for modeling devices is twofold. The device designer wants to understand how a device operates and hence is primarily interested in the internal device mechanisms. The circuit designer seeks a quantitative description of the terminal behavior only, which should be as accurate as necessary and as simple as possible. In his part of the overall design process he wants to predict circuit performance by numerically simulating a proposed circuit topology. Generally, he relies on an established process for device fabrication and hence is able to improve model accuracy by implementing empirical fitting parameters into the analytical formulas of his model. Extending this approach may lead to the point where the measured parameters constitute a table and the model acts only as an interpolation routine between neighboring table values. During this process, the connection to device physics is gradually lost gaining computational efficiency which is the uppermost concern in simulating large circuits.

However, the device designer is also somewhat interested in circuit performance at least of small-scale building blocks, since the devices he is designing are to operate in a circuit environment. But contrary to the circuit designer, he seeks to preserve the connection to device physics in order to be guided by circuit performance criteria in his design process. Ideally, the desired device performance should arise from those criteria and the device design process should result in specifications for a wafer process to be developed. In practice, however, process and device development are carried out simultaneously and device modeling should aid this iterative process by saving part of the otherwise necessary cycles of the iteration loop. Simplicity of the model must then be traded against accuracy at least to the extent enabling an engineering compromise between expenditures for increased processing complexity and resulting gain in device performance. At this point, computer-aided device modeling becomes mandatory.

This paper emphasizes the device designers' view on modeling and hence stresses numerical models. Section II reviews the device equations and the empirically founded models of the underlying physical parameters. It covers also the important mechanisms of bandgap narrowing and degeneration as well as carrier recombination and generation. These parameters and mechanisms are strongly reflected in device behavior, but can only be properly handled by numerical methods, if predictive capability of the modeling process is to be preserved.

Section III deals with exact and simplified numerical models. The term "exact" refers to the simulation of the device equations as treated in Section II without any simplifications. First, discretization methods are covered by one-dimensional examples to avoid lengthy formulas. It is hoped the reader will come to the conclusion that the sometimes controversial issue of finite difference versus finite element methods is not a highly important one compared with other aspects of the modeling problem. Second, solution methods are outlined stressing the respective properties of Gummel's successive procedure and the simultaneous one. In either case, a starting solution for the nonlinear system of equations has to be guessed, and the number of necessary iterations strongly depends on how good the initial guess was. Quite a different approach is guided by physical insight, where the starting solution results from solutions of simplified equations which are refined step by step. The solution techniques for the linearized system of equations are mentioned only briefly; for more details the reader is referred to the literature. A wide variety of simplified numerical models are possible where the nature of simplifica-

Manuscript received August 18, 1982; revised October 14, 1982.

The authors are with the Institut für Theoretische Elektrotechnik, University of Aachen, Aachen, West Germany.

Reprinted from *Proc. IEEE*, vol. 71, pp. 10–33, Jan. 1983.

tion is different for bipolar and MOS devices. But only a few examples can be given since exhaustive treatment could be the topic of a full paper.

Section IV summarizes a number of representative examples taken from the authors' own experience not only to demonstrate the power of computer-aided device modeling, but also to allow the reader to estimate respective cost by giving CPU times. Figures from different sources taken from examples in the literature cannot easily be compared or are often missing. The collection comprises an I^2L inverter in steady state, an n-p-n transistor in transient mode modeled in two dimensions by exact and simplified methods, and a similar transistor in steady state modeled in three dimensions. Furthermore, two MOST with moderate- and short-channel lengths are compared at four different bias points. All other parameters are left unchanged in order to clearly demonstrate short-channel effects. At this point, one remark on scaling seems appropriate. Its treatment has been deliberately omitted in this paper, despite the fact that it has acted as a buoy when sailing into VLSI waters and continues to be of importance there. Similarity transformations have been quite common in fluid mechanics for a long time. There, a down-scaled model of the real object is investigated. Likewise, physical parameters are changed in such a way as to leave the governing equations invariant under this transformation. In device scaling the same process is carried out in the opposite direction. However, scaling laws are more restricted, since due to their complexity the device equations scale only in simplified form. Hence, the MOST examples chosen here give an indication of what happens if scaling laws are violated for any reason.

Section V tries to give an overview of the vast area of analytical MOST models. In contrast with the short part on bipolar models where a standard, namely, the Gummel–Poon model, has evolved the MOST models have not converged to such a standard and it is unlikely they ever will. It seemed necessary to review the classical models along with the underlying assumptions. This forms the basis for covering what is usually called short-channel effects; namely, channel-length modulation, velocity saturation, and variation of threshold voltage and subthreshold current with drain voltage and channel length. Reference is made to numerical solutions given in Section IV indicating which of the classical assumptions are violated. By this approach it is hoped the reader will appreciate the problems which one faces in trying to improve the classical models and why so many different proposals have been and still are being made.

II. BASIC EQUATIONS

A. Field Equations and Boundary Conditions

The electrical behavior of electronic devices is governed by electromagnetic field equations, which have to be supplemented by constitutive relations. It can be shown that for silicon devices with linear dimensions of a few micrometers or less and for frequencies up to 10^{10} Hz, the quasi-static approximation of the field equations is valid. These equations are the continuity equation for the electrical current density J

$$\nabla J = - \frac{\partial \rho}{\partial t} \tag{2.1}$$

and Poisson's equation for the electrostatic potential ψ

$$\nabla^2 \psi = -\rho/\epsilon \tag{2.2}$$

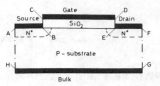

Fig. 1. Cross section of a MOS transistor.

where ϵ is the dielectric permittivity. Space-charge density ρ is composed of two different mobile carriers (electrons n and holes p) and the net impurity concentration N

$$\rho = q(p - n + N) \tag{2.3}$$

where q is the (positive) electronic charge and the net doping contains all ionized donors N_D and acceptors N_A

$$N = N_D - N_A. \tag{2.4}$$

From solid-state physics it is well known that for semiconductors the total charge transport consists of electron transport in the conductivity band and hole transport in the valence band

$$J = J_n + J_p. \tag{2.5}$$

This splitting requires a separate continuity equation for each type of carriers

$$\frac{\partial n}{\partial t} - \frac{1}{q} \nabla \cdot J_n = -R \tag{2.6}$$

$$\frac{\partial p}{\partial t} + \frac{1}{q} \nabla \cdot J_p = -R \tag{2.7}$$

where R is the net recombination rate. Irreversible thermodynamics teaches [1] that under isothermal conditions current densities for electrons and holes are proportional to the gradients of the corresponding electrochemical potentials or quasi-Fermi levels

$$J_n = -q\mu_n n \nabla \phi_n \tag{2.8}$$

$$J_p = -q\mu_p p \nabla \phi_p \tag{2.9}$$

where μ denotes mobility. These equations can also be derived from the Boltzmann transport equation, which, in turn, is being used for deriving expressions for mobility. For semiconductors with nonuniform band structure the use of (2.8), (2.9) avoids additional terms [2], [3], which are only necessary if a distinction between drift and diffusion currents is to be made.

The preceding field equations require boundary conditions in order to completely specify the boundary value problem to be solved. For the discussion of these boundary conditions we consider the cross section of an arbitrary MOS transistor (Fig. 1) as an example.

Ohmic contacts (e.g., source, drain, and bulk) are often idealized by assuming infinite contact recombination velocities and space-charge neutrality. Hence, carriers are in thermodynamic equilibrium and both quasi-Fermi levels equal to voltage applied there

$$\phi_n = \phi_p = V_{appl}. \tag{2.10}$$

Likewise, we have Dirichlet boundary conditions for the electrostatic potential and for both carrier densities at ideal contacts

$$\psi = \psi_0 + V_{appl} \qquad (2.11)$$

$$n = n_0 \qquad (2.12)$$

$$p = p_0 \qquad (2.13)$$

where ψ_0, n_0, and p_0 are the values of the corresponding variables for space-charge neutrality and at equilibrium.

For nonideal contacts, such as Schottky contacts, the boundary condition for ψ is still of the form (2.11), but ψ_0 includes now a barrier height. Carrier concentrations at Schottky contacts depend on the current density across the metal-semiconductor interface. A synthesis of the thermionic emission and diffusion theories has been proposed [4], which is based on the concept of a thermionic recombination velocity v_n, v_p at the contact. The resulting boundary conditions are

$$n \cdot J_n = -qv_n(n - n_0) \qquad (2.14)$$

$$n \cdot J_p = qv_p(p - p_0) \qquad (2.15)$$

where n is a unit vector normal to the interface. These equations reduce to (2.12) and (2.13) for infinite recombination velocities.

Likewise, surface recombination is assumed along all Si–SiO$_2$ interfaces (e.g., line B–E in Fig. 1) where the normal components of both particle current densities equal the surface recombination rate R_s

$$n \cdot J_n = -qR_s \qquad (2.16)$$

$$n \cdot J_p = qR_s. \qquad (2.17)$$

For the displacement vectors at both sides of such an interface we have the relation

$$n \cdot (\epsilon \nabla \psi) - n \cdot (\epsilon \nabla \psi) = Q_s \qquad (2.18)$$

where Q_s is the sum of all effective net oxide charges per unit area at the Si–SiO$_2$ interface (oxide fixed and trapped charge and interface trapped charge). For bipolar devices or field oxide, (2.18) can be simplified assuming zero electric field in the oxide layer, whereas for gate oxide two different approaches exist. One can either determine the field within the gate oxide region by solving Laplace's equation there, taking a Dirichlet boundary condition for the electrostatic potential at the gate contact into account; or one can assume a one-dimensional field perpendicular to the silicon surface.

At the remaining boundaries (e.g., lines B–C, D–E, F–G, and H–A in Fig. 1) the normal components of electron and hole current density and electric field strength are assumed to be zero, yielding

$$n \cdot J_n = n \cdot J_p = n \cdot \nabla \psi = 0. \qquad (2.19)$$

Since this Neumann boundary condition is somewhat artificial, one has to decide from case to case if the induced error can be tolerated or not. However, this error can be made negligibly small by placing the corresponding boundaries at a distance far enough from the region of interest (e.g., lines F–G and H–A).

B. Models of Physical Parameters

The field equations contain quantities—e.g., the recombination rate R and the mobilities $\mu_{n,p}$—which themselves are the result of rather complicated physical mechanisms. Therefore, these quantities are not constant but depend on the local

TABLE I
MOBILITY PARAMETERS

	μ_{max} $(cm^2v^{-1}s^{-1})$	μ_{min} $(cm^2v^{-1}s^{-1})$	N_{ref} (cm^{-3})	α $-$
Electrons	1360	92	$1.3 \cdot 10^{17}$	0.91
Holes	520	65	$2.4 \cdot 10^{17}$	0.61

values of carrier densities, current densities, and fields. Moreover, for the full set of equations, a relation between carrier densities, the corresponding quasi-Fermi potential, and the electrostatic potential is needed. This relation results from carrier statistics and has to take into account band-gap narrowing and degeneration.

Though considerable differences for bipolar and MOS devices exist, the aforementioned physical mechanisms are generally valid and affect more or less most of the devices. Thus experimental results from special test structures can be evaluated yielding empirical relations, which describe these mechanisms and which have been successfully used in numerical simulations for a large range of devices.

Carrier Mobility: Carrier mobility results from different scattering mechanisms. First of all, carriers are scattered by phonons and defects resulting in the relatively high bulk mobility of lowly doped material. This lattice mobility is reduced by additional Coulomb scattering at ionized impurity atoms. Caughey and Thomas [5] have given the following empirical expression fitting experimental data for majority-carrier mobilities:

$$\mu(N) = \mu_{min} + \frac{\mu_{max} - \mu_{min}}{1 + (N_T/N_{ref})^\alpha} \qquad (2.20)$$

where $N_T = N_D + N_A$ is the total doping concentration. Fitting (2.20) to more recent measurements [6] leads to the coefficients given in Table I. Usually, the same expressions are used for minority-carrier mobilities, because the few experimental data [7] do not differ significantly from majority-carrier mobilities.

Measurements have shown [8], [9] that for high excess carrier densities mobility is further reduced by electron–hole scattering. Following [10], the experimental data can be fitted replacing the total doping concentration in (2.20) by the expression

$$N_T = 0.34 \cdot (N_A + N_D) + 0.66 \cdot (\bar{n}) \qquad (2.21)$$

with $\bar{n} = p + n$ and using the coefficients of Table I. This approach is justified by the fact that both mobility reductions are due to Coulomb scattering.

The field dependence measured in lowly doped material can be taken into account by the expression [5], [11]

$$\mu(N, \bar{n}, E) = \mu(N, \bar{n}) \cdot [1 + (\mu(N, \bar{n})|E|/v_{max})^\beta]^{-1/\beta} \qquad (2.22)$$

with $\beta_n = 2$ and $\beta_p = 1$ resulting in doping-independent limiting drift velocities of

$$v_{max,n} = 1.1 \times 10^7 \text{ cm/s}$$

and

161

$$v_{\max, p} = 9.5 \times 10^6 \text{ cm/s.}$$

From a physical point of view it seems to be more reasonable to use in (2.22) the gradient of the quasi-Fermi level instead of the electrical field strength [12]. However, the resulting difference of device characteristics is quite small.

Concerning MOSFET simulations, channel mobility is further reduced by surface scattering or surface roughness. Following Yamaguchi [13], this effect can be taken into account by splitting the electrical field strength into components which are longitudinal $E_\parallel$ and transverse $E_\perp$ to current density. In this case, $E_\parallel$ is used in (2.22) and the resulting mobility is reduced by

$$\mu(N, E_\parallel, E_\perp) = \mu(N, E_\parallel)(1 + \alpha E_\perp)^{-1/2} \qquad (2.23)$$

with $\alpha_n = 1.54 \times 10^{-5}$ cm/V and $\alpha_p = 5.35 \times 10^{-5}$ cm/V. The resulting maximum drift velocity depends on $E_\perp$ which is in conflict with measurements [14]. This problem can be avoided if the field-independent mobility $\mu(N)$ is first reduced by $E_\perp$ using (2.23) and then the result $\mu(N, E_\perp)$ is substituted into (2.22) for drift-velocity saturation. Using this approach, carrier–carrier scattering is neglected as indicated by the absence of the argument $\bar{n}$ in (2.23). However, other approaches for channel mobility are possible. Some authors achieved good numerical results using mobilities which depend on doping, carrier density, longitudinal and transverse field, and the distance from the Si–SiO$_2$ interface [15].

Bandgap Narrowing and Degeneration: Fermi–Dirac statistics for both carriers yield the following relations between carrier concentrations, quasi-Fermi potentials and electrostatic potential:

$$n = \int_{-\infty}^{+\infty} \frac{\rho_n \, dE}{1 + \exp\left((E - F_n)/kT\right)},$$

$$\text{with } F_n = -q(\phi_n - \psi) \quad (2.24)$$

$$p = \int_{-\infty}^{+\infty} \frac{\rho_p \, dE}{1 + \exp\left((E - F_p)/kT\right)},$$

$$\text{with } F_p = -q(\psi - \phi_p) \quad (2.25)$$

where ρ_n and ρ_p denote the density of states functions. For nondegenerate semiconductors with a constant parabolic band structure these integral representations can be reduced to the classical Boltzmann approximation

$$n = n_i \exp\left(\frac{\psi - \phi_n}{V_T}\right) \qquad (2.26)$$

$$p = n_i \exp\left(\frac{\phi_p - \psi}{V_T}\right) \qquad (2.27)$$

where n_i is the intrinsic concentration.

In heavily doped regions, the band structure of the crystal is no longer independent of the impurity concentration. The splitting of discrete energy levels of the impurity atoms into an impurity band, as well as band-edge tailing narrows the effective bandgap E_G. This effect is of great importance for modeling bipolar devices because it influences strongly minority-carrier densities and currents within heavily doped regions. Bandgap narrowing with a position-depending band structure and degeneration can both be taken into account in the integral

expressions (2.24) and (2.25) without affecting the transport equations (2.8) and (2.9) [2], [16]. In earlier work on device modeling [17], [18] the density of states functions $\rho_{n,p}$ were assumed to have a rather complicated form depending on the impurity concentration and the screening length λ increasing considerably the overall complexity of the modeling problem.

Hence, a simpler approach is more common, which models heavy doping effects by the following expressions:

$$n = n_{ie} \exp\left(\frac{\psi - \phi_n}{V_T}\right) \qquad (2.28)$$

$$p = n_{ie} \exp\left(\frac{\phi_p - \psi}{V_T}\right) \qquad (2.29)$$

$$n_{ie}^2 = n_0 p_0 := n_i^2 \exp\left(\frac{\Delta E}{kT}\right). \qquad (2.30)$$

Equations (2.28), (2.29) do not imply Boltzmann statistics to hold, rather (2.30) is to be looked upon to model the electrical effects of bandgap narrowing and degeneration simultaneously in an empirical fashion. For this reason, the "effective bandgap narrowing" ΔE has to be taken from electrical measurements [19]–[21].

Recently, the origins of the bandgap reduction as a function of concentration were described by a microscopic theory by Selloni and Pantelides [22]. It was found that the bands shift rigidly so that the density of states retain their $E^{1/2}$ shape, except for a small knee at the band edge, which is a consequence of multivalley interactions. The same authors [23] have identified the sources of the discrepancies among values of the gap reductions that have been extracted from different experiments. In particular, they determined that the quantity ΔE appearing in (2.30) is given by

$$\Delta E = \Delta E_g + S(N, F, T) - D(N, T) \qquad (2.31)$$

where ΔE_g is the true bandgap reduction, S arises from statistics, and D arises from the disorder (fluctuations) in the impurity distribution. These two quantities tend to cancel each other, but their difference is not negligible ($\sim$20–30 meV). The consequences of these new developments on device modeling have not yet been investigated.

Recombination and Generation: For silicon, the net recombination rate R in (2.6), (2.7) is composed of Shockley–Read–Hall (SRH) recombination

$$R_{\text{SRH}} = \frac{np - n_{ie}^2}{\tau_p(n + n_t) + \tau_n(p + p_t)} \qquad (2.32)$$

Auger recombination

$$R_{\text{Aug}} = (c_n n + c_p p)(np - n_{ie}^2) \qquad (2.33)$$

and avalanche generation

$$G_{\text{AV}} = \alpha_n |J_n| + \alpha_p |J_p|. \qquad (2.34)$$

In (2.32), n_t and p_t depend on the energy level of the traps. Since this usually is unknown, the most effective trap level is assumed with $n_t = p_t = n_{ie}$. Different experiments (e.g., [24], [20]) show that SRH lifetimes decrease with increasing doping concentration. The empirical expression

$$\tau = \tau_{\min} + \frac{(\tau_{\max} - \tau_{\min})}{1 + (N_T/N_{\text{Ref}})^\alpha} \qquad (2.35)$$

TABLE II
AVALANCHE PARAMETERS

Electrons		Holes	
α_∞ (cm^{-1})	b (v/cm)	α_∞ (cm^{-1})	b (v/cm)
$7.03 \cdot 10^5$	$1.231 \cdot 10^6$	$1.582 \cdot 10^6$	$2.036 \cdot 10^6$

with $0.3 < \alpha < 0.6$ is used successfully in numerical methods. Recently, theoretical justification of an empirical relation like (2.35) has been given [25]. In contrast with SRH lifetimes, the Auger coefficients c_n and c_p are nearly independent of doping, carrier densities, and temperature as indicated by different measurements [26], [27].

From Chynoweth's law it follows that the ionization coefficients α_n and α_p for avalanche generation depend exponentially on the electrical field strength

$$\alpha = \alpha_\infty \exp(-b/|E|). \qquad (2.36)$$

Experimental data for the coefficients α_∞ and b are shown in Table II.

III. EXACT AND SIMPLIFIED NUMERICAL MODELS

A. Discretization Methods

In trying to achieve analytical solutions of the nonlinear basic equations, approximations are necessary, e.g., with respect to doping profiles, space-charge density, recombination models, etc. Though the resulting analytical models give some insight into physical device behavior, the underlying assumptions often yield an oversimplified picture. This disadvantage can be avoided if the device equations are solved by numerical means. The term "exact numerical models" refers to solutions of the complete system of basic equations without simplifications.

The numerical solution of the governing partial differential equations comprises two fundamental steps. First, the space domain is mapped on a grid of distinct points or nodes. Applying some discretization method to the field problem then yields an algebraic problem with respect to space of finite though large size. Second, this problem is solved for the unknown variables. The discretized equations are obtained from the field equations by approximating the derivatives or integrals by expressions, which involve only the nodal values of the unknown functions. This can be accomplished by using interpolation functions in the neighborhood of a node.

Following this general discretization procedure, there is a variety of possibilities for deriving discrete equations for a field problem. Most common are either finite-element or finite-difference methods. Often these two methods are considered mutually exclusive from the very beginning. The finite-difference method uses a local approximation of a differential operator by some difference operator and the finite-element method applies a collection of shape functions as trial functions to approximate the desired solution globally, whereby residual (Galerkin) or variational (Ritz) strategies are used in the approximation process [28]. However, for both methods, the starting point can be the field equations in differential or integral form or an equivalent variational problem. Likewise, the partitioning of the domain into subdomains and the use of trial functions is also applicable to both methods. An example will be given. It is generally accepted [28] that

finite-element methods always use trial functions which are defined subdomain by subdomain to have only compact support in the domain and which are then called shape or basis functions. This imposes a constraint on the choice of trial functions on the one hand and facilitates the adaption to the geometry of the domain on the other. In order to give some insight into the linkage between finite-difference and finite-element methods, they will be applied to Poisson's equation as a simple example.

From the various finite-difference methods the box integration method [29] is chosen here, which requires an integral representation, yielding

$$\oint_{\partial v} \nabla \psi \cdot dS = -\frac{1}{\epsilon} \int_v \rho \, dv \qquad (3.1)$$

for any subdomain v. The subdomains result from a partition of the domain into "boxes" without overlap or exclusion, where each box includes one grid point. In the one-dimensional case, the box for a grid point x_i is the interval $[(x_{i-1} + x_i)/2, (x_i + x_{i+1})/2]$, where x_{i-1} and x_{i+1} denote the neighboring grid points.

The resulting difference equations are obtained from approximations of the box integral in (3.1). Assuming a linear potential distribution between neighboring grid points

$$\psi(x) = \psi_i + (\psi_{i+1} - \psi_i) \frac{x - x_i}{x_{i+1} - x_i}, \qquad \forall x \in [x_i, x_{i+1}] \qquad (3.2)$$

the one-dimensional finite-difference equation becomes

$$\frac{\psi_{i+1} - \psi_i}{x_{i+1} - x_i} - \frac{\psi_i - \psi_{i-1}}{x_i - x_{i-1}} = -\frac{1}{\epsilon} \int_{(x_{i-1}+x_i)/2}^{(x_i+x_{i+1})/2} \rho(x) \, dx. \qquad (3.3)$$

The final result further depends on the approximation for $\rho(x)$. Assuming a constant space-charge density yields the classical finite-difference formulation of Poisson's equation

$$\frac{\psi_{i+1} - \psi_i}{x_{i+1} - x_i} - \frac{\psi_i - \psi_{i-1}}{x_i - x_{i-1}} = -\frac{1}{2\epsilon} (x_{i+1} - x_{i-1}) \rho_i. \qquad (3.4)$$

In the finite-element method, the domain is likewise discretized into subdomains. In the one-dimensional case, a subdomain or an element is simply the interval $[x_i, x_{i+1}]$ between two neighboring grid points. For the example considered here the same local approximation (3.2) yields the shape functions

$$u_i(x) = \begin{cases} \dfrac{x - x_{i-1}}{x_i - x_{i-1}}, & \forall x \in [x_{i-1}, x_i] \\[2mm] \dfrac{x_{i+1} - x}{x_{i+1} - x_i}, & \forall x \in [x_i, x_{i+1}] \\[2mm] 0, & \forall x \notin [x_{i-1}, x_{i+1}] \end{cases} \qquad (3.5)$$

which represent a basis for the global approximation of the unknown potential

$$\psi(x) = \sum_i \psi_i u_i(x). \qquad (3.6)$$

The finite-element equations can now be obtained for Poisson's equation by applying either Galerkin's method directly to the

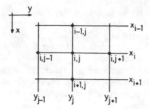

Fig. 2. Cell of a rectangular grid.

Fig. 3. Local refinement in a rectangular and a triangular grid.

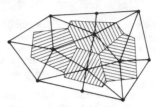

Fig. 4. Triangular grid and the boxes associated with the grid points.

differential equation or the Ritz method to an equivalent variational problem. Both methods result in the following equation:

$$-\int \nabla u_i \cdot \nabla \psi \, dv = -\frac{1}{\epsilon} \int u_i \rho \, dv \qquad (3.7)$$

where the integration domain covers only those elements which are incident with the considered node i, because u_i and ∇u_i vanish elsewhere. Evaluating (3.7) with the one-dimensional approximations (3.5) and (3.6) yields

$$\frac{\psi_{i+1} - \psi_i}{x_{i+1} - x_i} - \frac{\psi_i - \psi_{i-1}}{x_i - x_{i-1}} = -\frac{1}{\epsilon} \int_{x_{i-1}}^{x_{i+1}} u_i(x) \rho(x) \, dx. \quad (3.8)$$

This result differs from the finite-difference equation (3.3) only slightly in the way that space-charge density is taken into account at both right-hand side integrals. In (3.3), $\rho(x)$ is directly integrated over the domain of a box, whereas the finite-element approach requires a weighted integration over the larger domain covering adjacent elements. Moreover, both methods yield the difference equation (3.4), if a constant space-charge density is assumed within the integration intervals.

From the above considerations for Poisson's equation in one dimension one may conclude that nearly identical difference equations are obtained from the finite-difference and the finite-element methods if in both methods similar approximations are used. This is even true if more than one dimension is considered. For a node (x_i, y_j), the rectangular grid shown in Fig. 2, the standard difference formulation of Poisson's equation is

$$\frac{1}{2}(y_{j+1} - y_{j-1}) \left[\frac{\psi_{i+1,j} - \psi_{i,j}}{x_{i+1} - x_i} - \frac{\psi_{i,j} - \psi_{i-1,j}}{x_i - x_{i-1}} \right]$$

$$+ \frac{1}{2}(x_{i+1} - x_{i-1}) \left[\frac{\psi_{i,j+1} - \psi_{i,j}}{y_{j+1} - y_j} - \frac{\psi_{i,j} - \psi_{i,j-1}}{y_j - y_{j-1}} \right]$$

$$= -\frac{1}{4\epsilon}(x_{i+1} - x_{i-1})(y_{j+1} - y_{j-1})\rho_{i,j}. \qquad (3.9)$$

This equation can be obtained in either way, if appropriate approximations are used. Of course, other difference equations are possible evaluating the various integrals by different approximations.

It is widely accepted that the major advantage of finite-element methods becomes appearent if triangular grids are used, since triangular elements make local refinements more readily available without excessively increasing the total number of nodes. Depending on the specific example, the difference in the number of grid points can be much larger than for the simple example shown in Fig. 3. Moreover, nonplanar boundaries or interfaces can be more precisely

approximated by triangles than rectangles. On the other hand, such problems can also be solved with finite-difference methods by introducing triangular subregions within the rectangles [30] or, more generally, by using directly a triangular grid [29], [31]. If in the latter case the box integration method is applied, the perpendicular bisectors of the lines between neighboring grid points define the box associated with a grid point as indicated in Fig. 4. Usually the potential of triangular grids is not fully exploited because this demands an increased effort for mesh generation and bookkeeping. This is even more pronounced when three-dimensional tetrahedal elements are used [32].

Of equal importance, as matching the grid to the geometrical constraints of the problem, is the adaptation of the approximate solutions to the physics of the problem, in particular if the properties of the solutions are dominated by nonlinearities. In other words, trial functions to be used should primarily reflect the physics involved, whether they are simultaneously shape functions or not. Hence, trial functions, which use approximate analytical solutions of the problem, are a good choice.

As an example, the continuity equation for holes (2.7) is considered here. Assuming steady-state conditions, this equation is written as

$$\frac{1}{q} \nabla J_p = -\nabla \left(\mu_p n_{ie} \exp \left(\frac{\phi_p - \psi}{V_T} \right) \nabla \phi_p \right) = -R \quad (3.10)$$

where (2.9) and (2.29) have been used. A treatment of (3.10) and ϕ_p in analogy to (3.1) and (3.2), respectively, results in exponential current-density distributions in the neighborhood of each grid point. This would certainly be a poor approximation, since current densities vary only weakly with position. Hence, a different approach is mandatory reflecting this behavior.

Neglecting recombination within the one-dimensional interval $[x_i, x_{i+1}]$ and integrating (3.10) yields a constant current density $J_{pi+1/2}$

$$\frac{J_{pi+1/2}}{q} = -\frac{\exp(\phi_{pi+1}/V_T) - \exp(\phi_{pi}/V_T)}{\int_{x_i}^{x_{i+1}} \frac{\exp(\psi/V_T)}{V_T \mu_p n_{ie}} dx'}. \quad (3.11)$$

Because the interval considered is only small, the linear potential distribution (3.2) and a constant product of mobility and effective intrinsic density $(\mu_p, n_{ie})_{i+1/2}$ can be assumed there. Then (3.10) and (3.11) lead to

$$\exp(\phi_p(x)/V_T) = \exp(\phi_{pi}/V_T) + (\exp(\phi_{pi+1}/V_T)$$
$$- \exp(\phi_{pi}/V_T))$$
$$\cdot \frac{\exp(\psi(x)/V_T) - \exp(\psi_i/V_T)}{\exp(\psi_{i+1}/V_T) - \exp(\psi_i/V_T)}$$

$$(3.12)$$

and

$$\frac{J_{pi+1/2}}{q} = -(\mu_p n_{ie})_{i+1/2} \frac{\psi_{i+1} - \psi_i}{x_{i+1} - x_i}$$
$$\cdot \frac{\exp(\phi_{pi+1}/V_T) - \exp(\phi_{pi}/V_T)}{\exp(\psi_{i+1}/V_T) - \exp(\psi_i/V_T)} . \quad (3.13)$$

From the trial function (3.12) for $\phi_p(x)$ no basis function can be derived, since this expression is nonlinear in the nodal values ϕ_{pi}, ϕ_{pi+1}, which contradicts a representation of the form of (3.5) for $\phi_p(x)$. This could be corrected by a change in variables $\zeta_p(x) = \exp(\phi_p(x)/V_T)$ allowing for a representation $\zeta_p(x) = \Sigma_i \zeta_{pi} u_i(x)$ in this case [33]. But even then, keeping the coupled field equations for the dependent variables ψ, ζ_n, ζ_p in mind, the basis functions would depend on the potential $u_i(x) = u_i(\psi, x)$, which is uncommon in the concept of the finite-element method, as it is generally understood [28].

The approximate solution for the current density (3.13) can finally be inserted into the finite-difference equation

$$\frac{1}{q}(J_{pi+1/2} - J_{pi-1/2}) = -\frac{1}{2}(x_{i+1} - x_{i-1}) R(x_i) \quad (3.14)$$

resulting in a highly efficient approximation for the one-dimensional continuity equation.

The above discretization scheme, which was first used by Scharfetter and Gummel [34], has generally a much larger range of validity than other more conventional ones, where the current densities are derived from polynomial trial functions for the quasi-Fermi level or the carrier density. Equation (3.13) agrees with more conventional expressions if $|\psi_{i+1} - \psi_i| \ll V_T$ and $|\phi_{pi+1} - \phi_{pi}| \ll V_T$ are assumed. Since these assumptions have not been made here, the finite-difference approximation (3.13), (3.14) improves numerical accuracy or enables the use of coarse grids in regions where the assumptions of the analytical integral are not strongly violated.

Gummel's discretization scheme can be generalized if more than one dimension is considered. In this case, the current-density components along mesh lines are assumed to be constant between neighboring grid points and approximated by an expression of the form (3.13). This approach was the very key for the first accurate two-dimensional numerical simulations of bipolar devices [35]–[37] and can be applied to rectangular as well as triangular [32] grids.

Other examples for a physical approach to discretize the basic equations can be found in the literature; e.g., in [33], an accurate approximation for SRH recombination is developed from physical reasoning, and in [38], a first integral of the one-dimensional Poisson equation is incorporated into the discretization at oxide-covered surface regions.

Spatial discretization of the field equations yields at each

grid point one discrete equation for Poisson's equation and both continuity equations, respectively. The resulting system comprises coupled ordinary differential equations in the time domain because the spatially discretized continuity equations still contain derivatives of the carrier densities with respect to time. Condensing the nodal values of the unknown functions into vectors, this system is written as

$$f_\psi(\psi, \phi_n, \phi_p, t) = 0 \quad (3.15)$$

$$f_n(\psi, \phi_n, \phi_p, t) = \frac{\partial n}{\partial t} \quad (3.16)$$

$$f_p(\psi, \phi_n, \phi_p, t) = \frac{\partial p}{\partial t} \quad (3.17)$$

where the vector functions f_ψ, f_n, and f_p represent the spatial difference approximations of the field equations.

Integration of the system (3.15)–(3.17) requires again numerical algorithms discretizing the time domain and yielding difference approximations for the derivatives. Though semi-implicit methods can also be used [39], usually fully implicit backward-difference formulas are applied, in order to guarantee numerical stability without the imposition of small time steps [40]. In most cases, the first-order backward Euler formula is used [41]–[44], since it is "A-stable" for constant time steps and for increasing step size with a bounded rate of change [45]. This formula yields for (3.16)

$$f_n(\psi^m, \phi_n^m, \phi_p^m, t^m) = \frac{n^m - n^{m-1}}{t^m - t^{m-1}} \quad (3.18)$$

where the superscripts denote the values of the corresponding variables at time t^m. Moreover, implicit backward-difference formulas with variable step size and order of integration [46] can be profitably used [47], [48], ensuring accuracy as well as stability by an automatic control of steps and order [45]. Note, that for a fully implicit integration formula (e.g., (3.18)) the left-hand side function has to be evaluated at time t^m. This requires for each time step the solution of a system of coupled equations including Poisson's equation (3.15).

B. Solution Methods

In a transient analysis, space discretization and implicit time integration yield at each instant of time the coupled nonlinear system

$$F_\psi(\psi, \phi_n, \phi_p) = 0 \quad (3.19)$$

$$F_n(\psi, \phi_n, \phi_p) = 0 \quad (3.20)$$

$$F_p(\psi, \phi_n, \phi_p) = 0 \quad (3.21)$$

where the argument t^m and the superscripts m are omitted for simplicity. In a steady-state analysis, a system of the same form is obtained for each bias point. Thus in both cases $3N$ nonlinear equations have to be solved, where, e.g., in the two-dimensional case the number of grid points N is usually between 300 and 4000. The solution of this large system is the most time-consuming task during a numerical device simulation. Therefore, it is of great importance to choose an efficient numerical algorithm, especially if more than one dimension has to be considered.

Most simply, one treats each of the differential equations separately by decoupling the equations and solving the three

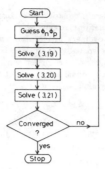

Fig. 5. Gummel's algorithm.

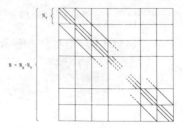

Fig. 6. Five-diagonal-band matrix. N_x and N_y are the numbers of grid lines in the x- and y-direction, respectively.

systems (3.19)–(3.21) successively. First, Poisson's equation (3.19) is solved assuming known quasi-Fermi levels. Next comes each of the continuity equations with ψ given from the first step. This sequence is iteratively repeated until self-consistent values of the desired accuracy for all unknown variables are obtained. Fig. 5 shows the flow diagram of this successive or decoupled method, which is due to Gummel [50]. It is advantageous for multidimensional simulations as it saves storage and converges quite well as long as the coupling of the three equations is only weak. Moreover, the result of the first cycle of this iteration is rather close to the exact solution if the first guess of the quasi-Fermi potential of the majority carriers is accurate enough.

Since each of the three systems (3.19)–(3.21), which have to be solved one after the other within Gummel's algorithm, is generally nonlinear, an iterative method has to be used. Because of its quadratic convergence, the Newton method is usually choosen. Applying this method, e.g., to Poisson's equation, the system (3.19) is linearized and the iteration process is defined as follows:

$$\frac{\partial F_\psi}{\partial \psi} \, \delta \psi_{k+1} = -F_\psi(\psi_k)$$

$$\psi_{k+1} = \psi_k + \delta \psi_{k+1}, \qquad k = 0, 1, 2, \cdots \quad (3.22)$$

starting with an initial approximation ψ_0. $\partial F_\psi / \partial \psi$ is the Jacobian matrix evaluated at ψ_k and $\delta \psi_{k+1}$ is the correction vector of the iteration step $k + 1$.

The relatively simple implementation of the successive method has to be paid for by its possible slow convergence if (3.19)–(3.21) are strongly coupled. Considering the steady-state analysis of a bipolar device, Gummel's algorithm converges well for low and moderate injection levels. But if for higher forward voltages the minority-carrier density approaches majority-carrier density, both carriers become strongly coupled via the electrostatic potential in order to maintain quasi-neutrality and convergence slows down rapidly [37]. For a FET analysis in the strong inversion regime, the mutual coupling between the potential and the dominating carrier density is likewise increased [51] though originating from a different physical mechanism. Moreover, in transient simulations, the displacement current can give rise to additional coupling [43].

These convergence problems can be overcome mathematically by solving (3.19)–(3.21) simultaneously rather than alternatingly. This simultaneous method has the advantage that the mutual coupling between all equations is taken into account by a quadratically converging overall Newton iteration

$$\begin{bmatrix} \dfrac{\partial F_\psi}{\partial \psi} & \dfrac{\partial F_\psi}{\partial \phi_n} & \dfrac{\partial F_\psi}{\partial \phi_p} \\[2ex] \dfrac{\partial F_n}{\partial \psi} & \dfrac{\partial F_n}{\partial \phi_n} & \dfrac{\partial F_n}{\partial \phi_n} \\[2ex] \dfrac{\partial F_p}{\partial \psi} & \dfrac{\partial F_p}{\partial \phi_n} & \dfrac{\partial F_p}{\partial \phi_p} \end{bmatrix} \begin{bmatrix} \delta \psi_{k+1} \\[2ex] \delta \phi_{n,\,k+1} \\[2ex] \delta \phi_{p,\,k+1} \end{bmatrix} = \begin{bmatrix} -F_{\psi,\,k} \\[2ex] -F_{n,\,k} \\[2ex] -F_{p,\,k} \end{bmatrix}. \quad (3.23)$$

Although this simultaneous Newton method is advantageous from a purely mathematical viewpoint, it is more involved with regard to program structure and storage requirements. Hence, comparisons between both methods [51] do not only depend on the device and its operating conditions but, in addition, also on the algorithms implemented for solving the different linearized systems.

For one-dimensional simulations, the simultaneous method is usually applied [42] and the linearized system (3.23) is best solved by Gaussian elimination or LU decomposition. An appropriate ordering of the columns and rows of the Jacobian yields a simple band matrix with mostly seven nonzero diagonals [48] allowing the efficient use of special band solver routines. For two-dimensional problems, this method proves to be also successful [52], provided that the bandwidth of the Jacobian matrix is not too large.

In Fig. 6, a five-diagonal band matrix is depicted, as it arises in the decoupled method from (3.22) assuming, e.g., the difference equation (3.9) and a rectangular grid of N_x and N_y grid lines in the x- and y-direction, respectively. For a direct elimination process, computation times and storage requirements are proportional to $N_y^3 N_x$ and $N_y^2 N_x$, respectively, if one takes into account the fill-in of nonzero coefficients within the bandwidth N_y. Threefold size and bandwidth of the Jacobian (3.23) for the simultaneous procedure leads to an increase of storage and computation time by a factor of nine compared with one Newton step for each decoupled equation. Hence, this approach is often prohibitive unless large computer resources are available [53].

If an irregular grid (as shown in Fig. 3 or Fig. 4) is used, both Jacobian matrices (3.22), (3.23) are still sparse but they lose their simple band structure, yet allowing the application of direct elimination methods if the increase of programming effort and program complexity is accepted. Such grids require special pre-processing for symbolic LU factorization and ordering of the sparse matrix equations [54], [44].

TABLE III
STEPSOLVING Model Hierarchy and the Underlying
Assumptions

MODEL		ASSUMPTIONS	NUMERICAL EFFORT	RESULT
1		A1 EVEN FOR MINORITY CARRIERS, A2 WITHIN QUASINEUTRAL REGIONS, (A3)	SOLUTION OF (3.19) WITHIN JUNCTIONS REGIONS	SRH-RECOMBINATION EARLY-EFFECT
2	L2	A1, Ψ FROM MOD. 1, (A3)	SOLUTION OF (3.20) OR (3.21) FOR MINORITY CARRIERS	AUGER-RECOMBINATION, CURRENT SPREADING FOR MINORITY CARRIERS
	H2	A1, A2, (A3)		
3	L3	Ψ FROM MOD. 1	SOLUTION OF (3.20) AND (3.21)	ALMOST EXACT RESULTS
	H3	A2		
4		NONE	SOLUTION OF (3.19), (3.20) AND (3.21)	EXACT NUMERICAL SOLUTION

Quite often restricted computer resources require an additional internal iteration for the solution of the large systems of linearized equations. This is especially true if the simultaneous method has to be used for two- and three-dimensional simulations. Various numerical algorithms can be successfully applied to the linear equations, e.g., Stone's strongly implicit procedure (SIP) [36], [15], the successive line over relaxation (SLOR) method [35], [37], [49], or the incomplete Choleski-decomposition and conjugate gradient (ICCG) method [55], [56]. The main disadvantage of these iterative methods is their linear convergence which is often rather slow and can limit considerably the available accuracy of the solution.

One common approach to escape convergence problems is to start with a solution for the device in thermal equilibrium and then try to climb up the operating dc characteristic to the requested bias point step by step using the solution of the preceding bias point as an initial guess to solve for the subsequent bias point. Since in many cases one is interested in a set of solutions for a number of bias points anyhow, this approach seems to be quite obvious. Although it is assured to stay within the radius of convergence for the simultaneous procedure, it fails to converge in the simpler successive procedure when coupling between the respective equations becomes strong.

A different approach can be applied for bipolar devices under steady-state conditions which allows one to maintain the advantages of a successive procedure, assures convergence, and reduces the computation time by about one order of magnitude. This approach is called STEPSOLVING [33], since it reaches the desired solution for an arbitrary bias point in four steps of a hierarchical nature (Fig. 7). The following assumptions

A1) constant quasi-Fermi potential of majority carriers: ϕ_{maj} = const = applied voltage;
A2) space-charge neutrality: $\rho = 0 \rightarrow \psi = f(\phi_n, \phi_p)$;
A3) negligible recombination for transport mechanisms: $R = 0$;

allow for a decoupling of the system (3.19)–(3.21) if proper subsets of them are applied within proper subregions of the device. Dropping the assumptions made at the beginning, step by step creates a hierarchy of numerical models which is shown in Table III. Because the validity of the assumptions depends on the operating conditions of the device, this hierarchy is split up into two branches for low (L) and high (H) injection levels, respectively. Medium injection levels can be dealt with using the L or H branch of the hierarchy resulting

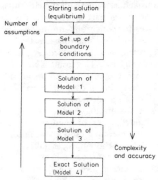

Fig. 7. STEPSOLVING model hierarchy.

in equal bounds of computation time and accuracy. Note that the quasi-neutrality assumption 2) is the most important one for the high-level injection branch.

The simplest model of the hierarchy requires the solution of only one equation within a subregion of the structure. At each level, the solution of the reduced system gives a good approximation of the corresponding internal variables. Therefore, the solution of the preceding model acts as a starting solution for the next model within the hierarchy. By this, only a few iterations are necessary in each case. Moreover, if more than one equation has to be solved, these equations remain weakly coupled at all times. Thus a successive procedure can be used profitably enabling the high numerical accuracy of a direct band solver routine. For the exact numerical solution of all three equations this decoupling is achieved by a generalization of quasi-neutrality yielding $\psi = f(\phi_n, \phi_p, \rho)$, which is then plugged into both discretized transport equations. Poisson's equations can now be understood as determining ρ rather than ψ.

C. Simplified Numerical Models

From an engineering point of view, the degree of accuracy which is achieved by an "exact numerical model" is not necessary in any case or even not justified, if the input data, e.g., doping profile, are known only with a limited accuracy. Hence, "simplified numerical models" may suffice. There is such a wide variety of possibilities, that within the framework of this paper only a few can be mentioned and reference to the literature must be made.

ENGL *et al.*: DEVICE MODELING

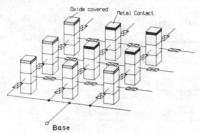

Fig. 8. Part of a quasi-three-dimensional model with nine one-dimensional subdevices and the coupling transportances.

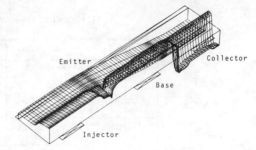

Fig. 9. Log-scaled hole density for an OXIL I²L inverter in the OFF state.

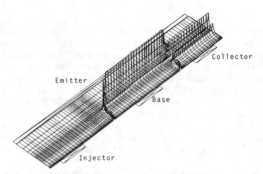

Fig. 10. Linearly scaled swing $P_{ON} - P_{OFF}$ of hole density.

For bipolar devices, each intermediate step of STEPSOLVING constitutes a simplified model in its own right (Fig. 7). Quite a different approach is called quasi-multidimensional modeling. There, a device is partitioned into a certain number of vertical subdevices for which one-dimensional device equations are set up together with network-like lateral coupling elements, called transportance, which symbolize the lateral carrier transport (Fig. 8). The result is a mixed system of distributed and lumped elements, the linearized equations of which have a bordered block diagonal form [47]. This system is solved with a mixed-mode device-circuit simulator MEDUSA [48], [57] for steady-state as well as transient behavior. For a steady-state model, a set of solutions for one-dimensional subdevices can be stored in a table allowing for a large number of subdevices [58]. The approach taken in MEDUSA was extended to handle ac analysis also [59].

For FET devices, the minimum number of space dimensions is always two, in contrary to bipolar devices, where one-dimensional models are meaningful in many cases. Simplified numerical FET models result from unipolar carrier transport, thus one transport equation is dropped [60] and, consequently, recombination is neglected [61].

One of the first programs for two-dimensional geometries based on these assumptions is CADETT [62]. It uses a stream function whose derivatives give the two components of the current densities. This approach had many followers, especially in Japanese literature [63]-[65]. Early versions of the program MINIMOS also used only two governing equations [66].

Further simplifications assume a constant quasi-Fermi level in the vertical direction [67] and lump the mobile channel charge into a charge sheet at the Si-SiO₂ interface [68].

IV. REPRESENTATIVE EXAMPLES

In the past, numerical solutions of the basic equations in one or two space dimensions and more recently in three dimensions [69]-[71] have been obtained for a large variety of different devices. These numerical models permit one to look into an operating device and watch the different internal mechanisms. By this, one can trace the dominating effects in the respective device regions and sharpen one's physical understanding of electrical device behavior. The knowledge gained during this process can quite often be valued higher than the numerical results themselves, since it may guide the course for improved device design. Several examples have been selected to support this view. All simulations were done with the programs GALATEA, GALENE, and MEDUSA developed at RWTH Aachen over the past 12 years, for two-dimensional bipolar, two-dimensional MOS, and quasi-multidimensional bipolar device analysis.

The first example is an OXIL I²L inverter [72]. A rectangular nonequidistant grid with 2511 nodes was used for the discretization of a vertical cross section of this device. Starting in each case at the equilibrium solution and using STEPSOLVING, the exact numerical model for injector voltages up to 900 mV required computation times between 20 and 30 min on a TR-440 computer which corresponds to 1.4 and 2 min, respectively, on a CYBER 175. Fig. 9 shows the two-dimensional distribution of hole density for the OFF state with an applied bias of $V_{Inj} = 720$ mV, $V_{BE} = 4$ mV, and $V_{CE} = 700$ mV. The crossed rectangles in the reference plane ($p = n_i$) indicate the ohmic contacts for injector, base collector, and emitter, respectively. Due to the forward voltage across the injector–emitter junction, the n-doped emitter region underneath the injector is completely flooded with holes. The excess carrier concentration of holes decays exponentially in the lateral direction underneath the base region. This decay results from recombination in the bulk and at the emitter contact. Moreover, holes are laterally injected into the epitaxial base of the lateral p-n-p transistor. Because this transistor is active, hole concentration shows a linear distribution there (diffusion triangle). Note that a log scale is used in Fig. 9. Fig. 10 shows the distribution of the swing $p(x, y)_{ON} - p(x, y)_{OFF}$, where for the ON state, $V_{BE} = 700$ mV and $V_{CE} = 4$ mV. The linear scale gives an indication of the excellent numerical accuracy achieved. For these bias conditions, a large difference of hole concentrations occurs at both junctions of the n-p-n transistor. Different acceptor doping profiles in the active and inactive region of the n-p-n transistor result in the step, which can be seen for $p_{ON} - p_{OFF}$ at the base–emitter junction underneath the collector edge.

168

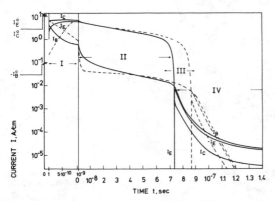

Fig. 11. Terminal currents versus time. In region I the time scale is enlarged by a factor of 40. I_E^0, I_B^0, I_C^0 are the initial values.

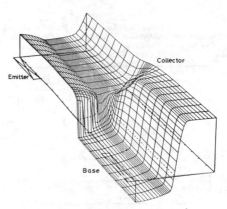

Fig. 12. Potential distribution at $t = 10^{-9}$ s.

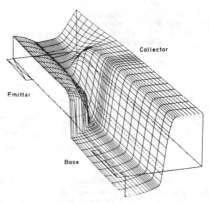

Fig. 13. Potential distribution at $t = 4 \times 10^{-8}$ s.

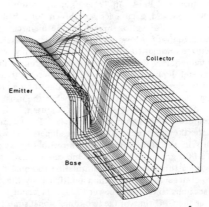

Fig. 14. Potential distribution at $t = 6.8 \times 10^{-8}$ s.

Though these results are obtained for steady-state conditions, they can be used to roughly calculate transient device behavior. Integrating $q(p_{ON} - p_{OFF})$ yields the charge, which has to be transported through the device terminals during the transition from the OFF to the ON state and vice versa. The usual quasi-static approximation gives a first estimation for the delay time, which differs only 20 percent from measured data for this example.

The second example concerns two-dimensional numerical solutions for a standard n-p-n transistor switched abruptly from $V_{BE} = 900$ mV to $V_{BE} = 0$ with a constant collector-base voltage of $V_{CB} = 1$ V [43]. Fig. 11 depicts the resulting terminal currents as a function of time (drawn lines). Note that the scale of the time axis changes at $t = 10^{-9}$ s. The numerical results show four time regions with different mechanisms in each:

I: $0 < t < 10^{-9}$ s,   discharge of the sidewall transistor,
II: 10^{-9} s $< t < 7 \times 10^{-8}$ s,   lateral wave,
III: 7×10^{-8} s $< t < 9 \times 10^{-8}$ s,   vertical discharge,
IV: $t > 9 \times 10^{-8}$ s,   emitter discharge.

These time regions are also indicated in Fig. 11. Due to the applied initial bias of $V_{BE} = 900$ mV, the active base has spread into the epitaxial collector. At the end of time region I, this base pushout is still present as can be seen from Fig. 12. Transient terminal characteristics are dominated by a lateral shockwave which propagates laterally through the active base region as demonstrated by the sequence of Figs. 12-14. In time region II, which dominates the total switching time, discharge of holes flowing laterally towards the base contact is the prevailing mechanism. Such a basically multidimensional mechanism is inherently excluded from one-dimensional simulations. Hence, the question arises how well this lateral shock wave can be approximated by a quasi-two-dimensional model. The result is shown by dashed lines in Fig. 11. The transistor was made up of only three one-dimensional subdevices. Compared with the exact two-dimensional model mainly two differences can be noticed: the propagation time is increased by approximately 15 percent and I_B decays faster at the beginning of the lateral discharge in the quasi-two-dimensional model. By extending the number of subdevices up to ten, it was found that the increase of the propagation time stems from the quasi-

two-dimensional approach itself, whereas the latter difference is due to discretization errors caused by the small number of only three subdevices. However, increased accuracy has its price, as can be seen from Table IV, which summarizes a comparison for the exact two-dimensional simulation and two examples of quasi-two-dimensional simulations.

TABLE IV

COMPUTATIONAL EFFORT FOR EXACT TWO-DIMENSIONAL AND
QUASI-TWO-DIMENSIONAL SIMULATIONS OF TRANSISTOR
TRANSIENTS—THE COMPUTATION TIMES REFER TO AN
ECLIPSE S200 COMPUTER

lateral gridpoints	3 (quasi 2D)	10 (quasi 2D)	27 (exact 2D)
vertical gridpoints	37	37	37
time steps	226	343	80
comp. time per time step	8	23	720
gain	90	31	1
relative cost	1	4	32

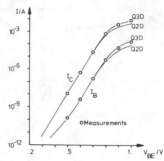

Fig. 15. Collector and base current versus V_{BE} from measurements and the quasi-two-dimensional (Q2D) and quasi-three-dimensional (Q3D) models.

TABLE V

COMPUTATION TIME AND ACCURACY OF THE MODELS OF THE
STEPSOLVING HIERARCHY APPLIED TO A TRANSISTOR AT
A MODERATE INJECTION LEVEL
(V_{BE} = 650 mV, V_{CB} = 1 V)

MODEL	COMPUTATION TIME (SEC)	ACCELERATION FACTOR	RELATIVE DEVIATION (%) FROM MODEL 4			
			R_{SRH}	R_{AUG}	I_B	I_C
1	4.3	83	26	---	20 for $V_{BE}<0.4$ V	20
L2	12.5(1+L2)	29	0.1	0.2	0.1	0.1
L3	25.1(1+...L3)	14	< 0.1	< 0.1	< 0.1	< 0.1
4	98.9(1+...4)	4	—	—	—	—

Different simplified numerical models result from the STEP-SOLVING method where each level of the hierarchy constitutes a model in itself. As an example, a standard n-p-n transistor is considered which is discretized using 34 lateral and 45 vertical grid lines. In Table V, computation times (on a CYBER 175) and accuracies are shown for the different models of the low-injection branch of the hierarchy. These results indicate that for low and medium injection levels model $L2$ is accurate enough (0.1 percent) for engineering purposes. This model requires only the numerical solution of the even simpler model 1 plus the solution of the continuity equation for minority carriers. Thus model $L2$ is almost by a factor 30 faster than the exact numerical model, when the usual successive procedure without STEPSOLVING is used. The latter model required 359 s for this example. If one intended to simulate the same example in three dimensions with ten grid points in the third dimension, one would have approximately 15 000 grid points totally. One can estimate the time required for a three-dimensional simulation to equal the time for a two-dimensional cross section multiplied by the number of cross sections to the third power [32]. The result would be 1000 times the CPU time of the two-dimensional simulation.

The last example of this series in Fig. 15 gives a quasi-three-dimensional simulation of an n-p-n transistor in comparison with a quasi-two-dimensional one [73]. The latter clearly overestimates base resistance and crowding because the model does not account for the spreading of the base current into the third dimension. However, the quasi-three-dimensional simulation and the measured characteristics are in good agreement. In the MEDUSA simulations, 35 and 6 one-dimensional sub-

devices and 65 and 7 transportances were used for the three-dimensional and two-dimensional case, respectively. For the device characteristic given in Fig. 15 and consisting of 20 operating points, the CPU time on a CYBER 175 was 478 and 83 s, respectively.

The next series of examples compiles plots of equipotential lines for four different bias points of a MOST with an effective channel length L = 3.3 μm with those of a MOST with L = 1.0 μm. The underlying simulations used a rectangular nonequidistant grid with 50 vertical and 29 lateral grid lines. In order to clearly work out the differences, caused by channel-length reduction only, all other technological parameters are kept constant. Among these, the most important are the oxide thickness d_{ox} = 22 nm, the homogeneous substrate doping N_A = 1.5 × 10^{15} cm^{-3}, and the junction depth of the arsenic source and drain implantation x_j = 0.36 μm. For comparison, the following bias points were chosen: two subthreshold points with low (V_D = 0.5 V, Figs. 16 and 17) and high (V_D = 5 V, Figs. 18 and 19) drain voltage, one bias point in the linear region (Figs. 20 and 21) and one in the saturation region (Figs. 22 and 23). The substrate voltage equals zero. The solutions for the different bias points were obtained without calculating the solutions for intermediate bias. The average CPU time on a CYBER 175 for one solution was 60 s. In all plots, the electrostatic potential of the first line is chosen to be one third of a thermal voltage above the potential in the neutral bulk. Therefore, this line indicates approximately the boundary of the space-charge region. The potential increment between two neighboring lines is equal for plots belonging to the same bias point. The plots for the shorter transistor are scaled by a factor of 2 in the lateral direction.

In order to demonstrate the influence of the effective channel length on the charge sharing between source, drain, and gate, the bulk charge shared by the gate is indicated by chain-dotted lines unless it vanishes (Fig. 19). It is apparent that the ratio of shared bulk charge to effective channel length decreases with channel length reduction. For higher drain voltages this effect is very pronounced (Figs. 22 and 23) and in the subthreshold case (Fig. 19) even punchthrough occurs. Moreover, it is evident that with constant L the bulk charge shared by the gate decreases considerably with increasing drain voltage (e.g., Figs. 16 and 18). At the device terminals, these effects cause the well-known short-channel effects of threshold voltage and subthreshold current dependence on drain voltage and effective channel length. The plots clearly indicate that charge sharing is a two-dimensional mechanism which is diffi-

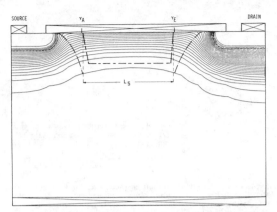

Fig. 16. Plot of equipotential lines for the n-channel MOST with $L = 3.3$ μm and $V_G - V_{TH0} = -0.2$ V, $V_D = 0.5$ V, $V_B = 0$ V. V_{TH0} is the threshold voltage of this transistor for $V_D \approx 0$ and has the same value for Figs. 17–23. The potential increment between two neighboring lines is 0.04 V. The chain-dotted and dashed lines indicate the bulk charge shared by the gate resulting from the numerical simulation and the analytical model by Taylor [74], respectively. Y_A and Y_E indicate the region where the gradual channel approximation is valid.

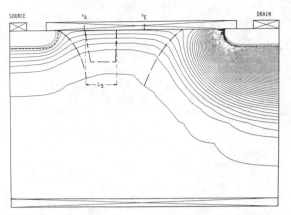

Fig. 18. Plot of equipotential lines for the MOST with $L = 3.3$ μm and $V_G - V_{TH0} = -0.2$ V, $V_D = 5$ V, $V_B = 0$ V. The potential increment is 0.1 V.

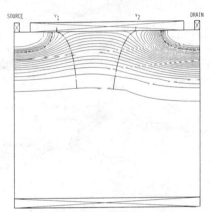

Fig. 17. Plot of equipotential lines for the n-channel MOST with $L = 1$ μm and $V_G - V_{TH0} = -0.2$ V, $V_D = 0.5$ V, $V_B = 0$ V. The potential increment is 0.04 V.

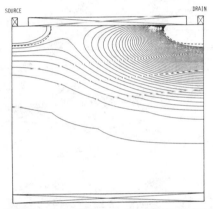

Fig. 19. Plot of equipotential lines for the MOST with $L = 1$ μm and $V_G - V_{TH0} = -0.2$ V, $V_D = 5$ V, $V_B = 0$ V. The potential increment is 0.1 V.

cult to model analytically. In order to support this view, the shared bulk charge for the subthreshold region as predicted by Taylor's model [74] is plotted by dashed lines in Figs. 16 and 18. Especially for $V_D = 5$ V (Fig. 18) it becomes clear that the analytical model overestimates the influence of drain voltage.

Fig. 24 shows, for the 1-μm transistor described above, a simulation of the output characteristic for $V_G = 2$ V and $V_B = 0$ V in comparison with measurements [75]. One can clearly draw the conclusion, that device behavior in saturation is dominated by carrier-velocity saturation and not by pinchoff.

The final example demonstrates the increase of hole density caused by avalanche generation in the pinchoff region of an n-channel MOST. It has a n^+-poly gate and its technological parameters are: $d_{ox} = 40$ nm, $L = 1.4$ μm, $N_A = 4 \times 10^{15}$ cm^{-3}, and $x_j = 0.5$ μm.

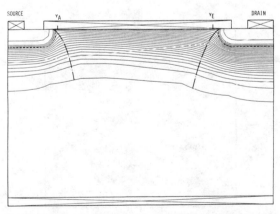

Fig. 20. Plot of equipotential lines for the MOST with $L = 3.3$ μm and $V_G - V_{TH0} = 2$ V, $V_D = 0.5$ V, $V_B = 0$ V. The potential increment is 0.05 V.

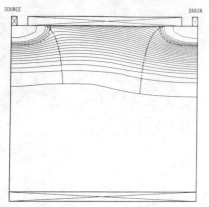

Fig. 21. Plot of equipotential lines for the MOST with $L = 1$ μm and $V_G - V_{TH0} = 2$ V, $V_D = 0.5$ V, $V_B = 0$ V. The potential increment is 0.05 V.

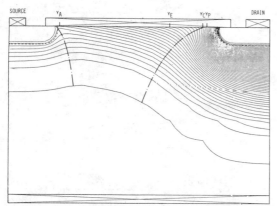

Fig. 22. Plot of equipotential lines for the MOST with $L = 3.3$ μm and $V_G - V_{TH0} = 2$ V, $V_D = 5$ V, $V_B = 0$ V. The potential increment is 0.1 V.

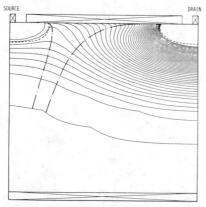

Fig. 23. Plot of equipotential lines for the MOST with $L = 1$ μm and $V_G - V_{TH0} = 2$ V, $V_D = 5$ V, $V_B = 0$ V. The potential increment is 0.1 V.

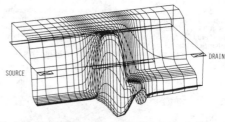

Fig. 24. Comparison of the output characteristics for $V_G = 2$ V of the MOST with $L = 1$ μm resulting from measurements ($\times$) and simulations with ($--$) and without ($-\cdot-$) velocity saturation.

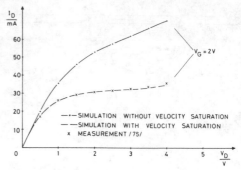

Fig. 25. Log-scaled hole density resulting from a simulation excluding avalanche generation of a n-channel MOST with n$^+$-poly gate.

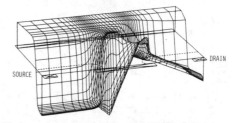

Fig. 26. Log-scaled hole density resulting from a simulation including avalanche generation. The underlying transistor is the same as in Fig. 25.

The bias conditions are $V_G = 1.5$ V, $V_D = 5$ V, $V_B = 0$ V. The two plots compare in a log scale the hole density resulting from simulations excluding (Fig. 25) and including (Fig 26) the avalanche generation. The drastic increase of the hole density in the pinchoff region near the drain is apparent. The peak value of the hole density (Fig. 26) is as large as the impurity concentration, and therefore influences the electrostatic potential in this region. Moreover, the considerable increase of hole density in the drain region and the slight increase in the source region are remarkable. The latter effect would become more pronounced or even dominant if the parasitic bulk resistance is important [76], [77].

In either case, the influence of avalanche generation is not a secondary effect which could be handled with sufficient accuracy in a simulation program which uses only one transport equation and calculates the rate of avalanche generation afterwards using the simulated electron density and potential. The

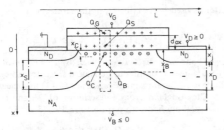

Fig. 27. Cross section of a MOS transistor indicating the different charge components.

coupling between majority- and minority-carrier flow and potential is such that it requires the solution of the three basic equations.

V. Analytical Models

A. MOS Transistor Models

The classical equations which form the basis for practically all analytical MOST models used in today's circuit analysis programs were derived by Ihantola, Moll [78] and Pao, Shah [79], [80] for the linear and saturation region and by Barron [81] and Swanson, Meindl [82] for the subthreshold or weak inversion region. With MOST geometries as required for VLSI, the classical models have their shortcomings which are generally summarized as short-channel effects. Examples are channel length modulation and mobility dependence on field and charge sharing. For each single effect, different modeling approaches have been proposed. In addition, the coupling of the respective models to form a complete MOST model can be done in many different ways.

In the literature it is not always clear whether the value for a certain parameter to be inserted into a given model is derived from device-independent measurements or from the device characteristics themselves to be described by the model. In the latter case, this parameter has to be considered as a fitting parameter. Hence, the accuracy of the resulting model depends, to a large extent, on how many of those parameters are used. Therefore, no effort was made to rate the different models on the basis of the resulting terminal characteristics. As an alternative, a comparison based on the underlying physical assumptions has been attempted.

In order to facilitate this attempt, first, the derivation of the classical equations is outlined briefly in order to clearly state the basic assumptions. Next, the short-channel effects are discussed and the different approaches to model them are outlined briefly. In order to simplify the expressions, the equations which follow are restricted to an n-channel MOST with uniform channel doping. Note that in the following section, the electrostatic potential is normalized in the neutral bulk by the condition $\psi_B = V_B$ (Fig. 27).

Threshold Voltage: For a MOST, whose channel length L and width W satisfy $L, W \gg x_D, x_S, x_B$, (Fig. 27) the field in the predominant portion of the channel region is approximately one-dimensional. Therefore, the following is valid:

1) Gradual channel approximation.

This means that the charges are governed by the vertical field only. Hence, the application of the one-dimensional Gauss's theorem is possible, yielding

$$Q_G + Q_S + Q_B + Q_C = 0 \qquad (5.1)$$

where Q_C is the mobile channel charge (Fig. 27). The gate charge Q_G results from electrostatics to

$$Q_G = (V_G - \phi_{MS} - \psi_S) \cdot C_{ox} \qquad (5.2)$$

where ϕ_{MS} is the work-function difference between gate and bulk, $C_{ox} = \epsilon_{ox}/d_{ox}$, and ψ_S is the electrostatic potential at the interface. Approximating Q_C as a surface charge [78], [83] in comparison with Q_B and applying the depletion approximation, yields

$$Q_B = -K \cdot C_{ox} \cdot (\psi_S - V_B)^{1/2} \qquad (5.3)$$

where $K = (2 \cdot \epsilon_{Si} \cdot q \cdot N_A)^{1/2}/C_{ox}$. (For a more accurate approximation see (5.27).)

The electron density at the surface n_S equals N_A at least near the source if

$$\frac{1}{2} \psi_S = \phi_F = V_T \ln \frac{N_A}{n_{ie}} \qquad (5.4)$$

where ϕ_F is the electron quasi-Fermi level near the source. Further increase of ψ_S by a few thermal voltages causes the mobile channel charge Q_C dominating Q_B because of the exponential dependence of n_S on ψ_S. Therefore, the gate voltage yielding (5.4) to hold is called threshold voltage V_{TH}. Under the condition (5.4), Q_C can be neglected in (5.1) resulting in

$$V_{TH} = 2\phi_F + V_{FB} - Q_B/C_{ox} \qquad (5.5)$$

where $V_{FB} = \phi_{MS} - Q_S/C_{ox}$ is the flat-band voltage and Q_B is given by (5.3) and (5.4), respectively. From the mechanism described above it is obvious that for $V_G > V_{TH}$ the device will be in the conducting state whereas the contrary is true for $V_G < V_{TH}$.

The Classical Drain Current Equation: The following assumptions are typical for an n-channel MOST models:

2) Recombination and Generation can be neglected.

3) Hole current can be neglected ($V_D \geqslant 0$, $V_B \leqslant 0$).

This yields the drain current I_D to be an electron current of vanishing divergence. Integrating (2.8) across the channel, therefore, results in

$$I_D = -W \cdot \int_0^{x_C} \left(q \cdot \mu_n \cdot n \cdot \frac{\partial \phi_n}{\partial y} \right) dx = \text{const} \qquad (5.6)$$

where x_C is the channel thickness. Assuming in addition that

4) $\partial \mu_n/\partial x$ can be neglected across the channel

5) $\partial \phi_n/\partial x$ can be neglected across the channel yields

$$I_D = W \cdot \mu_n \cdot Q_C(V) \frac{dV}{dy} \qquad (5.7)$$

where

$$V = \phi_n - \phi_n\big|_{\text{Source}}.$$

The Drain Current in the Linear and Saturation Region: The linear and saturation region implies $V_G > V_{TH}$. The assumption that the density of the mobile channel charge dominates the space-charge density in the whole channel region (strong inversion), leads to the following approximation [78], [79]:

6) Diffusion current can be neglected compared to drift current ($\partial \phi_n/\partial y \cong \partial \psi_S/\partial y$).

This implies

$$\psi_S(y) = \psi_S(0) + V(y). \qquad (5.8)$$

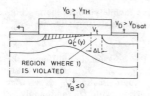

Fig. 28. MOS transistor in saturation.

Moreover, from the remarks made in connection with (5.4), (5.5), the following approximation is obvious and made quite often [84]:

$$\psi_S(0) = 2\phi_F. \tag{5.9}$$

Substitution of (5.8), (5.9) into (5.2), (5.3) yields

$$Q_C(V) = -C_{ox}(V_G - V_{FB} - 2\phi_F - V - K(V - V_B + 2\phi_F)^{1/2}). \tag{5.10}$$

Making the additional assumptions:
7) 1) is valid within the whole channel region;
8) the lateral dependence of μ_n can be neglected;

and using $V(0) = 0$, $V(L) = V_D$, (5.7) can be integrated yielding [78], [80]

$$I_D = -\beta((V_G - 2\phi_F - V_{FB} + \overline{Q}_B/C_{ox})V_D - V_D^2/2) \tag{5.11}$$

where $\beta = \mu_n \cdot C_{ox} \cdot W/L$ and

$$\overline{Q}_B = \frac{1}{V_D} \int_0^{V_D} Q_B(V)\, dV = -\frac{2K \cdot C_{ox}}{3V_D}$$
$$\cdot [(V_D + 2\phi_F - V_B)^{3/2} - (2\phi_F - V_B)^{3/2}] \tag{5.12}$$

is a special mean value of the bulk charge. Note that in view of (5.10) the condition of strong inversion within the whole channel region imposes the following constraint on the possible values of V_D:

$$V_D < V_{Dsat}(V_G) \tag{5.13}$$

where V_{Dsat} results from the pinchoff condition

$$Q_C(V_{Dsat}) = 0 \tag{5.14}$$

Q_C being given by (5.10). At least for $V_D > V_{Dsat}$, the channel region splits into two different regions (Fig. 28)—one on the source side where 1) is valid and a second on the drain side where 1) is violated. For long-channel MOST's, the second region is approximately identical to the pinchoff region near the drain where the mobile carriers are pushed away from the surface because of electrostatic interaction between gate and drain. In real long-channel devices, the extension of the pinchoff region ΔL, which depends on V_D, can be neglected
9)

$$L \gg \Delta L$$

and in such devices the condition

$$\left.\frac{\partial I_D}{\partial V_D}\right|_{V_D > V_{Dsat}} = 0 \tag{5.15}$$

is a good approximation to physical reality. Therefore, this condition is used to describe I_D in the saturation region [78], [80]

$$I_D(V_D) = I_D(V_{Dsat}), \qquad V_D > V_{Dsat}. \tag{5.16}$$

The right-hand side of (5.16) is given by (5.11). Note that (5.14) guarantees a continuous derivative at the transition.

In the past, different simplifications of (5.11) have been proposed. They originate from a description of Q_B and $Q_B(V)$, respectively, simplified with respect to (5.12), (5.3). In [79]

$$Q_B(V) = Q_B(0) = \text{const} \tag{5.17}$$

was used. Later publications proposed a linear dependence on V according to a first-order Taylor expansion of (5.3)

$$Q_B(V) = Q_B(0) - \gamma \cdot K \cdot C_{ox} \cdot (2\phi_F - V_B)^{-1/2} \cdot V. \tag{5.18}$$

Though $\gamma = 0.5$ is the exact mathematical value [85], better results were obtained by fitting γ to measured data yielding $\gamma = 0.4$ [86].

Mobility Dependence on Vertical Electric Field: For long-channel MOST's with small oxide thickness the model derived above is not yet accurate enough because it does not consider the mobility degradation with vertical electric field reported, for instance, in [87]. Mainly, two different models have been presented in order to take this effect into account. One was proposed by Frohman–Bentchkowsky [88] modeling the effect in the following manner:

$$\mu = \mu_0, \qquad E_\perp \leqslant E_S$$
$$\mu = \mu_0 \left(\frac{E_S}{E_\perp}\right)^C, \qquad E_\perp > E_S. \tag{5.19}$$

μ_0 is the low-field mobility and $E_\perp$ is some mean value of the vertical electric field in the channel which in the linear region can be given by [88]

$$E_\perp = \frac{C_{ox}}{\epsilon_{Si}}(V_G - V_{FB} - 2\phi_F - V_D/2). \tag{5.20}$$

From Frohmann–Bentchkowsky's experimental data E_S and C were found to be 6×10^4 V/cm and 0.15, respectively (for p-channel MOST's). The second model was reported by Crawford [89] proposing

$$\mu = \mu_0(1 + \theta(V_G - V_{TH}))^{-1} \tag{5.21}$$

where θ depends on oxide thickness and crystal orientation. It is possible to implement an analogous formula in (5.7) substituting $V_G - V_{TH}$ by the local field $E_\perp(V)$ and taking this dependence into account during integration [85]. But this results in more complicated equations.

Drain Current in the Subthreshold Region: For the case $V_G < V_{TH}$ (5.8), (5.9) are no longer valid and ψ_S becomes a function of V_{GS}. Furthermore, the rather crude approximation of Q_B in (5.3) is no longer sufficient to compute Q_C from (5.1) because now

$$Q_B \gg Q_C. \tag{5.22}$$

This problem can be overcome since assuming 1) it is possible to write a first integral of Poisson's equation (2.2) with (2.3) integrating from the surface to the neutral bulk and resulting in [80], [90], [91]

$$Q_B + Q_C = -K \cdot C_{\text{ox}}$$

$$\cdot \left(\frac{n_S - n_B + p_S}{N_A} \cdot V_T + \psi_S - V_B - V_T \right)^{1/2}. \quad (5.23)$$

n_B is the electron density in the neutral bulk. The assumption

$$2\phi_F > \psi_S > 3V_T \quad (5.24)$$

yields

$$n_B \ll n_S \ll p_S + \frac{1}{V_T} \cdot N_A (\psi_S - V_B - V_T). \quad (5.25)$$

Therefore, it is a good approximation to neglect n_B and to replace the square-root term in (5.23) by a first-order Taylor expansion [82], [83]. With (2.28) and (5.4) this results in

$$Q_B + Q_C = Q_1 + Q_2 \quad (5.26)$$

$$Q_1 = -K \cdot C_{\text{ox}} \cdot \left(\frac{p_S}{N_A} \cdot V_T + \psi_S - V_B - V_T \right)^{1/2} \quad (5.27)$$

$$Q_2 = V_T \frac{(K \cdot C_{\text{ox}})^2}{2Q_1(\psi_S)} \frac{n_S}{N_A} = V_T \frac{(K \cdot C_{\text{ox}})^2}{2Q_1(\psi_S)}$$

$$\cdot \exp\left(\frac{\psi_S - V - 2\phi_F}{V_T} \right). \quad (5.28)$$

Since Q_1 does not depend on the electron quasi-Fermi level $\phi_n = V + \phi_F$, the following splitting is obvious:

$$Q_1 = Q_R$$

$$Q_2 = Q_C. \quad (5.29)$$

The surface potential ψ_S results from (5.1). Omitting Q_C because of (5.22) and p_S because of (5.24) yields the following equation for ψ_S:

$$V_G - V_{\text{FB}} - \psi_S + Q_B(\psi_S, V_B)/C_{\text{ox}} = 0 \quad (5.30)$$

resulting in

$$\psi_S = V_G - V_{\text{FB}} - \frac{K^2}{2}$$

$$\cdot \left[\left(1 + \frac{4}{K^2} (V_G - V_{\text{FB}} - V_B - V_T) \right)^{1/2} - 1 \right]. \quad (5.31)$$

Note that ψ_S does not depend on V. Substitution of (5.28) into (5.7) and integration of (5.7) under assumptions 7), 8) results in

$$I_D = \beta V_T^2 \frac{K^2 C_{\text{ox}}}{2Q_1(\psi_S)} \left(\frac{n_{ie}}{N_A} \right)^2 \exp(\psi_S/V_T)$$

$$\cdot (1 - \exp(-V_D/V_T)) \quad (5.32)$$

where ψ_S and Q_1 are given by (5.31) and (5.27), respectively.
Note that for

$$V_D > 3V_T \quad (5.33)$$

I_D is independent of V_D and that in view of (5.31) I_D varies exponentially with V_G. Both features agree well with measurements for long-channel devices [92].

Limitations: Drain current in the subthreshold region is modeled in (5.32) as a pure diffusion current, whereas in the linear and saturation region it is modeled as a pure drift current. Hence, it is not to be expected that there is a smooth transition between the two respective regions. This is a severe drawback of the models treated so far, even for very-long-channel MOST's because smooth transitions are important if a model is to be implemented in a circuit simulator.

A possibility to overcome these limitations is a double-integral formula presented by Pao and Sah [90] including both current components but which results in a high computational effort and hence was not applied for circuit models. The charge-sheet model by Brews [83] reduces this effort considerably. The model by Swanson and Meindl [82] provides at least a continuous transition and may be considered a trade-off between the classical models and the ones mentioned earlier.

It is well known that for MOST's with shorter channels the measured characteristics deviate from those predicted by the long-channel model derived above. These deviations are usually called short-channel effects. Hence, there is no doubt that some of the assumptions made before are no longer valid.

Channel Length Modulation: The first assumption which must be dropped even for moderate channel lengths is 9). In this case, the channel length modulation ΔL (Fig. 28) becomes of increasing importance affecting the output resistance in the saturation region, which approaches finite values in contrast to (5.15). But if all other assumptions are restricted (if necessary) to the region at the source side, where 1) remains valid, they retain their validity at least for moderate channel lengths. In this case there are two unknowns. The first is ΔL the length of the region at the drain side where 1) is violated and the second is V_t the surface potential at the transition of the two regions. Assuming that these two quantities are known, the correct approach for $V_G > V_{\text{TH}}$ is the following:

$$I_D = f(V_G, V_B, V_D), \quad V_D \leqslant V_{D\,\text{sat}} \quad (5.34)$$

$$I_D = I_{D\,\text{sat}}(\Delta L, V_t) = \frac{L}{L - \Delta L} f(V_G, V_B, V_t),$$

$$V_D \geqslant V_{D\,\text{sat}} \quad (5.35)$$

where possible choices for f are the right-hand side of (5.11) or the formulas resulting from (5.17) and (5.18). But other relations describing I_D in the source region under the assumption of 1) are used, as well [85], [93]. In order to get a continuous transition the following constraints are sufficient:

$$\Delta L \big|_{V_D = V_{D\,\text{sat}}} = 0 \quad (5.36)$$

$$V_t \big|_{\Delta L = 0} = V_{D\,\text{sat}}. \quad (5.37)$$

To compute the exact values of ΔL and V_t is a difficult mathematical problem because of the two-dimensional nature of the field in the pinchoff region (Fig. 22). Therefore, all models proposed and in use provide only rather crude approximations for these unknowns. Frohmann–Bentchkowski et al. [94], [95] proposed

$$\Delta L = \frac{V_D - V_t}{E_T} \quad (5.38)$$

where E_T is the mean transversal electric field in the drain region. E_T is given by the empirical formula

$$E_T = E_1 + \alpha E_2(d_{\text{ox}}) + \beta E_3(d_{\text{ox}}) \quad (5.39)$$

where E_2 and E_3 are approximations of the vertical electric field at the beginning and the end of the drain section, E_1 is an approximation of the lateral electric field given by the one-dimensional depletion approximation, and α, β are empirical "field fringing factors." The continuity condition

$$\frac{\partial I_D}{\partial V_D}\bigg|_{V_D=V_{D\,\text{sat}}} = \frac{\partial I_{D\,\text{sat}}}{\partial V_D}\bigg|_{V_D=V_{D\,\text{sat}}} \tag{5.40}$$

is used to determine $V_t = V_{D\,\text{sat}}$. Most other approaches fall more or less into the following scheme.

A rearrangement of Poisson's equation at the interface yields

$$\frac{\partial^2}{\partial y^2}\,\psi_S = -\frac{\rho_S(y)}{\epsilon_{\text{Si}}} - g(y) \tag{5.41}$$

where g is given by

$$g(y) = \left(\frac{\partial^2}{\partial x^2}\,\psi\right)_S (y). \tag{5.42}$$

If the right-hand side of (5.41) is assumed to be known, the unknown lateral electric field at the transition of the two regions is denoted by E_t and the contribution of the mobile carriers to ρ_S is approximated using $I_{D\,\text{sat}}$, the solution of (5.41) together with the boundary conditions

$$\psi_S(L-\Delta L) - \psi_S(L) = V_t - V_D \tag{5.43}$$

$$\frac{\partial\psi_S}{\partial y}(L-\Delta L) = E_t \tag{5.44}$$

provides a relation of the form

$$F_1(V_t, E_t, \Delta L, I_{D\,\text{sat}}) = 0. \tag{5.45}$$

Two further relations are given by (5.35)

$$F_2(V_t, \Delta L, I_{D\,\text{sat}}) = 0 \tag{5.46}$$

and the differential equation (5.7) at the transition point

$$F_3(V_t, E_t, I_{D\,\text{sat}}) = 0. \tag{5.47}$$

These are three independent equations for the unknowns V_t, E_t, ΔL, $I_{D\,\text{sat}}$. If E_t or V_t (or both) are given by a further equation or an additional assumption, (5.45), (5.46), (5.47) can be used to compute the remaining unknowns.

Reddi and Sah [84] computed $V_t = V_{D\,\text{sat}}$ by the pinchoff condition (5.14) and used the approximations

$$E_t = 0 \tag{5.48}$$

$$\rho_S = -q \cdot N_A \tag{5.49}$$

$$g = 0. \tag{5.50}$$

In this case (5.45) is independent on $I_{D\,\text{sat}}$ resulting in explicit equations for ΔL and $I_{D\,\text{sat}}$. But this approach usually overestimates the influence of drain voltage on $I_{D\,\text{sat}}$ in the saturation region. Baum [96] did not use (5.14) and dropped (5.48). He assumed a linear relation between the velocity of the mobile carriers and the electric field in the source region (equivalent to 8) restricted to the source region) characterized by a constant μ. Moreover, he assumed a constant carrier velocity v_{sat} in the drain region due to velocity saturation. This yields at the transition

$$E_t = E_c = \frac{v_{\text{sat}}}{\mu} \tag{5.51}$$

where E_c is the critical electric field for velocity saturation. Using (5.49)–(5.51) results in implicit equations for ΔL and V_t, which have to be solved iteratively. In addition Merckel et al. [85] considered the influence of the mobile carriers on the space charge. They dropped (5.49) and used

the approximation

$$\rho_S(y) = -q \cdot N_A + \frac{I_{D\,\text{sat}}}{v_{\text{sat}} \cdot W \cdot x(y)} \tag{5.52}$$

where (Fig. 27)

$$x(y) = \frac{x_j - x_C}{\Delta L}(y - L + \Delta L) + x_C. \tag{5.53}$$

Moreover, utilizing (5.52), (5.51) and (5.50), they proposed a simplified solution of (5.45)–(5.47). Neglecting ΔL in (5.46) yields an implicit equation for $V_t = V_{D\,\text{sat}}$ ((5.46) combined with (5.47)). Substitution of V_t into (5.45) and (5.46) results in a cubic equation for $I_{D\,\text{sat}}$. Instead of (5.52), Rossel et al. [93] used

$$\rho_S = -q \cdot N_A + \frac{I_{D\,\text{sat}}}{W \cdot v_{\text{sat}} \cdot x_a} \tag{5.54}$$

where x_a is an empirical parameter, dropped (5.51), and derived another independent relation

$$F_4(V_{D\,\text{sat}}, E_t, I_{D\,\text{sat}}) = 0 \tag{5.55}$$

from the condition of continuity of $\partial^2\psi_S/\partial y^2$ at the transition. An advantage of Rossel's model is that $I_{D\,\text{sat}}$, determined by solving the full set of implicit equations (5.45)–(5.47), (5.55), guaranties (5.40) whereas the output characteristics resulting from all other models presented so far, except the first one, show a discontinuity of $\partial I_D/\partial V_D$ at the transition from linear to saturation region. Klaassen et al. [97] considered the two-dimensional structure of the electrostatic potential in the pinchoff region (Fig. 22) by incorporating results from two-dimensional numerical simulations. They identified the drain region with the pinchoff region, assumed (5.49), and derived from numerical results

$$E_t = E_p > 3E_c$$

$$g(y) = -\frac{\psi_S(y) - \psi_S(0) - V_G + V_{\text{TH}}}{X_0^2} \tag{5.56}$$

where E_p is the electric field at the pinchoff point and X_0 has a value of the order of the drain diffusion layer thickness. They used the simplified formula resulting from (5.18) in (5.35), and neglected ΔL in (5.46) yielding two explicit equations for $V_{D\,\text{sat}} = V_t$ ((5.46) combined with (5.47)) and ΔL ((5.45)). So far, most models presented approximated the region at the drain side, where 1), is not valid, by the pinchoff region or by the region, where $|\partial\psi_S/\partial y| > E_c$ is valid. In order to evaluate these approximations the region where the use of (5.10) causes an error of less than 10 percent is indicated in Fig. 22 by its boundaries y_A and y_E. Moreover, the pinchoff point y_P and the point y_C, where $\partial\psi_S/\partial y = E_C = 2.5 \times 10^4$ V/cm are indicated, too. It is likely that the approximations mentioned above may cause errors.

Popa [98] defined the transition by a condition based on 1)

$$\left(\frac{\partial^2\psi}{\partial x^2}\right)_S = K\,\frac{\partial^2\psi_S}{\partial y^2} \tag{5.57}$$

where K is some large number, e.g., $K = 10$, and yielded a relation of the form of (5.55). His remaining approach was similar to that of Rossel et al. [93], Höfflinger et al. [99] derived from (5.57), and additional assumptions

$$E_t = \frac{g}{L}(V_G - V_{\text{TH}}) \tag{5.58}$$

where g is a fitting parameter. Moreover, they applied (5.50) and (5.49) with an effective doping density $\tilde{N}_A = F^2 N_A$ and used the formula resulting from (5.17) in (5.35). El Mansy et al. [100] as well used (5.57) to determine the transition but used some explicit empirical formula to approximate the potential at the transition. Moreover, they described the drain region by a simplified boundary value problem based on Poisson's equation and solved it using further simplifying assumptions.

Velocity Saturation: So far, velocity saturation has only been mentioned in connection with some models described above which assume a constant carrier velocity v_{sat} in the drain region [96], [85], [93]. But for MOST's with shorter channel lengths 8) is no longer valid, even if it is restricted to the source region (Fig. 24). Trofimenkoff [101] showed that a hyperbolic velocity field characteristic fits well to measured data

$$\mu = \frac{\mu_0}{1 + |E_y|/E_c} \tag{5.59}$$

μ_0 is the mobility for low drain voltage and E_y is the lateral electric field. The proposal of Caughey et al. [5] agrees with (5.59) for holes but they showed that for electrons

$$\mu = \frac{\mu_0}{(1 + (E_y/E_c)^2)^{1/2}} \tag{5.60}$$

is a better fit. An advantage of the simpler expression (5.59) is that (5.7) with μ replaced by (5.59) and $E_y = -(dV/dy)$ can be integrated in closed form. If the boundary conditions $V(o) = 0$, $V(L) = V_D$ are used the solution (5.11) is only changed by the factor [102]

$$\frac{1}{1 + V_D/LE_c}. \tag{5.61}$$

Therefore, the hyperbolic velocity field characteristic or similar formulas are mostly applied [85], [97], [99], [102], [103]. Note that because of (5.51) and (5.19)–(5.21) E_c often depends on V_G.

Dependence of V_{TH} on L, W, and V_D: Comparison of Fig. 16 with Fig. 17 shows that the potential at the interface ψ_S is higher for the shorter transistor, although the technological parameters and the subthreshold bias condition are the same in both cases. This effect is known as barrier lowering induced by channel length reduction. In short-channel MOST's the same effect can be caused by increasing the drain voltage. This is easily verified by comparing Fig. 17 with Fig. 19. In the latter case, the extreme barrier lowering induced by the drain results in punch through. Therefore, it is evident, that in short-channel MOST's the threshold voltage depends on L and V_D. Unfortunately, if one of both effects has some influence, 1) is no longer valid within the whole channel region. Nevertheless, the relation

$$V_G - V_{FB} - \psi_S + \frac{\partial \psi_S^+}{\partial x}(y) \cdot \epsilon_{Si} \cdot C_{ox}^{-1} = 0 \tag{5.62}$$

which is a generalization of (5.30), is valid. Application of Gauss's law to the region occupied by the bulk charge Q_{BF}, which is shared by the gate, and noting that the lateral boundaries of this region are field lines and that the field vanishes at the bottom (Fig. 17) yields

$$Q_{BF} = \int_{y_1}^{y_2} \epsilon_{Si} \frac{\partial \psi_S^+}{\partial x}(y)\, dy \tag{5.63}$$

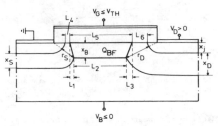

Fig. 29. Charge sharing in the subthreshold region as proposed by Taylor [74].

where y_1 and y_2 are the boundaries of the region at the interface (Fig. 17). Making the rather crude assumption that [74], [104]

$$\psi_S(y) = \text{const}, \qquad y_1 \leqslant y \leqslant y_2 \tag{5.64}$$

results in

$$V_G - V_{FB} - \psi_S + Q_{BF}/((y_2 - y_1) C_{ox}) = 0. \tag{5.65}$$

This approach at least guarantees charge conservation. Obviously, the threshold voltage is now given by

$$V_{TH} = V_{FB} + 2\phi_F - \frac{Q_{BF}(\psi_S - 2\phi_F)}{C_{ox} \cdot L_5} \tag{5.66}$$

where $L_5 = y_2 - y_1$.

For low drain voltages, Yau [104] used this approach and approximated the region occupied by Q_{BF} by a trapezoid. Taylor [74] generalized his approach imposing no restrictions on the possible values of V_D. Provided $L_2 \neq 0$, the trapezoid (Fig. 29) is determined, if L_4, L_6, r_S, r_D, x_B are known and a cylindrical underdiffusion profile of the source and drain junctions is assumed. Taylor approximated the unknown line segments applying the formula for an unsymmetrical plane junction

$$L_4 = (a(V_{Bi} - \psi_S))^{1/2} \tag{5.67}$$

$$L_6 = (a(V_D + V_{Bi} - \psi_S))^{1/2} \tag{5.68}$$

$$r_S = (a(V_{Bi} - V_B))^{1/2} \tag{5.69}$$

$$r_D = (a(V_D - V_B + V_{Bi}))^{1/2} \tag{5.70}$$

$$x_B = (a(-V_B + \psi_S))^{1/2} \tag{5.71}$$

where $a = 2\epsilon_{Si}/(q \cdot N_A)$ and V_{Bi} is the built-in voltage of the junctions. This yields

$$Q_{BF} = Q_{BF}(L, V_D, V_B, \psi_S) \tag{5.72}$$

and with the threshold condition $\psi_S = 2\phi_F$ and (5.66), an expression for the threshold voltage depending on V_D and L. Moreover, Taylor [105] and Chatterjee et al. [106] proposed extensions of this theory for the region above threshold incorporating another value of the bulk charge $\overline{Q}_B$ in (5.11), which they obtained by approximating Q_{BF} by a trapezoid or a quadrangle, respectively. Since one-dimensional approximations possibly are oversimplified (Fig. 18), Dang [103] incorporated into Yau's original theory, that assumed $L_4 = L_6 = 0$, the formula for an unsymmetrical cylindrical junction and assumed the boundary of the space charge shared by source or drain to take the form of an ellipse.

If W decreases and becomes comparable to the thickness of the space-charge layer, the threshold voltage is a function of W as well. This is obvious since, in this case, the charge Q_{BW}

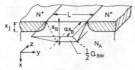

Fig. 30. Charge sharing for a narrow-channel transistor as proposed by Merckel [107].

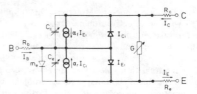

Fig. 31. Ebers–Moll model (EMM) for an n-p-n transistor.

(Fig. 30), which appears in the third dimension at the gate edges, can no longer be neglected compared to $Q_{BF} \cdot W$. Merckel [107] generalized Yau's theory using the same charge conservation argument. This leads to the following extension of formula (5.66):

$$V_{\mathrm{TH}}(W, L) = V_{\mathrm{FB}} + 2\phi_F - \frac{Q_{BF} \cdot W + Q_{BW}}{W \cdot L \cdot C_{\mathrm{ox}}} . \quad (5.73)$$

He assumed the shape of the space-charge region to be a trapezoid in the direction of channel width too and approximated the length of this trapezoid at the interface by $W + 2\alpha x_B$ (Fig. 30), where α is a fitting parameter assumed to be constant for a given technology and given design rules.

Other authors followed a different approach. Masuda *et al.* [108] derived from experimental results the empirical formula

$$V_{\mathrm{TH}} = V_{\mathrm{TH, long}} - (\eta/C_{\mathrm{ox}}) \cdot (V_D - 2V_B + 2V_{\mathrm{Bi}}) \quad (5.74)$$

where $V_{\mathrm{TH, long}}$ is given by (5.5) and

$$\eta = \eta_0(x_j, N_A) \cdot L^{-n}. \quad (5.75)$$

In the special case 10^{15} cm^{-3} $< N_A < 10^{16}$ cm^{-3}, 0.15 μm $\leqslant$ $x_j \leqslant 0.41$ μm, and $d_{\mathrm{ox}} = 50$ nm, they proposed $\eta_0/C_{\mathrm{ox}} = 4.1 \times 10^{-2} - 8.8 \times 10^{-3}$ and $n = 2.6 \cdots 3.2$. Toyabe *et al.* [109] proposed a model derived from an analytical approach which they optimized aided by various two-dimensional numerical simulations.

Variation of Subthreshold Current with V_D and L: The variation of the subthreshold current with V_D and L has two reasons. First, the region where 1) is valid cannot be approximated by the whole channel region for short MOST's and the extension of the remaining region is a function of V_D and L (e.g., Figs. 16 and 18). Therefore, the integration resulting in (5.32) has to be restricted to the region between y_A and y_E. In most cases, the boundary potential $V(y_E)$ has no influence because often $V(y_E) > 3V_T$. Therefore, the remaining modification of (5.32) is a substitution of L in $\beta = \mu C_{\mathrm{ox}}(W/L)$ by $y_E - y_A$. The second reason is the lowering of the ψ_S barrier induced by decreasing L and increasing V_D, which occurs in even shorter MOST's. Troutman [92] modeled these effects by substituting the modified surface potential

$$\psi_S = \psi_{S0} + V_D/\delta \quad (5.76)$$

into (5.32), where ψ_{S0} is given by (5.31) and δ is assumed to be a function of d_{ox}, N_A, and L. Taylor [74] used (5.65) in addition with (5.72) to get a new formula for ψ_S and approximated $y_E - y_A$ by $L_5 = L - L_4 - L_6$ (Figs. 29, 16, and 18), where L_4 and L_6 are given by the approximations (5.67) and (5.68), respectively.

B. Bipolar Transistor Models

Analytical models for bipolar devices are in most cases based on the regional approach [110], in which the device is subdivided into space-charge regions and quasi-neutral regions.

Approximate analytical solutions of the one-dimensional field equations are obtained within each region and then coupled at the corresponding interfaces yielding the desired model. Representative for bipolar devices, analytical models for a vertical n-p-n transistor will be reviewed without going into the details of their derivation.

For the Ebers–Moll model [111], [112] the dc currents of the intrinsic transistor are described as

$$I_{Ei} = I_{ES}[\exp(V_{BEi}/V_T) - 1] - \alpha_r I_{CS}$$
$$\cdot [\exp(V_{BCi}/V_T) - 1] \quad (5.77)$$

$$I_{Ci} = \alpha_f I_{ES}[\exp(V_{BEi}/V_T) - 1] - I_{CS}$$
$$\cdot [\exp(V_{BCi}/V_T) - 1] \quad (5.78)$$

$$I_{Bi} = I_{Et} - I_{Ci} \quad (5.79)$$

where forward and reverse current gains are denoted by α_f and α_r, respectively. Based on this simple model, further refinements have been introduced. A first necessary extension of the basic model is the addition of series resistors. Current-dependent current gain has been modeled by an additional base–emitter diode connected in parallel [113]; Early effect has been taken into account by introducing a current- and voltage-dependent output conductance [114], [115]. AC performance is achieved by adding transition layer capacitances and allowing frequency-dependent current-gain factors. The resulting model can be expressed in terms of network elements as shown in Fig. 31. Other models aim close contact to physics, like the Beaufoy–Sparkes model [116] or try to combine both aspects, e.g., in Linvill's lumped model [117].

A parallel line of development is based on Gummel's integral charge-control relation [118], which relates electrical terminal characteristics to the base charge. Because of its importance, a brief outline of the Gummel–Poon model will be given here. Details can be found in the literature [119]–[124].

Since the dominant electron current in an n-p-n transistor crosses the base region without significant recombination loss, one can analytically solve the transport equation for electrons there yielding the "transfer current" [52]

$$I_T = q A_E V_T \frac{\exp(-\phi_n(x_E)/V_T) - \exp(-\phi_n(x_C)/V_T)}{\displaystyle\int_{x_E}^{x_C} \frac{\exp(-\psi/V_T)}{\mu_n n_{ie}} dx'} \quad (5.80)$$

where A_E is the emitter area. This result corresponds to (3.11), which was obtained for hole current density. Note that the interval considered in (5.80) is extended to positions x_E and x_C beyond the transition regions of emitter and collector junction, respectively. Within this interval, a constant quasi-Fermi level of holes can be assumed. Yielding

$$I_T = qA_E V_T \frac{\exp(V_{BEi}/V_T) - \exp(V_{BCi}/V_T)}{\displaystyle\int_{x_E}^{x_C} \frac{p}{\mu_n n_{ie}^2} dx'}$$

(5.81)

where the internal voltages V_{BEi} and V_{BCi} are given by $\phi_p - \phi_n(x_E)$ and $\phi_p - \phi_n(x_C)$, respectively [52]. This result is often written as

$$I_T = I_s \frac{\exp(V_{BEi}/V_T) - \exp(V_{BCi}/V_T)}{Q_b/Q_{b0}}$$

(5.82)

where the base charge Q_b normalized to its value Q_{b0} at zero bias is defined by

$$\frac{Q_b}{Q_{b0}} = \frac{\displaystyle\int_{x_E}^{x_C} \frac{p}{\mu_n n_{ie}^2} dx'}{\displaystyle\int_{x_E}^{x_C} \left(\frac{p}{\mu_n n_{ie}^2}\right)_0 dx'}.$$

(5.83)

Note that Q_b is the charge of the majority carriers within the base.

According to both junction voltages, the transfer current is usually split into forward and reverse currents

$$I_T = I_f - I_r$$

(5.84)

with

$$I_f = I_s \frac{\exp(V_{BEi}/V_T) - 1}{Q_b/Q_{b0}}$$

(5.85)

$$I_r = I_s \frac{\exp(V_{BCi}/V_T) - 1}{Q_b/Q_{b0}}$$

(5.86)

In the Gummel–Poon model, the base charge Q_b is bias dependent and modeled as a sum of different components with different physical origin

$$Q_b = Q_{b0} + Q_e + Q_c + Q_f + Q_r.$$

(5.87)

Q_e and Q_c are the depletion-layer charges of emitter and collector junction, respectively. They are given by the expressions

$$Q_e = \int_0^{V_{BEi}} C_{je}(V)\, dV$$

(5.88)

$$Q_c = \int_0^{V_{BCi}} C_{jc}(V)\, dV$$

(5.89)

where both junction capacitances are usually described by equations of the form

$$C_j(V) = C_0 \left(1 - \frac{V}{V_d}\right)^{-\nu}$$

(5.90)

provided that the singularity at $V = V_d$ is avoided [124].

Charge storage of the diffusion capacitances is modeled by Q_f and Q_r, which are proportional to forward and reverse current, respectively

$$Q_f = B\tau_f I_f$$

(5.91)

$$Q_r = \tau_r I_r.$$

(5.92)

τ_f and τ_r are called transit times and the base push-out factor B is one at low injection levels and greater than one when the Kirk effect becomes of importance [119].

Dynamic transistor behavior is modeled by the following charge-control relations:

$$I_b = I_{\text{rec}} + \frac{dQ_b}{dt}$$

(5.93)

$$I_c = I_T - I_{\text{rec},r} - \frac{d}{dt}(Q_r + Q_c)$$

(5.94)

$$I_e = I_T + I_{\text{rec},f} + \frac{d}{dt}(Q_f + Q_e).$$

(5.95)

The steady-state base current I_{rec} sums recombination losses for forward and reverse mode of operation

$$I_{\text{rec}} = I_{\text{rec},f}(V_{BEi}) + I_{\text{rec},r}(V_{BCi})$$

(5.96)

where both components can again be split into an ideal part with unity injection factor and a nonideal part with an injection factor $m > 1$. Thus $I_{\text{rec},f}(V_{BEi})$ and $I_{\text{rec},r}(V_{BCi})$ are both modeled by equations of the form

$$I(V) = I_1 [\exp(V/V_T) - 1] + I_2 [\exp(V/m V_T) - 1].$$

(5.97)

The intrinsic Gummel–Poon model, as given by (5.84)–(5.97), accounts for many internal physical phenomena, like high injection in the base, base pushout, Early effect, and current-dependent current gain. Series resistances between the internal transistor nodes and the terminals account for the differences between internal junction voltages and applied voltages. Moreover, a charge-dependent base resistance [123]

$$R_b = R_{b\,ex} + R_{bi} \frac{Q_b}{Q_{b0}}$$

(5.98)

can be introduced to model the effect of base conductivity modulation. The resulting model is very accurate over a wide range of operation. The price to be paid for accuracy is that quite a few parameters have precisely to be extracted from measurements, which sometimes is not an easy task due to parasitics influencing the measured data.

VI. CONCLUSIONS

We have reviewed the present state of the art in device modeling with emphasis on computer-aided modeling. Our view was that of a device designer, who needs to retain the device physics during the design process. Starting with given data from a wafer process or a process simulator, he can look into an operating device and by doing so sharpen his understanding of device behavior, which in turn should guide him to improve his design. Present-day simulators for bipolar as well as MOS devices have matured to the point where this goal can be met at a reasonable cost. In addition, those simulators have been refined over the years of existence to allow prediction of device operation for devices to be built with an accuracy which is quite often limited only by the accuracy with which the input data for the simulator are known. This is true only for devices whose structure can be well approximated in two dimensions. Three-dimensional simulations with a sufficient number of grid points or elements require large computer resources. Hence, simplified treatment is still appropriate, but computation power also increases steadily.

Refinement of the models for physical parameters and the physics of the semiconductor material is an ongoing challenge as with shrinking device dimensions new effects are influencing device behavior. On the other hand, analytical models derived from basic principles seem to have been exploited a great deal and there emphasis is shifting towards simpler models with high computational efficiency.

The trend is pointing in the direction of merging process, device, and circuit simulation in some unified design system. One is then capable of having a direct correspondence between fabrication technology and circuit performance and one can likewise trace back circuit tolerances to tolerances occurring in production. However, one must bear in mind that a good understanding of device operation and verification by experiment will always be necessary for successful device design.

ACKNOWLEDGMENT

The authors wish to thank several colleagues for providing information on relevant results. Among these the discussion with S. T. Pantelides and A. Selloni on heavy doping effects (during an IBM International Symposium on "Methods and Materials in Microelectronic Technology" at Bad Neuenahr, West Germany) merits special mentioning. Also the cooperation with Dr. P. Lloyd and his co-workers from the Integrated Circuit Modeling Group at Bell Laboratories is gratefully appreciated. G. T. Pearman and G. M. Keltz provided accurate and detailed device measurements for Fig. 15.

REFERENCES

[1] O. Madelung, *Introduction to Solid-State Theory*. Berlin: Springer, 1978.
[2] A. H. Marshak and K. M. van Vliet, "Electrical current in solids with position-dependent band structure," *Solid-State Electron.*, vol. 21, pp. 417–427, 1978.
[3] K. M. van Vliet and A. H. Marshak, "The Shockley-like equations for the carrier densities and the current flows in materials with a nonuniform composition," *Solid-State Electron.*, vol. 23, pp. 49–53, 1980.
[4] C. R. Crowell and S. M. Sze, "Current transport in metal-semiconductor barriers," *Solid-State Electron.*, vol. 9, p. 1035, 1966.
[5] D. M. Caughey and R. E. Thomas, "Carrier mobilities in silicon empirically related to doping and field," *Proc. IEEE*, vol. 55, pp. 2192–2193, 1967.
[6] G. Baccarani and P. Ostoja, "Electron mobility empirically related to the phosphorus concentration in silicon," *Solid-State Electron.*, vol. 18, pp. 579–580, 1975.
[7] A. Méresse, H. Lévi, Y. Simon, and M. Blazquez, "Sur l'étude de l'influence de la mobilité sur la répartition des porteur dans la base d'une transistor on Silicium obtenu par double diffusion," *C. R. Acad. Sci. Paris*, vol. 270, sér. B, pp. 1394–1397, June 1970.
[8] F. Dannhäuser, "Die Abhängigkeit der Trägerbeweglichkeit in Silizium von der Konzentration der freien Ladungsträger–I," *Solid-State Electron.*, vol. 15, pp. 1371–1375, 1972.
[9] J. Krausse, "Die Abhängigkeit der Trägerbeweglichkeit in Silizium von der Konzentration der freien Ladungsträger–II," *Solid-State Electron.*, vol. 15, pp. 1377–1381, 1972.
[10] W. Anheier and W. L. Engl, "Numerical analysis of gate triggered SCR turn-on transients," in *IEEE IEDM Dig. Tech. Papers* (Washington, D.C.), pp. 303A–303D, 1977.
[11] K. K. Thornber, "Relation of drift velocity to low-field mobility and high-field saturation velocity," *J. Appl. Phys.*, vol. 51, no. 4, pp. 2127–2136, 1980.
[12] B. V. Gokhale, "Numerical solution for a one-dimensional silicon n-p-n transistor," *IEEE Trans. Electron Devices*, vol. ED-17, pp. 594–602, 1970.
[13] K. Yamaguchi, "Field-dependent mobility model for two-dimensional numerical analysis of MOSFET's," *IEEE Trans. Electron Devices*, vol. ED-26, pp. 1068–1074, 1979.
[14] J. Cooper and D. F. Nelson, "Measurement of the high-field velocity of electrons in inversion layers on silicon," *IEEE Electron Devices Lett.*, vol. EDL-2, pp. 171–173, 1981.
[15] S. Selberherr, A. Schütz, and H. W. Pötzl, "Minimos-A two-dimensional MOS transistor analyzer," *IEEE Trans. Electron Devices*, vol. ED-27, pp. 1540–1549, 1980.
[16] A. H. Marshak and K. M. van Vliet, "Carrier densities and emitter efficiency in degenerate materials with position-dependent band structure," *Solid-State Electron.*, vol. 21, pp. 429–434, 1978.
[17] M. S. Mock, "Transport equations in heavily doped silicon, and the current gain of a bipolar transistor," *Solid-State Electron.*, vol. 16, pp. 1251–1259, 1973.
[18] A. Nakagawa, "One-dimensional device model of the n-p-n bipolar transistor including heavy doping effects under Fermi statistics," *Solid-State Electron.*, vol. 22, pp. 943–949, 1979.
[19] J. W. Slotboom and H. C. De Graaff, "Measurements of bandgap narrowing in Si bipolar transistors," *Solid-State Electron.*, vol. 19, pp. 857–862, 1976.
[20] A. W. Wieder, "Emitter effects in shallow bipolar devices: Measurements and consequences," *IEEE Trans. Electron Devices*, vol. ED-27, pp. 1402–1408, 1980.
[21] R. P. Mertens, J. L. van Meerbergen, J. F. Nijs, and R. T. van Overstraeten, "Measurement of the minority-carrier transport parameters in heavily doped silicon," *IEEE Trans. Electron Devices*, vol. ED-27, no. 5, 1980.
[22] A. Selloni and S. T. Pantelides, *Phys. Rev. Lett.*, Oct. 15, 1982.
[23] S. T. Pantelidis and A. Selloni, to be published.
[24] D. L. Scharfetter, "Measured dependence of lifetime upon defect density and temperature in depletion layers of epitaxial silicon diodes," presented at the Solid-State Devices Res. Conf., Santa Barbara, CA, 1967.
[25] J. G. Fossum and D. S. Lee, "A physical model for the dependence of carrier lifetime on doping density in nondegenerate silicon," *Solid-State Electron.*, vol. 25, no. 8, pp. 741–747, 1982.
[26] J. Dziewor and W. Schmid, "Auger coefficients for highly doped and highly excited silicon," *Appl. Phys. Lett.*, vol. 31, pp. 346–348, 1977.
[27] J. O. Beck and R. Conradt, "Auger recombination in silicon," *Solid-State Commun.*, vol. 13, pp. 93–95, 1973.
[28] G. Strang and G. J. Fix, *An Analysis of the Finite Element Method*. Englewood Cliffs, NJ: Prentice-Hall, 1973.
[29] R. S. Varga, *Matrix Iterative Analysis*. Englewood Cliffs, NJ: Prentice-Hall, 1962.
[30] J. A. Greenfield and R. W. Dutton, "Nonplanar VLSI device analysis using the solution of Poisson's equation," *IEEE Trans. Electron Devices*, vol. ED-27, pp. 1520–1532, 1980.
[31] R. H. Mac Neal, "An asymmetrical finite difference network," *Quart. Appl. Math.*, vol. 11, pp. 295–310, 1953.
[32] E. M. Buturla, P. E. Cottrell, B. M. Grossman, and K. A. Salsburg, "Finite-element analysis of semiconductor devices: The Fielday program," *IBM J. Res. Develop.*, vol. 25, pp. 218–231, 1981.
[33] W. L. Engl and H. Dirks, "Numerical device simulation guided by physical approaches," in *Numerical Analysis of Semiconductor Devices*, B. T. Browne and J.J.H. Miller, Eds. Dublin, Ireland: Boole Press, 1979.
[34] D. L. Scharfetter and H. K. Gummel, "Large-signal analysis of a silicon read diode oscillator," *IEEE Trans. Electron Devices*, vol. ED-16, pp. 64–77, 1969.
[35] J. W. Slotboom, "Computer aided two dimensional analysis of bipolar transistors," *IEEE Trans. Electron. Devices*, vol. ED-20, pp. 669–679, 1973.
[36] H. H. Heimeier, "A two dimensional numerical analysis of a silicon n-p-n transistor," *IEEE Trans. Electron. Devices*, vol. ED-20, pp. 708–714, 1973.
[37] O. Manck, H. H. Heimeier, and W. L. Engl, "High injection in a two-dimensional transistor," *IEEE Trans. Electron. Devices*, vol. ED-21, pp. 403–409, 1974.
[38] G. D. Hachtel, M. Mack, and R. R. O'Brien, "Semiconductor device analysis via finite elements," in *Conf. Rec. 8th Asilomar Conf. on Circuits, Systems, and Computers 1974*, pp. 332–338, 1974.
[39] M. S. Mock, "Time-dependent simulation of coupled devices," in *Numerical Analysis of Semiconductor Devices and Integrated Circuits*, B. T. Browne and J.J.H. Miller, Eds. Dublin, Ireland: Boole Press, 1981.
[40] ——, "Time discretisation of a nonlinear initial value problem," *J. Comput. Phys.*, vol. 21, pp. 20–37, 1976.
[41] A. De Mari, "An accurate numerical one-dimensional solution of the p-n junction under arbitrary transient conditions," *Solid-State Electron.*, vol. 11, pp. 1021–1053, 1968.
[42] G. D. Hachtel, R. C. Joy, and J. W. Cooley, "A new efficient one-dimensional analysis program for junction device modeling," *Proc. IEEE*, vol. 60, pp. 86–98, 1972.

[43] O. Manck and W. L. Engl, "Two dimensional computer simulation for switching a bipolar transistor out of saturation," *IEEE Trans. Electron Devices*, vol. ED-22, pp. 339–347, 1975.

[44] G. D. Hachtel, M. H. Mack, R. R. O'Brien, and B. Speelpenning, "Semiconductor analysis using finite elements—Part I: Computational aspects," *IBM J. Res. Develop.*, vol. 25, pp. 232–245, 1981.

[45] H. P. Strohband, "New results on stability of the BDG-integration method with non-constant stepsize and order," in *Asilomar Conf. on Circuits, Systems and Computers, Conf. Rec.*, pp. 354–358, 1975.

[46] R. K. Brayton, F. G. Gustavson, and G. D. Hachtel, "A new efficient algorithm for solving differential-algebraic systems using implicit backward differentiation formulas," *Proc. IEEE*, vol. 60, pp. 98–108, 1972.

[47] R. Laur and H. P. Strohband, "Numerical modeling technique for computer aided circuit design," in *IEEE Int. Symp. Circuits and Systems, Proc.*, pp. 247–250, 1976.

[48] W. L. Engl and H. Dirks, "Functional device simulation by merging numerical building blocks," in *Numerical Analysis of Semiconductor Devices and Integrated Circuits. B. T. Brown and J.J.H. Miller, Eds:* Dublin, Ireland: Boole Press, 1981.

[49] D. Vandorpe, J. Borel, G. Merckel, and P. Saintot, "An accurate two-dimensional numerical analysis of the MOS transistor," *Solid-State Electron.*, vol. 15, p. 547, 1972.

[50] H. K. Gummel, "A self-consistent iterative scheme for one-dimensional steady state transistor calculations," *IEEE Trans. Electron Devices*, vol. ED-11, pp. 455–465, 1964.

[51] E. M. Buturla and P. E. Cotrell, "Simulation of semiconductor transport using coupled and decoupled solution techniques," *Solid-State Electron.*, vol. 23, pp. 331–334, 1980.

[52] W. L. Engl, O. Manck, and A. W. Wieder, "Modeling of bipolar devices," in *Process and Device Modeling for Integrated Circuit Design, F. van de Wiele, W. L. Engl, and P. G. Jespers, Eds.*, Leyden, The Netherlands: Noordhoff Int. Publ., 1977, pp. 377–418.

[53] J. D'Arcy, E. J. Prendergast, and P. Lloyd, "Modeling of bipolar device structures—Physical simulations," *IEDM Dig. Tech. Papers*, pp. 516–519, 1981.

[54] T. Adachi, A. Yishii, and T. Sudo, "Two-dimensional semiconductor analysis using finite-element method," *IEEE Trans. Electron Devices*, vol. ED-26, pp. 1026–1031, 1979.

[55] A. Yoshii, S. Horiguchi, M. Tomizawa, H. Kitazawa, and T. Sudo, "Three-dimensional analysis for semiconductor devices," Japan Inst. Electron. Comm. Engineers Tech. Rep. SSD-80-15, pp. 55–62, 1980 (in Japanese).

[56] T. Wada and R.L.M. Dang, "Modification of ICCG method for application to semiconductor device simulators," *Electron. Lett.*, vol. 18, pp. 265–266, 1982.

[57] W. L. Engl, R. Laur, and H. K. Dirks, "MEDUSA—A simulator for modular circuits," *IEEE Trans. Computer-Aided Des.*, vol. CAD-1, pp. 85–93, 1982.

[58] J. W. Slotboom and A.H.M. Goorman, "An efficient quasi three-dimensional bipolar transistor analysis program," in *Numerical Analysis of Semiconductor Devices, B. T. Brown and J.J.H. Miller, Eds.* Dublin, Ireland: Boole Press, 1979.

[59] K. Hanihara, H. Yanai, and T. Kamiya, "Efficient dc and ac analysis of I²L devices based on quasi-three-dimensional modeling," *IEEE Trans. Electron Devices*, vol. ED-29, pp. 418–429, 1982.

[60] M. B. Barron, "Computer aided analysis of insulated gate field effect transistors," Stanford Univ. Tech. Rep. 5501-1, Stanford, CA, 1969.

[61] M. Reiser, "A two-dimensional numerical FET model for dc, ac and large-signal analysis," *IEEE Trans. Electron Devices*, vol. ED-20, pp. 35–45, 1973.

[62] M. S. Mock, "A two-dimensional mathematical model of the insulated-gate field-effect transistor," *Solid-State Electron.*, vol. 16, pp. 601–609, 1973.

[63] R. Kasai and T. Kimura, "Two-dimensional structure analysis of short channel C-MOS and transient analysis of the C-MOS Circuits," Monograph of Technical Group of IECE Japan, ED76-5, 1976 (in Japanese).

[64] H. Masuda *et al.*, "Short channel MOS-IC based on accurate two-dimensional device design," Monograph of Technical Group of IECE Japan, SSD75-20, 1975 (in Japanese).

[65] M. Fukuma and Y. Okuto, "Analysis of short channel MOSFET's in saturation," Monograph of Technical Group of IECE Japan, SSD78-6, 1978 (in Japanese).

[66] S. Selberherr, W. Fichtner, and H. W. Pötzl, "MINIMOS—A program package to facilitate MOS design and analysis," in *Numerical Analysis of Semiconductor Devices. B. T. Brown and J.J.H. Miller, Eds.* Dublin, Ireland: Boole Press, 1979.

[67] F. H. De la Moneda, "Threshold voltage from numerical solution of the two-dimensional MOS transistor," *IEEE Trans. Circuit Theory*, vol. CT-20, pp. 666–673, 1973.

[68] C. L. Wilson and J. L. Blue, "Two-dimensional finite element charge-sheet model of a short-channel MOS transistor," *Solid-State Electron.*, vol. 25, pp. 461–477, 1982.

[69] E. M. Buturla, P. E. Cottrel, B. M. Grossmann, K. A. Salsburg, M. B. Lawlor, and C. T. McMullen, "Three-dimensional finite element simulation of semiconductor devices," in *IEEE Int. Solid-State Circuits Conf., Dig. Tech. Papers*, pp. 76–77, 1980.

[70] A. Yoshii, S. Horiguchi, and T. Sudo, "A numerical analysis for very small semiconductor devices," in *IEEE Int. Solid-State Circuits Conf., Dig. Tech. Papers*, pp. 80–81, 1980.

[71] A. Yoshii, H. Kitazawa, M. Tomizawa, S. Horiguchi, and T. Sudo, "A three-dimensional analysis of semiconductor devices," *IEEE Trans. Electron Devices*, vol. ED-29, pp. 184–189, 1982.

[72] J. Agraz-Güerena, P. T. Panousis, and B. L. Morris, "OXIL, A versatile bipolar VLSI technology," *IEEE J. Solid-State Circuits*, vol. SC-15, pp. 462–466, 1980.

[73] J. L. D'Arcy, P. Lloyd, E. J. Prendergast, H. Dirks, W. L. Engl, and W. Lunkenheimer, "Efficient 2 & 3D bipolar device simulations using MEDUSA," to be published.

[74] G. W. Taylor, "Subthreshold conduction in MOSFET's," *IEEE Trans. Electron Devices*, vol. ED-25, pp. 337–350, 1978.

[75] U. Niggebrügge, "Silizium-MOSFETs mit kleinen Kanallängen," thesis, TH Aachen, Aachen, Germany, 1981.

[76] A. Schütz, S. Selberherr, and H. W. Pötzl, "A two-dimensional model of the avalanche effect in MOS transistors," *Solid-State Electron.*, vol. 25, pp. 177–183, 1982.

[77] A. Schütz, "Simulation des Lawinendurchbruchs in MOS-Transistoren," thesis, TU Wien, Wien, Austria, 1982.

[78] H.K.J. Ihantola and J. L. Moll, "Design theory of a surface field-effect transistor," *Solid-State Electron.*, vol. 7, pp. 423–430, 1964.

[79] C. T. Sah, "Characteristics of the metal-oxide-semiconductor transistor," *IEEE Trans. Electron Devices*, vol. ED-11, pp. 324–345, 1964.

[80] C. T. Sah and H. C. Pao, "The effects of fixed charge on the characteristics of metal-oxide-semiconductor transistors," *IEEE Trans. Electron Devices*, vol. ED-13, pp. 393–409, 1966.

[81] M. B. Barron, "Low level currents in insulated gate field effect transistors," *Solid-State Electron.*, vol. 15, pp. 293–309, 1972.

[82] R. M. Swanson and J. D. Meindl, "Ion implanted complementary MOS transistors in low-voltage circuits," *IEEE J. Solid-State Circuits*, vol. SC-7, pp. 146–153, 1972.

[83] J. R. Brews, "A charge-sheet model of the MOSFET," *Solid-State Electron.*, vol. 21, pp. 345–355, 1978.

[84] V.G.K. Reddi and C. T. Sah, "Source to drain resistance beyond pinch-off in metal-oxide-semiconductor transistors (MOST)," *IEEE Trans. Electron Devices*, vol. ED-12, pp. 139–141, 1965.

[85] G. Merckel, J. Borel, and N. Z. Cupcea, "An accurate large-signal MOS transistor model for use in computer-aided design," *IEEE Trans. Electron Devices*, vol. ED-19, pp. 681–690, 1972.

[86] F. M. Klaassen, "Review of physical models for MOS transistors," in *Process and Device Modeling for Integrated Circuit Design, F. van de Wiele, W. L. Engl, and P. G. Jespers, Eds.* Leyden, The Netherlands: Noordhoff, 1977, pp. 541–571.

[87] O. Leistiko, A. S. Grove, and C. T. Sah, "Electron and hole mobilities in inversion layers on thermally oxidized silicon surfaces," *IEEE Trans. Electron Devices*, vol. ED-12, pp. 248–254, 1965.

[88] D. Frohman-Bentchkowsky, "On the effect of mobility variation on MOS device characteristics," *Proc. IEEE* (Lett.), vol. 56, pp. 217–218, 1968.

[89] R. H. Crawford, *MOSFET In Circuit Design.* New York: McGraw-Hill, 1967, pp. 51–69.

[90] H. C. Pao and C. T. Sah, "Effects of diffusion current on characteristics of metal-oxide (insulator)-semiconductor transistors," *Solid-State Electron.*, vol. 9, pp. 927–937, 1966.

[91] S. M. Sze, *Physics of Semiconductor Devices.* New York: Wiley, 1981, p. 437.

[92] R. R. Troutman, "Subthreshold design considerations for insulated gate field-effect transistors," *IEEE J. Solid-State Circuits*, vol. SC-9, pp. 55–60, 1974.

[93] P. Rossel, H. Martinot, and G. Vassilieff, "Accurate two sections model for MOS transistor in saturation," *Solid-State Electron.*, vol. 19, pp. 51–56, 1976.

[94] D. Frohman-Bentchkowsky and L. Vadasz, "Computer-aided design and characterization of digital MOS integrated circuits," *IEEE J. Solid-State Circuits*, vol. SC-4, pp. 57–64, 1969.

[95] D. Frohman-Bentchkowsky and A. S. Grove, "Conductance of MOS transistors in saturation," *IEEE Trans. Electron Devices*, vol. ED-16, pp. 108–113, 1969.

[96] G. Baum, "Driftgeschwindigkeitssättigung bei MOS-Feldeffekttransistoren," *Solid-State Electron.*, vol. 13, pp. 789–798, 1970.

[97] F. M. Klaassen and W.C.J. de Groot, "Modeling of scaled-down MOS transistors," *Solid-State Electron.*, vol. 23, pp. 237–242, 1980.

[98] A. Popa, "An injection level dependent theory of the MOS transistor in saturation," *IEEE Trans. Electron Devices*, vol. ED-19, pp. 774–781, 1972.

[99] B. Höfflinger, H. Sibbert, and G. Zimmer, "Model and performance of hot-electron MOS transistors for VLSI," *IEEE Trans. Electron Devices*, vol. ED-26, pp. 513–520, 1979.

[100] Y. A. El-Mansy and A. R. Boothroyd, "A simple two-dimensional model for IGFET operation in the saturation region," *IEEE Trans. Electron Devices*, vol. ED-24, pp. 254–262, 1977.

[101] F. N. Trofimenkoff, "Field-dependent mobility analysis of the field-effect transistor," *Proc. IEEE* (Corresp.), vol. 53, pp. 1765–1766, 1965.

[102] B. Hoeneisen and C. A. Mead, "Current-voltage characteristics of small size MOS transistors," *IEEE Trans. Electron Devices*, (Corresp.), vol. ED-19, pp. 382–383, 1972.

[103] L. M. Dang, "A simple current model for short-channel IGFET and its application to circuit simulation," *IEEE J. Solid-State Circuits*, vol. SC-14, pp. 358–367, 1979.

[104] L. D. Yau, "A simple theory to predict the threshold voltage of short-channel IGFET's," *Solid-State Electron.*, vol. 17, pp. 1059–1063, 1974.

[105] G. W. Taylor, "The effects of two-dimensional charge sharing on the above-threshold characteristics of short-channel IGFET's," *Solid-State Electron.*, vol. 22, pp. 701–717, 1979.

[106] P. K. Chatterjee and J. E. Leiss, "An analytic charge-sharing predictor model for submicron MOSFET's," *IEEE IEDM Dig. Tech. Papers* (Washington, DC), pp. 28–33, 1980.

[107] G. Merckel, "A simple model of the threshold voltage of short and narrow channel MOSFET's," *Solid-State Electron.*, vol. 23, pp. 1207–1213, 1980.

[108] H. Masuda, M. Nakai, and M. Kubo, "Characteristics and limitation of scaled-down MOSFET's due to two-dimensional field effect," *IEEE Trans. Electron Devices*, vol. ED-26, pp. 980–986, 1979.

[109] T. Toyabe and S. Asai, "Analytical models of threshold voltage and breakdown voltage of short-channel MOSFET's derived from two-dimensional analysis," *IEEE Trans. Electron. Devices*, vol. ED-26, pp. 453–461, 1979.

[110] W. Shockley, "The theory of p-n junction in semiconductors junction transistors," *Bell Syst. Tech. J.*, vol. 28, p. 435, 1949.

[111] J. J. Ebers and J. L. Moll, "Large signal behavior of junction transistors," *Proc. IRE*, vol. 42, p. 1761, 1954.

[112] J. L. Moll, "Large-signal transient response of a junction transistor," *Proc. IRE*, vol. 42, p. 1773, 1954.

[113] E. D. Johnson, C. T. Kleiner, L. R. McMurray, E. Steel, and F. A. Vassolla, "Transient radiation analysis by computer program (TRAC)," in *Users Guide* (Harry Diamond Labs., Autonetics Div., North American Rockwell, Anaheim, CA), vol. 1, 1968.

[114] J. M. Early, "Effects of space-charge layer widening in junction transistors," *Proc. IRE*, vol. 40, p. 1401, 1952.

[115] F. A. Lindholm and D. J. Hamilton, "Incorporation of the early effect in the Ebers-Moll model," *Proc. IRE*, vol. 59, p. 1377, 1971.

[116] R. Beaufoy and J. J. Sparkes, "The junction transistor as a charge-controlled device," *Automat. Teleph. Electric Commun. J.* (London), vol. 4, p. 310, 1957.

[117] J. G. Linvill, "Lumped models of transistors and diodes," *Proc. IRE*, vol. 46, p. 1141, 1958.

[118] H. K. Gummel, "A charge control relation for bipolar transistors," *Bell Syst. Tech. J.*, vol. 49, p. 115, 1970.

[119] H. K. Gummel and H. C. Poon, "An integrated charge control model of bipolar transistors," *Bell Syst. Tech. J.*, vol. 49, p. 827, 1970.

[120] H. C. Poon, "Modeling of bipolar transistor using integral charge control model with application to third-order distortion studies," *IEEE Trans. Electron. Devices*, vol. ED-19, p. 719, 1972.

[121] H. C. Poon and J. C. Meckwood, "Modeling of avalanche effect in integral charge control model," *IEEE Trans. Electron. Devices*, vol. ED-19, p. 90, 1972.

[122] H. C. Poon and H. K. Gummel, "Modeling of emitter capacitance," *Proc. IEEE*, vol. 57, p. 2181, 1969.

[123] B. R. Chawla, "Circuit representation of the integral charge-control model of bipolar transistors," *IEEE J. Solid-State Circuits*, vol. SC-6, p. 262, 1971.

[124] H. C. De Graaff, "Review of models for bipolar transistors," in *Process and Device Modeling for Integrated Circuit Design*, F. van de Wiele, W. L. Engl, and P. G. Jespers, Eds. Leyden, The Netherlands: Noordhoff, 1977, pp. 283–306.

Circuit Analysis, Logic Simulation, and Design Verification for VLSI

ALBERT E. RUEHLI, SENIOR MEMBER, IEEE, AND GARY S. DITLOW, MEMBER, IEEE

Invited Paper

Abstract—In this paper, we consider computer-aided design techniques for VLSI. Specifically, the areas of circuit analysis, logic simulation and design verification are discussed with an emphasis on time domain techniques. Recently, researchers have concentrated on two general problem areas. One important problem discussed is the efficient, exact-time analysis of large-scale circuits. The other area is the unification of these techniques with logic simulation and design verification technique in so called multimode or multilevel systems.

I. INTRODUCTION

THE FACT that this special issue is dedicated to VLSI design attests to the importance of the subject area. Many talented professionals are presently striving to find solutions to very challenging VLSI problems. The increase in complexity is the one fundamental issue which confronts both chip and Computer-Aided Design (CAD) tools designers [1]. The techniques and tools and algorithms which were successfully applied to LSI are inadequate for VLSI. Mainly, algorithms which are of $O(N^3)$ or worse in time for practical computations may not be extendable to VLSI with a larger number of subcircuits N.

Fundamental design methodologies like structured design [1], hierarchical, and "divide and conquer" strategies [2] are proposed by many authors. The interaction between the design methodology, the designer, and the CAD techniques is of key importance to the ease with which the VLSI chip design is achieved. This paper is mainly concerned with CAD techniques for circuit design and timing-oriented problems. We assess the status of three important areas, circuit analysis, logic simulation, and design verification. Here, we de-emphasize the historical aspects since review papers and texts are available which include extensive references on design tools and techniques pertinent for the electrical chip and package design [1]–[14]. Also, simulation for testing is beyond the scope of this paper.

We will first define the terminology used before giving an introduction to the three main topics—circuit analysis, logic simulation, and verification or checking.

A. Terminology

We start this paper with the definition of a few frequently used terms to be able to give a clear account of the subject. One source of ambiguity is the fusion of the languages of circuit theorists and computer scientists. The subject of this paper is an illustration of a classical "EECS" subject.

Here, *circuit* is used in two ways. It may be used to describe a collection of gates with possible interconnection models. Unfortunately, this ambiguity is unavoidable since *circuit* can also mean a fraction of a gate or a single gate. We use the term *subcircuit* for a smaller portion of a circuit, especially when we talk about partitioning concepts. Another ambiguity exists in the usage of the term *gate*. We will use gate to mean a logical gate or subcircuit. If we refer to the gate electrode of an MOS transistor, we call it an MOS transistor gate.

Analysis rather than simulation is used to describe techniques which are based on mathematics as opposed to heuristics. The reasons become clear if we consider a dictionary definition for *analysis*: 1) to separate into parts of basic principles so as to determine the nature of the whole; 2) examine methodically; 3) to make mathematical analysis; 4) opposite to synthesize.

The mathematical or physics (basic principles) foundation of analysis is clear from these definitions.

We contrast this definition to the meaning of *simulation* in dictionary terms: 1) to have or take the appearance; 2) assume or imitate a particular appearance or form; 3) counterfeit; 4) to reproduce the conditions of a situation.

The empirical nature of a *simulation model* is apparent from these definitions. Analysis techniques are a subset of simulation approaches since by some lucky insight we may intuitively conceive a model or technique which is mathematically accurate. Simulation techniques span an extremely wide range even if we restrict ourselves to subjects of a technical nature. Here we are interested in topics like *logic* or *circuit simulation* rather than, for example, airplane flight simulation. We use *circuit simulation* to imply that we use approximate, heuristically based models. *Logic simulation* is the conventional process where we replace electrical signals by two or more values, e.g., 0 and 1.

Another specification of a model pertains to its "granularity." Three terms are useful, *micromodel*, *model*, and *macromodel*. A circuit *model* describes the physical situation at an intermediate level. If we desire to analyze at a far more detailed level as, for example, at the level of the transistor physics, we construct very detailed *micromodels* [5], [15], [16]. On the other hand, the need to simulate large VLSI systems has generated much interest in *macromodels* which are designed to trade off internal complexity for speed, e.g., [3], [17], [18]. A macromodel may not necessarily be less accurate than a model, but it may have fewer parameters or exclude unimportant dependencies.

Recently, the usage for the terms *mixed and multilevel (mode) simulation and analysis* techniques has become clear [19], [20]. A *mixed-mode* technique includes two techniques

Manuscript received May 13, 1982; revised October 15, 1982.
The authors are with the IBM Thomas J. Watson Research Center, Yorktown Heights, NY 10598.

Reprinted from *Proc. IEEE*, vol. 71, pp. 34–48, Jan. 1983.

in the same system at the same level [19] while a *mixed-level* technique includes different hierarchical levels which interact with each other. Details are discussed in Section IV.

Another term which we use frequently is *verification* which is the following according to a dictionary: 1) evidence that establishes or confirms the accuracy or truth of; 2) process of research, examination required to establish authenticity.

Verification enters in many aspects of the design processes as will be discussed in Section V. In fact, the major purpose of the techniques in Section II is *timing verification*.

B. Circuit Analysis and Simulation

From the sixties until recently, the emphasis in computer-aided circuit analysis was on general-purpose programs. ECAP [21], which was one of the earliest widely available programs, was replaced by many newer ones. Today, the most used programs are SPICE [22]–[24], ASTAP, [25] and ADVICE [26]. These programs employ techniques which were innovated in the last decade such as 1) sparse tableau analysis method (STA) [27]; 2) modified nodal analysis method (MNA) [28]; 3) implicit integration methods; and 4) sparse matrix techniques.

In the early seventies a few researchers devised techniques suitable for larger circuits [29]–[31]. For a while the field of large-scale circuit simulation and analysis (LSSA) was called macromodeling [31], [17], [32]. Today, the term *macromodeling* is more correctly applied to the *modeling* aspect of large-scale circuits. The field of LSSA has expanded in the last few years due to its importance for *timing verifications* for VLSI circuits.

A multitude of new ideas have been conceived in LSSA in the last few years. MOTIS [33] is one of the first programs where simplified analysis techniques are employed for MOSFET circuits. Other programs include MACRO [34], DIANA [17], and MOTIS-C [35]. The specific techniques employed will be discussed in Section II-A.

We differentiate between *incremental* time techniques which have their origin in circuit analysis and *waveform* techniques which include logic simulation with delay times. In the *incremental* approach the analysis proceeds globally in time steps which are usually smaller than the signal rise times. All the above programs are based on *incremental* time updating techniques. The local circuit waveforms are computed for a sizable time segment in a *waveform* approach [36]–[38]. Two major sources of time saving result from the sparsities present in the space–time relationship of the circuits and from employing *decomposition techniques*. The waveform technique, and *latency*, e.g., [34], [40] are approaches which take advantage of time domain or *temporal* sparsity. Section II-B details these techniques. The other area of *decomposition* pertains to the structure of the logic circuits. The average fan-out for a logic gate is between two and three. Thus the connectivity of most circuits is extremely sparse leading to *structural sparsity*. Usually, for an exact representation of the gates the number of internal nodes of the circuits is much larger than the external nodes. This leads to a *natural* decomposition of the circuits in terms of the gates. Numerous papers referenced give techniques for the exploitation of this structure, e.g., [3], [90], [92]. For MOS devices the MOS transistor gate represents an almost unidirectional node with the exception of the gate-to-drain and -source capacitances. The approach given in [37] exploits this, and the so-called one-way (1-way) scheduling technique is based on this. Here, we discuss mostly

graph-based algorithms, while a recent paper [4] concentrates on equivalent sparse matrix techniques. Some of these techniques are detailed in Section II-B.

A source of inaccuracy may be the approximate inclusion of feedback in the solution. Feedback may be *local* or *global*. Further, the strength of the feedback may be *weak* or *strong*. For example, a flip-flop is locally coupled with strong feedback. The Miller feedback in an MOS circuit is local and weak. Further, the feedback extending over several subcircuits in sequential logic is global and strong. Techniques will be discussed below for the inclusion of feedback. For example, the basic waveform 1-way modeling technique [37] works for the flip-flop case. Two recent general methods are the waveform relaxation (WR) technique for a *waveform* analysis [36] and the symmetric displacement [41] for an *incremental* system.

Logic simulation is performed at the functional gate and recently at the transistor level. In this paper we concentrate on simulation for design verification rather than testing. Gate level simulation is an area which evolved over the last two decades. Even the early work was concerned with efficiency improvement techniques, e.g., [42], [43] since the logic circuits of interest were already large and computers were less powerful. Since then a continuous progress has been made towards the simulation of very large circuits, e.g., [7]–[10], [44]–[48]. Both temporal and structural sparsity is exploited in these techniques. Mainly, logic simulation is an area where the need for large-capacity CAD programs is very evident. Many of these simulators include crude timing information.

Transistor level simulation [49], [52] has recently emerged as an important problem due to the emergence of new complex MOS transistor designs which cannot easily be cast into standard logic gates, e.g., [53]. This new field is presently receiving attention from many researchers.

Another area of importance is mixed-mode and multilevel systems. In a mixed system two techniques are used like circuit analysis and simplified macromodels [54] or logic simulation with an electrical WR technique [19]. Many multimode and/or multilevel systems include several simulation/analysis levels combining many of the above-mentioned techniques. [19], [20], [54]–[64]. Detailed aspects on multilevel systems are given in Section IV.

C. Verification

There are two fundamental processes in VLSI-CAD. *Design* is the process of construction while *verification* ensures the correctness of the design [65]–[78]. The following are general examples of *verification* steps: timing; layout; mask; electrical connectivity; functional correctness; and design rule.

Some of the verification steps involve mask and layout steps, e.g., [65]–[70] for which we refer the reader to another paper in this issue [70] since we want to concentrate on timing aspects in this paper.

Verification of the functional correctness of the logic design is another area which has intrigued computer scientists for more than two decades [71]–[75], [8], [14], [44]–[48]. This topic is obviously closely related to timing verification since functional correctness is a prerequisite and therefore a subset of timing verification, which is discussed in Section V. Simulation for design verification [48], [75] was successfully applied to truly large-scale problems with more than 0.5×10^6 gates more than a decade ago. However, the chips themselves were LSI rather than VLSI.

Timing verification is perhaps the most evasive aspect of verification, e.g., [76], [78]. Specifically, the physical design may be perfect, but still the electrical performance of the design may be incorrect or insufficient. This is why we concentrate on timing design and timing verification in this paper. The spectrum spans from exact circuit analysis to extremely efficient algorithms designed for timing simulation and verification. A discussion of verification techniques is given in Section V.

II. CIRCUIT ANALYSIS AND SIMULATION

A. General-Purpose Circuit Analysis

The most widely used tools for circuit analysis are the *general-purpose* or *standard* circuit analysis programs like SPICE [22]–[24] or ASTAP [25], based on the modified nodal analysis (MNA) approach and the sparse tableau analysis (STA), respectively. They are designed for the detailed analysis of a large variety of circuits and are characterized by having a multitude of features. For VLSI, these tools have a place in the detailed design of special circuits. Specifically, the following applications are a natural for them.

They can serve as an interface to the usually elaborate models used for semiconductor device analysis, e.g., [15], [16]. In this capacity they are used to verify the validity of the semiconductor circuit models from the detailed usually two-dimensional micromodels.

The individual subcircuits or gates are designed and optimized using these programs. The compute time for this type of work is moderate since usually only a few devices are involved.

The correctness of newly developed large-scale programs is verified using these well-proven exact circuit analysis programs.

Thus even for VLSI, they play an important part in the early design phases where the semiconductor devices and the menu of subcircuits are established. Importantly, the process of circuit analysis is exact within the accuracy of the models used and the mathematical numerical techniques employed.

The circuit equation in both the MNA and the STA approaches lead to a set of coupled equations of the form

$$f_1(x, \dot{x}, y, t) = 0 \tag{1a}$$

$$f_2(x, y, t) = 0 \tag{1b}$$

where x are the differentiated variables and y the nondifferentiated variables. The formulation of the equations in terms of f_1 and f_2 results naturally from both formulations although the STA formulation is a larger, more sparse matrix while the MNA matrix is smaller and more dense.

We are interested in the solution for the analysis time which usually is $t \in [0, Tmax]$ where $Tmax$ is the final time. Two main techniques are used today to solve (1). The time derivatives are in the most simple case replaced by the backward Euler (BE) formula where

$$\dot{x}_n \cong \frac{x_n - x_{n-1}}{h_n} \tag{2}$$

where n represents the "now" time, $n - 1$ the time step before, and $h_n = t_n - t_{n-1}$ is the present time step. Equation (2) is the most simple A-stable formula. However, other integration methods like the second-order backward-differentiation formula [79], [80] and the ACA methods [81] are more desirable for general purpose programs. Numerical damping [82] is severe for the BE formula (2), and misleading results may be

obtained especially for oscillatory solutions which are present in high-performance logic. In this discussion, we will proceed using the BE formula for time integration for clarity. The result of applying (2) to the system (1) is

$$\tilde{f}_1(x_n, x_n - x_{n-1}, y_n) = 0 \tag{3a}$$

$$f_2(x_n, y_n, t_n) = 0 \tag{3b}$$

which is a system of nonlinear algebraic equations.

To transform the nonlinear equations into a system of linear equations, we usually apply Newton's method to the system (3) which is written as $g(z) = 0$ for

$$\frac{\partial g}{\partial z} z^i = -g(z)^{i-1} + \frac{\partial g}{\partial z} z^{i-1}. \tag{4}$$

Here $z = \begin{bmatrix} x_n \\ y_n \end{bmatrix}$ and $g = \begin{bmatrix} \tilde{f}_1 \\ f_2 \end{bmatrix}$ and i is the index of the iteration. Usually, (4) is written in the form of a linear system of equations

$$Az = b \tag{5}$$

where A is the Jacobian

$$A = \frac{\partial g}{\partial z} \tag{6}$$

and b is evident from (4) and (5).

The above mathematical procedure for incremental circuit analysis is summarized in ALG. 1. Again, *incremental* refers to the small increments with which time proceeds for all circuits.

ALGORITHM 1: Incremental Circuit Analysis

Inputs:	Circuit	C
	Input Waveforms	IW
	Time Step	h
	Stop Time	$Tmax$
Results:	Waveforms of node voltages $v(t)$	
	Waveforms of branch currents	
Note:	$z(n, i)$ Vector of voltages and currents at time n and Newton iteration i	

Procedure   CircuitAnalysis $(C, I, h, Tmax)$
BEGIN

    Fill in Jacobian Matrix A and right-hand side b with MNA stamps for time invariant circuit elements
    dc solution at time = 0
    time = h
    $n = 1$

TIMEloop: for time $\leq$ $Tmax$ do
    BEGIN $i = 1$
NEWTONloop: for ABS$(z(n, i) - z(n, i-1))$
    $<$ EPSILON do
    BEGIN Fill in A and b
    with MNA stamps for time variant and nonlinear circuit elements
    Solve $A z(n, i) = b$
    $i = i + 1$
    END
    time = time + h
    $n = n + 1$
    END
END

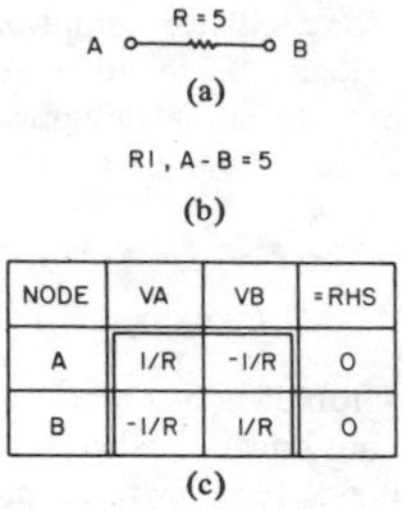

R = 5
A o——WW——o B

(a)

RI, A - B = 5

(b)

NODE	VA	VB	= RHS
A	I/R	-I/R	O
B	-I/R	I/R	O

(c)

Fig. 1. Processing of resistor R. (a) Graphical representation. (b) Input language statement. (c) Entries into the A-matrix.

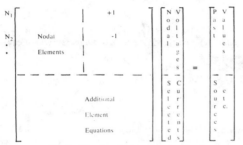

Fig. 2. Circuit analysis matrix $Az = b$.

The relevant aspects of the techniques outlined in ALG. 1 are detailed next. The input data may be supplied to the program in one of three forms. Fig. 1(a) shows a circuit element which may be entered with a graphics system. Fig. 1(b) shows the equivalent language statement where A and B are the connecting nodes. In the third way, the circuit element is extracted from the layout with the assistance of a preprocessing program. As shown in Fig. 1(c) the circuit element data are "stamped" directly into the A matrix in the locations which are identified by the connecting nodes. The linear resistor used in this example is a particularly simple case for the way A is assembled inside the NEWTONloop in ALG 1.

Other circuit elements like transistors, capacitors, inductors, current and voltage sources are stamped into the A matrix in a similar way. A schematic representation of A for the MNA approach is shown in Fig. 2.

Many other algorithms are implemented in an efficient program. In the following, a few are enumerated which are not evident from the discussion above: conversion of node-names into program internal numbers; efficient numerical integration techniques for inductances and capacitances; sparse matrix techniques for storing A and solving the system $Az = b$; efficient assignment of variable time steps h; and convergence improvements for the Newton loop (NEWTONloop) which solves the nonlinear equations.

General-purpose analysis programs of the SPICE and ASTAP type may contain many features which add to their flexibility such as the following: statistical analysis; ac sinusoidal steady-state analysis; built-in source time waveforms; changeable parameters and restart facilities; design centering for design improvement, e.g., [83]; and transmission line analysis.

The growth of the solution time for sophisticated circuit analysis programs is $O(N^m)$ where $1.2 \leqslant m \leqslant 1.5$ and N is the number of nodes. These programs are mostly limited to

the applications listed in Section I-B since they are exhausted for most practical cases for 50–100 gates. Further, improvements of perhaps factor 3 can be envisioned in the future from the application of techniques like node tearing [84], and programming improvements.

Another effort to improve the speed of circuit analysis programs is based on *vector processing* [85], [86]. Basically, repetitive subcircuits can be analyzed in parallel, which results in time savings. To evaluate the potential gain with this approach, a comparison has been made between SPICE2 and CLASSIE, a vector processing circuit program. For a sufficiently large and regular circuit like an adder, the speed up is about an order of magnitude compared to SPICE2.

B. Large-Scale Circuit Simulation and Analysis

Clearly, substantial improvements must be made for large circuits in the *simulation/analysis* (S/A) techniques above the analysis approaches presented in Section II-A for VLSI. A new technique must lead to at least an order of magnitude improvement in the number of circuits to be analyzed to offer a distinct advantage above the general-purpose circuit analysis programs. Thus we expect to analyze at least 500 subcircuits in several minutes of compute time on a high-performance machine. In the recent past, the following areas of potential gain have been identified: special-purpose programs; repetitive subcircuit structure (modularity); structural sparsity, approximation and simplification techniques; and time domain or temporal sparsity (latency, etc.).

Special-purpose programs can lead to substantial gains in performance. As an example, the analysis of a digital filter subcircuit is efficiently performed by special techniques, e.g., [87] while a general-purpose program lead to an inefficient, time-consuming solution. Another special-purpose program may be involved in the solution of the linear package or interconnection equations [5], [88], [89]. Efficient techniques may involve the symbolic solution [88] of subcircuits like the interconnections and the exploitation of the special sparsity structure [89]. Specifically, if we employ the general solution in ALG. 1 for interconnection circuits, we can completely eliminate the NEWTONloop since f_1 and f_2 in (1) are linear for this case.

Repetitive substructures or modularity lead to gains in several areas of a S/A system. First, we notice that gains can be made in the DATA specifications of ALG. 1. A large amount of repetitive data is present in the input obtained from a VLSI chip. The essential information is usually a very small repertoire of fundamentally different devices and subcircuits. This is in contrast to the general-purpose circuit analysis program where the inherent data structure must accommodate large amounts of data of a different nature. Internally, each element is individually processed. As an example, in a coarse gate oriented MOS circuit simulator, we may specify a few different gates, the interconnections, and perhaps a single capacitance value per interconnection. In this case, we can severely limit the data handling and tailor the algorithms. So-called *modular* methods are based on the regularity of the subcircuits from an analysis point of view [34], [40], [90]–[92]. The major gain in employing modularity is a reduction in storage requirements and convenience in the implementation of other saving concepts rather than time. One of the modular methods will be discussed below in more detail.

Structural sparsity must be exploited beyond the conven-

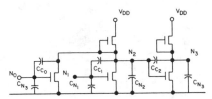

Fig. 3. Example of an MOS circuit.

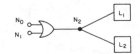

Fig. 4. Illustration of loading.

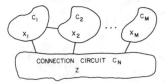

Fig. 5. Circuit with modular subcircuits.

tional sparse matrix techniques for linear systems in circuit analysis programs [93], [94]. Most digital circuits exhibit even more structural sparseness at the global level than analog circuits. The typical fan-out of a logic gate is between 1 and 3 while an analog circuit has about 3 connections per node with other dependent coupled sources. Following this concept, we clearly want to avoid stamping each subcircuit into a single large A matrix as it is done in the general-purpose circuit analysis ALG. 1. Two basic formulations based on the subcircuit structure are widely used. For low- and medium-performance MOS generally connected transistor circuits, a specialized set of nodal equations can be written in the form

$$I(v_N, V_{DD}) + C\frac{dv_N}{dt} = 0 \qquad (7)$$

where $I(v_N, V_{DD})$ corresponds to the MOS transistors which are connected between the nodes as exemplified in Fig. 3. C is the matrix of node capacitances, which are of two types, the node-ground C_N and the node–node capacitances C_C. The node capacitance C_N usually lumps several device and wire capacitances into a single value, and the coupling capacitances C_C is C_{gd} the gate-to-drain capacitance in simple cases. This type of model is used in MOTIS [33], MOTIS-C [35], SPLICE [55], MACRO [34], and MEDUSA [92], and other programs with variations. Usually, the voltage sources are treated as having zero internal resistance in this scheme. The time discretization employed is similar to (2) in Section II-A, and the overall time solution approach is *incremental* like ALG. 1.

In the other approach where more elements are present in a subcircuit model, the number of external connections is usually small or sparse compared to the internal connections. For this case, the modular approach is employed at the subcircuit level. Examples of modular techniques are [40], [61], [83], and [90]. Each of the subsystem of equations for the subcircuit is of the form (1) or (7). If we take the discrete time form of the nonlinear equation (3) for the first subcircuit in Fig. 3, it can be written in the form

$$g(v_{n_0}, v_{n_1}, v_{n_2}, v_{n_3}) = 0 \qquad (8)$$

where n is the "now" index of time. This model is ideally suited to show how the various approximations employed in the different programs operate.

First, we will exemplify the Gauss–Jacobi and Gauss–Seidel iterative solution methods for the simple example of a system of linear equations $Ax = b$. We decompose the matrix A into $A = L + D + U$ with L being strictly lower triangular, D diagonal, and U strictly upper triangular. Then the system of equations can be written as

$$Lx + Dx + Ux = b. \qquad (9)$$

In the Gauss–Jacobi method, we evaluate Dx^k at the present iteration k while Lx^{k-1} and Dx^{k-1} are evaluated at the previous iteration $k - 1$. This leads to a very simple solution. In the Gauss–Seidel method, only Ux^{k-1} is evaluated at iteration $k - 1$. Thus the Gauss–Seidel case corresponds to a lower triangular system of equations

$$(L + D)x^k = b - Ux^{k-1} \qquad (10)$$

which is related to levelizing the circuit graph using 1-way models [37] and can easily be solved by back substitution.

Returning to (8) for the linear case, L corresponds to elements in the inputs or the previously iterated variables v_{n_0} and v_{n_1}, v_{n_2} corresponds to the diagonal or variable to be updated while v_{n_3} corresponds to the not-yet-evaluated voltage, or the Ux contribution. Taking the analogous nonlinear case [95], Gauss–Jordan corresponds to the iterative scheme

$$g(v_{n_0}^{k-1}, v_{n_1}^{k-1}, v_{n_2}^{k}, v_{n_3}^{k-1}) = 0 \qquad (11)$$

while the Gauss–Seidel results in

$$g(v_{n_0}^{k}, v_{n_1}^{k}, v_{n_2}^{k}, v_{n_3}^{k-1}) = 0. \qquad (12)$$

The scheme in (12) needs updated input variables before it can update node 2. A source of confusion exists since the Gauss–Seidel and Gauss–Jordan schemes can be applied to the solution of the nonlinear equation as exemplified here, or to the linear equations, (9) and (10). Both approaches are practiced, and the notation employed is usually hard to understand.

Circuit theorists have a similar way of reducing forward coupling among the subcircuits. A circuit motivated approach to reduce the coupling variables in (8) is *loading*. Fig. 4 gives a loading circuit for the analysis of the two input gates in Fig. 3 with the output node $N2$. $L1$ is an approximate circuit for the coupling capacitance C_{c_2}, which is discussed below, while $L2$ approximates the transistor input. Loading models are employed in many programs, e.g., MACRO [34] and RELAX [38].

Many of these approximation techniques apply to both the incremental and waveform approaches. Clearly, the intent is to save computations. In MOTIS [33], transistor characteristics are approximated by secants which results in a linear local equation which does not require multiple Newton iterations. In MOTIS-C [35], table look-up procedures are used for the nonlinear MOS device characteristics to save function evaluations.

MEDUSA [92] is used as an example of a modulator treatment of the circuit matrix A. The circuit is partitioned into "natural" subcircuits with least connections, as shown in Fig. 5.

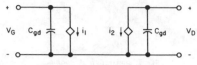

Fig. 6. Equivalent circuit for C_{gd}.

The modular subcircuits C_m with internal variables x_m are embedded in a general interconnection circuit C_N with variables z. The A-matrix (5) can be represented in terms of the modularity as (13)

$$\begin{bmatrix} \dfrac{\partial f_1}{\partial x_1} & & & \dfrac{\partial f_1}{\partial z} \\[2mm] & \dfrac{\partial f_2}{\partial x_2} & & \dfrac{\partial f_2}{\partial z} \\[2mm] & & \dfrac{\partial f_m}{\partial x_m} & \dfrac{\partial f_m}{\partial z} \\[2mm] \dfrac{\partial f_n}{\partial x_1} & \dfrac{\partial f_n}{\partial x_2} & \dfrac{\partial f_n}{\partial x_m} & \dfrac{\partial f_n}{\partial z} \end{bmatrix} \begin{bmatrix} \Delta x_1 \\[2mm] \Delta x_2 \\[2mm] \Delta x_m \\[2mm] \Delta z \end{bmatrix} = \begin{bmatrix} -f_1 \\[2mm] -f_2 \\[2mm] -f_m \\[2mm] -f_n \end{bmatrix} \qquad (13)$$

where the circuit variables are again combinations of voltages and currents like in ALG. 1.

With $\partial f_m / \partial x_m = A_m$, each row of the matrix is easily solved for Δx_m, or

$$\Delta x_m = -A_m^{-1} f_m - A_m^{-1} \frac{\partial f_m}{\partial z} \Delta z \qquad (14)$$

for the mth subcircuit. Δz is found by inserting (14) into the last row of (13). Thus the solution of the structurally bordered block diagonal matrix is formally simple. However, to gain decoupling, the second term on the right-hand side in (14) is ignored in [92]. The omission of these terms results in a lower block triangular system which is used in a Gauss–Seidel iteration scheme.

Approximations for the feedback coupling capacitance C_{c_1} in Fig. 3 are discussed next. It is natural for incremental techniques to attempt to achieve decoupling by replacing unknown values at the "now" time $x(t_n)$ by known values $x(t_{n-1})$ at the previous time steps [105]. This is equivalent to having 1-way properties for t_n.

Explicit forward Euler schemes were used by some authors to eliminate the coupling due to the "floating" capacitances by

$$i_{c,n} = C_{gd} \frac{v_{n-1} - v_{n-2}}{h}. \qquad (15)$$

Unfortunately, this scheme severely limits the time step h for the response to be stable. Fig. 6 shows an improved model for a floating capacitor where

$$i_1 = -C_{gd} \frac{dv_2}{dt} \cong -C_{gd} \frac{v_{2_{n-1}} - v_{2_{n-2}}}{h} \qquad (16)$$

$$i_2 = -C_{gd} \frac{dv_1}{dt} \cong -C_{gd} \frac{v_{1_n} - v_{1_{n-1}}}{h}. \qquad (17)$$

Equations (16) and (17) together with Fig. 6 represent an equivalent circuit interpretation of the IIE method proposed in [96]. Note that this model maintains the 1-way coupling property by restricting the forward Euler integration to the

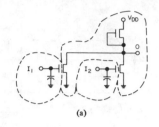

(a)

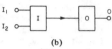

(b)

Fig. 7. (a) Two-input gate with strongly connected components. (b) One-way model for gate.

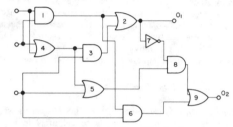

Fig. 8. Example of an adder circuit.

current which represents feedback. A further refinement of this approach is the symmetric displacement method in [41].

In a recent paper a method has been proposed of the form

$$g(v_{n_0}^k, v_{n_1}^k, v_{n_2}^k, v_{n_3}^*) = 0 \qquad (18)$$

corresponding to (18) and Fig. 3. Here $v_{n_3}^*$ is computed from

$$v_{n_3}^* = v_{n-1_3} + h v_{n-1_3} \qquad (19)$$

which is again a prediction of the feedback variables in the time coordinate.

The "now" time step h_n is more or less synchronized among all subcircuits in the incremental approaches. An attempt has been made at decoupling the time steps by using a master clock with subcircuit running at their own h_n [98]. In a waveform approach, complete decoupling among the subcircuit is achieved and the subcircuits are allowed to run at their own maximum time step [36], [37]. This may result in considerable time saving due to the reduction in the number of computations. This approach is illustrated on the example circuit of Fig. 8, where the model of Fig. 7 is used to represent the 1-way circuits. The interaction graph G of Fig. 9 results if the individual gates or subcircuits are replaced by 1-way models. The key insights gained from this graph are the portions which should be analyzed simultaneously. For example, the subcircuits inside the dashed line B may be strongly connected. Note that the interconnections are conveniently accommodated in this approach. We form a new graph from Fig. 9 which has the strongly connected subcircuits as its nodes. Fig. 10 shows G'' where additionally the nodes have been assigned to levels to further simplify the processing. The levelizing ensures that we analyze the circuit such that all the input information is available for each subcircuit at the processing time. Interpolation must be used in this approach to obtain the input

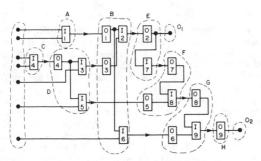

Fig. 9. One-way interaction graph G for Fig. 8.

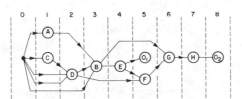

Fig. 10. Levelized graph G'' for circuit.

waveforms at the appropriate time points due to the unequal time steps in the subcircuits [37]. The processing of the subcircuits and the subsequent discarding of this portion of a circuit, is a desirable approach to the time analysis for large-scale circuits. In this process, the waveforms of interest are stored on disk and thus the amount of data present in active store is limited. The accuracy of the solution techniques in the straightforward 1-way technique depends on the size of the gate-to-drain capacitance. Accuracy is always a key issue in the S/A techniques discussed since inaccuracies may lead to faulty chip designs [99]. The WR technique leads to an approach for which the compute time can be reduced at the expense of accuracy and vice versa.

The basic WR approach is easily illustrated for C_{gd} with the assistance of the equivalent circuit Fig. 6. Again, full-time waveforms are involved and we choose

$$i_1(t) = -C_{gd} \frac{dv_2(t)}{dt} \tag{20}$$

$$i_2(t) = -C_{gd} \frac{dv_1(t)}{dt}. \tag{21}$$

The left circuit portion is evaluated first for $t \in [0, T]$ where T is the final time. We iterate between the left and right circuits until convergence, with $i_1(t)$ and $i_2(t)$ being the waveforms at the previous iteration. This process is generalized in ALG. 2.

ALGORITHM 2: Waveform Relaxation for Multiple Circuits

Inputs:	Circuit	C
	Start time	Tmin
	Stop time	Tmax
	Input waveforms	IW
Result:	Waveforms for each node	
Note:	$S(i, j)$	= subcircuit j for iteration i
	NS	= number of subcircuits
	$X(i, j, k, t)$	= voltage of node k in subcircuit j iteration i at time t

Procedure WaveformRelaxation $(T$min$, T$max$, C, I)$
BEGIN
    Partition C into subcircuits S
    Schedule the subcircuits
    $X(0, *, *, t) = IW$
    $i = 0$
    Repeat
      For $j = 1$ to NS do
      BEGIN
        Solve each subcircuit $S(i, j)$ for voltages
        $X(i, j, k, t)$ at iteration i using the results
        of iteration $i - 1$
        Note: use the Incremental Circuit Analysis
                Algorithm to solve each $S(i, j)$
      END
    until max norm $(x(i, j, k, t) - x(i - 1, j, k, t))$
      $<$ ERROR for all j, k, t
END

Different techniques are employed for choosing the subcircuits in ALG. 2. In [100], [19] the decomposition is by *strongly connected component* while in [36], [38] the decomposition is *by circuit* given by the topology of the logical gate.

In the beginning of this section, the desirable goal of at least an order of magnitude speed enhancement over a general-purpose circuit analysis program was stated and a multitude of methods for improving the solution speed are given. A comparison among the methods may be somewhat misleading due to the different implementation, computers, and accuracy demanded in the solution. An indication of the state of the art may be a factor 50 in speed improvement for RELAX [38] as compared to SPICE for a medium-size circuit.

C. Time Waveform Representation

A key aspect of a circuit S/A program and also a logic simulator is the representation of the time waveforms. This is true for incremental as well as waveform techniques. Some of the factors to take into account are the number of circuit, application, intended accuracy, available computer, and storage space, as well as the compute time to be consumed by a typical run. We easily can think of these considerations as well as the waveform representation as more fundamental than the S/A techniques which lead to the waveforms. Fig. 11 illustrates different time waveform representations. In circuit analysis which has the potential of retaining a better than 1-percent accuracy, all of the details of the waveforms are represented as shown in Fig. 11(a). The high accuracy is obtained at the cost of both high storage and time requirements. For example, at the circuit analysis level, 10^3 time points for a single waveform is not unusually high. If we analyze a problem with $N = 10^4$ nodes we may want to retain 10 percent of the node results for future observation of the resultant waveforms. The storage for these waveforms (time, voltage pairs) will require 2×10^6 words of storage. Usually, this will be a secondary store database. Clearly a form of *data compression* is desirable for realistic large-scale systems. In general, point of the amount of information H in a signal with k levels occurring with probability P_i is

$$H = -\sum_{i=1}^{k} P_i \ln P_i. \tag{22}$$

From this point of view it is clear that the binary simulator (0, 1) employs the minimum waveform representation which

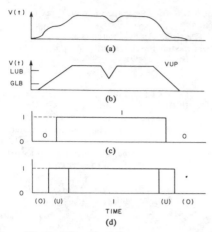

Fig. 11. Different waveform representations.

contains any information at all. However, adding a few additional intermediate levels between the "scaled" levels 0 and 1 is not the most practiced approach to increasing the amount of useful information. Fig. 11 illustrates a few other examples. In (b) a linear rise and fall time has been used as well as a half-signal spike representation. The pure binary signal is given in (c), while in (d), the unknown U- or X-state is added. Both (c) and (d) may ignore the spike shown.

Simulators with 7 or more states are in use, e.g., [102] today attempting to maintain sufficient accuracy while keeping compute time and storage to a minimum. In terms of (22), adding an X-state may increase the useful information content far more than adding an intermediate signal level. It is obvious that the concepts earlier presented unify the techniques employed in analysis and simulation programs. However, new challenges are introduced when different level representations are used simultaneously in a multilevel system. Two fundamentally different types of transitions are necessary: high-to-low information; and low-to-high information.

The first transition is obviously accomplished by discarding information, although challenges remain like the matching of many different waveform representation like the ones with X or high impedance state, etc. The transition from logic variables, Fig. 11(d), to circuit voltages is interesting since information needs to be added. Assume that we want to obtain the constant slope representation of Fig. 11(b). First, the amplitude is scaled by associating a logical 1 with a typical up-level voltage VUP = 4.5 V. Further, the slope of the rise time is

$$SL = \frac{V_{LUB} - V_{GLB}}{t_{LUB} - t_{GLB}}. \qquad (23)$$

Thus the constant slope in Fig. 11(b) can be constructed. This obviously only works for X-states corresponding to transitions. Most likely, this waveform will be the input to the circuit analysis portion in a multilevel system obtained from the simulation portion.

The concepts given in this section show the similarities between the fundamental aims of the simulation and analysis techniques which is the computation of waveforms. However, it should be clear at this point that the means of obtaining them may be quite different.

D. Temporal Sparsity

The last fundamental technique mentioned in Section II-B which we have not considered so far is temporal sparsity. We choose *temporal sparsity* [90] to describe the basic fact that not all subcircuits are active at the same time. Typically, for sufficiently large circuits only between 0.01 to 10 percent of the gates are active at the same instant.

Numerous clever techniques have been devised to take advantage of temporal sparsity. One of the first techniques reported is the event-driven logic simulation method [43], [44], [103]. In this section we restrict ourselves to the event mechanism while in Section III-B we will discuss the simulation. Usually the events are represented in a time event queue for the actions to be taken. In the scheme in ALG. 3, the actions taken at the present or "now" time t_n are illustrated.

ALGORITHM 3: Time Event Scheduling

Inputs: Circuit C
         Subcircuit Delays $ScD(i)$
         Event Queue EQ
         Initial events IE
Result: Updating of event queue for circuit scheduling

Note: tn is present time

Procedure EventScheduling(C,ScD,time)
BEGIN
  $EQ = IE$
  While EQ is not empty do
    BEGIN
    tn is smallest new next event time on EQ
    P = Pop from EQ all events at tn
    For all $P(j)$ do
    BEGIN
      S = Successors($P(j)$)
      For all $S(j)$ whose states have changed do
      SelectiveTracing:
      Push onto EQ the event $[S(i),tn+ScD(i)]$
    END
    END
END

The kernel of ALG. 3 is the *selective tracing* which finds all new events which are caused by the present events at t_n. Then the event queue EQ is updated by these events. A further refinement may be if they actually switch and cause new events before we execute the successors. This scheme leads to an excellent exploitation of temporal sparsity since actions are taken only if they lead to activities, or equivalently computations must be performed. It is noted that the number of computations is directly related to how busy the event queue is. Selective tracing usually assumes the logic circuits models to be simple having 1-way properties. It should be noted that special algorithms must be employed for a circuit with pass-transistors which are 2-way [55].

Temporal sparsity was not taken into account in circuit analysis and large-scale circuit simulation until recently when the latency concepts were introduced, e.g., [34], [84], [90]. Before, all subcircuits were analyzed with the same time-step h, whether the subcircuits were latent or not. In a modular or subcircuit oriented program, the inactive subcircuits can be singled out and no computations are done inside the subcircuit. Then, in an incremental analysis, the internal variables are simply [40]

$$z_n = z_{n-1} \qquad (24)$$

which is a zeroth-order integration method with a local truncation error in the variable k is

$$E_{0_k} = \dot{z}_n(t_{n-1})h. \qquad (25)$$

Thus a latency detector keeps track of the derivative of all variables in a subcircuit.

The computations for the subcircuit are resumed if changes in one of the subcircuit variables occur which exceed an error criterion. Thus many of the new incremental programs are taking latency into account, e.g., [35], [61], [84], [90]. The waveform programs have independent time steps in the subcircuits. Therefore, if a subcircuit is inactive, its variable time step algorithm will choose a very large time step which is equivalent to the latency concept [36], [37], [19].

Thus it can be concluded that temporal sparsity can be exploited for both general-purpose circuit analysis, as well as for large-scale programs. In logic simulators, the computations are reduced using event scheduling illustrated in ALG. 3.

III. Logic Simulation

By *logic simulation* we mean the simulation of two (0, 1) or more states like H, X, etc. For many years, logic simulation was performed at the *gate type level* only. However, with the advent of custom VLSI pass-transistor designs, logic simulation at the *transistor level* was devised, e.g., [49]. Simply, these designs cannot efficiently be represented by gates. A logical gate is a higher level representation since usually several transistors are mapped into a single gate. Obviously, for a large-scale circuit this reduction in complexity is important if it can be accomplished for at least a portion of the logic at hand.

A. Gate Level Simulation

Today, the majority of simulators are of the gate or subcircuit level type. Logic design is most easily performed in terms of gates which perform logic functions like AND, OR, NAND, etc. This implies that groups of transistors are easily identifiable as one of a few standard gates like an AND or a NOR subcircuit.

Gate level simulation of high-performance machines is perhaps the only discipline which has so far been executed at a large-scale level. In these machines the number of gates per integrated circuit is small by VLSI standards due to the power dissipation required to obtain the high-performance operation. However, simulation runs involving 0.5×10^6 gates have been made already several years ago, e.g., [48]. The simulation methodology does not strongly depend on whether the physical location of the gates is on VLSI chips or on separate chips at least at the gate level for high-performance logic.

The following factors contribute to the convenience and efficiency by which gate-level simulation can be executed.

The gates almost directly correspond to the logical operators OR, AND, NAND, etc., and these operations can efficiently be executed in most computers.

Delay equations for timing verification may yield accurate answers for bipolar transistors. An accuracy of 10 percent is achievable in some cases especially if the interconnections add a large portion to the delay.

The structure of the circuits is extremely sparse since the number of connections per subcircuits is limited for high performance and since the overall size of the circuit is very large.

Temporal sparsity is large since the percentage of active gates usually decreases with increasing circuit size.

Some of the concepts implemented in gate level simulators which were developed in the last two decades are outlined next. Mainly, the design and verification of large, high-performance machines with up to $\sim 10^6$ gates depend heavily on this simulation capability. While simulation is used for both verification and testing, we consider verification only to limit the scope of this paper. Some of the techniques which make the simulation of large-scale circuits possible are these.

Parallel simulation is a technique where for example each bit in a word is used to represent an input variable, e.g., [42]. Thus this process allows for the simulation of 32 input patterns to a circuit in parallel for a 32-bit word machine. Thus this method has the potential of speeding up the simulation time of almost a factor of 32.

Compiled-code simulation is a technique which takes advantage of the high speed of execution of compiled code. The circuit description is programmed in a suitable language like Pascal or Assembler. Either logical macros or the entire circuit is compiled and then run simultaneously. Clearly, scheduling is required which specifies the sequence in which the logical functions are processed similar to G'' in Fig. 10. Hard problems in compiled-code simulators are the methodology for taking advantage of the temporal sparsity and also to efficiently change the logic configuration represented by the compiled code.

Table lookup is a frequently used technique where the truth table and other important information are stored in a table for the logic gates, e.g., [104]. These models are accessed using the input values to determine the resultant output. This approach is quite flexible and is widely used.

As mentioned above, gate level simulation is widely applied to large-scale, high-performance machines where standard gates are employed. The techniques in this discipline are well established and are sophisticated. Timing delay approximations are relatively accurate for high-performance circuits since the delay is mainly in the interconnections [6]. Thus far more accuracy is obtained by this type of timing simulation for high-performance machines than for MOS-VLSI circuits even if standard logical gates are employed.

B. Transistor Level Simulation

Transistor level logic simulators are a relatively new addition to the CAD tools used especially in the design of MOS transistor circuits. Mainly, new circuit designs have been invented which cannot efficiently be treated by a gate simulator. More function per transistor can be obtained by direct transistor designs rather than gate designs [53].

A good example of an MOS logic simulator is MOSSIM [49], [50], which takes the actual transistor circuit into account. MOSSIM is a three-logic level (0, 1, X) simulator. At each *state* of the circuit the steady-state levels (SSL) are established. Note that the transients from one state to the next state are *not* calculated in contrast to the techniques discussed in the last section. However, the SSL (0, 1, X) must be distinguished from the "*dc*" levels since the SSL may in some case be a dynamic level held by a ratio of capacitances. Dynamic elements like capacitances and inductances are ignored in these simulators unless they are involved in determining the SSL. The fundamental transistor level simulator requires a circuit diagram description where we need to specify the type of each transistor.

Fig. 12. (a) Simplified transistor model. (b) Two resistances in parallel.

The conventional way to solve for the SSL is to apply ALG. 1 with the time-step loop fixed where the time step h is chosen sufficiently large. This large h assures that the companion resistances corresponding to the capacitances are sufficiently large [93], [94]. This approach is both accurate and time consuming. Approximate solutions are of interest since the approximate knowledge of the logic levels suffices in many cases and since we are interested in simulating very large transistor circuits.

The basis of the technique in MOSSIM is what we can call *approximate circuit theory*. The interpretation of the transistor model is best done in terms of resistances of the device. In Fig. 12(a), we show the model for an MOS transistor where R depends on the type of device. For example, a load device may have $R_1 = 10$, while the active devices may have $R_2 = 1$. The switch for an enhancement load is always closed while the active device in an inverter is controlled by the input. Thus the logic output levels v at the inverter are a logical 1 for a 0 input and for a 1 input

$$ v = \frac{R_2}{R_1 + R_2} = 0.0909 \qquad (26) $$

which is equivalent to a logical zero, since we divide the logical range for v

$$ v = 0, \quad \text{for} \quad v < v_L $$
$$ v = x, \quad \text{for} \quad v_L \leqslant v \leqslant v_H $$
$$ v = 1, \quad \text{for} \quad v_H < v. \qquad (27) $$

Computations are saved if we use approximate computations. For example, in Fig. 12(b) the parallel resistance is given by

$$ R = \min(R_1, R_2) \qquad (28) $$

which saves a multiplication, an addition, and a division compared to the exact parallel resistor formula. A similar simplification can be worked out to avoid the computation in (26) for the voltage divider, where one of the conditions is

$$ v = 0, \quad \text{if} \quad R_1 > \frac{1 - v_L}{v_L} R_2. \qquad (29) $$

A complete set of equations can be worked out for an approximate circuit theory.

A MOSSIM simulator algorithm is outlined below. Here, the nodes are classified as *internal* and *external*. *Clock nodes* are casually called inputs NE which have a state $E(NE)$. The internal nodes NI have a state $I(NI)$ in ALG. 4.

ALGORITHM 4: Transistor Level Logic Simulator

Inputs: Circuit C
   State of each node $E(NE), I(NI)$
   State of each transistor $T(NE, NI)$
Result: Updated States (SSL) $I(NI), T(NE, NI)$

Procedure TransistorSimulation (C, S, T, E)
 For all MOS-transistor gates
 connected to NE's update the state
 $T(NE) = E(NE)$
BEGIN
 For all internal nodes NI do until no changes
 occur
 BEGIN
 Internal NI connected transistors are
 held fixed in state $T(NI)$
  Compute new nodal states $I(NI)$
  using approximate circuit theory
  Update transistor $T(NI)$ states from
  new nodal states $I(NI)$
 END
END

All nodal states are fully determined for each input set or time phase. Since the MOS transistor gates form ideal 1-way connections at dc, they control the MOS transistor source and drain nodes. Groups of MOS transistors are formed by the interconnections [50] between the source and drain nodes. These groups suggest another level of hierarchy which is left out of ALG. 4 for simplicity. Specifically, strong components or groups can be formed which are isolated by FET gates while the interconnections join the members of a group. It is interesting to note that for FET circuits, these groups closely resemble the 1-way components in Section II-B.

The relaxation procedure used in MOSSIM given in ALG. 4 starts from one steady-state level defined by all inputs and clock signals $E(NE)$ at the input or external nodes NE. Then a new input excitation $E(NE)$ is applied and the new internal states $I(NI)$ are computed where $E \in [0, 1]$ and $I \in [0, X, 1]$. This basic transistor level MOS simulation procedure is an iterative procedure to avoid the solution of large, sparse matrices in the form of (4). The transistor states $T(NI)$ connected at internal nodes NI are updated simultaneously only once per iteration while the internal computations are performed with fixed transistor states. The nodal states for internal nodes are computed from the simplified computations of the voltage dividers.

MOSSIM [49] has been applied to circuits with 10^4 transistor on a DEC-20 using about 10 s of compute time per input clock cycle. This suggests that the methodology is applicable to about 10^5 transistors corresponding to approximately 3×10^4 logical gates. Presently, many researchers are active in this general area of MOS transistor level simulation.

The question of approximate time-domain simulation at a far coarser level than the techniques reported in Section II-B is of general interest. In [60], [106] an approximate delay simulation is attempted for MOS circuits. The delays are computed using a table lookup and delay equation-type procedure. In [109] the MOSFET problem is formulated in terms of a switching theory in contrast to the resistive model approach discussed here.

IV. Mixed- and Multilevel Simulation/Analysis Systems

A VLSI circuit may be represented at several levels of complexity depending on the level of the model which may be architectural; functional; gate; device, transistor, circuit; and detailed device macromodel.

In fact, a complete VLSI design of a new technology usually

spans all of these levels. Thus it is very desirable for a design system to encompass as many of these levels as possible.

In the literature a distinction is made between a *multilevel* and a *multimode* system. The multilevel system is based on a hierarchical structure where a common database is employed. Each lower level adds more detail and accuracy to the simulation results like the above list. *Mixed* systems involve two levels and *multi* systems may involve more than two levels.

The first mixed and multilevel systems were different in scope. For example, at the high end logic level simulation was combined with the functional level, e.g., [62]. In the circuit domain, the first macromodels for digital logic were incorporated in a circuit analysis program leading to mixed circuit analysis/simulation systems [32], [55].

The technology of multilevel S/A systems is presently evolving. An early example of such a system is DIANA [87]. Here, the techniques span the digital as well as the analog circuit domain which include analog to digital (A/D), D/A converters as well as filters. With the advent of digital filters, this capability is becoming increasingly important. The internal structure of DIANA is such that even the circuit-analysis-oriented portion can be event driven.

In *mixed-mode* and *multimode* systems, the different programs operate at the same level but the function is different. For example in [19], a logic simulator is employed in the mask design task of the system while the WR time S/A program is used for the timing verification of design. An interesting combined mixed-level and mixed-mode piecewise linear modeling technique is given in [20].

Two recent papers report on CAD systems at Sandia [107] and Hughes [108]. They have a multilevel S/A "engine" as a central part of the system. This approach has many advantages for large-scale VLSI circuits. First, the problems of data conversion from one program to another is avoided in a well-designed system. This is only one reason why the design time is reduced. Other, more important time and storage savings result from the "magnifying glass" technique where, for example, the overall simulation proceeds at a high level while only a few circuits are analyzed accurately at a more detailed level. The potential increase in the number of subcircuits which can be analyzed is substantial. Clearly, a multilevel system provides the environment for these tradeoffs. Further, the danger of losing relevant information by using a too-simple implementation always exists. In a multilevel system the results can always be checked by a lower level technique which ultimately may be the exact circuit analysis level.

V. VERIFICATION

As mentioned above, *design* and *verification* are the two key purposes of a CAD system. The former is the "creation" process while the latter insures the "correctness" of the design. Verification is of concern at all levels in the design. Examples of verification steps are the following: functional design from architectural design; correctness of gate level implementation; electrical connectivity; design rules violations; and timing verification.

Verification is not only of importance in the initial design, but also in the engineering design changes which follow each design phase. The verification process must establish the correspondence among all the models used for the representation of the design [76]. The design and verification processes span the entire spectrum from the system architecture to the implementation of the shapes on silicon wafers. Some of the

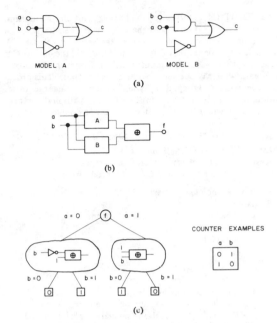

Fig. 13. (a) Example models. (b) Comparison circuit. (c) Expansion procedure.

design procedures at the shapes level involve automatic translation programs [64]–[65], [72] which guarantee correctness. This shifts the burden of verification to the CAD programs. This is a desirable trend since the designs obtained by such a CAD system are automatically correct. Some of the design steps are more amenable to automation, e.g., [71] while others like timing verification are much more difficult to quantize. Here, we give more details on two verification levels, the functional equivalence and timing verification.

A. Functional Equivalence of Logic Circuits

One form of design verification is to determine whether two implementations of the same specification are equivalent. In the IBM 3081 machine, the Static Analysis program [74] was used to find input conditions which would cause two implementations to differ. The two implementations were at the gate level and register transfer level (RTL). Usually the RTL level design is considered correct since a large amount of simulation is possible at this level. However, the 3081 experience demonstrated that errors were found at each level.

The fundamental idea behind this form of design verification is the efficient solution of a set of Boolean equations. The RTL level design is translated to Boolean equations and then each output is exclusive-ored with the corresponding output in the gate level description. All the outputs are ored together to form a single output function f. Solving $f = 1$ is equivalent to finding input patterns which cause the gate level and RTL level designs to differ. If no solutions are found, the two models are declared equivalent. If solutions are found, they represent counter examples which cause at least one of the outputs to be different. Fig. 13 demonstrates the design verification algorithm for comparing two models A and B for equivalence.

ALGORITHM 5 solves for $f = 1$ using symbolic simulation. Inputs are set to 0 or 1, and the effect is propagated through the graph. For example, consider the gate $C = \text{AND}(A, B)$. When $B = 0$, this implies $C = 0$. But for $B = 1$, the output C is equal to A. $C = A$. The input A now becomes the input of a new gate which is one level closer to the output. This procedure is recursively applied by expanding around the other inputs until either $f = 1$ or until $f = 0$. Any path in the expansion process which causes $f = 1$ is a counter example.

ALGORITHM 5: Functional Equivalence

Inputs: Two combinational circuits $C1, C2$
Result: Input patterns which cause output
values of $C1$ and $C2$ to be different

Procedure BooleanCompare($C1,C2$)
BEGIN
    C = Exclusive-Or($C1,C2$) connections as Fig. 13
    Stack = empty
    Expand(C)
END

Procedure Expand(C)
BEGIN
    Choose input variable X from C
    $CX0 = C(X = 0)$ Symbolic simulate (expand around 0)
    $CX1 = C(X = 1)$ Symbolic simulate (expand around 1)
    Traversc($X,0,CX0$)
    Traverse($X,1,CX1$)
END

Procedure Traverse(X,Direction,C)
BEGIN
    Push onto Stack (X,Direction)
    If C not = 0 or 1 then   BEGIN Expand(C)
                                     RETURN
                        END
    If $C = 1$ then Print Stack
    Pop Stack(X,Direction)
END

The main advantage of this form of verification is that no simulation is required. The algorithm formally proves the equivalence of two designs. The computational complexity of this algorithm is known to be NP-complete. However, for most practical problems the algorithm exhibits polynomial time behavior. One reason for this is that during the expansion process, two subgraphs may be identical to one another. In this situation, recursively solving for counter examples in two subgraphs reduces to solving for counter examples in one. This verification step clearly precedes the timing verification step given in the next section.

B. Timing Verification

As discussed above, timing verification is an important aspect of the process unless the circuits are designed for a very low performance technology. Here we again will distinguish between high-performance *bipolar* circuits which are packaged on multichip modules and MOSFET circuits where most of the communication among the circuits is on chip.

Again, the *bipolar* transistor delay may be dominated by the interconnection delay [6] and the subcircuits are usually gates which can be described by delay equations. Thus rather accurate delay equation macromodels can be obtained which can

be added to obtain path delays. Algorithms for timing verification based on this delay model are applicable for large-scale systems.

Timing verification algorithms using path delays are discussed in [13]. They have the capability of selectively disabling unused paths. This is useful in detecting long functional paths which are hidden by unused paths with worse timing problems. Their implementation propagates a null signal through unused paths which no longer participate in the delay calculation. To approximate statistical delay, they use a min. and a max. range for the rising and falling delays. Furthermore, logic gates fall into one of three categories—positive unate(and,or), negative unate(inverter), and nonunate(xor). A rising delay through a negative unate gate becomes a falling signal. Their implementation also includes the analysis of clock skew, pulsewidth, and both long and short paths. Since the algoritm is block oriented rather than path oriented, the performance is linear with the number of gates in the circuit. The implementation is sufficiently general for large problems of 100 000 logic gates and consumes only 2 ms/gate.

The SCALD timing verifier [76] uses timing assertions based on a calculus of 7 values to verify the design. Here a signal can take the value 0,1,stable,changing,rising,falling, or unknown. During a block cycle, SCALD determines when a signal is changing and when it is stable. By setting inputs to 0 or 1, certain paths are eliminated from the analysis since changing signals no longer propagate. This is necessary to achieve the proper timing for variable length cycles. To verify the correct functioning of memory chips, a setup and hold check is performed. This guarantees that the data are stable before the clock arrives and that it is held long enough before the clock falls. Finally, a minimum pulsewidth is checked for because of the large variations in circuit rising and falling delays. The algorithm is event driven and is computationally efficient on problems as large as 100 000 gates.

The Timing Analysis (TA) technique [78] is the only algorithm which creates slack diagnostics. The slack for a logic gate is defined as the difference between the expected arrival and the actual arrival time. Slack is a measure of how bad a long or short path is. Another feature of the algorithm is that path lengths are statistical rather than worse case. This allows for process variation rather than worse case. A three sigma design allows for process variation which naturally occurs in the manufacturing cycle. The analysis of paths is block oriented rather than by path enumeration so that an entire IBM 3081 processor of 700 000 gates can be handled efficiently. For problems of this magnitude, a software paging scheme is necessary. Another way of avoiding the data explosion problem for 700 000 gates is to use TA to solve small partitions of the machine and then combine the solutions together. Delay modifiers are also a feature of the TA technique. This allows the user to cut paths that are never active or to adjust delays for multicycle paths. All gates are considered as either inverting or noninverting. The rising and falling delays for each gate use this information to accurately predict delay values as is carefully illustrated in Fig. 14 and (30). The meaning of the labels used is as follows:

a_0, b_0 = rising arrival times
a_1, b_1 = falling arrival times
    d_0 = delay if output is rising
    d_1 = delay if output is falling
    c_0 = rising output arrival
    c_1 = falling output arrival.

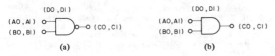

Fig. 14. (a) TA model for an inverting gate. (b) Model for a noninverting gate.

For the late mode the following equations hold for Fig. 14(a)

$$c_0 = \text{MAX}(a_1, b_1) + d_0$$

$$c_1 = \text{MAX}(a_0, b_0) + d_1 \qquad (30a)$$

while for the early mode

$$c_0 = \text{MIN}(a_1, b_1) + d_0$$

$$c_1 = \text{MIN}(a_0, b_0) + d_1. \qquad (30b)$$

Similarly, for a noninverting circuit in Fig. 14(b) the late mode equations are

$$c_0 = \text{MAX}(a_0, b_0) + d_0$$

$$c_1 = \text{MAX}(a_1, b_1) + d_1 \qquad (30c)$$

while for the early mode

$$c_0 = \text{MIN}(a_0, b_0) + d_0$$

$$c_1 = \text{MIN}(a_1, b_1) + d_1. \qquad (30d)$$

Using this gate or block model, ALG. 6 gives the timing verification for a large-scale clocked circuit.

ALGORITHM 6: Timing Analysis (TA)

Inputs: Combinational Circuit C
            Primary input arrival times Tin
            Expected Output times $Tout$
            Circuit delays D
Results: Worst case arrival times $t\text{ARR}$
            Slack times for each circuit $t\text{SLACK}$

Procedure TimingVerification($C, Tin, Tout, D$)
BEGIN
    Levelize C by a topological sort
    Schedule gates in levelized order
    For each gate i do
        $t\text{ARR}(i) = D(i) + \text{MAX}(t\text{ARR}(\text{predecessors of } i))$
    For all outputs j do
        $t\text{SLACK}(j) = Tout(j) - t\text{ARR}(j)$

    Schedule gates in reverse levelized order k
    For each connection Edge(m, k) do
    BEGIN
        Edge $t\text{SLACK}(m, k) = t\text{ARR}(k) - D(k)$
        $+ t\text{SLACK}(k) - t\text{ARR}(m)$
    END
END

Worst case arrival times are computed in linear time by making only one sweep through the circuit from primary inputs to primary outputs. Slacks are useful as diagnostics for timing verification. They represent how late (or early) a signal is with respect to the expected arrival time at the primary outputs. The computation of slacks is done in linear time by making one sweep through the circuit in the backward direction from primary outputs to primary inputs. However, it needs the arrival times computed during the forward propagation phase.

The critical path in the circuit is the one with the smallest slack. There are many ways to fix these timing problems. One way is to change low-power subcircuits to high power on nets which drive a high capacitance load. For chip-to-chip timing problems, designers may change to IO assignment or driver and receiver types to prevent electrical reflections. This is another example of how innovative algorithms extend the capabilities of the design procedure to VLSI dimensions.

The area of verification tools is presently evolving [62]–[78] as is illustrated by the above examples. For timing verification at the transistor level, the techniques given in Section II are used. Again, the procedures at the transistor level are more complicated than at the gate level. Mainly MOS transistor responses are highly dependent on the interconnections and the capacitances and thus the delay and rise times include much more variability than the corresponding bipolar transistor gates. This forces the verification to a much more refined level especially for passtransistor circuits.

VI. CONCLUSIONS

At present, the areas reported on in this paper are receiving considerable attention from industry as well as universities since they are of key importance for the design of realistic VLSI circuits. As is evident from the recent references in this paper, much progress has been made in the last few years across the entire spectrum of VLSI problems. The main task that needs to be performed is to find algorithms and implementations which yield acceptable running times at the VLSI level. Programs are in use today in some areas like logic simulation and timing verification which accommodate circuits at the VLSI level without excessive running time and storage requirements.

ACKNOWLEDGMENT

The authors would like to thank G. Almasi for the valuable suggestions and careful reading of the manuscript. They would also like to acknowledge the contributions made by the discussions with other researchers active in the field. Within the space given here they can only mention a few names: C. Carlin, W. Donath, G. Hachtel, I. Hajj, E. Lelarasmee, F. Odeh, G. Rabbat, A. Sangiovanni-Vincentelli, and V. Visvanathan.

REFERENCES

[1] C. H. Sequin, "Managing VLSI complexity: An outlook," this issue, pp. 149–166.
[2] C. Niessen, "Hierarchical design methodologies and tools for VLSI chips," this issue, pp. 66–75.
[3] A. E. Ruehli, N. Rabbat, and H. Y. Hsieh, "Macromodeling— an approach for analyzing large-scale circuits," *Comput. Aided Design*, vol. 10, pp. 121–130, Mar. 1978.
[4] G. D. Hachtel and A. L. Sangiovanni-Vincentelli, "A survey of third generation simulation techniques," *Proc. IEEE*, vol. 69, pp. 1264–1280, Oct. 1981.
[5] A. E. Ruehli, "Survey of computer-aided electrical analysis of integrated circuit interconnections," *IBM J. Res. Develop.*, vol. 23, pp. 627–639, Nov. 1979.
[6] E. E. Davidson, "Electrical design of high speed computer package," *IBM J. Res. Develop.*, vol. 26, pp. 349–361, May 1982.
[7] M. A. Beuer, Ed., *Digital System Design Automation: Languages, Simulation and Data Base*. Woodland Hills, CA: Computer, Sc. Press, 1975.
[8] M. A. Breuer and A. D. Friedman, *Diagnosis & Reliable Design of Digital Systems*. Potomac, MD: Comp. Sc. Press, 1976.
[9] M. A. Breuer, A. D. Friedman, and A. Iosupovicz, "A survey of the state of the art of design automation," *Computer* (IEEE), pp. 58–75, Oct. 1981.
[10] L. Bening, "Developments in computer simulation of gate level physical logic," in *Proc. 16th Design Automation Conf.*, San Diego, CA, June 1979, pp. 561–567.
[11] E. Ulrich and D. Herbert, "Speed and accuracy in digital network simulation based on structural modeling," in *Proc. 19th*

Design Automation Conf., Las Vegas, NV, June 1982, pp. 587–593.

[12] R. B. Hitchcock, Sr., "Timing verification and the timing analysis program," in *Proc. 19th Design Automation Conf.*, Las Vegas, NV, June 1982, pp. 594–604.

[13] L. C. Bening, T. A. Lane, and C. R. Alexander, "Developments in logic network path delay analysis," in *Proc. 19th Design Automation Conf.*, Las Vegas, NV, June 1982, pp. 605–613.

[14] J. P. Roth, *Computer Logic, Testing, and Verification*. Potomac, MD: Comp. Sc. Press, 1980.

[15] D. A. Antoniadis and R. W. Dutton, "Models for computer simulation of complex IC fabrication process," *IEEE J. Solid-State Circuits*, vol. SC-14, pp. 412–422, Apr. 1979.

[16] W. L. Engl, H. K. Dirks, and B. Meinerzhagen, "Device modeling," this issue, pp. 10–33.

[17] G. Arnout and H. De Man, "The use of threshold function and boolean-controlled network elements for macromodelling of LSI circuits," *IEEE J. Solid-State Circuits*, vol. SC-13, pp. 326–332, June 1978.

[18] H. De Man, "Computer aided design for integrated circuits: Trying to bridge the gap," *IEEE J. Solid-State Circuits*, vol. SC-14, pp. 613–621, June 1979.

[19] H. De Man, "Mixed mode simulation for MOS VLSI: Why, Where and How?" in *Proc. IEEE Int. Symp. Circuits System*, Rome, Italy, May 1982, pp. 699–701.

[20] W.M.G. Van Bokhoven, "Mixed-level and mixed-mode simulation by a piecewise-linear approach," in *Proc. IEEE Int. Symp. Circuits System*, Rome, Italy, May 1982, pp. 1256–1258.

[21] R. W. Jensen and M. D. Lieberman, *IBM Electronic Circuit Analysis Program*. Englewood Cliffs, N.J.: Prentice-Hall, 1968.

[22] L. W. Nagel, "SPICE2: a computer program to simulate semiconductor circuits," Univ. of California, Berkeley, ERL Memo ERL-M520, May 1975.

[23] E. Cohen, "Program reference manual for SPICE2," Univ. of California, Berkeley, ERL Memo ERL-M592, June 1976.

[24] A. Vladimirescu, K. Zhang, A. R. Newton, D. O. Pederson, and A. Sangiovanni-Vincentelli, "SPICE Version 2G User's guide," University of California, Berkeley, Tech. Memo., Aug. 10, 1981.

[25] "Advanced statistical analysis program (ASTAP)," Program reference manual, Pub. No. SH20-1118-0, IBM Corp. Data Proc. Div., White Plains, NY 10604.
W. T. Weeks, A. J. Jimenez, G. W. Mahoney, D. Mehta, H. Quassemzadeh, and T. R. Scott, "Algorithms for ASTAP—a network analysis program," *IEEE Trans. Circuit Theory*, vol. CT-20, pp. 628–634, Nov. 1973.

[26] L. W. Nagel, "ADVICE for circuit simulation," in *Proc. IEEE Int. Symp. Circuits and Systems*, Houston, TX, Apr. 1980.

[27] G. D. Hachtel, R. K. Brayton, and F. Gustavson, "The sparse tableau approach to network analysis and design," *IEEE Trans. Circuit Theory*, vol. CT-18, pp. 101–113, Jan. 1971.

[28] C. Ho, A. E. Ruehli, and P. A. Brennan, "The modified nodal approach to network analysis," *IEEE Trans. Circuits Syst.*, vol. CAS-22, pp. 504–509, June 1975.

[29] N. B. Rabbat, W. D. Ryan, and S. Q. Hossain, "Computer modeling of bipolar logic gates," *Electron. Lett.*, vol. 7, pp. 8–10, Jan. 1971.

[30] O. Wing and E. B. Kozemchak, "Computer analysis of digital integrated circuits," in *NERM Conf. REC.*, Boston, MA, Nov. 1971, IEEE Cat. No. 71C51, pp. 189–191.

[31] S. C. Bass and S. C. Peak, "Terminal models of digital gates allowing waveform simulation," in *Proc. IEEE Int. Symp. Circuit Theory*, Apr. 1973, pp. 287–289.

[32] N. Rabbat, A. E. Ruehli, G. W. Mahoney, and J. J. Coleman," A survey of macromodeling," in *Proc. IEEE Int. Symp. Circuits Systems*, Apr. 1975, pp. 139–143.

[33] B. Chawla, H. K. Gummel, and P. Kozah, "MOTIS—a MOS timing simulator," *IEEE Trans. Circuit Syst.*, vol. CAS-22, pp. 301–310, Dec. 1975.

[34] N. Rabbat and H. Y. Hsieh, "A latent macromodular approach to large-scale sparse networks," *IEEE Trans. Circuit Syst.*, vol. CAS-22, pp. 745–752, Dec. 1976.

[35] S. P. Fan, M. Y. Hsueh, A. R. Newton, and D. O. Pederson, "MOTIS-C: a new circuit simulator for MOS LSI circuits," in *Proc. IEEE Int. Symp. Circuits Systems*, 1977, pp. 700–703.

[36] E. Lelarasmee, A. E. Ruehli, and A. L. Sangiovanni-Vincentelli, "The waveform relaxation method for time-domain analysis of large-scale integrated circuits," *IEEE Trans. CAD Integ. Circ. Syst.*, vol. CAD-1, pp. 131–145, Jul. 1982.

[37] A. E. Ruehli, A. L. Sangiovanni-Vincentelli, and N.B.G. Rabbat, "Time analysis of large scale circuits containing one-way macromodels," *IEEE Trans. Circuit Syst.*, vol. CAS-29, pp. 185–189, Mar. 1982.

[38] E. Lelarasmee and A. Sangiovanni-Vincentelli, "RELAX: A new circuit simulator for large scale MOS integrated circuits," Electronic Research Laboratory, Univ. of California, Berkeley, Memo UCB/ERL M82/6, Feb. 1982.

[39] M. Tanabe, H. Nakamura, and K. Kawakita, "MOSTAP: An MOS circuit simulator for LSI circuits," in *Proc. IEEE Intl.*

[40] *Symp. Circuits Systems*, Houston, pp. 1035–1038, Apr. 1980.

[40] N. G. Rabbat, A. L. Sangiovanni-Vincentelli, and H. Y. Hsieh, "A multilevel Newton algorithm with macromodeling and latency for the analysis of large-scale nonlinear circuits in the time domain," *IEEE Trans. Circuits Syst.*, vol. CAS-26, pp. 733–741, Sept. 1979.

[41] G. DeMicheli and A. L. Sangiovanni-Vincentelli, "Numerical properties of algorithms for the timing analysis of MOS VLSI circuits," in *Proc. 1981 Europ. Conf. on Circuit Theory and Design*, Aug. 1981, pp. 387–392.

[42] M. A. Breuer, "Techniques for the simulation of computer logic," *Commun. Ass. Comput. Mach.*, pp. 443–446, Jul. 1964.

[43] E. G. Ulrich, "Time sequenced logical simulation based on circuit delay and selective tracing of active network path," in *Proc. ACM Nat. Conf.*, 1965, pp. 437–448.

[44] E. Ulrich, "Exclusive simulation of activity in digital networks," *Commun. Ass. Comput. Mach.*, vol. 12, no. 2, pp. 102–110, Feb. 1969.

[45] S. A. Szygenda, "TEGAS-Anatomy of a general purpose test generation and simulation at the gate and functional level," in *Proc. 9th Design Automation Conf.*, June 1972, pp. 116–127.

[46] E. G. Ulrich and T. Baker, "The concurrent simulation of nearly identical digital networks," in *Proc. 10th Design Automation Conf.*, June 1973, pp. 145–150.

[47] S. A. Szygenda and E. W. Thompson, "Digital logic simulation in a time-based table-driven environment: part 1, design verification," (IEEE) *Computer*, pp. 24–36, Mar. 1975.

[48] H. E. Krohn, "Design verification of large scientific computers," in *Proc. 14th Design Automation Conf.*, June 1977, pp. 354–361.

[49] R. E. Bryant, "MOSSIM: A switch-level simulator for MOS LSI," in *Proc. 18th Design Automation Conf.*, Jul. 1981, pp. 786–790.

[50] R. E. Bryant, "An algorithm for MOS Logic simulation," *Lamda Mag.*, Fourth Quarter, pp. 46–53, 1980.

[51] J. Watanabe, J. Miura, T. Kurachi, and I. Suetsugu, "Seven value logic simulation for MOS LSI circuits," presented at the IEEE Intl. Conf. Circuits and Computers, Port Chester, NY, Oct. 1980, pp. 941–944.

[52] W. Sherwood, "An MOS modeling technique for 4-state true-value hierarchical logic simulation," in *Proc. 18th Design Automation Conf.*, Nashville, TN, Jul. 1981, pp. 775–785.

[53] C. Mead and L. Conway, *Introduction to VLSI Systems.* Reading, MA: Addison-Wesley, 1980.

[54] N. Rabat, A. Y. Hsieh, and A. E. Ruehli, "Macromodeling for the analysis of large-scale networks," in ELECTRO-76 Professional Program 21, May 1976, pp. 1–8.

[55] A. R. Newton, "Techniques for the simulation of large-scale integrated circuits," *IEEE Trans. Circuits Syst.*, vol. CAS-26, pp. 741–749, Sept. 1979.

[56] D. Hill and W. van Cleemput, "SABLE: a tool for generating structural, multi-level simulation," in *Proc. 16th Design Automation Conf.*, San Diego, CA, June 1979, pp. 403–405.

[57] V. D. Agrawal, A. K. Bose, P. Kozak, H. N. Nham, and E. Pacas-Skewes, "A mixed-mode simulator," in *Proc. 17th Design Automation Conf.*, Minneapolis, MN, June 1980, pp. 1–8.

[58] T. Sasaki, A. Yamada, S. Kato, T. Nakazawa, K. Tomita, and N. Nomizu, "MIXS: a mixed level simulator for large digital system logic verification," in *Proc. 17th Design Automation Conf.*, Minneapolis, MN, June 1980, pp. 626–633.

[59] V. D. Agrawal, A. K. Bose, P. Kozak, H. N. Nham, and E. Pascal-Skewes, "A mixed model simulator," in *Proc. 17th Design Automation Conf.*, Minneapolis, MN, June 1980, pp. 618–625.

[60] H. H. Nham and A. K. Bose, "A multiple delay simulator for MOS LSI circuits," in *Proc. 17th Design Automation Conf.*, Minneapolis, MN, June 1980, pp. 610–611.

[61] P. H. Reynaert, H. De Man, G. Arnout, and J. Cornelissen, "DIANA: a mixed-mode simulator with a hardware description language for hierarchical design of VLSI," in *Proc. IEEE Intl. Conf. Circuits and Computers*, Port Chester, NY, Oct. 1980, pp. 356–360.

[62] D. D. Hill and W. M. Van Cleemput, "SABLE: Multilevel simulation for hierarchical design," in *Proc. IEEE Int. Symp. Circuits and Systems*, Houston, TX, Apr. 1980, pp. 431–434.

[63] W.M.G. van Bokhoven, "Macromodeling and simulation of mixed analog-digital networks by piecewise-linear system approach," in *Proc. IEEE Intl. Conf. Circuits and Computers*, Port Chester, NY, Oct. 1980, pp. 361–365.

[64] M. E. Daniel and C. W. Gwyn, "Hierarchical VLSI circuit design," in *Proc. IEEE Intl. Conf. Circuits and Computers*, Port Chester, NY, Oct. 1980, pp. 92–97.

[65] L. Scheffer and R. Apte, "LSI design verification using topological extraction," in *Proc. 12th Asilomar Conf. Circuits and Systems, and Computers*, Nov. 1978, pp. 149–153.

[66] C. R. McCaw, "Unified shapes checker—A checking tool for LSI," in *Proc. 16th Design Automation Conf.*, June 1979, pp. 81–87.

[67] R. Auerbach, "FLOSS: Macrocell Compaction system," presented at the 1979 IEEE Design Automation Workshop, East

Lansing, MI, 1979.

[68] C. S. Chang, "LSI layout checking using bipolar device recognition technique," in *Proc. 16th Design Automation Conf.*, June 1979, pp. 95–101.

[69] T. Mitsuhashi, T. Chiba, M. Takashima, and K. Yoshoda, "An integrated mask artwork analysis system," in *Proc. 17th Design Automation Conf.*, June 1980, pp. 277–284.

[70] J. P. Avenier, "Digitizing, layout, rule-checking—The everyday tasks of chip designers," this issue, pp. 49–56.

[71] H. C. Godoy, G. B. Franklin, and P. S. Bottorff, "Automatic Checking of Logic design structures for compliance with testability ground rules," in *Proc. 14th Design Automation Conf.*, June 1977, pp. 469–472.

[72] C. M. Baker and C. Terman, "Tools for verifying integrated circuit designs," *Lambda Mag.*, Fourth Quarter, pp. 22–30, 1980.

[73] R. N. Gustafson and F. J. Sparacio, "IBM 3081 processor unit: Design consideration and design process," *IBM J. Res. Develop.*, vol. 26, pp. 12–21, Jan. 1982.

[74] G. L. Smith, R. J. Bahnsen, and H. Halliwell, "Boolean comparison of hardware and flow charts," *IBM J. Res. Develop.*, vol. 26, pp. 106–116, Jan. 1982.

[75] M. Monachino, "Design verification system for large-scale LSE designs," *IBM J. Res. Develop.*, vol. 26, pp. 89–99, Jan. 1982.

[76] T. M. McWilliams, "Verification of timing constraints of large digital systems," in *Proc. 17th Design Automation Conf.*, Minneapolis, MN, June 1980, pp. 139–147.

[77] S. Newberry and P. J. Russell, "A programmable checking tool for LSI," in *Proc. IEE Europ. Conf. Electrical Design Automation*, Brighton, U.K., Sept. 1981, pub. no. 200, pp. 183–187.

[78] R. B. Hitchcock, Sr., G. L. Smith, and D. D. Chang, "Timing analysis of computer hardware," *IBM J. Res. Develop.*, vol. 26, pp. 100–105, Jan. 1982.

[79] C. W. Gear, "The automatic integration of ordinary differential equations," in *Proc. Information Processing 68*, A.F.H. Morrel, Ed. Amsterdam, The Netherlands: North-Holland, 1968, pp. 187–193.

[80] L. O. Chua and P. M. Lin, "Computer-aided analysis of electronic circuits: algorithms and computational techniques." Englewood Cliffs, NJ: Prentice Hall, 1975, chap. 10, pp. 410–431.

[81] F. Odeh and W. Liniger, "On A-Stability of second-order two step methods for uniform and variable steps," in *Proc. IEEE Intl. Conf. Circuits and Computers*, Port Chester, NY, 1980, pp. 123–126.

[82] A. E. Ruehli, P. A. Brennan and W. Liniger, "Control of numerical stability and damping in oscillatory differential equations," in *Proc. IEEE Intl. Conf. Circuits and Computers*, Port Chester, NY, Oct. 1980, pp. 111–114.

[83] V. M. Vidigal and S. W. Director, "A design centering algorithm for non convex regions of acceptability," *IEEE Trans. CAD Integ. Circ. Syst.*, vol. CAD-1, pp. 13–24, Jan. 1982.

[84] P. Yang, I. N. Hajj, and T. N. Trick, "Slate: A circuit simulation program with latency exploritation and node tearing," in *Proc. IEEE Intl. Conf. Circuits and Computers*, Port Chester, NY, Oct. 1980, pp. 353–355.

[85] D. A. Calahan, "Multilevel vectorized sparse solution of LSI circuits," in *Proc. IEEE Intl. Conf. Circuits and Computers*, Port Chester, NY, Oct. 1980, pp. 976–979.

[86] A. Vladimirescu and D. O. Pederson, "Performance limits of the CLASSIE circuit simulation program," in *Proc. Int. Symp. on Circuits Systems* (Rome, Italy, May 1982), pp. 1229–1232.

[87] H. De Man, J. Rabaey, G. Arnout, and J. Vandervalle: "DIANA as a mixed-mode simulator for MOS LSI Sampled-data circuits," in *Proc. IEEE Intl. Symp. on Circuits and Systems*, Houston, TX, Apr. 1980, pp. 435–438.

[88] P. Penfield, Jr. and J. Rubinstein, "Signal delay in RC tree networks," in *Proc. 18th Design Automation Conf.*, June 1982, pp. 613–617.

[89] A. E. Ruehli, N. B. Rabbat, and H. Y. Hsieh, "Macromodular latent solution of digital networks including interconnections," *Proc. IEEE Int. Symp. Circuits and Systems*, New York, NY, Apr. 1978, pp. 515–521.

[90] K. A. Sakallah and S. W. Director, "An activity-directed circuit simulation algorithm," in *Proc. IEEE Intl. Conf. Circuits and Computers*, Port Chester, NY, 1980, pp. 1032–1035.

[91] ——, "An event driven approach for mixed gate and circuit level simulation," in *Proc. IEEE Int. Symp. Circuits and Systems*, Rome, Italy, May 1982, pp. 1194–1197.

[92] W. L. Engl, R. Laur, and H. Dirks, "MEDUSA—A simulator for modular circuits," *IEEE Trans. CAD Integ. Circ. Syst.*, vol. CAD-1, pp. 85–93, Apr. 1982.

[93] L. O. Chua and P-M Lin, *Computer-Aided Analysis of Electronic Circuits*. Englewood Cliffs, NJ: Prentice-Hall, 1975.

[94] J. Vlach and K. Singhal, *Computer Aided Circuit Analysis*. New York: Van Nostrand, 1983.

[95] J. M. Ortega and W. Rheinboldt, *Iterative Solution of Nonlinear Equations in Several Variables*. New York: Academic Press, 1970.

[96] A. R. Newton, "The analysis of floating capacitors for timing simulation," in *Proc. 13th Asilomar Conf. on Circuits Systems and Computers*, Pacific Grove, CA, Nov. 1979.

[97] Y. P. Wei, I. N. Hajj, and T. N. Trick, "A prediction—relaxation based simulator for MOS circuits," in *IEEE Intl. Conf. Circuits and Computers* (New York, NY, Sept. 1982), pp. 353–355.

[98] A. L. Sangiovanni-Vincentelli and N. G. Rabbat, "Techniques for the time domain analysis of LSI circuits," *IEE Proc.*, vol. 127, part G, pp. 292–301, Dec. 1980.

[99] R. Bernhard, "Technology '82/82 solid state VLSI/LSI components," *IEEE Spectrum*, pp. 49–63, Jan. 1982.

[100] E. Lelarasmee, A. E. Ruehli and A. S. Sangiovanni-Vincentelli, "Waveform relaxation decoupling (WRD) method," *IBM Techn. Discl. Bulletin*, vol. 24, no. 7B, pp. 3720–3721, Dec. 1981.

[101] P. Goel, H. Lichaa, T. E. Rosser, T. J. Stroh, and E. E. Eichelberger, "LSSD fault simulation using conjunctive combinational and sequential methods," in *Proc. IEEE 1980 Test Conf.*, Nov. 1980, pp. 371–376.

[102] E. M. DaCosta and K. G. Nichols, "MASCOT," *IEE Proc.*, vol. 127, part G, no. 6, pp. 302–307, Dec. 1980.

[103] P. W. Case, H. H. Graff, L. E. Griffith, A. R. LeClercq, W. B. Murley, and T. M. Spence, "Solid logic design automation," *IBM J. Res. Develop.*, vol. 8, pp. 127–140, 1964.

[104] E. Ulrich, "Table lookup techniques for fast and flexible digital logic simulation," in *Proc. 17th Design Automation Conf.*, Minneapolis, MN, June 1980, pp. 560–563.

[105] R. A. Rohrer and H. Nosrati, "Passivity Considerations instability studies of numerical integration algorithms," *IEEE Trans. Circuits Syst.*, vol. CAS-28, pp. 857–866, Sept. 1981.

[106] V. B. Rao, T. Trick, and M. Lightner, "Hazards in a multiple delay logic simulation," *Proc. IEEE Int. Symp. on Circuits and Systems*, Rome, Italy, May 1982, pp. 72–75.

[107] M. E. Daniel and C. W. Gwyn, "CAD system for IC design," *IEEE Trans. CAD Integ. Circ. Syst.*, vol. CAD-1, pp. 2–12, Jan. 1982.

[108] H. W. Daseking, R. I. Gardner and P. B. Weil, "VISIA: A VLSI CAD system," *IEEE Trans. CAD Integ. Circ. Syst.*, vol. CAD-1, pp. 36–51, Jan. 1982.

[109] J. P. Hayes, "A unified switching theory with applications to VLSI design," *Proc. IEEE*, vol. 70, no. 10, pp. 1140–1151, Oct. 1982.

Part VI

Design Methodologies and Testing of VLSI Chips

DIGITIZING, layout, and rule checking is the everyday task of the chip designer. J. P. Avenier describes these techniques in the next paper. The most frequently used methods are compared and rated. For high integration levels, hierarchical methods offer a pragmatic solution to cope with the increasing number of parameters to be optimized simultaneously.

The interconnection of components in VLSI chips is becoming an increasingly complex problem. In the second paper of this part, S. J. Hong and R. Nair discuss several approaches to solving this problem with emphasis on special wire routing machines. With such machines, the wire routing time can be reduced significantly; their use in the design of future VLSI chips may become mandatory. Whether there should be many machines, each of which specializes in some aspect of VLSI physical design automation, or a "consensus" machine that can be used for most of the critical computational needs, is an emerging question.

In the third paper, C. Niessen discusses in detail the methodology of hierarchical design approaches, including their advantages and disadvantages. The partitioning of complex networks into several hierarchic levels ("gates," "cells," "blocks," "macros") simplifies the design effort considerably. The design and the structuring of the various hierarchic levels are simpler and less complex compared to the unpartitioned treatment of the system as a whole. In most cases, the hierarchic structuring is done heuristically, refraining thereby from a complete optimization of the whole system, in favor of a tradeoff with regard to a considerable reduction in design effort. Such suboptimizations are quite often reasonable compromises.

The use of computers to design newer computer systems automatically has been a dream of computer system designers since the early days of digital computers. None of the systems proposed and developed so far is completely automatic. Human interaction of varying degree is needed to guide the synthesis process. Methodical aspects of logic synthesis are discussed in the fourth paper of this part, by H. M. Lipp. The author especially compares top-down with bottom-up optimization. He predicts that in the VLSI era the bottom-up optimization approach will lose influence in favor of new top-down design tools for logic synthesis.

With the emerging VLSI technology, it has become apparent that considerable care will have to be taken in the design stage in order to ensure testability. If necessary, provision must be made for specific additional circuits to facilitate and improve the testing. In the last paper of this part, by T. W. Williams and K. P. Parker, the various concepts to serve this purpose are described and compared. Design and testability are closely interrelated. With a suitable and carefully structured design, the mastering of the testing problems should be possible even for higher integration levels. Increased sophistication and increased expenditures, however, will become mandatory.

Digitizing, Layout, Rule Checking—The Everyday Tasks of Chip Designers

JEAN PIERRE AVENIER

Invited Paper

Abstract—The layout phase is most critical in the design of integrated circuits (IC's) because of the cost of the phase itself, since it involves expensive tools and a large amount of human intervention, and also because of the consequences for production cost. Several approaches are used that need more or less computer and/or man time.

The compromise is difficult because of the number of parameters to be taken into account. This paper presents the methods most commonly used with their advantages and disadvantages.

I. INTRODUCTION

THE DESIGNER who has the task of drawing the layout of an integrated circuit (IC) is confronted with a large set of methods. The main compromise is related to the ratio between design cost and production cost. An IC with a high-density layout will be long and expensive to draw, but the small area will induce a higher production yield and a higher number of dies per wafer as well. So the main criterion to be taken into account for the choice of a layout methodology is the production volume. The design duration is next. Today, the size and complexity of circuits impose hierarchy and symbolic approaches. These techniques advocated by MEAD and CONWAY are not yet fully established in the industrial world, but they prefigure the state of the art. It is important, also, for high-cost, complex circuits to have the opportunity of following the technology improvements. The symbolic methods generally allow such transformation, but other tools offer the ability to shrink the layout with some intelligence, sizing the patterns in accordance with their electrical functions.

As the cost and duration are increasing rapidly, it is of prime necessity to run a maximum of verification programs on the layout before the mask generation. These checks refer to the design rules, the electrical rules, and the consistency with a reference wiring diagram.

II. HAND-DRAFTED METHOD

A. Hand-Drafted Layout

1) Presentation: Although the size of VLSI circuits has made the use of manual drawing for a complete layout almost impossible, these methods are widely used and their limits have been pushed away by the new graphic systems available on the market. The growing number of systems installed in various semiconductor companies is proof of a large success. But the kind of work is changing at the same time. They are used as the front end of more complex CAD systems—for the

Manuscript received June 22, 1982; revised October 24, 1982.

The author is with Thomson-EFCJS, F-38019 Grenoble Cedex, France.

definition of the basic cell library, for example. However, in spite of the increasing part of regular structures (ROM, RAM, PLA) in the designs, a great deal of the layout is still done manually. Why? The main reason is the good density of the hand-drafted layout and, above all, its aptitude to fill the remaining areas left by the regular blocks. There is no doubt, again, that for VLSI circuits the shift to more sophisticated methods (that we shall examine later) is compulsory.

B. Methodology

1) Digitizing: It is the oldest approach. The work is split into two phases. The first is drawing of the several layers of the artwork on mylar at a large scale (1000, 2000 for up-to-date technologies). This requires a very good knowledge of the design rules. Generally, the designer himself has to do the major part of the job. A second phase of coding on a large-scale (more than 1 m $\times$ 1 m) and accurate (0.1-mm) digitizer inputs the layout into the computer. Associated is a screen that allows a feedback control of the operation.

This process is obviously very cheap in computer resources. The coding phase represents only 5 percent of the total time. Human interaction with the computer is very poor. The drawing of the artwork is long and extremely tedious, and the digitizing itself requires sustained care.

2) Interactive Input on a Graphic Terminal: The availability on the market of high-quality color displays for a relatively low price and the wide spread of computer use have incited people to go to more interactive methods. The layout is done directly on the screen, often starting from a manual sketch [4].

Some functions (design rules checking (DRC), electrical values extraction) can be used for a quick feedback. The computer system investment is naturally far more important than for the previous method, but the realization times are shorter and the job is more pleasant.

3) Description Language: There is another way to define the geometrical patterns; it is to use a description language instead of a graphic input. This method, seldom developed, has the great advantage of offering all the wealth of a procedural programming language, that is, parameters, conditional and inconditional branches, labels, do-loops computed variables, and so on. This allows the description of parametrizable cells that can be rather independent of the technology.

The drawback of this method is its batch mode process. It is, however, very interesting for the description of the basic elements of a technology (transistors with their W/L ratio as a parameter, for example). It is the essential accessory of a more sophisticated approach for the definition of bristle blocks or

Reprinted from *Proc. IEEE*, vol. 71, pp. 49–56, Jan. 1983.

201

stretchable cells used in interactive methods. Another advantage is the trace that is automatically kept, which limits the effect of any computer failure.

III. Symbolic Approach

A. Introduction

Symbolic layout methodologies are a means of abstracting the detailed and often laborious task of mask design of IC's. They offer the advantages of hand-packed mask design with regard to density of layout, while also having advantages over manual layout for design duration and correctness. In essence, the use of symbology reduces the complexity of the IC design process, and, in addition to the advantages mentioned, allows experienced designers to undertake more complicated circuits than would otherwise be possible, and, more importantly, allows novice designers to complete designs with a high degree of confidence. This last point is regarded as especially important as system designers move to using silicon as an implementation medium, rather than more conventional techniques.

B. Symbolic Layout Methodologies

Symbolic layout methods attempt to abstract the detailed task of designing IC masks to clarify this operation. Normally, this is achieved by simplifying the design rules for a given process. These design rules include the minimum spacings and widths of the mask layers used in the technology. They also include electrical rules for interconnecting layers and the formation of active devices. These simplified rules ideally result in a quicker turnaround of designs and a reduction in errors compared to manual layout.

1) Fixed-Grid Layout: Fixed-grid layout systems divide the chip surface into a uniformly spaced grid in both the x and y directions. The grid size represents the minimum feature or placement tolerance that is desired in a given process. For each combination of mask layers that exists at a grid location, a symbol is defined. Given a particular design system, these symbols are then placed on the grid to construct the desired circuit much in the same way one would tile a floor. Symbol sets may be defined as characters, or perhaps graphical symbols, if a graphics display is used for design.

American Microsystems International (AMI) and Rockwell International have made use of character-based symbolic layout for some time.

The Symbolic Interactive Design System (SIDS) uses a color character terminal as a design station which provides a high degree of user feedback. In addition to these character-based systems, Hewlett–Packard has developed an interactive graphics system (IGS), which is capable of accepting symbolic input on a fixed grid. The IGS also uses symbolic representations to reduce the time to display hand-designed layouts.

The design process in these systems consists in laying symbols down on the coarse grid. The use of fixed-size symbols simplifies geometric design rules but does not totally alleviate them. SIDS, therefore, provides on-line DRC for geometric design rules violations, and a "trace" facility to trace circuit nets to visually check for electrical connectivity. Similarly, the IGS provides "bumpers" which surround symbols to aid designers in placing them.

2) Sticks Layout: The term "sticks" [1], [3] is a generic term given to symbolic design systems that do not necessarily

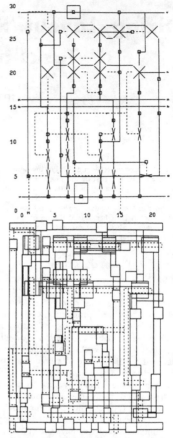

Fig. 1. Input and output of the symbolic program with compaction. "TRICKY" (CMOS technology).

constrain the designer to a grid and generally require the designer to enter a free-form topological description of a layout via an IGS (digitizer, tablet, color work station, etc.).

Graphical symbols are placed relative to each other rather than in an absolute manner. Following the definition phase, the symbolic descriptions are converted into valid mask descriptions using a variety of compaction strategies designed to space symbols in accordance with the process design rules.

The TRICKY system [2], developed by Thomson-EFCIS, Grenoble France, uses a grid-based placement scheme. Grid-based placement allows grid entry of geometric topology by "snapping" elements to the grid (and also aids the capture of the circuit details and the subsequent processing needed prior to preparing a valid set of masks). TRICKY accepts free composed and arranged input sketches and results in good layout density and reliability, using a spacer for this purpose; a one-direction algorithm is used successively in both directions, starting in a user-selected one, and can be repeated in alternate directions either a given number of times or until no more space is saved (Fig. 1).

Moreover, STICKS from CALMA removes the grid as a design

consideration. This results in the designer being totally freed from geometric design rules and accessing the layout through a symbolic editor.

Unfortunately, there are two major disadvantages in these methods. The first one is the lack of diagonals because of the complexity of the compaction process. The second one is the fact that the spacer is a batch processed program.

3) Benefits of Symbolic Layout: The simplification of geometric design rules relieves the designer of details that can cloud more global and important issues, such as achieving the correct circuit or communication requirements.

Transparent design rules also make designs relatively process independent. If a process design rule changes, the mask descriptions for a circuit may be regenerated with a minimum effort.

The more recent sticks systems have, in addition to the perceived benefits of a design rule free environment, the basis for capturing circuit connectivity, although few have treated this benefit in detail. This is due to the fact that specific problems have been addressed, in particular compaction, rather than the complete design cycle and the relevant tools required. The time saving and quick turnaround allow a better layout optimization. As opposed to manual methods, DRC is not necessary for this approach. Finally, a loss of 10 to 20 percent of density has to be compared to a reduction of 50 to 75 percent of layout time.

IV. BUILDING-BLOCK APPROACH

This design method is very fast and secure and especially well suited for logic circuits of medium size; density and performances are not critical.

For each technology and range of applications, the designer builds his circuit with standard cells stored in libraries.

The building-block approach consists of a set of blocks arranged in regular bands separated by channels dedicated to interconnections.

Thus the regular layout is able to support automatic placement and routing algorithms.

An important investment of this method is associated with the definition of the standard cells library, a necessary condition for an efficient method.

A. Definition of the Library

For a given technology, a set of standard cells is selected: a two-input NOR gate, a three-input NOR gate, elementary latches and flip-flops with and without asynchronous inputs, input–output buffers, and so on.

Then the layout shape of each cell is chosen; it is generally rectangular with fixed height and variable width.

The global density of the circuit depends strongly on the position of the input–output pads of each cell as follows:

a) I/O pad on each side: important loss of density inside the cell (Fig. 2);

b) no duplication of I/O pad: high density inside the cell but necessity of foreseeing cross cells for interchannel connections (Fig. 3);

c) lateral I/O pad for regular cell structure (register–counter) self-connection (D–Q) just by cell juxtaposition: important gain of density in interconnection area, but necessity to design three types of cells: first, current, and last one (Fig. 4).

Once these basic choices are made, each cell is laid out and

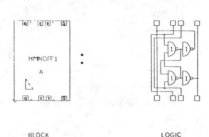

NOR LATCH

Cell Name : HMNOFF1   Iss:A

BLOCK   LOGIC

Fig. 2. Example of case a) in Section IV-A (extracted from *COMIC User's Manual*, Hughes Me. Ltd.).

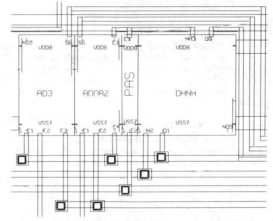

Fig. 3. Example of case b) in Section IV-A. PAS cells are pass-through.

the library contains: logical features—function or logical diagram; electrical features—propagation delay, maximum fan-out; and graphical features—outline rectangle, I/O pads level and coordinates, geometrical details of masks.

B. Layout

The starting point is a logic diagram containing only standard cells. The layout consists in the placement and interconnection of these cells. This task may be performed by means of a graphical station (display and tablet); in this case, the area dedicated to interconnection may be used by the designer to insert some parts of random logic (for instance, transmission gate logic). More frequently, this task is performed by a CAD program that, from a wiring list of cells and from some constraints (critical path and proximity), determines the cells' placement and the coordinates of each interconnection wire. According to the performances of the algorithms used, this process can be either a fully automatic approach, or a semiautomatic tool with manual modifications of automatic placement and completion by hand of unsuccessful wirings.

A main advantage of this method is that the same circuit

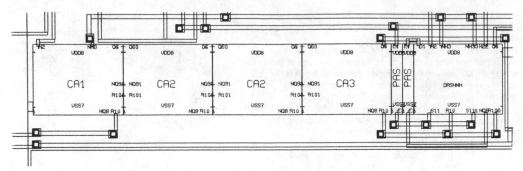

Fig. 4. Example of case c) in Section IV-A, *CA* 1—first cell; *CA* 2—current cell; *CA* 3—last cell.

description (wiring list) is used for layout and also for logic simulation and test pattern generation.

C. Enhancement of this Approach

Many building-block CAD systems offer the opportunity to take into account nonstandard cells, such as blocks of any rectangular shape designed by other methods (PLA's ROM's, RAM's) [5], [6]. Thereby, the placement and routing algorithm had to be modified to support these non-regular structures.

V. Gate Array Approach

In the custom design area, it is of prime importance to get very short design delays. So the enhancement of the quality of process has updated gate array approach. The basic concept is to stock nearly fully processed wafers, waiting for the last mask layers, the ones which correspond to the interconnections. The following different kinds of arrays are possible.

1) *Transistors arrays:* Basic elements (transistors) are first interconnected to build elementary gates or blocks (these interconnections can often be stored in library), then the gates themselves are interconnected to realize the whole circuit.

2) *Gate arrays (ULA):* Basic elements are already logic elements (elementary gate, D flip-flop, etc.) and design work consists only in blocks wiring.

Once the logic description has been simulated to obtain the layout of the circuit, it is possible to use either an interactive display station or automatic tools such as partitioning, placement, and routing.

The loss of silicon area due to the gate array approach in comparison with the hand-drafted method has been reduced by the development of optimization tools. A great amount of work and money has been invested in this area by large companies (IBM, Motorola, Fujitsu, AMI, Signetics) and CAD software companies such as Silvar Lisco, V-R, Information Systems Inc., Scientific Calculations Inc., Compeda, etc.

It is possible to find on the market a wide range of tools starting with fully hand-drafted layout up to fully automated process with 100-percent placement and routing performed by CAD. This type of "always successful" algorithm requires special gate arrays arrangement with sufficient size of routing channels. But the absence of manual operation and graphical associated tools may justify such an approach. Generally, a semiautomatic technique is used, with only about 5 to 10 percent of unsuccessful wiring completed by the user on a graphical display.

Main Remarks: The CAD systems associated with the gate array method, according to the type of concerned circuits, can be very highly integrated (schematic entry, simulation, test generation, automatic layout).

VI. Automated Placement and Routing

A. The Problem

The goal is to place the elements (transistors, gates, functions) and to route the wires corresponding to the equipotentials, taking into account the design rules and using a minimal chip area. The task is done automatically, using algorithms. When problems arise, human intervention tries to solve them. The man–machine, manual–automatic interaction is the key to good tools able to work on various technologies.

B. The Placement

This problem is mathematically hard to define. Several measures are taken for optimization. The initial goal may be total length of the wires, number of contacts, or channel density. Moreover, the placement is simplified by the suppression of trees in the equipotentials (only pairs are treated).

There are generally two steps, as follows.

1) *Automatic Elaboration of an Initial Placement:* Various methods are used.

Static baycenter: Starting from the position of some elements, forces between modules (generated by the connections) are computed and a balanced position is searched.

Branch and bound: Given an evaluation function, the tree of possible solutions is tracked.

Linear order: In the case of linear placements, the problem is to find an optimal order.

Heuristic and constructive methods: The modules are placed one by one, by maximal conjunction or minimal disjunction with others already placed. The associated measures vary. They are the most used.

Min-cut algorithms: The set of modules is cut in two parts to satisfy a law (minimum number of wires between the two parts, equal size of the subsets...). These methods are best suited for modules of various size.

2) *Automatic Improvement of the Placement:* Local modifications are tried. All the measures described before may be improved. However, starting from the initial placement, the routing is simulated to introduce real constraints in the algorithms.

The static baycenter is computed module by module to allocate new positions.

Pair exchange is the most used method, with various measures according to the exchange test. Some difficulties arise when the exchanged modules are of different sizes.

3) Interactive Placement: The designer may preplace some modules or choose between algorithms. He can also, during the improvement phase, modify the placement of a module, specify its form, and change the choice for an I/O allocation.

C. The Routing

The equipotentials are drawn between the modules. Some choices such as the following must be made as a preliminary in accordance with the density or the technology: ON or OFF grid routing (OFF grid is mandatory for high density); EQUI-POTENTIAL TREE cutting; routing order (depending on the length or the strategic position of the wires); and number of interconnection levels.

As for the placement, the routing is now done in two phases.

1) Global Router: This phase results in the allocation of the connections to the various areas of the chip.

Channels definition: The area available between the modules is divided into channels. The wiring is done afterwards channel by channel. The various methods cut the area in rectangles defined by the block boundaries. Association between rectangles depends on the local router.

Connections allocation for each channel: The methods vary with the router. A Lee-type algorithm may be used. A graph of contiguous channels is used to find the wires. First of all, the wires are allocated to some channels. Then the wires of the most chocked channels are redrawn.

Channel wiring order: This point is fundamental because the preliminary allocation of the wires to the channels does not solve the communication problem between channels. The graph of contiguous channels can be used.

2) Local Router: Three approaches exist.

Expansion algorithms on a grid: A wave is propagated from the starting to the ending point of a connection.

Aim algorithm: Two orthogonal lines are drawn from a point until they reach an obstacle. An escape point is then chosen on the line. The process is restarted from this new point. The same process is run from each end of the wire. When the lines cut, the routing is done. This method is much faster than the previous one but the solution is not always found.

Channel algorithms: These methods are widely used. Given a number of connections, several tracks defined in the channel, and I/O positions on each side of it; the routing is done inside the channel. Some connections may be impossible because of the positions on the I/O on the side of the channel.

The order of the routing must be defined previously for the two first algorithms and is given by the third one.

3) Interactive Router: Automatic routers often follow a manual process, and this eases this understanding of the task by the designer. In an interactive system, the user can intervene by commands before or during the routing step for several decisions: allocation of I/O pads; allocation of wires to the channel; modification of the already-drawn connections to relieve some channels; and introduction of underpasses or modification of mask layer for a wire.

VII. SILICON COMPILATION

A. Regular Parametrizable Blocks

If one observes present VLSI circuits, a large amount of silicon area is dedicated to blocks with a repetitive structure, such as PLA's, ROM's, RAM's, Registers stacks, and ALU.

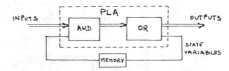

Fig. 5. Example of a synchronous automation using PLA.

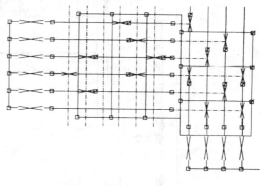

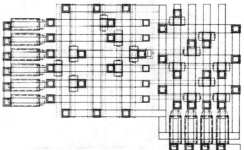

Fig. 6. Example of PLA automatic generation.

Thus in order to save time and to increase reliability, it is very interesting to automatize the design of such elements, that will be called macrofunctions.

To speak about this concept, we take the example of a PLA because it can be taken into account from functional level to layout level.

PLA's are very often used to implement synchronous automation: combinational two-levels logic (AND–OR) and feed-back-loop state variables register (see Fig. 5).

The functional description can be described by a language or a flowchart. The logic part consists in deriving a logic equation from flip-flop type and state assignment. This set of equations may be minimized. The final layout is obtained by fixing the sizes of transistors and by specifying the order and position of inputs/outputs (Fig. 6).

B. Silicon Compilers

The trend is to continue the automation process towards the definition of the macrofunctions and the final layout of the whole circuit. The design time can become very short with high reliability. Unfortunately, critical circuits for area, timing, or consumption reasons are not subject to such methods. Silicon compilation starts from the functional description of the circuit. Automatic synthesis and automatic definition of the macrofunctions give the description of the major blocks.

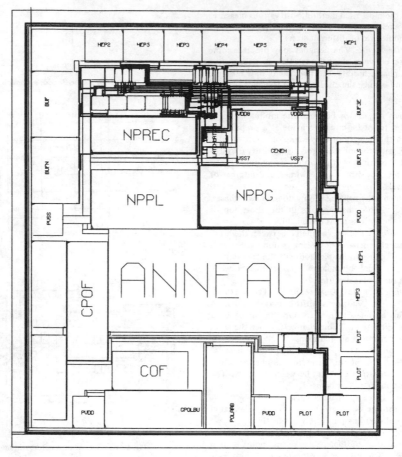

Fig. 7. Output of chip assembler.

A chip assembler (automated placement and routing) draws the final layout. The loss of silicon area is generally high [8].

C. Advantages

These automatic techniques of implementation for complex and programmable blocks allow one to speed up the design and to increase the reliability due to minimal human intervention.

The increase of abstraction level allows one to push the limits in design area (analog to software engineering).

VIII. Hierarchical Approach

Although several methods of structured design have been known for a long time (simultaneously with structured programming), they were far slower to reach an industrial use. The optimization constraints and the need of a high performance level were a powerful brake to this evolution that will be mandatory for VLSI.

A. Introduction

The design methodology must be roughly top-down with stepwise refinement; the layout by itself, on the contrary, has to be bottom-up to reach a good result.

The first step is a general floor plan at a jumbo cell level with their global connections (buses). The number of elements manipulated must remain under thirty. The shape, the area, the I/O positions are already known for several blocks such as ROM, RAM, PLA, ALU. This first approach will allow the definition of remaining unknown parameters using the general floor plan. The allocation of the PLA lines to variables is made, for example. The remaining area is allocated to the logic not yet implemented. Reshaping of some block of main importance may be decided to fit with its proximity. For example, an $8 \times 2n$ ROM will be better than a $16 \times 1n$. Starting from this point, the work can be divided among several teams for which a more accurate layout process is defined. The same approach may also be used at a lower level.

B. Tools

1) Database: All this process must be supported by only one database for the whole circuit to allow consistency checking between the several parallel tasks. To improve the design security, the layout has to be associated with the previous design steps (functional and logic synthesis) that must be themselves structured. It is interesting to speak about a database that accepts all the data of the various design levels: functional, register-transfer, logic, electric, and layout. This single

TABLE I
ADVANTAGES AND DISADVANTAGES OF VARIOUS DESIGN STYLES

Evaluation Implantation methods	DENSITY	SPEED	SECURITY	DATA PROCES. COSTS implantation	COMPANIES
DISPLAY DIGITIZER LANGUAGE	+ + + + + + + + +	- - - - - - - - -	- - - - - - - - - DRC obliga- tory	- - - - - - - - - (with DRC) + + + +	CALMA.APPLICON CALMA.APPLICON
MANUAL AUTO ROUTING FULL AUTOMATIC	- - - - - - - - -	+ + + + + + 200 blocks a week	- + + + + +	0 + + + + +	COMIC (Hughes) PHILIPS MPS2D (RCA) CALMOS (LISCO)
GATE ARRAYS	- -	+ +	+ +		
GRID Max. Min. Multi step	- 0 0	+ + +	+ - 0	0 0 0	MASKS (ROCKWELL) MASKS (ROCKWELL) SLIC ou SIDS (AMD)
DEFORMATION	0	+	⟊	+	ABRAITIS
COMPACTION 1 DIR 2 DIR	+ + +	0 0	+ + + + + +	+ + + + +	STICKS (CALMA) BERKELEY (TRICKY) SLIP (BELL)

+ Good
0 Medium
- Poor

description of the circuit under a blocks + connections form, whatever the level of abstraction, and the memorization of the correspondence between these levels offers the opportunity of an accurate control on the project evolution.

2) Evaluators: In order to avoid a number of loops in the definition of the circuit layout, it is of prime importance to have an idea as soon as possible of the shape and the size of the blocks that will be drawn.

It is the goal of the evaluators, which, given a technology (that is design rules and circuitry) and a specific function to design, will compute some characteristics of the block.

3) Chip Planning:

Chip planning and chip assembler: In connection with the database, two programs are useful for the layout: the chip planning program that helps in the establishment of a general floor plan during the top-down phase and a chip assembler for the accurate definition of the block positions.

The first one must be highly interactive to allow a large number of tries of the placement of the cells. An automatic placement program may be used to propose some solutions. At the current state of the art, only rectangular blocks may be handled by these programs. The connections must be taken into account for the placement because of the large impact they have on the total area of the chip. (Half of the circuit is devoted to connections.)

The chip assembler [7], on the contrary, is involved in the bottom-up phase to get the layout. Each time a block is placed, all the connections are made with respect to the I/O positions and the design rules. Automatic routers can be used to ease the work (to run buses, for example). The lack of diagonals in such routers unfortunately greatly reduces their utility (Fig. 7).

Main Remarks: This approach requires a parallel between the cutting up at the various levels.

Advantages: The process structuration allows the design of very large circuits, preserving realistic security and delays.

IX. ARTWORK ANALYSIS

The design of integrated circuits is not fully automated but contains more or less manual steps. Therefore, error-free design is practically impossible. If an error is found after the fabrication process, it costs much time and money because new masks must be prepared again. Thus complete checkout for design errors becomes a necessary step of the design. Several types of errors may appear in a mask, such as violations of geometrical rules, connectivity errors, or topological errors. So artwork analysis computer programs must be able to perform a wide range of functions. These functions include verifying design rules, discovering electrically conducting paths, and recognizing devices. Several approaches are possible to realize these functions: a "figure-based" method, an "edge-based method," or a "scanning" method. Hierarchical design of the artwork allows checks on basic cells and avoids checks on multiple repetitions of a cell. Using special representation of the border region of the cells, a check can then be performed on all the artwork.

A. "Figure-Based" Approach

This is the most commonly used method. The smallest entity is a closed figure, and various operations are performed on these figures to check for design violations. These operations are Boolean combinations, contraction or expansion, calculation of area and perimeter, and labeling of figures (partitioning the artwork to avoid useless comparisons) or bit map procedures. With this method, one rule can be checked at a time, since the Boolean operations (and expansion or contraction) can be performed on a single layer or between two layers. In order to increase the efficiency of the process, "layer splitting" can be used; this means the elements of one layer are split into several sublayers, each with logically identical components. The bit map procedure presents the difficulty of dealing with the nonorthogonal edges of figures. This approach is quite general and is being used in many programs, with little differences about the partitioning of the artwork. It tends to be expensive.

B. "Edge-Based" Approach

Another checking method is based on "line segments." This approach is more economical since less data must be processed (vertical edges are not part of the data). Each segment is oriented, and the procedure is based on comparisons between segments (check for intersection, test if a point is within a figure, etc.). This method is similar to the "figure-based" one and seems to have the same efficiency.

C. "Scanning" Method

This third method assumes that the artwork is in the form of segments (or points) sorted in lexicographic order. All mask levels are merged into one file before the sort, so all layers will be checked in parallel. Then the artwork can be scanned from left to right by a virtual vertical line drawn across the mask, searching the data to locate all segments which cross this line. The position of the scan line is incremented from the left side of the mask to the right side. It can be stepped by a user-defined increment or by variable increment auto-scan based on "when the data changes" (each point in the data represents a data change). The design rules to be checked or the devices to be recognized are described in technology-dependent subroutines or are compiled separately before the scan begins. This method has two main advantages. All mask levels can be checked in one pass. Besides, interlevel checks can be performed simultaneously.

X. Conclusion

Until today the design methods have evolved rather slowly, the layout remaining the larger part of the work. For VLSI circuits, the trends are evolving rapidly because of the growing need for security and control. The compromise between the various parameters may be done using Fig. 8 and Table I.

More academic approaches are used for the synthesis at the functional and logical levels. Naturally, the layout follows the same evolution. Hierarchic methods are mandatory for large circuits for two main reasons. First, the need of reliability offers the possibility to split the work into several subtasks.

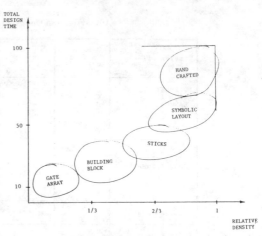

Fig. 8. A diagram of the density versus design time for the various design styles.

The first point refers to the delays. Second, the need of security in the conduct of a process is more and more complex due to the large number of parameters to optimize at the same time. But old methods are still in use and will remain in use for a while each time a difficult problem arises. The evolution towards silicon compilation will cut the design time and the design cost, allowing a large number of small companies to design VLSI circuits mainly for small production volume.

References

[1] N. Weste, "MULGA: An interactive symbolic layout system for the design of integrated circuit," Bell Syst. Tech. J., vol. 60, no. 6.
[2] A. Hanczakowski, "TRICKY symbolic layout system for integrated circuits," in Proc. Spring Compcon 81 (San Francisco), pp. 374–376.
[3] J. Williams, "STICKS: A new approach to LSI design," thesis, Massachusetts Institute of Technology, Cambridge, MA, June 1977.
[4] J. Ousterhout, "CEASAR: An interactive editor for VLSI layouts," VLSI DESIGN, Fourth Quarter, 1981.
[5] A. Feller and R. Noto, "A speed oriented, Fully R automatic layout program for random logic VLSI devices," presented at the Nat. Computer Conf., 1978.
[6] H. Beke, W. Sansen, and R. Van Overstraeten, "CALMOS: A computer aided layout program for MOS/LSI," IEEE J. Solid-State Circuits, vol. SC-12, pp. 281–282, June 1977.
[7] S. Trimberger, "RIOT: A simple graphical chip assembly tool," presented at the 19th Design Automation Conf.
[8] A. Szepieniec, "SAGA: An experimental silicon assembler," presented at the 19th Design Automation Conf.

Wire-Routing Machines—New Tools for VLSI Physical Design

SE JUNE HONG, FELLOW, IEEE, AND RAVI NAIR, MEMBER, IEEE

Invited Paper

Abstract—Interconnection of components in a VLSI chip is becoming an increasingly complex problem. In this paper we examine the complexity of the wire routing process and discuss several new approaches to solving the problem using a parallel system architecture. The machines discussed range from compact systems for highly specialized applications to more general designs suited for broader applications. The process speedup due to parallelism and the cost advantage due to the use of large numbers of identical VLSI parts make these new machines practical today.

I. INTRODUCTION

THE PROCESS of designing a chip becomes more challenging as the number of components that it can accommodate increases. Many design automation problems, e.g., logic synthesis, testing, partitioning, placement, and wire routing, are known to be NP-complete or worse in complexity. The optimal solution to these problems requires computation times which could grow exponentially with the number of components. Practical algorithms, therefore, use heuristic techniques with polynomial complexity which lead to near-optimal solutions. Unfortunately, in most aspects of VLSI design, the heuristics for even these suboptimal solutions involve polynomials with degrees higher than 1 that make them prohibitively more costly to apply as the number of components increases.

Physical design of a chip refers to the process of placing the component elements on the chip and determining wire routes to interconnect the terminals of the components. A component may occasionally be a large functional macro (ALU, PLA, ROM, RAM, register, etc.) with terminals on the periphery, a logic gate/circuit (NAND, NOR, driver, flip-flop, etc.), or even an isolated transistor or resistor. Integrated circuits today have components ranging up to a few hundred thousand transistor equivalents in custom designed chips or up to ten thousand logic gates in *gate array* or *master-slice* chips.

The interconnections of terminals are made through one or more wiring planes where wire tracks generally run in either horizontal or vertical direction on alternating layers. A physical wire changes direction usually by means of a *via* connecting the two wiring planes at the intersection of a horizontal wire track with a vertical one. The density of wires today approaches several hundred tracks per millimeter, implying thousands of wire tracks on a chip of size 5 mm × 5 mm. The number of grid points (via sites) defined by such dense wire tracks on a chip can be well over a million.

Manuscript received May 10, 1982; revised September 28, 1982.
The authors are with IBM Thomas J. Watson Research Center, Yorktown Heights, NY 10598.

The active devices and wires compete for space on the chip surface, although multilayer wiring may alleviate this problem. It has been observed that wiring can occupy more than half of the chip area. As the device size becomes smaller, the wiring space would dominate the space needed for the devices by far. A good placement and wiring technique that minimizes the number of wire tracks used is essential for the VLSI chip density, except for highly repetitive structures with regular interconnections such as PLA chips, memory chips, or arrays of identical processing elements. Placement of components and wiring of interconnections between them are conventionally carried out in successive phases for computational convenience. In the "custom" approach which occupies one end of the VLSI design spectrum, the process of physical design also determines the final dimensions of the chip. It is desirable in this case to closely couple the process of positioning the components on the chip with the routes of the interconnecting wires. Often, in order to reduce the number of parameters involved in the optimization process, the positions of the active area of devices and service terminals are fixed before the routing is done. On the other end of the spectrum is the "master-slice" approach where the size of the chip is fixed, components occupy prespecified positions, and wires are limited to predefined tracks. In such cases, not much is sacrificed by separating the processes of placement and routing, provided appropriate wireability measures are considered during the placement. In discussing the wire routing process in this paper we will assume that the precise physical locations of the points to be interconnected are known.

Consider a master-slice chip as shown in Fig. 1. The number of horizontal and vertical tracks associated with a gate/circuit cell is fixed by the chip designer guided by some theoretical analysis of wire demands [1]–[3]. For a given size of chip area, the more the components, the less the available area for wiring. It has been observed that in designing these master-slice chips the channel demands are generally underestimated, at least in certain areas of the chip. This puts a strain on the physical design automation programs especially when the logic designer expects to use most of the active devices on the chip. It is not unusual then to find systems which specify that only a certain fraction (between 50 and 90 percent) of the active devices on the chip should be used by the logic designer. It is also not unusual that a small fraction of connections remain unconnected, as *overflow wires*, by the automatic wiring programs for LSI chips. The overflow connections are then manually routed by rerouting some of the existing wires if necessary, which may take days, weeks, and sometimes months.

Reprinted from *Proc. IEEE*, vol. 71, pp. 57–65, Jan. 1983.

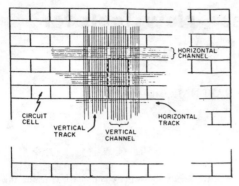

Fig. 1. A typical master-slice chip.

Fig. 2. The waves of forward propagation.

If the current wire routing programs were employed for complex VLSI chips, the hours of computation that it would require would be intolerable. Furthermore, the percentage of overflows is not likely to decrease. Even 1 percent of interconnections for a ten thousand gate chip amounts to hundreds of wires. Manual embedding of even a single wire segment becomes progressively more difficult as the chip size gets denser and larger. Therefore, what is required for VLSI chip wiring is a new technique that is both fast and reduces, or preferably eliminates, overflows.

There are two approaches to meet this challenge. One is to develop better serial algorithms to run on bigger and faster conventional mainframe computers. The other is to construct a parallel processing machine with effective parallel algorithms. The latter seems more promising on two accounts. 1) The complexity of serial computation is too high even for the fast new mainframes. 2) The economy of VLSI chips, especially that of microprocessors, makes it cost effective to build a large parallel machine.

Before we discuss these special-purpose machines, let us examine some of the characteristics of wire routing problems in more detail in the next section. We refer to Soukup [4] for a comprehensive overview of current practices in VLSI physical design in general.

II. THE WIRE ROUTING PROBLEM

The signal lines in the schematic diagram of a logic network are now to be embedded as connected wires along the given wire tracks on the chip. (Many of the concepts to be discussed apply not only to chips but also to higher levels of packaging like cards and boards.) The grid of wire tracks in a chip contains numerous blockages due to internal wiring of the components (component personalization). Wires of different nets obviously cannot occupy the same wiring space. Further, technology rules often limit the position of vias adjacent to one another or even the routing of wires on adjacent tracks in certain directions. These restrictions transform the wire routing problem to an allocation problem with limited track resources and complex constraints. The quality of routing is measured primarily by the overflow count. Secondary considerations include the total wire length, the number of vias used, and the maximum length of a net.

An important and often employed simplification is to find a shortest wiring path on the rectilinear grid between two given points. The length of a shortest path may be and often is

longer than the rectilinear distance between the two points because of blockages. The basic technique by Moore [5] and Lee [6], commonly referred to as the Lee–Moore (LM) algorithm can be informally stated as follows. For simplicity of argument we take a single wiring plane. The technique can be adapted easily to situations where multiple planes are involved. Let one of the points be called the source and the other the sink. We make use of two lists of nodes called OLD and NEW and two status markers per node for recording whether the node has been visited, and if so from which direction.

Lee–Moore Algorithm

LM1) Initialization:
    Mark source node as visited
    OLD ← source node.

LM2) Propagation: Starting with empty NEW list
    For each node in the OLD:
        new ← the neighbor nodes of the current node that are not visited and not blocked.
        Mark *new* nodes as visited and the direction visited from.
        If sink ∈ NEW, go to LM3, else append *new* to NEW
        Let OLD ← NEW (if NEW is empty, the path does not exist, i.e., an overflow)
        GO to LM2).

LM3) Backtrace: Starting from the sink node, follow the directions noted on the nodes to the source node.

This description of the shortest path finding algorithm is not unique and many variations of the above have been implemented. The important aspects are as follows: 1) the propagation step, LM2, is iterated p times where p is the shortest path length, and 2) the time taken for the backtrace step, LM3, is linear in the length p, but processing at each step during the backtrace is much simpler than that during the propagation.

During the propagation iteration, nodes are processed in a wave-like fashion where each NEW list represents a fresh wavefront. When there are no blockages, each node within the diamond shaped area with rectilinear radius p must be processed once for propagation. Fig. 2 shows the nodes labeled by the numbered iteration of the propagation step, LM2, from a given source, assuming no blockages. The wire length p is easily identified as the total number of times LM2 is invoked.

The number of nodes within the diamond area of radius p is asymptotically $2p^2$ and hence a serial computer takes computation time that grows as the square of p. Of course, if the chip is known to have no blockages, a greedy progression from source to sink would take just $p = q$ steps where q denotes the rectilinear distance between the two points. A routing tech-

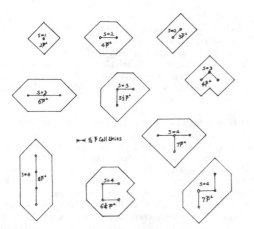

Fig. 3. Examples of sources that are wire segments and their forward propagation areas.

nique based on this greedy approach, called the line probe technique, performs well when wire routes are not constrained by existing blockages or by wires already routed on the chip.

Many techniques [7]-[11] have been developed to reduce the number of nodes processed in finding a path, of which the line probe technique is just one example. Reduction is often accomplished by expanding only within the minimum rectangle area[1] or by target directed depth first expansion. While these techniques tend to reduce the average processing time, the worst case computational complexity remains $O(p^2)$.

The basic Lee–Moore algorithm can be extended to find a shortest path between one piece of wire to another simply by marking initially all nodes representing one wire as sources and all nodes of the other as sinks. The propagation waves in this case emanate from the entire length of the source wire. Suppose a wire source contains s of the t terminals in a net already connected. Assume, for simplicity, that all connections are of length $p = \overline{p}$. The total area within distance $\overline{p}$ of such a wire of length $(s-1)\overline{p}$ ranges between $(s/2)\overline{p}^2$ to $2s\overline{p}^2$ depending on the wire configuration. Fig. 3 shows some of the configurations and the corresponding areas. It can be seen that if one uses the method of wiring a t terminal net by wiring to one additional terminal at a time from a partially connected wire [7], the total serial time complexity becomes $O(t\overline{p})^2$. The same can be accomplished in $O(t\overline{p})$ time using a parallel machine.

Consider a mesh connected complex of simple processing elements, one per track intersection of the chip being wired. Suppose each processing element can perform the following basic operations (among some other equally simple operations) in parallel:

[1] Minimum rectangle refers to the smallest rectangle enclosing the given nodes. Given two points distance q apart, it can be enclosed in minimum rectangle of size $a \times b$ where $q = a + b$. If propagation is restricted to this area, the average number of nodes processed would be asymptotically

$$\frac{1}{q}\sum_{a=0}^{q} a(q-a) = (q^2 - 1)/6 \approx \frac{1}{6}q^2$$

in contrast to $2q^2$ of the full diamond area. However, in the presence of blockages, a path may not be found inside the area or the path found may not be of the shortest length.

Parallel Lee–Moore Algorithm (Kernel of Propagation)

PLM1) Receive wavefront tokens from neighbors, if any.
PLM2) Ignore the token if blocked or already visited.
PLM3) Mark itself visited and mark the direction from where the token was received.
PLM4) If sink node, signal halt, else send wavefront tokens to all four neighbors simultaneously.

Clearly, all nodes on the wavefront (the entire LM2 invocation) during the propagation can be processed in parallel. This is true whether the source is a single point or a piece of wire. The parallel propagation time is the same as the path length p. The Breuer and Shamsa's L-machine [12] designed at the University of Southern California and the SAM machine proposed by Blank, Stefik, and van Cleemput [13] at the Stanford University both implement the parallel Lee–Moore algorithm in efficient hardware. These machines will be discussed in more detail later on.

Let us now return to the wire routing problem with all the constraints mentioned before. It cannot be solved by a series of path finding steps alone. One approach is to judiciously employ a fast path finding machine as a subroutine in conjunction with a more sophisticated routing technique using a conventional computer as the main processor. Another approach is to route each wire more carefully with due considerations from the beginning to the wire congestions on the chip. That is, when a path is to be found, the goal is not an arbitrary shortest path, but the path with the best cost among all acceptable paths. Here the cost may include an estimate of the congestion, number of available wire tracks in the local area, the length, etc. Other heuristic measures that help steer the path to the "right" one in the overall wire allocation task can also be utilized. Because the cost measures are of heuristic nature, it may be necessary to have rip-and-rerouting feature in any VLSI automatic routing schemes to get rid of overflows. The Lee–Moore algorithm addresses a special case of minimum cost path finding: namely, uniform cost per unit length over the whole area. The algorithm employs a breadth-first search technique which is efficient for uniform costs. (The labels of nodes in Fig. 2 also represent the partial path cost from the source.) Akers [7] presented a modified algorithm that finds the minimum cost path in rectilinear geometry with arbitrary nonnegative cost distribution. His algorithm is a mixture of breadth-first and depth-first search where the propagation initially spreads out like the Lee–Moore algorithm until the sink is reached. The propagation then continues only if some partial path cost is less than the current best cost seen at the sink node. The serial complexity of this scheme again remains the square of the path length. The path length for this case is usually longer than the shortest path length p which, in turn, is greater than or equal to the distance between the two points.

The best cost path algorithm requires much more complex processing per node. Besides, it is extremely difficult to compute a reasonable cost function for track-to-track fine resolution. An effective strategy is to attack the problem in two phases: divide the chip into an array of cells, where each cell contains a reasonable number of horizontal and vertical wiring tracks. During the first phase, routes are determined in cell resolution, this operation is called *global wiring* [14], [15], or *loose wiring* [16]. The number of wiring tracks at the boundary between two adjacent cells is called the channel capacity. Global wiring ensures that all wires are routed without violating the channel capacities of the cells. The second phase deter-

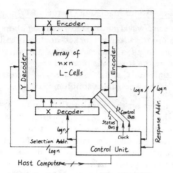

Fig. 4. An overview of the L-machine.

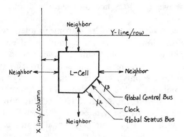

Fig. 5. I/O signals of an L-Cell.

mines the fine track routes within the global route. This is called *exact embedding*. This division into cells comes naturally in the case of master-slice chips. Similar to the machines alluded to earlier, a mesh connected structure of more general-purpose processing elements (microprocessors), one per cell of the chip being wired, can be employed to carry out these two phases efficiently. The Wire Routing Machine (WRM) [17] and associated wiring algorithms being developed at IBM Thomas J. Watson Research Center is aimed at this and other broader applications.

III. THE L-MACHINE

Breuer and Shamsa's L-machine [12] is the first published design of this nature. The L-machine consists of a control unit that communicates with a host computer and sequences the operations of an array of simple processing elements, called L-Cells (see Figs. 4 and 5). This is expressly designed to implement the parallel Lee–Moore (PLM) algorithm. The L-Cells are simple (about 75 gates) and hence many of them can be laid out on a VLSI chip to form a subarray. The machine is capable of performing the following tasks:

1) Initialization: This involves the loading of source, sink, and blockages information into the L-Cells.

2) Parallel Propagation: This essentially implements the PLM described earlier. In addition a BUSY-status signal is raised by those L-Cells which are active during a step of processing the wavefront. The controller receives the wired-OR of BUSY signals from all the L-Cells. Thus the BUSY signal is high as long as some cell is active. If the controller sees the BUSY signal go down before the sink is reached, an overflow is indicated.

3) Backtrace: This process determines the wire path by following the stored direction flags from an activated sink back to the source. The X, Y coordinates of each node on the path of the wire are output by the machine.

4) Clear: Cells along the backtraced wire path are marked as blockages for subsequent wire routing. The internal status of all other L-Cells is cleared to an idle state.

Each L-Cell communicates with its four neighbors through bidirectional lines, one per neighbor. These lines are used during the propagation and the backtrace. In addition there are 7 more signal I/O's and a clock input line per cell:

a) Global Broadcast Bus (3 bits of control signals) from the control unit to all cells in the array.

b) Global Status Bus (2 bits) from all cells to the control unit in wired-OR lines.

c) X and Y (1 bit each) Select/Response wired-OR bidirectional lines along each column and each row of L-Cells.

The control signal lines are used to sequence the loading of blockage, source and sink status (in conjunction with X, Y selection), the forward propagation, the backtrace, and clearing operations. The two status bits inform the control unit of the busy status of the wavefront, whether the sink is reached during the propagation phase, and whether the source is reached during the backtrace phase. The X and Y select/response lines are used for communicating the cell addresses between the control unit and the array. The control unit selects a specific L-Cell, through the X and Y addresses of the cell. These addresses are decoded by X and Y decoders, the outputs of which activate the appropriate column and row signal lines. When an L-Cell raises its X and Y lines the column and row encoders translate these signals to X and Y addresses for the control unit or for other I/O lines of the system.

The machine is capable of processing an entire wavefront of propagation in one clock cycle. Contrast this with tens of instructions necessary to process just one node of the wavefront for the Lee–Moore algorithm in a conventional serial computer. For two wiring planes, the number of L-Cells double and each L-Cell has five neighbor connection lines. To accommodate the two wiring planes in three dimensions, the authors propose to interweave rows of L-Cells of top and bottom layers in a plane. While the arrangement is perfectly capable of finding a shortest path, the current design can neither accommodate preferred wire directions in the wiring planes nor treat vias as anything other than one unit of length, should such technology constraints exist.

For an $n \times n$ track wiring surface, the wiring array contains n^2 L-Cells each of which contains about 75 gates. The total number of pins of the array including two power pins and the row and column decoder and encoder is $4 \log_2 n + 8$ (this can be reduced to $2 \log_2 n + 8$ if the row and column select/response address signals share one bidirectional bus). Breuer and Shamsa envision using one VLSI chip for the entire array of size ranging from 64×64 (300K gates 32 I/O pins) to 256×256 (5M gates and 40 pins) depending on the available VLSI chip technology. In general, when the problem size is in the range of a VLSI chip or of a large board (say 1024×1024), a single chip array is not realizable. The array must then be partitioned into subarrays, each of which is a VLSI chip. One subarray of size $m \times m$ would have $75m^2$ gates for the L-Cells. Due to their desire to incorporate the decoders and encoders, the authors resort to the following three chip types; a corner chip, a side chip, and a mid-array chip. The corner and side chips realize portions of encoder and decoder structure besides the subarray. The mid-array chip now needs $4m$ neighbor lines, $4m$ X, Y lines plus six global wires.

To reduce the pin counts, Iosupovicz [18] suggests a scheme involving serial transfer of information between subarray boundaries. That is, all neighbor communication between a subarray boundary are serially transmitted by encoding the active cell positions, and then passed on to the next chip which, in turn, serially decodes the correct neighbor cell position on the boundary. A substantial reduction in the chip pin count, as well as a complete modularity of subarray chips is accomplished at the expense of lengthening the operation of the machine. The processing time is still more or less proportional to the length of the path.

The array size of the L-machine must be as large as the wiring surface (twice as large for two-layer wiring). If a large enough machine is built, perhaps all practical problems can be handled. But no problem larger than the physical size of the machine can be processed. The L-Cell processor is compact and very fast. However, it is inflexible and limited to a very narrow field of applications; namely, finding a shortest path between two points.

IV. THE SAM-MACHINE

The machine proposed by Blank, Stefik, and van Cleemput [13] is also aimed at a compact design suitable for subarray packing in a VLSI chip. One main difference between this machine and the L-machine is that this was designed with a somewhat broader range of applications in mind. Examples include most of the bit map oriented spatial processing algorithms such as the Lee–Moore algorithm, image processing algorithm, and many elements of design rules checking. This emphasis is expressed in the name given to the machine as Synchronous Active Memory (SAM) machine. The node processor is called a SAM-Cell. It supports 20 assembly level instructions operating mainly on the data width of 1 bit. Similar bit-oriented parallel computing structures had been proposed earlier by Unger [19] and more recently by Reeves [20] and Duff [21].

A SAM-Cell consists of a local control unit, a 2-bit Boolean logic unit, a multiplexor feeding a 1-bit accumulator, a neighbor masking unit, and 16 1-bit registers, as shown in Fig. 6. A cell is enabled by X and Y selection lines from the array control logic. A global data line, five register address lines, and five control lines also enter the chip from the control logic. The cell communicates to each of its four neighbors through four separate bidirectional lines which are not explicitly shown in the figure. The global data output line connects to a wired-OR bus running through all the SAM-Cells. There is a total of 18 signal I/O lines per cell. The first prototype design used approximately 350 transistors in $900 \times 900 \ \mu m^2$ in NMOS technology.

The SAM-machine operates by the controller broadcasting each instruction which every cell obeys.[2] The program control and storage can be provided either by the host computer or by the SAM system depending on implementation. The SAM array control logic works as an interface between the host and the array.

One of the most powerful SAM instructions is called NEIB, which masks the 5-bit data (4 neighbor input and self data in the accumulator) by the 5-bit address and ORs the result into the accumulator in one clock cycle. This instruction enables a fast implementation of node processing for the Lee–Moore propagation. The authors programmed a variant of propagation labeling technique known as the 1–1–2–2 scheme (see

<hr>

[2] This mode of parallel processing is called the Single Instruction Multiple Data (SIMD). On the other hand, if each processor node follows its own instruction stream, it is called the Multiple Instruction Multiple Data (MIMD) [32].

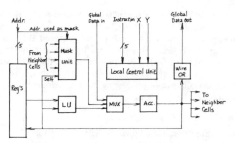

Fig. 6. A SAM-Cell overview.

[7]), where successive wavefronts are labeled 1 twice and 2 twice alternately.

They envision packaging a 16×16 subarray of SAM-Cells on a VLSI chip. To process a 1000×1000 grid wiring, it would require about 4000 such chips in the SAM system. A more cost-effective way of realizing such a large machine is to use a folding technique as proposed by the SAM and as practised with the WRM to be discussed later. In folding, the chip area is divided into the machine size frames and the machine serially processes each frame. In such a scheme, the run time and the memory size of node processors will increase, but the fixed size machine can act as a virtual machine of much larger size, limited only by the node memory capacity. Some of the overhead for this flexibility are

1) optional but worthwhile addition of end-around neighbor connections between the opposing edges of the array;
2) software overhead of managing frame by frame computation;
3) much of the communications may require tags to indicate the frame identification, especially the array boundary cells communicating across the frame boundary to their (folded) neighbors.

The SAM proposal chose to fold actually like an accordion without the end-around neighbor connections. As a consequence, the cells at the boundary of the array have themselves as neighbors across the frame, and the neighborhood directions change to their mirror images between adjacent frames. For the SAM virtual machine design, the SAM-Cells are modified by replacing the accumulator and the registers with 1K and 16K RAM, respectively. This amount of memory would allow the machine to process problems 1000 times larger in size.

The speed advantage of the SAM-machine is illustrated by the following run-time estimate. Unlike the L-machine, it now takes many clock cycles to process one wavefront (hard-wired L-Cell versus assembly level instructions in SAM-Cell). Assuming 300-ns instruction cycle time (100 ns for virtual machine), an estimate is made for routing 1000 two-point nets on a 512×512 grid wiring surface, with average connection length of $\bar{p} = 200$ units. (M refers to the time for initial loading of the problem estimated between 1 and 5 s.)

Machine	Run Time
$1K \times 1K$ full size SAM	$0.4 \ s + M$
32×32 virtual SAM	$15 \ s + M$
Conventional computer	5 h

Although it was not specified in [13] which conventional computer was used for comparison, the contrast is clear. The same example on a more specialized L-machine with the same clock cycle would take only $0.12 s + M$.

Conceptually, the SAM machine can be used for general-purpose applications. However, the limited instruction set, small data width (1 bit), and SIMD operation together restrict the effective range of other applications to bit-map problems arising in certain image processing, bit-vector operations, and simple design rules checking.

V. THE WIRE ROUTING MACHINE (WRM)

The machine described by Hong, Nair, and Shapiro [17] was originally conceived for two-phase wire routing strategy (global wiring and exact embedding). It is also a mesh-connected multiprocessor complex, as the two machines just described. The major difference in the design philosophy between this and the others lies in the power and scope of the node processing element. It is clear that even for the path finding problem alone, the compact L-Cells and SAM-Cells are not flexible enough if there are complex technology constraints on the wire routes. How general and powerful should the node processor be may be a difficult question to answer. Our feeling is that the processing elements must support almost the full range of a general-purpose instruction set and perhaps even some additional special hardware enhancements. The total speed gain of the machine comes not only from the parallelism but also from hardwired instructions for often used kernel operations (for example, NEIB instruction of the SAM-Cell, or even the whole L-Cell mechanism). Each node of WRM requires one or more VLSI chips or even a circuit board for implementation, trading versatility for compactness.

The WRM system consists of three major parts: the *processing array*, the *control processor*, and the *array control unit* that interfaces the array and the control processor. The control processor connects to the host computer, disk units, console, printer, and the array. In the experimental machine at IBM Thomas J. Watson Research Center, the processing elements are implemented using commercial microprocessors. The machine was first constructed in 1979 and has been upgraded in memory and the disk capacity during the past two years.

All communication within the system occur by a memory map mechanism invoked by the microprocessors. All I/O operations and some control operations are performed by accessing special addresses in the memory. The node processors in the array operate in a slave mode to the controller. The controller can select any subset of rows and columns (X, Y selection lines) of node processors and communicate with them. Besides the global I/O ports, the controller has Direct Memory Access (DMA) capability to all node memories, for fast bulk loading, unloading, and broadcasting.

The node processor has a *local neighbor bus* to communicate with neighbors. It has individual *strobe* lines to each neighbor, which latch the local neighbor bus contents to the appropriate neighbor's *receiver latch*. The action of strobing a neighbor also sets his *neighbor flag*. The neighbor's action to read the latch resets the flag. This mail box flag protocol provides for an asynchronous communication. A similar protocol arrangement is made for global port communication. It is envisioned that a more ambitious design would have individual neighbor output ports as well as banks of neighbor input buffers. Fig. 7 shows the I/O ports of the node processor. Global communication is enabled by the X, Y selection mechanism.

An overview of the node processor is shown in the Fig. 8. The local control logic intercepts all memory mapped special

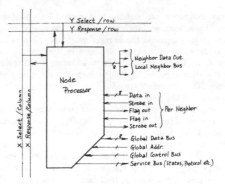

Fig. 7. I/O signals of WRM node processor.

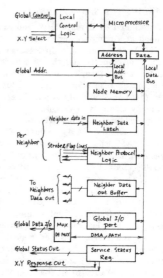

Fig. 8. An overview of WRM node processor.

addresses and controls the local buses, I/O buffers, and the service status register which includes the X, Y reponse bits. The node memory capacity in the current machine, capable of folding operation, is 15K bytes. The whole node processor, except the local memory, can be realized in one VLSI special processor chip.

The machine operates mainly in MIMD fashion, although identical programs are loaded into all the node processors. The node processor programs are sufficiently complex and general so that depending upon the data, the node status, and the node position, each node often processes different program sequences. An SIMD machine would lose the advantage of parallelism in such applications.

During the global wiring process the nets are wired one at a time. For each net, one of the terminals is designated as the initial source, and all the rest of the terminals are designated as sink cells. The WRM finds the optimum cost route from the source to a sink cell within a *deferential detour limit*, that is, the allowed detour length from the shortest possible connection. The connected wire now becomes the source, and the

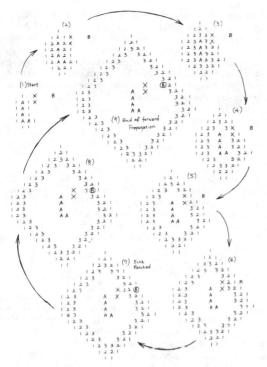

Fig. 9. An example of forward propagation in WRM.

For one net, the complexity is of $O(\overline{tp})^2$ as discussed earlier. The average number $\overline{t}$ of terminals per net is in the range of 2 to 4. The average connection length $\overline{p}$ is a slow growing function of N, the number of circuits, the number of nets, or the size of the chip, all of which are proportional quantities. Feuer derives [23] that $\overline{p}$ is proportional to $N^{1/6}$. Therefore, the serial complexity for N nets would be $O(N^{4/3})$.[3] On the other hand, the parallel processing complexity is $O(N^{7/6})$. The difference here seems small. However, if the detour limit is about the same as $\overline{p}$, the serial complexity increases to $O(N^{3/2})$ while the parallel complexity remains the same. We shall discuss later how the parallel complexity can be reduced even further. Additionally, the simplifying assumption of identical connection length $\overline{p}$ causes an underestimation of the serial complexity, which is not the case for the parallel complexity because each connection takes linear time in p, the actual connection length.

Often the quality of wiring can be improved by iterating on the global wiring already obtained. In some dense examples iteration is a powerful measure to remove overflows. The number of iterations can be a constant so as to not change the complexity of the computation. The need for a high-speed wiring process is more acutely felt when iterative procedures are used.

The exact embedding algorithm currently implemented on the WRM has two major components, *cell boundary assignment* and *cell embedding*. The nets globally routed through the cells are first assigned to exact tracks at all cell boundaries considering the terminal locations and eventual destinations. This process takes $O(N^{1/2})$ time on the WRM, mostly involving sweeping of various information in two orthogonal directions. The remaining task is for each cell to honor the assigned boundary and the internal terminals of the net. This represents a small area (at most about 16 tracks in each direction) wiring problem with small number of internal nets (typically less than 10). During the cell embedding process each node processor wires its own cell in track-to-track resolution considering all the technology restrictions. It is during this cell embedding that the WRM achieves its maximum parallelism, i.e., all node processors are busy.

The degree of restrictions imposed by the technology varies greatly from chip to chip. It is not uncommon to find a masterslice chip that necessitates some representation of restriction status for every track intersection and every track interval. Hence, minimally, the entire length of an embedded wire segment must be examined at every track interval. For an average net of length $(\overline{t}-1)\overline{p}$ cell units, the length is multiplied by the number of tracks per cell in one direction (assuming square cells). The total serial complexity for the exact embedding is then bounded from below by $O(N^{7/6})$. The WRM complexity for the same depends on the serial time taken by a node processor to do the cell embedding. The number of nets that has to be internally wired is of the order $\overline{p}$, estimated roughly by dividing the total net length in cell units, $N(\overline{t}-1)\overline{p}$, by the total number cells, N. We conclude that the parallel com-

process repeats. Each time, a connection is made to the lowest score sink cell that is within the detour limit D from the nearest one. Similar to the Lee–Moore process, a connection is established by forward propagation and backtrace. The propagation of partial path costs emanate out from the source in a wave fashion. This forward propagation differs from that of simple Lee–Moore in that the active nodes are not just the thin wavefronts but a band of cells of width D. The computation that is required for each node in the active propagation zone is quite a bit more complex also (see [22] for details).

The advantage of parallel processing in the WRM can be illustrated by the following small example. Fig. 9 shows the forward propagation at each time step of parallel operation. The numbers in the cells denote the number of times the cell was processed for the detour limit of 2. In the example, a source cell is denoted by A a sink cell by B, and a cell having no wiring tracks at the boundary by X. The shortest connection length between A and B is 7 cell units. For the given detour limit of 2, the parallel forward propagation takes nine steps as shown in the figure. However, the total number of nodes processed during these nine steps sums up to 602, which will be the number of steps required for a serial processor. The speed advantage is even higher for a large detour limit or for a larger body of source wire segment.

Let us now consider the computational complexity of the global process. For simplicity, assume that all connections made are of the same length $\overline{p}$ and that all nets have the same number of terminals $\overline{t}$. Furthermore, assume that the detour limit is given as 0, that is, the forward propagation proceeds as in the Lee–Moore case except with more involved node processing.

[3] $O(N^{4/3})$ is higher than some empirical complexities obtained from experiences on wiring programs run on conventional machines. For instance, Feuer *et al.* [24] reports $O(N^{1.1})$ for combined global and exact embedding. The algorithm they use does not seek the best cost route during global phase as does the algorithm used in the WRM. The serial algorithm uses many techniques to reduce the average computation and the result of wiring may not necessarily be inferior to the exhaustive method used in the parallel WRM algorithm. The $O(N^{4/3})$ would result if the serial computer is to do exactly all the computations done by the parallel algorithm.

plexity is bounded from below by $O(N^{1/6})$. This ignores the boundary assignment complexity of $O(N^{1/2})$, as the multiplicative constant is negligible compared to that of cell embedding even for the numbers (N) involved in VLSI range. Similarly, $O(N)$ process of problem loading is ignored. We also ignored the fact that the number of tracks per cell is a function of chip size for the simplicity of arguments (see [1]–[3]).

The experimental WRM has an array size of 8 × 8. The memory size of 15K bytes per node is adequate to process wire routing for a chip of 24 × 24 cells, making use of the folding technique. The array has end-around neighbor connections in both directions for a convenient program implementation of the folding. (Recall the accordion folding of SAM virtual machine without the end-around connections.) The speed penalty due to folding will not be discussed in much detail here. Briefly, for any foreseeable VLSI chip, if the size of the array, $m \times m$, is about 32 × 32, the time penalty during global wiring is about a factor of 2 over a full size machine. For the exact embedding process, full parallelism penalty of $(n/m)^2$ would incur to process for a chip size $n \times n$ cells. In general, the machine size can be smaller with increased folding, but the processing time would increase, while the total memory capacity of the system would stay constant, that is, the amount of memory per node would have to increase. We feel that the most cost-effective system would have $16 \leqslant m \leqslant 32$.

The main purpose of the experimental machine was to develop efficient parallel wiring algorithms. Performance was not the design objective. The microprocessors used in the machine have 8-bit operands and 250-ns cycle time, the fastest instructions taking 1 μs. Today's technology provides much more powerful microprocessors with 16-bit operands and faster cycle times. Additional hardware features to implement special instructions (such as 4-port compare or NEIB-like operations), and to facilitate neighbor communications, would also contribute to the speedup. It is expected that a production machine with a reasonable array size would improve the speed relative to our experimental system by a factor of 50 or more.

The global wiring experiments performed on 19 × 23 cell chip examples ($n \approx 400$, folded nine times on the experimental 8 × 8 machine) took about 1 min of CPU time. An almost identical algorithm was programmed in PL/1 and run on IBM 3033. The run time was about 45 s. Considering the order of computation time involved, the projected speed advantage at the VLSI range ($N \approx 10\,000$) is significant, though not so dramatic as simple Lee–Moore processors for path finding applications.

The global wiring algorithm of WRM uses the parallel speed advantage to compute a more elaborate cost function for the routes as mentioned earlier (see [22] for details). The WRM computation for each node during the forward propagation is more involved than that performed by existing global wiring programs for serial machines. The objective here is to reduce the overflows. Experimental results are encouraging in that more uniform wiring track usage have been observed and fewer overflows have resulted.

Let us return to the complexity of parallel global wiring. Wiring one net at a time, the computational complexity is of $O(N^{7/6})$. It is indeed possible to wire more than one net at a time provided the propagation areas of the nets do not overlap. Suppose all the terminals of a net are enclosed within a minimum rectangle which, for the sake of simplicity, is assumed to be of size $l \times l$. The propagation activity for the entire net would be confined to within $(D + l) \times (D + l)$ area where D is the detour limit. The side l is proportional to the average connection length $\bar{p}$ which, in turn, is proportional to $N^{1/6}$. Therefore, the propagation activity of the net requires an area proportional to $N^{1/3}$. If the machine size is $m \times m$ and $m \gg \bar{p}$, we may assure that some number of nets, proportional to $m^2/N^{1/3}$ can be simultaneously wired on the machine with only a small probability of overlap in their propagation areas. The controller can schedule groups of nets in such a fashion using a heuristic packing algorithm. If the machine size matches the chip size, $n \times n = N$ and $n \gg \bar{p}$, some number of nets proportional to $N^{2/3}$ can be wired simultaneously. Of course, there is a programming overhead as well as a performance overhead in implementing such a scheme. It is also true that packing of the nets into such groups may not be efficient. However, one can argue that the complexity of global wiring in this manner has to be at most linear in N for the range of VLSI. Taken together with exact embedding complexity, we see that the total WRM routing with simultaneous global wiring would take time at most linear to the size of the chip N. Similar simultaneous path finding tasks can be implemented on a full size L-machine or a SAM-machine.

VI. SUMMARY AND DISCUSSIONS

We have examined the complexity of various wire routing stages. It is shown that special-purpose machines with a rectangular array of mesh connected processors can significantly reduce the wire routing time. These machines range from the highly specialized L-machine, and slightly more general SAM-machine to the WRM designed with fully general microprocessors in the array. These machines can be constructed using today's VLSI parts at a fraction of cost that a mainframe computer would require. These machines gain speed over a conventional machine by special-purpose hardware and by use of parallel computation. High-speed wire routing in VLSI would allow fast feedback to the designers and even enable the designer to interactively improve the design through a series of applications.

The WRM has been discussed in greater detail than the others because it is more general and it addresses the total wire routing problem. Although, master-slice chip wiring is obviously a natural application for WRM, the machine could also route wires on any carrier that has regular wiring tracks and placed net terminals.

Parallel processing machines are organized for many different levels of generality. On the one end, there are general-purpose machines with general-purpose interconnection schemes. On the other end, there are machines with highly specialized simple processing elements that are packed in one (or more) VLSI chip, such as the L-machine or the systolic processors [25]. The WRM and the SAM-machine lie somewhere in between these two ends of the spectrum. So are many two-dimensional array machines designed originally for other applications such as BAP [20], CLIP4 [21], ILLIAC IV [26], DAP [27], MPP [28], FEM [29], CHiP [30], and WISPAC [31]. Most of these machines could be programmed for wire routing and other physical design algorithm, with varying degrees of effectiveness. Problems that require two-dimensional processing, in general, benefit from the obvious match with machine structure. Image processing, matrix operations, and structural analysis of surfaces are examples of such problems. So are specific physical design automation problems in routing, placement, shape generation and checking, timing analysis, chip simulation, rules checking, etc.

Analyses and experiments to date point to practical usefulness of wire routing machines. Whether there should be many machines each of which specializes in some aspect of VLSI physical design automation, or a "consensus" machine that can be used for most of the critical computational needs is an emerging question. For the complexities involved in VLSI physical design, it is clear that some form of parallel processing tool will come to be used. Much of the issues concerning data width, instruction capability, neighbor communication mechanism, MIMD/SIMD, and local memory organization need further research and development. There is also the exciting area of parallel algorithm development for problems solved by such machines.

ACKNOWLEDGMENT

The authors gratefully acknowledge the leadership and encouragement given them by E. Shapiro during the course of WRM development. They also thank H. M. Brauer, M. Denneau, S. Liles, and R. Villani for the invaluable contributions to the design and development of the machine and programs. Finally, they wish to thank M. Dietrich for the typing of this manuscript.

REFERENCES

[1] W. R. Heller, W. F. Mikhail, and W. E. Donath, "Prediction of wiring space requirements for LSI," *J. Design Automation and Fault Tolerant Computing*, pp. 117–144, 1978.
[2] W. E. Donath and W. F. Mikhail, "Wiring space estimation for rectangular gate array," in *VLSI 81 Conf. Proc.*, J. P. Gray, Ed. New York: Academic Press, 1981.
[3] A. ElGamal, "Two-dimensional stochastic model for interconnections in master-slice integrated circuits," *IEEE Trans. Circuits Syst.*, vol. CAS-28, pp. 127–138, Feb. 1981.
[4] J. Soukup, "Circuit layout," *Proc. IEEE*, vol. 69, no. 10, pp. 1281–1304, Oct. 1981.
[5] E. F. Moore, "Shortest path through a maze," in *Annals of Computation Laboratory*, vol. 30. Cambridge, MA: Harvard Univ. Press, 1959, pp. 285–292.
[6] C. Y. Lee, "An algorithm for path connections and its applications," *IRE Trans. Elec. Comput.*, vol. EC-10, pp. 346–365, Sept. 1961.
[7] S. Akers, "Routing," in *Design Automation of Digital Systems: Theory and Techniques*, vol. 1, M. A. Breuer, Ed. Englewood Cliffs, NJ: Prentice Hall, ch. 6, pp. 283–333, 1972.
[8] F. Rubin, "The Lee path connection algorithm," *IEEE Trans. Comput.*, vol. C-23, no. 9, pp. 907–914, Sept. 1974.
[9] S. Akers, "A modification of Lee's path connection algorithm," *IEEE Trans. Elec. Comput.*, vol. EC-16, pp. 97–98, Sept. 1967.
[10] J. Soukup, "Fast maze router," in *Proc. 15th Design Automation Conf.* (Las Vegas, NV, 1978), pp. 100–101.
[11] J. Soukup and U. W. Stockburger, "Routing in theory and practice," in *Proc. 1st Annual Conf. on Computer Graphics in CAD/CAM Systems* (MIT, Apr. 1979), pp. 126–146.
[12] M. A. Breuer and K. Shamsa, "A hardware router," *J. Digital Syst.*, vol. 4, no. 4, Computer Sci. Press, 1980, pp. 393–408.
[13] T. Blank, M. Stefik, and W. van Cleemput, "A parallel bit map processor architecture for DA algorithms," in *Proc. 18th Design Automation Conf.* (Nashville, TN, 1981), pp. 837–845.
[14] K. A. Chen, M. Feuer, K. H. Khokhani, N. Nan, and S. Schmidt, "The chip layout problem: An automatic wiring procedure," in *Proc. 14th Design Automation Conf.* (New Orleans, LA, 1977), pp. 298–302.
[15] H. Shiraishi, and F. Hirose, "Efficient placement and routing technique for master-slice LSI," in *Proc. 17th Design Automation Conf.* (Minneapolis, MN, 1980), pp. 458–464.
[16] J. Soukup and J. C. Royle, "On hierarchical routing," *J. Digital Syst.*, vol. V, no. 3, Computer Sci. Press, 1981, pp. 265–289.
[17] S. J. Hong, R. Nair, and E. Shapiro, "A physical design machine," in *VLSI 81 Conf. Proc.*, J. P. Gray, Ed. New York: Academic Press, 1981.
[18] A. Iosupovicz, "Design of an iterative array maze router," in *Proc. IEEE Int. Conf. on Circuits and Computers*, pp. 908–911, Oct. 1980.
[19] S. H. Unger, "A computer oriented toward spatial problems," *Proc. IRE*, pp. 1744–1750, Oct. 1958.
[20] A. P. Reeves, "A systematically designed binary array processor," *IEEE Trans. Comput.*, vol. C-29, pp. 278–287, Apr. 1980.
[21] M.J.B. Duff, "CLIP 4: A large scale integrated circuit array parallel processor," in *Proc. Pattern Recognition and Image Processing Conf.*, pp. 728–733, Nov. 1978.
[22] R. Nair, S. J. Hong, S. Liles, and R. Villani, "Global wiring on a wire routing machine," presented at the 19th Design Automation Conf., Las Vegas, NV, 1982.
[23] M. Feuer, "Connectivity of random logic," *IEEE Trans. Comput.*, vol. C-31, no. 1, Jan. 1982.
[24] M. Feuer, K. H. Khokhani, and D. Mehta, "Computer-aided design wires 5000-circuit chip," *Electronics*, pp. 144–145, Oct. 9, 1980.
[25] H. T. Kung, "The systolic (VLSI) system: A powerful computing engine," presented at the ICASE Workshop Array Architecture for Computing in the 80's and 90's, Hampton, VA, 1980.
[26] G. H. Barnes *et al.*, "The Illiac IV computer," *IEEE Trans. Comput.*, vol. C-17, pp. 746–757, Aug. 1968.
[27] S. F. Reddaway, "DAP architecture and algorithms," presented at the ICASE Workshop Array Architectures for Computing in the 80's and 90's, Hampton, VA, 1980.
[28] C. Michelson, "MPP architecture and system software," presented at the ICASE Workshop Array Architectures for Computing in the 80's and 90's, Hampton, VA, 1980.
[29] D. Loendorf, "The finite element machine: an array of asynchronous microprocessors," presented at the ICASE Workshop Array Architectures for Computing in the 80's and 90's, Hampton, VA, 1980.
[30] L. Snyder, "Overview of the CHiP Computer," in *Proc. VLSI 81 Conference*, J. P. Gray, Ed. New York: Academic Press, 1981.
[31] M. J. Redmond and S. D. Smith, "Permutation function simulation on the Wisconsin parallel array computer (WISPAC)," presented at the ICASE Workshop Array Architectures for Computing in the 80's and 90's, Hampton, VA, 1980.
[32] M. J. Flynn, "Some computer organizations and their effectiveness," *IEEE Trans. Comput.*, vol. C-21, no. 9, pp. 948–960, Sept. 1972.

Hierarchical Design Methodologies and Tools for VLSI Chips

C. NIESSEN

Invited Paper

Abstract—Hierarchical design methods are considered to be a means of managing the VLSI design problem. This paper will consider why this problem exists and discuss alternative means that can be used to arrive at a solution. The merits of design methodologies, with emphasis on hierarchical techniques, will be compared with those of automated design approaches. The discussion of hierarchy will lead to the conclusion that the method requires formal abstraction facilities in order to be effective. Hierarchical design methods permit the creation of a new generation of CAD programs that can both give a designer better support and can be much more efficient than the present generation of tools. An example of such a tool, VOILA, will be given.

I. INTRODUCTION

HIERARCHICAL design methods are considered as a means of managing the VLSI design problem. Remarkably, the discussion on such a methodology mainly happens in the CAD environment and less among chip designers. In discussing the method of hierarchical design it is necessary to examine the nature of the IC design problem and to compare this method with alternative ones. As we do so it becomes more obvious that the discussion of design methods originated in the CAD domain, because the underlying complexity of the problem can be perceived more readily there.

Today's design problem is caused by the ever-increasing ability of technologists to integrate more components in a single integrated circuit. The maximum number of components in a chip has on average doubled annually for almost two decades [1]. The maximum number of components is at present in excess of 100 000. An analysis of technological possibilities and limitations [2] leads to predictions of future densities that may well be two orders of magnitude greater. Despite this technological potential, present circuits, with the exception of memories and other very regular circuits, contain a significantly smaller number of components. This has been caused by, *inter alia*, the increased difficulty of designing such complex circuits.

The exponential growth of IC complexity has had a dramatic impact on the time needed to design a circuit. It has increased exponentially from a few weeks for small-scale integrated circuits (SSI) to tens of man-years for large-scale circuits. Simple extrapolations [3] would yield future design times in the order of thousands of man-years. Obviously this cannot take place, it demonstrates, however, that continued use of current design procedures will be a barrier to growth of IC complexity in the future. The progress in circuit integration, again with the exception of memories and very regular structures, will no

Manuscript received May 17, 1982; revised October 18, 1982.
The author is with the Philips Research Laboratories, Eindhoven, The Netherlands.

longer be limited only by technology, but also, and to a much greater extent, by our design capability [1].

Today's design methods, which emerged in the SSI and MSI period, apparently need adaptation. In the early days of IC design, almost unlimited freedom was required in order to achieve the best possible results. The limited technological possibilities were the prime justification for this attitude, while the restricted design problem allowed for this. That freedom is now the main cause of the increase in design time. The justification for that freedom has, however, disappeared. The sheer fact that our design capability is going to impede progress, means that we have to explore methods to enhance designer productivity. The purpose of such methods is a drastic reduction of the number of detailed design decisions to be taken by a designer. The products made using these methods will inevitably be less optimal than those designed with all possible freedom. It appears that many designers are reluctant to realize that some trade-in of design efficiency may well yield a decrease of the sum of design plus production cost, thus opposition has to be anticipated. Yet one has to head for that opposition. The former controversy between synchronous and asynchronous logic may serve as an example. Asynchronous logic, because of its freedom in timing, utilizes the time domain inherently better than synchronous logic. For some time synchronous logic has been banned from IC's. Nevertheless, the difficulty of designing and debugging large asynchronous circuits has finally led to acceptance of the concept of synchronous logic.

For a long time now automation has been explored as a means to enhance design productivity. Although a massive amount of work has been and is still being done on the subject and although some of the results are impressive, the degree of acceptance is on the whole disappointing. Automated design produces results that are inferior in most cases to manual designs [4]. Still more unfortunately, the quality of the result deteriorates as the size of the problem increases. This might be a "contra indication" for its use in VLSI. Be that as it may, one of the aims of this paper is to indicate a feasible position for automation in a superimposed design architecture.

Another alternative for improving designer productivity is the exploration of various design architectures. Although it has to be admitted that this subject is still an area of research from which significant results are to be expected, it is already widely accepted that hierarchical design techniques must be a cornerstone for a VLSI design methodology.

In this paper we shall try to find the most important deficiencies of current design methods and the associated CAD

Reprinted from *Proc. IEEE*, vol. 71, pp. 66–75, Jan. 1983.

tools. On that basis we shall formulate concepts that should be included in a VLSI design environment. We shall then depict a VLSI design method that adheres to such concepts and sketch a hierarchical CAD system that supports that method. Finally, we shall present some details of VOILA, a hierarchical CAD system, which we are currently implementing.

II. Present-Day IC Design Methods

A designer who has to create a function by means of discrete components on a printed-circuit board is confronted with many constraints. As a general rule, he cannot define the components to be used, but can merely select them from a standard catalog. Only in rare cases will he find components with precisely the specifications he needs; normally, he has to be content with components that approach without exactly satisfying his specifications. Similarly, he is confronted with limitations regarding the printed-circuit board. All such boundary conditions lead to less perfect results than those obtained with components specially designed for the needs of that application. These limitations are, of course, not created to tease the designer. They are necessary when a catalog of standard components is compiled, with a manufacturing infrastructure for general use in mind. Against this disadvantage there is an obvious advantage; namely, that it is almost inconceivable how time-consuming printed-circuit board design would be without such an infrastructure.

Quite in contrast, the pioneers of IC design were equipped with a blank sheet of paper, a ruler, a pencil, and an eraser. The potentials and the unknowns of the new technology demanded unlimited freedom. The results are familiar, astonishing innovations have come about. Currently designers are not standing with empty hands, but their primary tools are still paper, ruler, pencil, and eraser. Design styles have, of course, changed in the meantime, but is that enough?

In the pioneering phase IC design meant making a circuit diagram; a breadboard model was used to predict the ultimate behavior on the chip as accurately as possible. The layout was drawn by hand, CAD was an unknown term. The first breakthrough was the introduction of computer aids for layout design. Layout design was cumbersome and error-prone, even for small circuits. The laborious tasks of the designer were taken over by programs. Important contributions to design methodology date back to that period. The use of computers meant that precise circuit descriptions had to be made available. The ability of the computer to take over much of the boring repetitive work required the development of concepts for the description of regular and repetitive structures. Formal layout description languages satisfying these requirements were evolved. Precise textual design descriptions rather than drawings became the design documents.

Tools for electrical analysis and logical simulation rapidly succeeded each other. Languages were again designed to describe analog and digital circuits accurately. This led to a design procedure which is still typical of most present-day design activities (Fig. 1).

A typical feature of this figure is that the synthesis activity from left to right is performed manually. The task of transforming a required function into a chip by successively adding detail is inherently difficult. Up till now this has best been dealt with by a creative designer. By contrast, the time-consuming and boring task of checking whether a subsequent step in a design is in effect the implementation of the preceding specification cannot be done effectively by a human being.

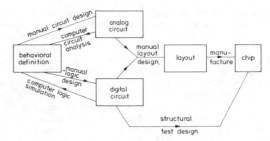

Fig. 1. Traditional IC design procedure.

There have been many examples of design errors overlooked by the designer, while the computer excels in performing the verification task with great accuracy.

As has been mentioned, description languages exist for analog circuits, digital circuits, and layout, but hardly any exist for the behavioral definition. In many cases, such definitions reside only in the designer's mind, or at best are written down in natural language. As a result, the analog and/or digital circuit description is the first document that accurately defines the intended functions. The disadvantages are many. The feedback of accurate design data to customers is delayed considerably. Hence it is difficult to do electrical and logic design as a team and if it is so done, misunderstanding and different interpretations can result.

Despite its disadvantages, the method described has been applied successfully for many circuits. Increasing chip sizes have created a need for additional methodology.

The cumbersome task of designing and verifying asynchronous designs has resulted in the acceptance of synchronism as a means to master complexity, notwithstanding the related disadvantages. The time-consuming nature of layout design activity has led to methods that reduce its complexity. Standard cell approaches and cells in row organizations are examples. These methods have now gained wide acceptance despite some loss of efficiency.

The possibility of shifting parts of the design work to CAD by exploiting the capability of CAD to handle regularity and repetition resulted in a design style which is referred to as "informal hierarchy" [5]. The macro facilities available in many of the IC description languages were used to describe circuits as a collection of modules rather than as a monolithic entity. The underlying thought is, of course, that the repeated design of modules is simpler than the design of one complex circuit. The notion underlying the word "informal" will be explained more thoroughly later. Roughly, it means that designs are broken down into modules, but that rules enabling modules to be designed independently of each other do not exist. The simplification that can be obtained by the use of hierarchical methods is severely diminished by the absence of such rules.

In addition to these approaches aimed at reducing design effort by the introduction of methodological concepts, another approach has been tried whereby design tasks are shifted from the designer to the computer, design automation proper. The main topics of design automation have been automation of the layout task and automatic test pattern generation. Although automatic layout tools have gained some acceptance, there is a disproportionate ratio between the effort spent in creating such tools and their utilization. The resulting products of the automatic programs are large compared to their manually designed counterparts. The difference between the two in fact increases with increasing design size. In the present state of affairs, automatic layout tools are useful only for small volumes and circuit sizes that are not at the far end of the complexity range.

Automatic test pattern generation has led to an even more profound trauma. In contrast to layout automation, which was to provide an alternative for manual layout, automatic test pattern generation had to replace a manual task which had already become impossible. Automatic test pattern generation itself proved to be an unrealistic tool. With excessive computer run times and incomplete sets of tests, IC testing threatened to become an unsolvable problem. It was design methodology that came to the rescue. Scan testing [6], [7] proved to be the method of transforming an unsolvable problem into an easy one. Provided that a designer fulfills a simple set of requirements that makes a circuit scan testable, test pattern generation can be done automatically. In fact, the impact of scan testing is so dramatic that IC testing can almost be considered a mechanistic issue that needs no further attention from the designer.

In summary, present-day design methods have emerged from an initial situation with almost total freedom. The difficulty of designing ever larger circuits has been dealt with by the introduction of some methodological concepts and the application of passive analytical tools. Automated design has until now played a less important role. The best prospects for the future seem to lie in devising methodological concepts which further simplify the design activity.

III. PRESENT POSITION OF IC DESIGN TOOLS

The extremes in IC design are total manual design and fully automated design. Computer aids for design have been developed on the basis of these extremes. One line being followed is the assisting role, the intention of which is to aid the designer in the evaluation of his work and to take over from him the more laborious and dreary routine tasks. This approach is usually referred to as CAD. The other approach attempts to replace human design tasks by computerized counterparts. This latter situation is called design automation, DA. However, quite often the term DA is used when actually CAD is meant. The term DA has been in existence since at least 1964 [8].

There is a significant difference between the two approaches. Manual design assisted by CAD can yield highly optimized results at the cost of long design time. Because of the restrictions imposed by the automatic tools, automated design leads to much less efficient solutions, which are, however, obtained with considerably reduced design effort. In fact, these approaches represent two extremes in a much larger design space. This can be represented graphically as in Fig. 2, in which design cost and circuit cost are related. One can arrange the drawing in a number of areas. There is an area, below the indicated design space, that is inaccessible because a certain minimum effort is required to obtain a desired result. The area above the design space is unattractive because it yields results that are inferior to the state of the art. Within the design space, a variety of design methods can be located. The better methods are, of course, located near the lower left boundary. The design space symbolizes the design limitations, inventions are needed to shift it towards the origin.

In appraising CAD and DA, their purpose and their location in the design space have to be considered. The search for alternatives has also to take into account the design space for variants meeting the requirements of the application. In this

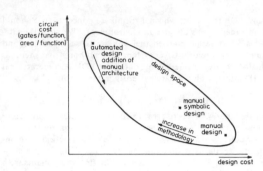

Fig. 2. Design space: acceptable design methods are located within the design space. Cost of design can be substituted for circuit cost.

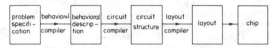

Fig. 3. The ultimate in design automation.

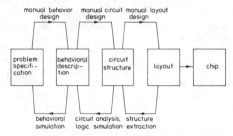

Fig. 4. Manual design with computer aids.

process, it becomes clear that the popular proposal to replace manual design by automated design ignores properties of the problems in hand.

The overall reach of the design process is from problem specification to final realization. Synthesis is both the step-wise refinement of the initial specification towards its realization via a number of intermediate specifications (behavioral definition, circuit structure, layout) and the addition of design detail at each of the intermediate specification stages. Analysis is the verification of a newly created intermediate specification against the preceding one.

If this view is combined with the view of design methods, the resulting extremes are a totally automated design (Fig. 3) and a manual computer-aided design (Fig. 4). The view with regard to design space shows that many intermediate situations are possible.

Similarly to the previously mentioned lack of description languages for problem specification and behavioral description, the set of tools to transform a problem specification into a circuit structure is also meagre. Automation of the transformation from behavioral description to circuit structure is in its infancy and a research topic [9]. Analytical tools for verifying the correct operation of a circuit structure with respect to the original specification are the main achievements. Circuit analysis and gate level logic simulation tools are used extensively. They may be considered as two different tools, but it is much better to regard them simply as two items in a hierarchy of

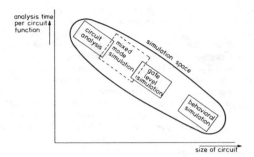

Fig. 5. Simulation space. Simulation tools must be located within the area shown. The area above it is unsuitable because simulation cost becomes excessive. The area below it is unattractive because it gives lower quality result than are essential.

simulation tools. Circuit analysis examines in detail circuits composed of transistors, resistors, etc., limiting it to circuits of modest size. Logic simulation can deal with much larger circuits, because of the abstraction from analog-to-digital circuits. *As will be discussed later, correct abstraction techniques are the key towards hierarchical design techniques.* Abstraction can only be properly applied if certain rigid abstraction rules are given, as in the case of analog-to-digital abstraction. An immediate consequence of the use of abstraction techniques is the need to have facilities to verify that the abstraction rules have been adhered to, for analog-to-digital abstraction simulators of this kind are being made [10].

Although gate-level logic simulators can handle several thousands of gates, the corresponding computer runtime then becomes large. Considerable increases in the number of gates will result in prohibitive run times. Further abstraction is thus unavoidable. This gives rise to the notion of simulation space (Fig. 5), according to which circuit granularity must grow with increasing circuit size in order to keep cost under control.

The majority of tools presently available are for the transformation of a circuit structure into a layout. The tools for assisting manual design are especially well known. Some examples are interactive graphic programs for assisting the designer to enter a layout, design rule checkers, and layout-to-structure checkers. Among the tools for automation are automatic placers and automatic routers. There is much concern at present about the applicability of these programs in the future. The increase in circuit complexity has caused a dramatic increase in the run time of the layout-analysis programs. Automated tools are equally affected in that the compactness of their results, which is not too good for small designs in the first place, degrades further with the increase of problem size. A solution to these problems is not simple. The problems are caused by the intrinsic computational complexity of the tool [11], which is roughly polynominal for analysis and exponential for synthesis tools. Attempts to perform program optimizations which yield decrease in run times by a constant factor have no long-term effect. Such improvements will be consumed rapidly by the growth of the circuits to be designed.

The real problem with design aids is that they deal with layouts as monolithic entities. Solutions are required which support abstraction techniques, similar to the ones mentioned for circuit structure design. Investigations are now in progress which examine whether present design methods can be further exploited to improve CAD performance. The informal hierarchy in particular is receiving much attention, the idea being

to do as much work as possible on lower level modules in a hierarchy of this kind, e.g., by using filtering techniques [12]. The thesis referred to indeed shows that given good organization in a design, significant savings can be obtained. It also shows that the method is very dependent on and sensitive to the quality of the structure presented. With badly structured designs the intended savings aimed at can turn into dramatic increases in computer run times.

It must be concluded that present-day informal design methods are like quicksand, they are too weak a foundation on which to construct a set of VLSI design tools.

IV. CONCEPTS FOR A VLSI DESIGN METHODOLOGY

The goals to be met by a VLSI design methodology are in order of importance:

a) It must provide complexity control such that a reasonable confidence in the correctness of designed circuits is made possible.

b) The method must comprise the whole design traject.

c) An efficient utilization of technological possibilities should be provided.

d) A considerable increase in design productivity should result.

e) It must enable the creation of efficient CAD tools.

From the preceding section on IC design tools it may be concluded that a further automation of the design activity is in conflict with requirements b) and c). Layout design, the main subject of design automation, is just a fairly small portion of the design activity as a whole. The replacement of human creativity by automatic algorithms is an impoverishment of the design process, of which increase of chip area is just one symptom in a larger spectrum of resulting drawbacks. In short, it is questionable whether automated design on VLSI scale is at all feasible.

This brings us back to methodology. Hierarchical design has been already referred to several times in this connection. It is, however, just one method though probably the most important for dealing with complexity. Design methodology is not an established speciality, but has to be subjected to further investigations. At present, the primary concepts are abstraction, repetition, and, perhaps somewhat trivially, the use of past experience.

Abstraction: Abstraction is a method to replace an object by a simplified one that only defines the interactions of the object with its environment, while deleting the internal organization of the object.

The abstraction of analog-to-digital circuits is an example. Such an abstraction is often only valid within certain constraints. A logic gate, for instance, only behaves as a gate when certain load conditions are not exceeded.

The virtue of abstraction is data reduction, sometimes by one or more orders of magnitude. For very large systems, one level of abstraction may not suffice, it has to be applied a number of times in succession, "hierarchical abstraction." A system can thus be considered as being broken down into a number of subsystems, each of which is further broken down into smaller entities, and so on. The building block in such a breakdown is often called a module. Fig. 6 shows a possible representation of a system composed of modules.

The hierarchy, when properly implemented, is the self-evident implementation of the divide and conquer principle. Dividing and conquering itself is a principle that can be applied hierarchically, as is the case in many human organizations. To

221

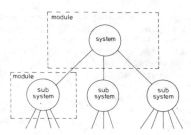

Fig. 6. A hierarchical representation of a system.

do so, concepts are consequently needed for the implementation of both "division" and of "conquering." Division necessitates means to delegate responsibilities, i.e., principles for *communication*. Conquering implies a need to express *local autonomy*. A so-called hierarchical system that does not embody these principles is not a hierarchical system at all. Such a hierarchy is informal, it can provide some intellectual help, but it does not simplify the problem in hand. The main drawback of the informal hierarchy is its lack of rigid abstractions. A hierarchy that does contain these principles will be called a formal hierarchy instead.

Locality of concern is an extremely important attribute of a hierarchical design system. Simplification of the design problem is its predominant virtue. However, it introduces a disadvantage for which a price has to be paid. A module at a higher level in the hierarchy expresses requirements applying to a lower level module in global terms (e.g., as a transfer function $Y = f(x)$). The detailed implementation is a matter for the lower level module. Neighboring modules thus possess only limited knowledge about each other's implementation. It may well happen that certain similar subproblems are solved in adjacent modules. It can also happen that modules are given requirements that cannot be fulfilled within the constraints of the local autonomy. This can be partially overcome by supplying the local module with an oversized set of resources. The disadvantage of the clean hierarchy concept introduces the necessity to make iterations through the hierarchical levels possible. In principle, it is possible to perform so many iterations through a hierarchy that its disadvantage is eliminated; unfortunately, this is achieved at the cost of a complete loss of the simplification provided by the hierarchy. The other extreme is the total absence of iterations. This is pure top-down or pure bottom-up design. The realistic approaches are somewhere in between these extremes.

As such, this reasoning tells us that hierarchical design methods are not restricted to certain problem classes, whether low or high volume, whether custom circuits or whatever. *It does, however, also tell us that a hierarchical CAD tool which prohibits such iterations restricts itself to a limited set of problem classes.*

Repetition: Repetition is an easy and often applied method of simplifying design. It can be used in a regular array type manner (RAM's, ROM's) but also irregularly. Ratios such as the total device count versus the drawn device count give a measure of the use of repetition. This ratio [13] has increased with more recent designs. The concept of hierarchy is of advantage to that of repetition because it provides the module as the atom for repetition.

Use of Past Experience: It is a waste of effort not to use experience gained in previous activities. Stated more concretely

in the context of IC design, it is wasteful to design each chip from scratch rather than to use modules that have been done previously. The advantages are many. The time taken to design a chip is reduced. The risk of errors is reduced because modules copied from previous designs are more likely to be error-free. The disadvantages, too, are worth mentioning. It is difficult to define standard circuits other than the familiar ones. Moreover, such standard circuits probably do not precisely match the requirements of the new application, causing a certain degree of inefficiency. The most important reason not to use standardized modules for IC design is the absence of facilities for precisely defining the interface requirements of the standard module.

Perhaps the concept of formal hierarchy will come to the rescue. It provides the necessary grips for formulating the interface requirements of the standard module. Not improbably, it will have a similar effect on IC design as the dual-in-line package standard has had on printed-circuit board design.

To sum up, the primary concept for a VLSI design methodology must be one that permits design to be done modularly, the formal hierarchy. This concept leads to well-defined interactions between the various modules in a design, yielding simplified design as an advantage and some inefficiency as a disadvantage. It may also be the carrier for a design style which makes use of standardized modules.

Hierarchical design may even provide the infrastructure on which design automation will flourish. Instead of design automation being regarded as a replacement for human design, it might be seen as subordinate to human design. In a hierarchical environment the human being can assume responsibility for design at a high level, i.e., the architecturing tasks, while the computer can undertake design at the lower levels, i.e., the implementation tasks. Experiments in silicon compilation [14] are, in fact, supportive of this idea.

V. The Architecture of a Hierarchical VLSI Design Environment

Scope of Hierarchy

Hierarchical design is often associated with layout design. From the preceding it may be clear that hierarchical concepts also have to be extended to the stage of circuit structure and behavioral definition (Fig. 4), such that every design specification can be created with the aid of abstraction facilities. But even that is not enough. The creation of a new design specification refers back to a previous one, the circuit structure is created with reference to the behavioral definition, and the layout is created with reference to the circuit structure. If during such an activity reference has to be made to hierarchical structures which are different, the complexity issue returns in all its magnitude. The transformation from one hierarchy to another requires an intermediate stage in which the structure is eliminated by expansion, which is undesirable. This drastically broadens the scope and the impact of the hierarchy concept. The same hierarchical breakdown should be present, in principle, throughout the whole design trajectory, although compromises may sometimes be possible and justified. These compromises, however, ought to be of limited scope.

A good example of such a compromise is the organization of standard cells in rows. The distribution of power and clock lines over standard cells makes any other organization very inefficient (Fig. 7).

This means that the layout structure has to be different

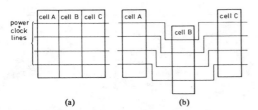

(a)   (b)

Fig. 7. Power and clock distribution may force a layout organization in rows (a), as other arrangements (b) are very inefficient.

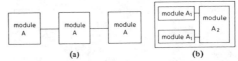

(a)   (b)

Fig. 8. Example of aliasing: a module A used three times in a circuit structure may need different implementations in layout owing to constraints present here. (a) Circuit structure. (b) Layout.

from that present in the circuit structure. However, the applicability of this layout technique has shown to be limited. Beyond a certain complexity, the transformation of a circuit structure into a row-type layout becomes cumbersome, while the area occupied for signal distribution tends to increase disproportionately. In addition, the inefficiency of an irregular power distribution, though significant at the standard cell level, is of less importance at the level of larger modules.

Finally, because modules tend to be distributed over several rows in a layout, alterations that are local at the circuit stage have a more global impact on the layout. This layout technique consequently does not lend itself to redesigns.

Given these limitations of the standard cell approach, it is not a threat to the ambition to have similar hierarchy in circuit structure and layout. A limited discrepancy in hierarchical organization can be easily eliminated via selective expansion.

Similarity of hierarchical structure at the various design specification stages does not come about spontaneously. If the constraints of the other stages are not considered, detailed design at, for example, the behavioral stage may not be implementable at those stage. Since rejection of the considerable work done up to this point seems wasteful, there is only one conclusion which can be drawn; namely, that the hierarchy at the next design stage must be different.

If the constraints at the various design stages had been taken into account simultaneously, however, a uniform hierarchical organization might have been possible. This leads to the conclusion that a hierarchical design environment requires decisions taken at the high level of design to be taken simultaneously at all the specification stages. Floorplanning [15] is becoming the accepted term for denoting this kind of activity. This word, with its geometrical undertones, was first used in the context of layout planning but its meaning is now extending to the circuit and behavioral design stages as well.

The uniformity of hierarchy in the various design phases was so far not used in the proposed rigid form. Although it seems that it is being used more and more as circuit size increases, general acceptance cannot yet be said to exist. The provision of flexibility within the given constraints may well help confidence in the method to become established.

One such provision may be the aliasing concept. When a module has been used several times at a certain design stage, its instances at a subsequent stage may need to be different owing to conditions at that stage. A good example can again be found in layout, where geometrical boundary conditions may oblige one or more module instances to be deformed (Fig. 8).

The design of alternative implementations for a particular

module certainly does increase the design effort. A decision to do so thus must, therefore, be taken carefully. It does not affect the similarity of hierarchy concept as such, its impact being limited to a single module.

The Implementation of "Divide and Conquer"

In the section headed "Concepts for a VLSI Design Methodology" it was stated that a formal hierarchy requires means, so far as implementation of communication is concerned, delegating responsibilities as well as means to express local autonomy. Globally, these concepts must be the same at all design stages in order to allow hierarchies to be mapped. More detailed examination of these aspects will reveal that there are also differences in order to cope with specific aspects.

An important architectural decision is whether these concepts must be the same from top to bottom in a hierarchy or whether there is a need for them to be different. Identity of concept is a useful property as it enables design to be tackled recursively with the same approach.

The recursive concept has an important consequence, namely that the "grammar" for the atom of recursion, in our case the module, can only be defined once. This means that the grammar has to incorporate all the primitives needed for composition.

It is not at all clear yet whether this recursion concept is applicable throughout the IC design trajectory.

We will treat the "divide-and-conquer" subject in the reverse order as design normally proceeds, viz., starting from layout because the concepts there can be more easily identified and visualized. We will not discuss all the primitives needed for design but restrict ourselves to the discussion of such aspects as are of concern to the hierarchical structure.

a) Layout: A layout composed in a hierarchical manner consists of a number of modules which are mutually interconnected with interconnection tracks, often called nets. Every module can, in turn, be broken down in a similar fashion.

The concept of locality must clearly be expressed in terms of area. We will call the area occupied by a module its domain. Rules for the definition of domains can be given with various degrees of refinement. The roughest method is to allocate every module a single rectangular area as its domain. A more subtle method is to associate each mask in the layout with one or more polygons as its domain, permitting more efficient management of silicon area. This approach makes it possible for a module to provide (partially) unused masks for use at the next design level.

The layout of a module has to be designed inside its domain in the usual manner, making use of design rules prescribed by the relevant technology. The concept of locality means that the designer need not bother about details outside a module while the details inside a module are being designed. For that purpose, design rules applying between details in a layout must be replaced by new design rules expressing relations between details and domains. There have to be rules to express rela-

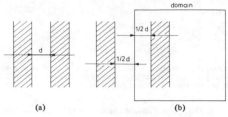

Fig. 9. An example showing how a design rule (minimum distance *d*) between layout details (a) can be expressed as a design rule with respect to domains (b) in hierarchical environment. The latter rules eliminate the need to varify the relations inside and outside a module.

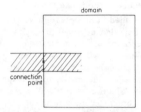

Fig. 10. Communication in a layout hierarchy is effected with the aid of connection points. Details outside and inside a domain are enabled to connect at a connection point.

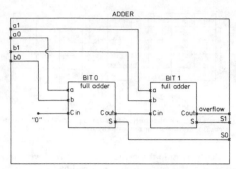

Fig. 11. A circuit structure of a 2-bit adder composed of full adders. Each of the modules, a 2-bit adder and a full adder, has its own domain and signal names.

tionships between details inside a domain and the domain and rules for those between details outside the domain and the domain. The situation obviously becomes simplest when the inside and outside rules are symmetrical (Fig. 9).

A good set of design rules relating to domains makes the application of the normal design rules on details inside and outside the domain superfluous. Hence it also makes any communication from the inside to the outside and vice versa impossible.

In addition to the domain as a means expressing local autonomy, a primitive for communication is also needed; namely, the connection point. The connection point is the means for controlled intervention in details inside and outside a module. Just as rules are needed for domains, also rules are needed regarding connection points.

Connection points must be located at domain boundaries. Each connection point is available for connection from both the outside and the inside of a domain (Fig. 10). Apart from these rules for connection points—rules concerned with geometrical aspects—connection points can also be given certain attributes. One example is electrical loading. For instance, the supply current drain can be passed from the lowest level modules up to the bonding pads via the connection points. Derivation of the width required for supply lines in every module is then a simple and local problem.

The domain and the connection point, in combination with rules on how they are to be used, are the necessary and sufficient primitives needed to make hierarchically structured layout design possible.

It may be appropriate at this point to discuss the effect which hierarchical concepts have on layout (in)efficiency. There are two sources affecting efficiency, the first being the local treatment of layout modules without detailed knowledge of the environment. As has been explained, this source can be eliminated to any degree by multiple top-down and bottom-up iterations. The other source is the desired introduction of design rules specifically for hierarchical modules. At domain boundaries, these rules result in inefficiencies which would not otherwise have occurred. It will be clear that the penalty is more severe for small than for large modules.

b) Circuit Structure: The locality concept of a circuit module is more complex than it is for layout. A circuit structure not only expresses connectivity of circuit modules but it also expresses timing relationships, adding a new dimension to the problem [16].

The connectivity aspects can be arranged in similar fashion to program structures. For a circuit module one can define a domain, in this case expressed in terms of signals. The set of signals available to a module may be composed of three subsets. First, there is the set of signals which are created and used locally; their scope is limited to the particular module. Second, there are signals which are passed from outside the module via a mechanism still to be described. Finally, there are global signals of which clocks and system resets are examples.

The counterpart of a global signal, the global net, does not exist in layout. A global net might perhaps be implemented as a solid layer of metal, completely dedicated to that net. From a design point of view the absence of such layers is a deficiency of the technology.

Communicaton between modules can be established by specification of the set of signals to be passed. By analogy with terminology used in programming languages, that set may be called a formal signal list. A higher level module using the particular module has to define the signals it passes. Again by analogy, this is called an actual signal list. This mechanism binds actual and formal signals while retaining local names. Fig. 11 shows how this works out for a simple example.

Unlike the domain and connection-point concepts for layout which are relatively new and not yet in general use, the corresponding concepts for circuit modules are not new at all and widely used. They can be used recursively at any level in a design. This seems not to be the case with regard to timing aspects. Timing concepts are expressed in terms such as asynchronous, synchronous, handshakes, self-timed [16], etc. They cannot be used interchangeably. An elegant solution appears to be to associate attributes with a module, e.g., asynchronous module, self-timed module, etc.

A quick look into the possibility of mapping a circuit hierarchy on to a layout counterpart reveals that it must be relatively easy to accomplish. Circuit domains and layout domains map easily on to each other. In outline this also applies to the mapping of signals in a circuit module onto nets in layout, except for two problems. Difficulties may be encountered when the signals are to be mapped on to two-dimensional space, a limitation not present in the circuit module. A more difficult problem, however, is that global signals at the circuit stage have no counterpart in layout but must be embedded in the hierarchy of intermodular interconnections.

c) Behavioral Description: The use of behavioral descriptions for IC design is as yet very limited [17]. Expertise and experience are still lacking in this field. A discussion of the subject cannot present solutions but is rather restricted to indicate directions that may be taken.

A circuit exhibits both sequential and parallel behavior. Apart from measures of scale there is thus similarity to operating systems in computers that also exhibit sequentialism and parallelism. In the computer, the sequential behavior is expressed in terms of programs. Parallelism is obtained by having multiple programs running concurrently. Each such program then is called a process. The possibility to create and control a number of processes is obtained by having facilities in the programming language to create, terminate, and communicate with processes. There is recursion in this scheme, a process can launch and control a number of processes, while each of the created processes can do the same. All the processes running at a given point in time are the ultimate result of a single start-up process.

The behavioral description of an integrated circuit can be modeled along similar lines. One needs the concept of process, one needs to be able to describe sequential behavior, and one needs constructs to create and interact with other processes. Such a scheme seems to contain the necessary primitives to describe circuit behavior. The manner how behavior has to be mapped on to circuit structure seems as yet to be unresolved. An interesting question in view of uniformity of hierarchies is whether there can be an association between a process in a behavioral description and a circuit module in the circuit structure.

VI. THE ROLE OF CAD IN A HIERARCHICAL DESIGN ENVIRONMENT

CAD for hierarchical design has to satisfy three conditions. First, it must support the hierarchical design methods. Second, it must provide improvements in capacity and efficiency that can be expected from hierarchical tools. Finally, it should open up new possibilities that become feasible in this environment.

Support Given by CAD Tools

Precise hierarchical languages in which structured designs can be described are the chief sources of support of the design method. For example, a description language for layout must, besides permitting the description of components, facilitate the description of domains and connection points.

CAD programs must ensure fast excursions through the hierarchical structures, both through the levels at a certain design stage and also between design stages. A typical use of CAD could be

a top level behavioral description is created;
simulation is done at this level;
a floorplan for the circuit structure is created, using a hierarchical graphic editor;
the top level behavior is made more detailed, the top level itself is translated to circuit structure;

a mixed mode behavioral, circuit simulation is done;
a floorplan for layout is created;
etc.

This picture shows that there will be a need for high-level simulators, mixed-level simulators, hierarchical graphic editors, etc.

Capacity and Efficiency of Hierarchical CAD Tools

As explained, most of the classical CAD tools do not use structure in a design, it is even eliminated when present. This has resulted in inefficient programs with limited capacity, considering present requirements. New CAD tools have to and can do away with the disadvantages of the classical tools.

By retaining the hierarchy of a design in internal data structures, the problem of data storage is completely eliminated. Where a data structure for a VLSI design may consume hundreds of megabytes of storage in the classical approach, a hierarchical approach only needs at the most a few megabytes. What is more, any increase in circuit complexity that is obtained by better utilization of structure and repetition does not increase the size of a hierarchical data structure, in complete contrast to the classical. Hierarchical tools can solve the capacity problem of design data storage once and for all.

The run time of CAD programs is affected in a similar way. The execution of CAD programs on modules instead of on a complete circuit in itself constitutes an advantage because program run time increases faster than linearly with problem complexity. But the main advantage derives from the fact that in a hierarchy a CAD task needs only be performed once per module, regardless of the number of times it occurs in the design. The classical CAD program does the task as many times as there are occurrences. Hence the run time of a hierarchical CAD program is hardly affected by an increase in circuit complexity as long as it is obtained by a better utilization of structure and repetition.

New Possibilities in CAD

Hierarchical design may do much to encourage the silicon compilation approach. Especially layout automation of the design of small modules is within reach of present-day design automation tools. A recursive application of the tool on modules at various levels in the design hierarchy may result in a situation where considerable parts of an IC are done automatically: This will then be due to the symbiosis of man and the computer, the hierarchy, i.e., the architecture, being ascribable to man and the implementation to the computer.

The efficiency improvements to be expected from new CAD tools promise that certain former batch programs will become interactive. Graphic editors containing interactive design rule checkers are within reach of hierarchical CAD.

VII. VOILA—A HIERARCHICAL VLSI LAYOUT DESIGN SYSTEM

At our laboratories we are currently implementing a hierarchical CAD system for VLSI layout which is based upon previously described principles. It is aimed at circuit complexities to be expected in the next decade (10^7 components on a chip as a guideline). The approach adopted is a combination of manual design of chip architecture and automatic implementation of modules in a design. Consequently, emphasis is placed on high-quality and high-speed man–machine interaction, while using state-of-the-art interactive color graphics. Integrity of design will be achieved by having check programs which complement manual design activities in such a way that layouts developed with VOILA are proven to be correct prior to manufacturing. VOILA takes as a starting point a circuit structure described in NDL (a proprietary network description language). From there, a symbolic layout having the same hierarchy is produced, which is an abstracted form of the detailed geometrical layout that will be implemented on the chip. The abstraction employed in the symbolic layout agree with methods which have been described in literature [18]; namely, simplification of geometries and the replacement of actual mask layers by symbolic mask layers. For the symbolic layout, we have developed a hierarchical description language SLDL (symbolic layout description language). The detailed geometrical layout is described in GLDL (geometric layout description language). The detailed layout is compiled from the symbolic layout supplemented with blocks designed at this level.

In this presentation we will first concentrate on the design languages and then provide some information about CAD programs that have been developed in VOILA.

Design Languages

a) Network Description Language, NDL: The network language used to describe circuit structures has now been in use for several years, during which it has proved its capability. Basically, a network is a module, called a block, which is broken down into a number of smaller blocks, etc. Every block consists of an interface to its environment, described in a block header, and a block body which defines its contents. The body contains references to lower level blocks. In outline the adder block in Fig. 11 would be described as

```
ADDER:  2BIT ADDER  I(A0, A1, B0, B1)
                    O(S0, S1, OVERFLOW)
BEGIN

        BIT0:  FULLADDER  I(A0, B0, 0)
                          O(S0, C1)
        BIT1:  FULLADDER  I(A1, B1, C1)
                          O(S1, OVERFLOW)
END
```

In this example all signals except C1 are passed from the outside, C1 is an internal signal with a scope limited to the 2-bit adder.

This network language, though simple in concept, is powerful enough to express any degree of hierarchical structure.

b) Symbolic Layout Description Language, SLDL: This language has been newly developed to express hierarchically structured layouts. In symbolic layout, the module has been called a cell, a layout being a cell which can be broken down into a number of smaller cells, etc.

The major subdivision of a cell is into a cell header, describing the interface to its environment, and the cell body, describing its contents. The cell header declares the name of the cell, its domain in a domain part, and its connection points in a pin part. The cell body consists of a contents part describing its detailed contents and a drawing part in which a symbolic drawing can be specified. The drawing part can be used as a replacement of the cell contents if one is not interested in that degree of detail. Before examining some of these parts more closely we will look at some other aspects of the symbolic environment which are relevant to cell description.

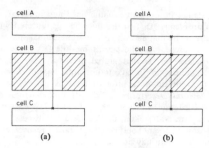

Fig. 12. Alternative crossover approaches. The hatched area denotes the cell domain. An unused area in cell *B* can be made available for use by others using a disjunct domain ((a), VOILA approach) or filled with a crossover track (b).

Cells have to be described in symbolic masks. Many actual masks, e.g., masks for contact holes, are omitted. Their function is replaced by a symbol, for example, the contact hole providing vertical connection is replaced by a VIA symbol.

The x, y coordinate system is selectable. The unit of size can be specified (micrometer, mil, etc.), by default it is micrometer. In addition to this unit, a grid to which all coordinates are rounded off can also be specified.

The selectable grid concept makes design rule violations possible. To permit checking, the design rules must be stated.

Cell geometries are restricted: they must be orthogonal at symbolic level.

Careful consideration was devoted to the domain part and the pin part. Two objectives had to be met, clear demarcation of a cell in relation to its environment had to be possible with a minimal loss of chip area. We adopted the following domain concept: A cell can have in each of the symbolic masks any number (including zero) of orthogonal polygons defining its domain. Polygons in a mask need not be tied together. Unused and partially unused masks can then be made available to other cells. This approach is the consequence of a fundamental decision on how to deal with "crossovers" by other cells over an area of a cell that is unoccupied. The other approach would be to incorporate the crossover as part of the cell (Fig. 12). We rejected the latter alternative because it is less flexible and presents a threat to equality between layout and circuit structure. Design rules versus domains are as already explained (Fig. 9).

The pin part defines the locations of the connection points (pins) on the perimeter of the domain and associates signals to pins. This provides a reference to the NDL description. More than one pin can be associated with a signal, providing alternative connection points. Nets inside a domain can be connected to a pin as can nets outside the domain. We ran into a difficulty with regard to design rules for unconnected pins; namely, that the symmetry in design rules cannot be maintained near such pins (Fig. 13) It was for this reason that we created the "automatic pin." An automatic pin is also located at the domain boundary, but a net inside the domain may approach the pin to within a distance of $1/2d$. A CAD program will automatically close the "gap" when a connection is done from the outside.

In the cell contents part one can describe nets and cell references as could be expected.

c) Geometrical Layout Description Language, GLDL: This language has a great similarity to SLDL. The constructs for

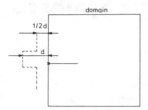

Fig. 13. The symmetrical design rule concept for domains as shown in Fig. 9 becomes more complex in the vicinity of a pin.

the description of domain and connection points are the same. The main difference is the larger degree of freedom to describe geometry, plus the fact that actual layout dimensions are used.

CAD Programs

We intend to create the VOILA CAD programs in a number of phases. In the first phase we are implementing the more traditional programs, interactive graphics, design rule checkers, checkers verifying layout to circuit, mask manipulators, post processors for pattern generation, etc., but with a drastic improvement of program capacity and efficiency by exploiting the advantages of the hierarchy. In later phases we will provide more advanced man–machine symbiosis by creating programs that automatically implement detailed design of modules.

Our aim is to have CAD programs work directly from a hierarchical design description. Since hierarchical descriptions are compact they can consequently be held in main memory, dramatically improving program performance. We will not discuss all the VOILA programs exhaustively, but take a selection that illustrates the benefits most clearly.

The VOILA graphics editor works directly from the hierarchical description. It can provide a detailed view of a part of a layout as well as overviews of larger portions. For overviews it uses the SLDL drawing part to replace layout details by a simplified presentation. It creates a picture using a selective trace through the hierarchy with the aid of bounding boxes. The efficiency of this approach is startling, a picture of a portion of a layout can be selected in a short time (1 s on a VAX 780) irrespective of the overall complexity of the layout. The simplicity of the algorithm is astonishing. Edit operations can be performed on any module of the layout, which automatically affect all its instances.

Rule checkers in VOILA, both design rule checkers and checkers verifying that a layout is in conformity with the required function, also benefit from the hierarchy concept. The batch rule checker will do its job in a fraction of the time needed by a conventional checker. Moreover, incremental checks, i.e., checks verifying that a component added to a good design still yields a good design, can be executed in real time. Incremental checks are an integral part of VOILA graphics.

We have also incorporated in VOILA a program named LOCAL, which was developed in our group but outside the VOILA project. Its function is to extract an electrical schematic from a layout, providing layout to circuit verification. Although circuit extraction is technology dependent, LOCAL has been designed as a technology-independent and circuit-description-language-independent program. The dependencies are concentrated in so-called application files which describe the design context. Another technology only requires a re-write of a compact application file. Initially developed for the extraction of limited sized circuits, its efficiency allows it to be used for complex circuits as well. Many thousands of transistors can be extracted from a layout in a reasonable computer run time. It turns out that VOILA and LOCAL can be combined nicely. LOCAL provides a verification of modules designed at a detailed level, making use of the module's domain, VOILA is used for system integration.

The programs referred to are in the domain of aids for manual design. Further tools are envisaged beyond this level. If the VOILA coordinate space is interpreted as mouldable, compaction programs can be incorporated. Module design can be automated with placers and routers, e.g., for irregularly shaped blocks. As already stated, such programs will be economically viable because they can work on a module after module basis.

VIII. Conclusion

The design of complex circuits is becoming difficult and time consuming. Hierarchical design is gaining in popularity as a remedy for that problem. However, the introduction of hierarchical design methods is not a simple matter. It requires a change of attitude to design, calls for new concepts to support hierarchical design, and a new generation of CAD tools. But once the capital expenditure on these innovations has been made, the reward will be proportionately great. They will enable us to go on designing increasingly complex circuits.

References

[1] G. E. Moore, "Are we really ready for VLSI?" presented at the CALTECH Conf. on VLSI, Pasadena, CA, Jan. 1979.
[2] J. D. Meindl, K. N. Ratnakumar, L. Geizberg, and K. C. Saraswat, "Circuit scaling limits for ultra large-scale integration," presented at the Int. Solid State Circuits Conf., 1981.
[3] D. P. Siewiorek, D. E. Thomas, and D. L. Scharfetter, "The use of LSI modules in computer structures: Trends and limitations," *Computer*, July 1978.
[4] W.G.J. Kreuwels, "CAD at Philips-Europe reviewed in a historical perspective," presented at the Custom Integrated Circuits Conf., May 1982.
[5] W. M. van Cleemput, "Hierarchical design for VLSI: Problems and advantages," presented at the CALTECH Conf. on VLSI, Pasadena, CA, Jan. 1979.
[6] E. B. Eichelberger and T. W. Williams, "A logic design structure for LSI testability," presented at the 14th Design Automation Conf., June 1977.
[7] C. Mulder, C. Niessen, and R.M.G. Wijnhoven, "Layout and test design of dynamic LSI structures," presented at the Int. Solid State Circuits Conf., 1979.
[8] The First Share Design Automation Conf., 1964.
[9] J. A. Darringer, W. H. Joyner, L. Berman, and L. Trevillyan, "Experiments in logic synthesis," presented at the IEEE Int. Conf. on Circuits and Computers, ICCC, 1980.
[10] H. de Man, J. Rabaey, G. Arnout, and J. Vandewalle, "DIANA as a mixed-mode simulator for MOSLSI sampled-data circuits," presented at the IEEE 1980 Int. Symp. on Circuits and Systems.
[11] S. Sahni and A. Bhatt, "The complexity of design automation problems," presented at the Design Automation Conf., 1980.
[12] T. Whitney, "A hierarchical design-rule checking algorithm," *LAMBDA*, first quarter 1981.
[13] B. Lattin, "VLSI design methodology, the problem of the 80's for microprocessor design," presented at the CALTECH Conf. on VLSI, Pasadena, CA, Jan. 1979.
[14] D. L. Johannsen, "Bristle blocks: A silicon compiler," in *Proc. 16th Design Automation Conf.*, 1979.
[15] S. Trimberger, J. A. Rowson, C. R. Lang, and J. P. Gray, "A structured design methodology and associated software tools," *IEEE Trans. Circuits Syst.*, vol. CAS-28, pp. 618–634, July 1981.
[16] C. L. Seitz, "System timing," in C. Mead, L. Conway, *Introduction to VLSI systems.* Reading, MA: Addison-Wesley, ch. 7.
[17] M. R. Barbacci, "Instruction set processor specifications (ISPS): The notation and its application," *IEEE Trans. Comput.*, vol. C-30, pp. 24–40, Jan. 1981.
[18] N.H.E. Weste, "MULGA, an interactive symbolic layout system for the design of integrated circuits," *Bell Syst. Tech. J.*, vol. 60, no. 6, July-Aug. 1981.

Methodical Aspects of Logic Synthesis

HANS MARTIN LIPP, MEMBER, IEEE

Invited Paper

Abstract—The increasing complexity of integrated circuits demands improved design quality. For system developments with small- or medium-scale integrated circuits, successive steps of the design process are interconnected loosely. Therefore, design checks, tests, and even redesigns could be performed without affecting large fractions of the overall design. With large scale integration (LSI) and especially very large scale integration (VLSI), the situation has changed drastically. The technological capability of these techniques allows designers to put a whole digital system on a few chips or even on one single chip. Consequently, all design steps between the definition of the system and its realization as a semiconductor structure must be strongly interconnected to yield successful and economic solutions. Reduced possibilities for testing and correcting design errors do not permit design concepts that follow the principle of trial and error. But up to now, the so-called logic design has been dominated by manually generated solutions. Because of the inherent possibilities of misinterpretation of the design task or of local design errors, analytical tools like simulation have to demonstrate the correctness of a design. But the restricted model accuracy, incomplete sets of test data, and excessive request for computing time are limiting factors of this design strategy in the context of VLSI. Therefore, other concepts for logic design are necessary that avoid analytical tools as much as possible but support the design process by synthesis. This paper discusses some methodical aspects of this problem, and it mentions some properties of logic design tools that are of practical importance.

I. INTRODUCTION

THE CONSTRUCTION of a digital system from small functional parts like small- and medium-scale (SSI, MSI) integrated circuits results in a design process where successive steps are only loosely connected to each other. Decisions within a single design step do not affect the overall design significantly, and tests for correct functional behavior can be performed easily. As a result, errors in a design due to misinterpretations of the functional description or to design errors may be checked locally; redesign or repair refer only to a small fraction of the whole system without increasing development time and cost too much. This is especially true for the step which is called logic design. Therefore, the problems of logic design have not been in the center of interest for years. After a first period of activity in the sixties when a large number of principles and methods were created, a certain stability has characterized the field of logic design. It has remained at a level appropriate for manual designs, despite the fact that some of the algorithms were programmed to support typical tasks like minimization of Boolean expressions, etc. But most of these experiments were restricted to academic work. The main emphasis during that period was on problems of modeling and simulation, physical design (layout), and related fields.

Manuscript received April 26, 1982; revised October 4, 1982. The development of the design system LOGE has been supported by the Department of Research and Technology of the Federal Republic of Germany.

The author is with the Institut für Technik der Informationsverarbeitung, University of Karlsruhe, D-7500 Karlsruhe 1, Germany.

With the increasing complexity of integrated circuits in the area of LSI and especially VLSI, the step of logic design is attracting more and more attention and is becoming a topic in the design of modern digital systems. There are several different motivations for this situation: ever increasing development costs and shorter design cycles put a tremendous pressure on the designers; the wide use of integrated circuits adapted to specific tasks increases the number of customized designs; and also, there is a certain lack of skilled designers. In addition, VLSI does not tolerate design errors and repairs to the same extent that previous generations of integrated circuits did. It is obvious that classical design methods for manual design in conjunction with modeling and simulation in the future cannot guarantee design correctness to the degree necessary for successful developments.

Whereas other design activities, especially layout, testing, and documentation, are already supported with powerful design tools, the area of logic design today is still characterized by manually performed designs. A recent survey of tools for design automation [5] contains the following comment on aids for logic design automation: "We were rather disappointed by the complete lack of automated techniques in the area of logic design, although two companies reported the existence of (seldom used) aids for logic minimization and translation and several companies do have the ability to automatically map from T^2L (SSI, MSI) to CMOS (LSI)." These findings confirm the results of a comparative study which was published by the Commission of the European Community in 1978 [16].

The reports cited earlier do not, however, give an explanation for the situation. From our own experience with the development of computer-aided design (CAD) tools in this field and with their introduction into industrial use, we know that the range of arguments stretches from poor design performance to psychological effects (for some details, see [12]). Before we discuss questions related to the use of logic design tools, we will refer to an abstract schematic of the design process [13] and demonstrate some of its typical properties.

II. THE DESIGN PROCESS

The design process for a digital system comprises at least two layers of development. One refers to the conceptual phase where a specific processing task has to be defined in the form of a functionally complete but abstract description. The second one deals with the problem of realizing the system as a semiconductor structure which correctly maps the defined functional behavior. In practice, more steps are inserted to cope with the complexity of the design task; normally, they are labeled functional block design, logic design, circuit design, and finally physical design or layout. In addition, every intermediate level itself is broken down into smaller steps to create

Reprinted from *Proc. IEEE*, vol. 71, pp. 88–97, Jan. 1983.

228

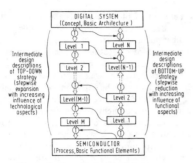

Fig. 1. A schematic for the design process.

subtasks of "adequate" size. "Adequate" in this context means that the corresponding design tasks are small enough to be tackled manually by the designer or automatically by design tools. The design then may be understood as a sequence of small design actions which interconnect the two primary layers of concept formulation and semiconductor realization. Fig. 1 shows a simple schematic to illustrate the situation. The design actions are referred to as transformations T which generate the intermediate design description of the next level based on that of the preceding one.

Connecting the two boundary levels of Fig. 1 by a sequence of transformations may be performed in either of two directions. As a result, two main design strategies are possible—the "bottom-up" and the "top-down," which at a glance seem to be completely contradictory and independent of each other.

The *bottom-up design* (the sequence at the right-hand side of Fig. 1) starts with basic components of the semiconductor layer and proceeds by joining an appropriate set of these elements to generate units of the first level, functionally more complex than the basic ones. Then, repeating this procedure with units of level 1, the transformation yields even more complex parts at level 2, etc. The last transformation step then finishes the design process by forming the desired system.

This design strategy was widely used in early periods when digital systems were constructed from single elements like diodes, resistors, transistors, and also SSI circuits. Because of the limited complexity of those systems, the number of intermediate design steps was quite small. Thus the designer was aware of most design decisions with regard to the whole design process.

The bottom-up style has proven to be a very efficient strategy under the aspect of a perfect use of given elements or units. Today, this still holds as long as only a small number of design steps are necessary. Normally, the bottom-up style guarantees the best performance with regard to given properties of elements, and it allows a nearly perfect use of technological innovations.

But the number of intermediate design steps is growing rapidly for complex systems. Thus the bottom-up strategy is of decreasing interest in system design. Combining given units of level i to form more powerful ones at level $i + 1$ proves to be a combinatorial problem with an exponential growth function. If the design process proceeds over a large number of successive design steps, the number of possible design variations will be excessively large, far from any practical interest. Therefore, the transition from one design level to the adjacent one not only constitutes a transformation problem but also one of selection. Only a small fraction of alternative possibilities can be regarded in the next design step. For complex designs it

seems to be very difficult to obtain powerful selection criteria for a specific design level that reflect the needs of more distant steps of the design process. Thus a pure application of the bottom-up style results in a largely undirected sequence of design transformations which is not very efficient with regard to the overall system design.

If only a few steps are involved, this style is still of great interest under special conditions. The use of layout libraries with elements reaching from basic cells to complicated cell assemblies like stack registers and memories, or the use of prefabricated integrated circuits with arrays of gates and macrocells is a typical situation.

The *top-down design* (the sequence at the left-hand side of Fig. 1) is preferred today for several reasons. With the increasing number of computers or, more generally speaking, of digital electronic systems, users have to finance large investments in software, periphery, and education of their personnel. Therefore, the stability of the interface between the user and the digital system resp. between large functional parts within a system is of crucial interest. Preserving a certain amount of compatibility under these conditions is an essential aspect of the design philosophy which is mapped best by the top-down design. In addition, it is often necessary to start hard- and software development at an instant when important parameters of a new technology are still unstable and, therefore, when the use of the bottom-up principle is not possible. Often, systems and modules will be realized with different semiconductor processes, e.g., first with a bipolar solution and later on with a CMOS version. This also asks for a top-down development which is independent of a specific technology as long as possible. Finally, a top-down approach seems to be more adequate to support design constraints where different parts of a system have to be constructed at different times or by different design groups.

The main disadvantage of this design style is opposite to that of the bottom-up strategy. Breaking down large units into smaller ones under technical constraints also poses a combinatorial problem with exponential growth function, and the transformation sequence yields an excessive number of different solutions. Consequently, efficient selection criteria are necessary to reduce that large variety to a very small fraction of interesting designs. But for a long design sequence, most criteria do not properly reflect technological aspects to guarantee acceptable designs.

As a consequence, pure design styles never occur in practice. Real developments normally make an alternate use of both design strategies, or refer to the information extracted from the other branch to guide the selection process properly and efficiently (indicated in Fig. 1 by some arrows which interconnect horizontally the two different design sequences). A closer inspection reveals that design processes are characterized by a complicated net of mutual influences and cyclic iterations of a part or even of the whole design sequence. The main problem then consists in the decision at which level and to what amount this information transfer should be activated (for an example, see [11]).

III. ALGORITHMIC TRANSFORMATIONS

A. Bottom-Up versus Top-Down

Obviously, logic design represents a very difficult step in the overall design of a complex system. The correctness of manual designs decreases rapidly with the growing size of a design, and simulation or other analytical design verification tools cannot

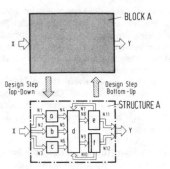

Fig. 2. Relations between two adjacent design descriptions.

compensate for this trend because they need excessive amounts of computing time. Already today in many cases only functionally based test sequences with restricted data sets are possible for simulation. In the future this type of logic design will be too inefficient with regard to design time and too expensive with regard to design cost. An improvement of the analytical tools seems to be limited. Therefore, a different approach for logic design has to be taken which yields good solutions in a shorter design time and with a degree of correctness that (in most cases) avoids simulation for the purpose of design verification.

To derive a new concept for logic design, we should discuss some of the properties of a design process in more detail. The basic structure as described by Fig. 1 relies on the principle that each system must be described explicitly at each level of design. This description should be self-contained and not depend on information from subsequent levels. Thus what we need is a comprehensive set of description languages for different levels of a design. In the last few years, activities have been started that especially support such an approach [19]. But collections of existing hardware description tools may be an acceptable compromise for the next time.

Such tools do not support the transformation itself; they are primarily aids for describing a system at a certain level of specification. The creative part of the design consists in generating those descriptions following a given set of transformation rules and observing given constraints. To demonstrate some of the relations of two adjacent design steps, we will use a small example as given in Fig. 2.

For the top-down design the functional behavior of unit A may be given by an appropriate set of input–output relations referring to A as a black box. Applying the desired transformation to that description, the designer normally has to generate a more detailed one that consists of a set of functionally smaller units which are interconnected by nets. In our example units $a–f$ may be necessary together with nets $N1–N12$. The transformation will be correct if the overall behavior of structure A equals the black box behavior of block A whenever the latter is specified. Normally, expansion of a less detailed description into a more detailed one adds some fraction of unspecified relations (e.g., don't care entries). Consequently, correctness can only be demonstrated by using a covering rather than an equivalence relation.

For the bottom-up design an inverse operation must take place. The detailed structure A with its aggregate of units and nets has to be replaced by a single block A. Therefore, details are lost. The applied transformation will be correct when the

black box behavior of block A equals the overall behavior of structure A. Because this direction of the design sequence does not add unspecified relations (structure A is completely defined), the proof of correctness is based on an equivalence relation. If we repeat, correspondingly, the design process for different structures B, C, etc., we receive a set of blocks A, B, C, etc., which themselves may be interconnected by nets. Block A then will be part of a higher structure. It is likely that in such a restricted environment only a fraction of the whole set of input–output relations of A is really used for the description of that level (e.g., a structure made up from gates may realize a JK flip-flop, but in the next step the input condition $J = K = 1$ will never be used when the flip-flops are forming a shiftregister).

If we now try to replace manual design transformations by automatic ones, we have to discuss the question of whether the bottom-up or the top-down strategy, or both, are candidates for such an approach. Most problems arising in the context of logic design automation are interesting from the academic point of view, and none of the two styles should be preferred. But under practical aspects, the top-down strategy seems to be the most promising one at the moment. Some arguments for this preference have already been mentioned in Section II. An additional and very important motivation is the necessity to have tools for automated logic design as soon as possible to cope with the upcoming problems of complex designs.

Transformations within a bottom-up sequence must realize an extraction algorithm to derive subsets of a functional behavior which are essential for further design steps. At the moment, no solutions are known for the use under practical conditions. Logic design tool for the bottom-up approach, therefore, are an unrealistic expectation for the near future.

The situation looks better for top-down design transformations because this direction of a design sequence implies algorithms based on principles like prime implicant calculations, covering and equivalence relations, (maximal) compatible sets, etc. The theory has already developed a large number of corresponding methods. Design of units at the level of Boolean equations may serve as a well-known example, but tasks like finding optimal input assignments to multiplexer nets, realizing a minimal number of read/write operations of microprocessor I/O ports, and reducing the word length of a control memory belong to problems with the same mathematical background. Nevertheless, logic synthesis for the top-down design has also failed in the past because of poor design performance of the tools compared to manual designs, excessive demands for computing time, and memory capacity. Therefore, logic synthesis is not very attractive to designers as long as small- and medium-sized design tasks are concerned. However, for LSI and VLSI the superiority of the designers is vanishing at least in special fields. For example, with an efficient PLA optimization method [10] the number of product terms of existing manually optimized PLA designs can still be reduced by some percent, and for new designs with several hundreds of product terms, savings of up to 50 percent are realistic compared with manual approaches.

B. Decision Criteria and Cost Functions

If we intend to introduce logic synthesis, we must first develop improved and carefully adapted design algorithms which can accept complex tasks. The goal of the development should be to replace tiring and error-prone manual subtasks with syn-

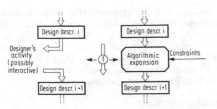

Fig. 3. Modes of a transformation step.

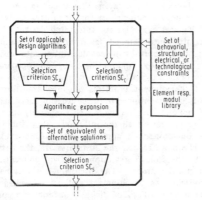

Fig. 4. Structure of an algorithmic expansion.

thesis (as indicated by Fig. 3) to shorten design cycle time and to enable the designer to control the design process more globally.

The work of a designer is characterized by a certain mixture of intuitive reasoning, experience, and application of some design algorithms. If we materialize the replacement, we must formalize the corresponding activities to derive methods and to construct programs that are equivalent to the manual design behavior. Besides the basic transformation procedure, three decision-making domains can be extracted from manual design despite the fact that most designers cannot express their reasons and motivations explicitly. Fig. 4 will give an impression of the problems we are confronted with. In real environments and for interesting applications, the type of the algorithmic expansion is not defined uniquely by one single algorithm. In most cases a set of different procedures may be available that also emphasize different aspects of a transformation. Consequently, a design by synthesis should rely on a variety of algorithms combined with the corresponding decision criterion that guides the selection (labeled SC_A in Fig. 4). As an example, we mention the minimization problem of (incompletely defined) Boolean functions where several quite different algorithms are known.

The attribute "different" includes some ambiguity in the context of logic design automation. It may refer to the situation that expanded descriptions of the adjacent design level may (slightly) differ for different algorithms. On the other hand, the performance of these algorithms may be different with regard to processing time and memory requests. For logic synthesis the second aspect is of central interest.

During the discussion of Fig. 1, we have already mentioned that pure design styles are unrealistic and some pre-known structural information must be added to the top-down se-

quence to direct the design process properly. This additional information may come from already performed bottom-up designs or from experience of preceding design transformations with "good" results at the semiconductor level. Therefore, all sensitive transformation steps are connected to a library or other source of structural information. Since the whole set of references will not apply for all tasks, a decision criterion SC_C must be added to insert the proper information into the expansion. As typical examples for structural constraints, we may mention the number of input–output terminals and product terms of a PLA, prescribed properties of a multiplexer net, or organizational aspects of bus structures.

Finally, many design algorithms include features which allow the generation of a set of possible solutions. Therefore, for automated synthesis we need some selection principle to reject unfavorable versions and to extract the best one which then may serve as the reference solution for further design steps. The selection criterion SC_S normally is based on cost functions. They assign a defined value (sometimes combined with a weight factor) to essential parameters of a solution. Selecting then means the comparison of metric relations, with search procedures for minimal or maximal values, the so-called optima. That is, a familiar but not too realistic cost function is the length of a Boolean expression as used for minimizing purposes.

Formalizing selection criteria and finding adequate cost functions poses a hard problem for automated synthesis and is the object of sophisticated studies. Such control elements of a design process should reflect as many influences and constraints as possible but, on the other hand, must be computable without too much effort. If one tried to copy the behavior of designers, he would realize that manual designs in general are not guided by a set of formalized criteria. Instead of pure metrical measures, a complicated mixture of metrically and intuitively based evaluation rules prevails which cannot be mapped successfully for automated design. But the price the designer has to pay for this adaptive evaluation principle must be seen in the fact that he has no unique decision criterion to detect when his solutions are optimal and then stop this part of a design definitely. He will always be uncertain to some degree that he has really found the best solution (whatever "best" means). However, for logic synthesis with automated transformations, the existence of metric cost functions is a necessary condition for guiding transformations and for stopping correlated optimization procedures. But it seems unrealistic or even impossible to derive criteria and cost functions that completely map all aspects of a manual design style. Existing design algorithms, therefore, cannot compete on an average with manual designs, and some small fraction of additional units and circuits has to be accepted. But if "optimality" also includes the whole environment of a design process like design time, cost for simulation, degree of correctness, testability, and completeness of design documentation, automated synthesis will be the only possible alternative for VLSI.

C. Local Transformations

The inherent difficulties of formalizing selection criteria and defining appropriate cost functions combined with some other reasons have split the development strategies of logic synthesis tools into two distinct branches, the so-called synthesis by local resp. global transformations. No precise measure exists to decide whether a transformation is local or global. But to some extent we may establish a basis for distinction by the way design descriptions will be altered. If a transformation

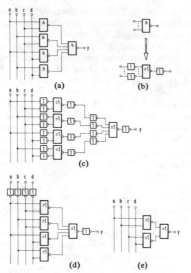

Fig. 5. Example of a local transformation.

does not change the design significantly or does not solve a design task as a whole, we may refer to it as a local one. For example, if a combinatorial circuit has to be transformed from a two-level AND–OR representation to a pure NAND one with input restrictions of the gates, local operations may act only on a small fraction of the whole net. Then a sequence of changes at the same level of description must be performed to complete the task (e.g., see Fig. 5(b) where the transformation NAND → NOR replaces one gate after another). Local transformations are also used for redesigns when existing solutions in one technology will be realized in a different one [6], [17].

The preference for local transformations is due to the fact that decision criteria and cost functions can be very simple, or—if interactive tools are provided—the designer can act on this part of the task. Then, the tool consists mainly of a menu of local operations which are selected by the designer. After application, he evaluates the transformed result and decides if this step should be undone or fixed. Local transformation techniques sometimes are derived by copying typical actions of the designer [6].

But there are some hard problems associated with this style of design operations. One question is how large the scope of a local design step should be; another is related to the question of whether a design would be optimal or not. However, the main difficulty originates from the observation that a sequence of local operations may miss the optimal solution altogether because they focus on a target area too small. Typically, they will introduce additional units at the edge of their field of operation. Therefore, postprocessing must be executed for the elimination of unnecessary parts (if they can be isolated at all). A very simple example will demonstrate this problem. Given a combinational circuit with five NAND gates (Fig. 5(a)) which should be transformed locally into a representation of NOR gates (Fig. 5(b)), if we perform all necessary steps, we will receive an intermediate solution with some unnecessary inverters (Fig. 5(c)). Postprocessing then yields the final (and optimal ?) solution (Fig. 5(d)). But if we had reworked the design from the preceding level of formal representation, a

better solution would have emerged (Fig. 5(e)). It is unlikely that the menu will contain another local transformation to come from the solution of Fig. 5(d) to that of Fig. 5(e), especially if the situation is not as simple as in this example. Thus local operations do not guarantee good solutions. But they may allow technological aspects to be taken into consideration better than other strategies will.

D. Global Transformations

The opposite approach concentrates on global transformations. Referring to the definition given above, we expect for this type of synthesis operations that it covers a greater distance of the design sequence or that it deals with designs as a whole. Typical examples are automated designs of a data path description into detailed descriptions at the component level [18] or of a control sequence description into finite state machines realized by random logic, by microprogrammed controllers, or even by software for microcomputers.

Some of the inherent problems of global transformations have already been mentioned in the context of decision criteria and cost functions. Despite the fact that relatively poor metric relations do not reflect all the influences, they still may be efficient enough for special applications to outperform manual designs. The more regular the structures are, the better the results. In the following sections, we will concentrate on aspects of global synthesis. The discussion is mostly based on experience with the development and use of a large CAD system for logic synthesis of digital sequential and combinational circuits (especially of adapted controllers) which is now widely used both in scientific and industrial environments (for details of the design system LOGE see [9], [14], and the Appendix).

Besides the evaluation problem, global logic synthesis poses a second severe difficulty. Many procedures are based on algorithms that have been shown to be np-complete. This property reflects a measure for the complexity of a given task. It refers to the fact that the number of necessary calculations to solve the problem will exceed any expression which is of a polynomial form. But from a practical point of view, those estimates must be seen as worst case calculations which do not include additional information about some structural properties of an actual design problem. Therefore, realistic approaches make use of the so-called heuristics that cut down the number of calculations within certain limits to acceptable values. On an average the calculated solutions will be quite good, but generally they cannot guarantee optimal solutions. It is a typical situation for global synthesis that transformations under the control of heuristics will yield attractive solutions for complex problems but may perform poorly for small ones. For global transformations it is extremely necessary to select and analyze algorithms very carefully to avoid all superfluous intermediate results and calculations. A recent study [20] has shown that for the well-known problem of finding the set of all prime implicants of a Boolean function the number of intermediate results will be limited to at most $(2 \cdot n - 1)$ if n is the number of variables. Similar bounds can be derived for the calculation of sets of maximal compatibles or for covering problems. Correspondingly, the demand for computing time is also reduced. Accurate tuning of algorithms and of data structures will overcome the problem of complexity for logic synthesis. For example the LOGE system will allow automated global designs of fairly large digital controllers (several dozens of in- and outputs and several hundreds of transition statements) within some minutes of computing time on a SIEMENS 7760 [14]; minimization of combinational circuits and PLA's typically takes some seconds to some minutes for large problems.

Powerful tools with this level of performance also can ease the problem of cost functions. A designer can run such or similar design programs several times for the same task using different structural or technological constraints. He then may collect a set of globally transformed solutions and perform an additional selection following guidelines which are not mapped by the cost functions of the applied algorithms.

Detailed investigations of design tasks demonstrate that the theoretically defined limits for computing time and memory space are not very helpful for realizing successful design runs. Complexity only refers to the fact that these algorithms show bad growth functions. But a comparable bad aspect is the fact that for a given task the actual request for computer resources cannot be estimated at all. Since we are not able to assign memory space and computing time for the worst case, logic synthesis computations are always in danger of being finished by external interrupts like timeout or storage overflow without any useful result for the designer. This possible behavior of a synthesis tool will not stimulate the acceptance of global transformations.

To overcome this severe drawback, another property of design algorithms has to be noticed. There are two main classes. One consists of those algorithms performing design calculations in such a way that only the very last step will create the desired solution. Intermediate results are worthless for the designer. The other class is quite different. The corresponding algorithms always start their transformation with a valid (but sometimes trivial) solution and then perform operations which iteratively improve the solution until the optimum has been reached. Normally, the first class seems to be more attractive because the average computing time is less than for the second class. But for industrial tools where unsuccessful design runs are costly, the second class will be of greater importance. In this case, a premature end of a design run yields some more or less improved intermediate solution, and the designer will be able to decide whether this approximation is good enough, or if it is necessary to set up an auxiliary run with extended computing resources. This allows a tradeoff between optimality of a design transformation and use of computer resources.

In the LOGE design program for random logic, we have realized an additional strategy [9]. The minimization procedure contains two different algorithms, an optimizing and a fast but approximating one. The associated selection criterion has been constructed in such a way that it controls the transformation with regard to demands for computer resources. When starting a design run, a scheduler will assign a certain amount of computing time and memory space to every optimization task. During the run the consumption of these two resources will be monitored by the program. If a certain fraction of the assigned values has already been used and the resources for a subtask are likely to run out during optimization, the program switches to the approximating algorithm which is fast but not very powerful. This strategy assures that all design runs will end with results; nearby solutions are identified to inform the designer where approximation has been used.

Global logic synthesis is studied for several reasons. The most important ones in the era of VLSI are the expectation of being able to reduce design time significantly and the hypoth-

esis of creating correct designs. At least for certain classes of designs, industrial applications have proven that design time for automated synthesis will be a small fraction of that for manual designs despite the need to spend a lot of time at the front end of a design process to produce a formal task description. For our LOGE system we know that average design time has been reduced to about 30–50 percent of that for manual design. Sometimes the amount of additional circuits will be up to about 20 percent with regard to manual designs because the program supports well-structured solutions.

The second goal of synthesis—the confidence of functionally correct solutions—has not yet been reached sufficiently. From a theoretical point of view, correctness must be demonstrated by static, mathematically based verification techniques. In general this task has not been solved, but some studies for restricted environments have been published (e.g., [15]). For complex tasks and for large design descriptions, such proofs may be quite unrealistic. Synthesis tools are an urgent need, and designers cannot wait for improved verification principles, so we have to attack this problem pragmatically. For a large number of synthesis algorithms, one can show by using covering relations and set theoretical proofs that they perform correct alterations of a design description (during the development of LOGE we have widely used this principle). But to create design tools we have to map the proven algorithms into programs and demonstrate that these are correct, which is very hard to do. At this point, some pragmatism may be allowed.

If we check manual designs by simulation, we have principally the same problem for the simulation model and the simulation program. But up to now no such program has undergone a comprehensive proof for correctness. Therefore, we can reduce the problem of correctness to that of acceptance. If a synthesis program yields solutions which on an average contain significantly fewer design errors than manual ones verified by simulation, a logic design tool will be accepted by designers.

Additional principles allow an increase in the probability of generating correct designs. For one of our most important LOGE programs [3], we have realized a special program which decompiles detailed design descriptions with methods different from those used in the synthesis program. The result is a specific table that is equivalent to the information contained in a sequence diagram. "Correctness" then will be demonstrated for the whole cycle (consisting of logic synthesis algorithm, corresponding program, decompilation algorithm and program), if for a carefully selected set of design tasks the primary and the reconstructed sequence diagram follow a certain covering relation. This still does not replace a sound mathematical proof, but our experience shows that this strategy ensures an excellent reliability for this design program. The limitations of our approach are not given primarily by the performance of the design tool but by the limited ability of the designer to define and describe his design task correctly and completely.

E. Interface Stability

Every transformation step of the top-down approach replaces a block by a structure of several blocks which are properly interconnected. This separation always introduces the need for interface definitions that describe the relations between parts of the structure (for a systematic study at the system level see [21]). But in this paper another methodical aspect of the interface problem should be discussed. For the top-down design the decomposition of a block into a set of smaller blocks must be done at an instant when the consecutive expansions of each sub-block have not yet been performed. Therefore, the definition of the interface relations and signals will be fixed without any knowledge of the internal situation of the sub-blocks. But during following design steps it may be recognized that those definitions have been chosen inadequately with regard to optimal implementations of the sub-blocks. For small designs it may be permissible to go back in the design sequence, rearrange the interface definition more properly, and start the design again. But for complex designs with many parallel developments, an interface definition must be stable in any case to avoid excessive design iterations and problems of incompatibility. Logic design tools then must support a different way of adaptation. The solution may exist in some preprocessing of the interface signals preserving the external behavior as it has been defined. In Fig. 2, block f in structure A demonstrates this strategy by the hatched area. Recent studies [7], [8] have shown that for microprogrammed controllers savings of up to 90 percent in the capacity of the microprogram memory can be achieved for existing designs. Besides that improvement, in some cases the speed of a controller can be increased significantly.

F. Differential Design

The use of optimizing algorithms for logic synthesis is necessary for the development of successful tools. But to some extent they cause acceptance problems in industrial environments. Normally, design specifications are not completely stable; they may change to some degree during a development cycle due to previously unknown conditions or constraints. Later on, engineering changes and redesigns may also introduce some alterations. If a designer now applies optimizing algorithms (especially those for global transformations), he may realize that the obtained results are quite different with regard to the already existing ones. Because all the following steps like physical design, mask generation, testing, etc., are heavily influenced, such a procedure would be too time consuming and costly. In practice, designers up to now overcome this severe drawback by omitting design tools. But, on the other hand, the way in which designers often modify existing solutions to adjust for engineering changes or to remove design errors cannot be accepted from our methodical point of view. To speak in terms of Fig. 1, designers usually tend to realize modifications at a certain level by actions on design descriptions much later in the design sequence. For example, a small change in a Boolean equation would be mapped immediately by some small alterations of the layout, thus avoiding a new and consequent design. But this technique is not very reliable because new design errors may be added unnoticed, destroying the consistency of the whole design.

What we really need for logic synthesis is a new class of algorithms which we may call differential synthesis algorithms (DSA's). They are under industrial conditions a necessary completion for optimizing algorithms. Their essential quality is demonstrated by the schematic of Fig. 6. Given two levels i resp. $i+1$ of designs with description P_i. If we apply an optimizing algorithm, we may receive the transformed description $P_{0, i+1}$ at level $i+1$. If we now introduce an engineering change at level i which moves P_i to P_i' by a small distance ϵ, the optimized solution $P_{0, i+1}'$ may be completely different from $P_{0, i+1}$, a result which cannot be tolerated, e.g., by economical reasons. A DSA, however, would yield solution $P_{D, i+1}'$ which will

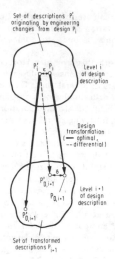

Fig. 6. Basic property of a differential synthesis algorithm.

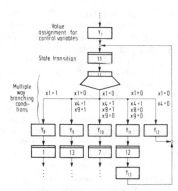

Fig. 7. Section of a control flow description (example).

differ only by a small distance δ from $P_{0, i+1}$. In general, a DSA should be constructed using the following guidelines:

1) There must be a metric relation to express the property "neighborhood" of two descriptions at the same level.

2) A DSA must be able to map a small deviation ϵ at level i into a small change δ at level $i+1$ (if such a solution exists) under given constraints.

Let us demonstrate this situation by a small example. Fig. 7 shows part of a sequence diagram which maps the control flow of a digital controller. (The symbols together with the interconnecting edges are a special representation of a finite state machine of the Mealy type.) Fig. 8 illustrates the optimized solution as a microprogrammed structure which was synthesized completely by the corresponding LOGE design program [3]. Now let us assume that an engineering change takes place that introduces a new decision variable $x10$ and a slightly modified sequence diagram (Fig. 9). The value ϵ may then be calculated as the fraction of modified entries with regard to the existing ones. If ϵ is less than a given limit (e.g., $\epsilon < 0.1$ for a normalized representation $0 \leqslant \epsilon \leqslant 1$), then we expect a solution similar to that of Fig. 8. But the application of the

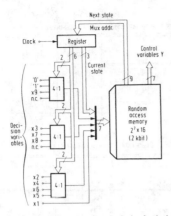

Fig. 8. Block diagram of an optimized solution.

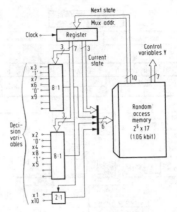

Fig. 10. Block diagram of a new optimized solution.

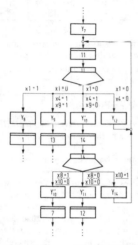

Fig. 9. Example of a small change within the control flow description.

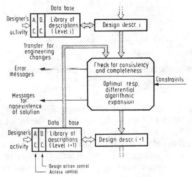

Fig. 11. Complete structure of a design step for synthesis.

Fig. 11 demonstrates the structure of a design step which will support differential designs as well as optimizing ones. An appropriate control mechanism (labeled *D.C.* in Fig. 11) should prevent the designer from acting incorrectly on the design data if changes of a task description occur.

The consequence of applying a DSA normally consists in a tradeoff between an optimized new solution and the smallest alteration of an existing one. (In our example the optimized memory size would be 1.07 kbits versus 2 kbits of the modified one.) For that reason, DSA tools should never be used to improve carelessly derived design descriptions. At the moment, only few papers mention the need for DSA's [4], [6], [13]. But it is the author's opinion that in the future DSA will be an essential part of industrial design automation systems.

IV. SUMMARY

At the moment logic synthesis is still in a rudimentary phase of development. But in the last few years an increasing number of investigations have been performed. Since a general approach to logic synthesis is still missing, several design strategies are dominating, based on different restrictions to reduce the complexity of the problem. Three main principles are important: data path resp. control flow oriented logic synthesis, and approaches which try to reduce the number of intermediate design steps drastically. Automated logic synthesis will ask for powerful decision and selection procedures

same program will yield the structure of Fig. 10 different from Fig. 8 in all essential parameters (number and size of multiplexers, size of memory). The cost of realizing this solution would be correspondingly high. To overcome this problem we have designed a DSA for microprogrammed controllers [4] that allows us to keep design changes as small as possible. For that reason, we define a hierarchy of actions that may alter an existing design description by:

1) modification of memory contents (the highest priority);
2) use of hitherto redundant components;
3) use of hitherto redundant input and output connections of components;
4) adding or removing of interconnections;
5) adding of components.

Assigning costs to each of these actions according to the priority scheme, the value δ can be calculated. The best solution $P'_{D,i+1}$ then is characterized by a minimum of δ. For our example, only actions 1) and 3) apply. A minimal change is reached by connecting variable $x10$ to the unused input of the upper multiplexer and calculating a new memory contents.

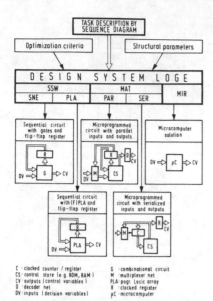

Fig. 12. The LOGE system for the global synthesis of digital controllers.

TABLE I
LIMITS FOR SOME ESSENTIAL PARAMETERS OF LOGE

Limits for the number of		SSW/SNE SSW/PLA	MAT/PAR MAT/SER	MIR
Inputs (decision var.)	DV	64	64	64
Outputs (control var.)	CV	64	96	96
States	S	128	512	512
Lines of trans.statements	LT	806	1024	1024

TABLE II
CPU TIME FOR SOME REALISTIC EXAMPLES

Ex. No.	Number of				CPU time in seconds				
	DV	CV	S	LT	SSW/ SNE	SSW/ PLA	MAT/ PAR	MAT/ SER	MIR
1	11	15	35	431	275	166	48	112	192
2	16	25	18	48	134	16	25	9	15
3	7	9	21	73	33	19	13	15	18
4	9	11	23	70	24	16	11	14	25
5	29	6	94	183	111	56	48	33	62
6	9	12	13	38	15	3	7	8	11

to guide the design sequence efficiently. For economic reasons a new class of design aids (the so-called differential synthesis algorithms) has to be studied intensively. For the era of VLSI technological aspects and optimization goals with regard to the efficient use of silicon will lose some influence in favor of efforts that generate powerful design tools for logic synthesis.

APPENDIX

The CAD system LOGE has been developed for the automated synthesis of synchronously operated digital controllers, including single- and multiple-output combinational circuits. The basic idea is to generate all the necessary specifications of a solution by global transformations starting from an abstract task description for the control flow. (For details see [1], [2], [3], [4], [9], [10], [12], [14], [20].) As a description aid we are using a special graph (called sequence diagram; for examples see Figs. 7 and 9) which allows a representation following the finite state machine concept. Partially specified entries for input and output information as well as multiple branches allow rather compact descriptions. The sequence diagram was introduced by the author for lectures and laboratory exercises in 1967 and has also proven since to be a valuable tool under industrial conditions. For computer input the diagram has to be transformed into a list of transition and output statements. Each row of this list contains the necessary information to identify the current state of the control sequence, the next state, the branch condition, and the output information; comments may be included.

At the moment LOGE consists of five program modules for automated and optimized synthesis (see Fig. 12):

SSW/SNE for realizations with random logic;
SSW/PLA for realizations with PLA logic;

MAT/PAR for seven types of microprogrammed structures with parallel input and output operations;
MAT/SER for a microprogrammed structure with serialized input and output operations;
MIR for software solutions based on given microcomputer structures.

The module MAT/KOR is available for differential design referring to five of the seven structures of the module MAT/PAR.

The whole system comprises at the present state of development about 50 000 lines of Fortran IV code. It has been installed on a series of computers. Versions with some loss of performance are running on small minicomputers.

Table I lists some of the limits for the system; they are of more theoretical interest because practical designs have shown that designers usually cannot describe correctly and completely control flows which contain more than several dozens of input and output variables and some hundred lines of transition statements.

Table II demonstrates the efficiency of the synthesis programs (values refer to a SIEMENS 7760 computer system). As may be seen from the corresponding entries, a complete design with five detailed but completely different structures will be synthesized in less than 14 min of CPU time, for example no. 1. The design descriptions contain all necessary information concerning the number and type of functional elements, their interconnections, the size of control stores, the programming information for PLA's resp. control stores, the I/O-port assignment for microcomputers, etc. Postprocessing may be necessary with regard to some technological aspects.

REFERENCES

[1] G. Biehl, "Automatic generation of optimal microcomputer programs for software-driven controllers," in *Proc. Symp. on Microcomputer and Microprocessor Application*, vol. II, Budapest, Oct. 1979, pp. 571–586.
[2] G. Biehl and A. Ditzinger, "Computer aided design of microprocessor-based digital controllers," *Microproc. Microprog.*, vol. 7, no. 5, pp. 326–333, 1981.

[3] G. Biehl, W. Grass, and S. Hall, "OOGE-MAT—a program for the synthesis of microprogrammed controllers," in *Proc. 4th Intern. Conf. on Computers in Design Engineering*, CAD 80, Brighton, 1980, pp. 543–558.

[4] G. Biehl, W. Grass, and S. Hall, "Optimization of the influence of problem modifications on given microprogrammed controllers," in *Proc. 17th ACM-IEEE Design Automation Conf.*, Minneapolis, 1980, pp. 309–317.

[5] M. Breuer, A. Friedman, and A. Iosupovicz, "A survey of the state of the art of design automation," *IEEE Comput. Soc. Mag.*, vol. 14, no. 10, pp. 58–75, Oct. 1981.

[6] J. Darringer, W. Joyner, C. Berman, and L. Trevillyan, "Logic synthesis through local transformations," *IBM J. Res. Develop.*, vol. 4, pp. 272–280, 1981.

[7] A. Ditzinger, "Optimierung des Realisierungsaufwandes digitaler Steuerungen durch Modifikation der internen Schnittstellen," Fortschr.-Ber. VDI Z Reihe 9, Nr. 33, Düsseldorf: VDI-Verlag, 1982.

[8] A. Ditzinger and J. Beister, "Word reduction in microprogrammed controllers by state-dependent preprocessing of the inputs," *Microproc. Microprog.*, vol. 9, no. 3, pp. 161–173, Mar. 1982.

[9] W. Grass and H. M. Lipp, "LOGE—a highly effective system for logic design automation," *SIGDA Newslett.*, vol. 9, pp. 6–13, 1979.

[10] W. Grass and B. Thelen, "Ein leistungsfähiger Algorithmus zur Optimierung von Funktionsbündeln," *Dig. Proces.*, vol. 7, pp. 1–19, 1981.

[11] G. W. Leive and D. E. Thomas, "A technology relative logic synthesis and module selection system," in *Proc. 18th ACM-IEEE Design Automation Conf.*, Nashville, 1981, pp. 479–485.

[12] H. M. Lipp, "Conditions for the development of an effective CAD system for digital controllers," in *CAD in Medium Sized and Small Industries*, J. Mermet, Ed. Amsterdam: North-Holland, 1981, pp. 397–410.

[13] ——, "Strukturiertes Entwerfen in der Digitaltechnik," *NTZ Archiv 1*, vol. 4, pp. 3–10, 1982.

[14] H. M. Lipp, M. Nolle, and K. Sutter, "LOGE—Ein leistungsfähiges CAD System zum Entwurf digitaler Steuerungen," in *Proc. 10th Inter. Cong. Microelectronics*, Munich, 1982, to be published.

[15] M. C. McFarland, "On proving the correctness of optimizing transformations on a digital design automation system," in *Proc. 18th ACM-IEEE Design Automation Conf.*, Nashville, 1981, pp. 486–493.

[16] G. Musgrave, Ed., *Computer-Aided Design of Digital Electronic Circuits and Systems*. Amsterdam: North-Holland, 1979.

[17] S. Nakamura, S. Murai, and C. Tanaka, "LORES—logic reorganization system," in *Proc. 15th ACM-IEEE Design Automation Conf.*, Las Vegas, 1978, pp. 250–260.

[18] A. Parker, D. Thomas, D. Siewiorek, M. Barbacci, L. Hafer, G. Leive, and J. Kim, "The CMU—design automation system: an example of automated data path design," in *Proc. 16th ACM-IEEE Design Automation Conf.*, San Diego, 1979, pp. 73–80.

[19] R. Piloty, M. Barbacci, D. Borrione, D. Dietmeyer, F. Hill, and P. Skelly, "CONLAN—a formal construction method for hardware description languages," in *Proc. NCC*, Anaheim, 1980, vol. 49.

[20] B. Thelen, "Untersuchungen von Algorithmen für den rechnergestützten logischen Entwurf digitaler Baugruppen," Ph.D. dissertation, Dep. of Elec. Eng., Univ. Karlsruhe, 1981.

[21] C. A. Vissers, "Interface—definition, design and description of the relation of digital system parts," Ph.D. dissertation, Technische Hogeschool Twente, 1977.

Design for Testability—A Survey

THOMAS W. WILLIAMS, MEMBER, IEEE, AND KENNETH P. PARKER, MEMBER, IEEE

Invited Paper

Abstract—This paper discusses the basics of design for testability. A short review of testing is given along with some reasons why one should test. The different techniques of design for testability are discussed in detail. These include techniques which can be applied to today's technologies and techniques which have been recently introduced and will soon appear in new designs.

I. Introduction

INTEGRATED Circuit Technology is now moving from Large-Scale Integration (LSI) to Very-Large-Scale Integration (VLSI). This increase in gate count, which now can be as much as factors of three to five times, has also brought a decrease in gate costs, along with improvements in performance. All these attributes of VLSI are welcomed by the industry. However, a problem never adequately solved by LSI is still with us and is getting much worse: the problem of determining, in a cost-effective way, whether a component, module, or board has been manufactured correctly [1]–[3], [52]–[68].

The testing problem has two major facets:

1) test generation [74]–[99]
2) test verification [100]–[114].

Test generation is the process of enumerating stimuli for a circuit which will demonstrate its correct operation. Test verification is the process of proving that a set of tests are effective towards this end. To date, formal proof has been impossible in practice. Fault simulation has been our best alternative, yielding a quantitative measure of test effectiveness. With the vast increase in circuit density, the ability to generate test patterns automatically and conduct fault simulation with these patterns has drastically waned. As a result, some manufacturers are foregoing these more rigorous approaches and are accepting the risks of shipping a defective product. One general approach to addressing this problem is embodied in a collection of techniques known as "Design for Testability" [12]–[35].

Design for Testability initially attracted interest in connection with LSI designs. Today, in the context of VLSI, the phrase is gaining even more currency. The collection of techniques that comprise Design for Testability are, in some cases, general guidelines; in other cases, they are hard and fast design rules. Together, they can be regarded essentially as a menu of techniques, each with its associated cost of implementation and return on investment. The purpose of this paper is to present the basic concepts in testing, beginning with the fault models and carrying through to the different techniques associated with Design for Testability which are known today in the public sector. The design for testability techniques are divided into two categories [10]. The first category is that of the ad hoc technique for solving the testing problem. These techniques solve a problem for a given design and are not generally applicable to all designs. This is contrasted with the second category of structured approaches. These techniques are generally applicable and usually involve a set of design rules by which designs are implemented. The objective of a structured approach is to reduce the sequential complexity of a network to aid test generation and test verification.

The first ad hoc approach is partitioning [13], [17], [23], [26]. Partitioning is the ability to disconnect one portion of a network from another portion of a network in order to make testing easier. The next approach which is used at the board level is that of adding extra test points [23], [24]. The third ad hoc approach is that of Bus Architecture Systems [12], [27]. This is similar to the partitioning approach and allows one to divide and conquer—that is, to be able to reduce the network to smaller subnetworks which are much more manageable. These subnetworks are not necessarily designed with any design for testability in mind. The forth technique which bridges both the structured approach and the ad hoc approach is that of Signature Analysis [12], [27], [33], [55]. Signature Analysis requires some design rules at the board level, but is not directed at the same objective as the structure approaches are—that is, the ability to observe and control the state variables of a sequential machine.

For structured approaches, there are essentially four categories which will be discussed—the first of which is a multiplexer technique [14], [21], Random Access Scan, that has been recently published and has been used, to some extent, by others before. The next techniques are those of the Level-Sensitive Scan Design (LSSD) [16], [18]–[20], [34], [35] approach and the Scan Path approach which will be discussed in detail. These techniques allow the test generation problem to be completely reduced to one of generating tests for combinational logic. Another approach which will be discussed is that of the Scan/Set Logic [31]. This is similar to the LSSD approach and the Scan Path approach since shift registers are used to load and unload data. However, these shift registers are not part of the system data path and all system latches are not necessarily controllable and observable via the shift register. The fourth approach which will be discussed is that of Built-In Logic Block Observation (BILBO) [25] which has just recently been proposed. This technique has the attributes of both the LSSD network and Scan Path network, the ability to separate the network into combinational and sequential parts, and has the attribute of Signature Analysis—that is, employing linear feedback shift registers.

For each of the techniques described under the structured approach, the constraints, as well as various ways in which

Manuscript received June 14, 1982; revised September 15, 1982.
T. W. Williams is with IBM, General Technology Division, Boulder, CO 80302.
K. P. Parker is with Hewlett-Packard, Loveland Instrument Division, Loveland, CO 80537.

Reprinted from *Proc. IEEE*, vol. 71, pp. 98–112, Jan. 1983.

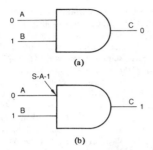

Fig. 1. Test for input stuck at fault. (a) Fault-free AND gate (good machine). (b) Faulty AND gate (faulty machine).

they can be exploited in design, manufacturing, testing, and field servicing will be described. The basic storage devices and the general logic structure resulting from the design constraints will be described in detail. The important question of how much it costs in logic gates and operating speed will be discussed qualitatively. All the structured approaches essentially allow the controllability and observability of the state variables in the sequential machine. In essence, then, test generation and fault simulation can be directed more at a combinational network, rather than at a sequential network.

A. Definitions and Assumptions

A model of faults which is used throughout the industry that does not take into account all possible defects, but is a more global type of model, is the Stuck-At model. The Stuck-At model [1]–[3], [9], [11] assumes that a logic gate input or output is fixed to either a logic 0 or a logic 1. Fig. 1(a) shows an AND gate which is fault-free. Fig. 1(b) shows an AND gate with input "A," Stuck-At-1 (S-A-1).

The faulty AND gate perceives the "A" input as 1, irrespective of the logic value placed on the input. The pattern applied to the fault-free AND gates in Fig. 1 has an output value of 0 since the input is 0 on the "A" input and 1 on the "B" input, and the AND'ing of those two leads to a 0 on the output. The pattern in Fig. 1(b) shows an output of 1, since the "A" input is perceived as a 1 even though a 0 is applied to that input. The 1 on the "B" input is perceived as a 1, and the results are AND'ed together to give a 1 output. Therefore, the pattern shown in Fig. 1(a) and (b) is a test for the "A" input, S-A-1, since there is a difference between the faulty gate (faulty machine) and the good gate (good machine). This pattern 01 on the "A" and "B" inputs, respectively, is considered a test because the good machine responds differently from the faulty machine. If they had the same response then that pattern would not have constituted a test for that fault.

If a network contained N nets, any net may be good, Stuck-At 1 or Stuck-At 0; thus all possible network state combinations would be 3^N. A network with 100 nets, then, would contain 5×10^{47} different combinations of faults. This would be far too many faults to assume. The run time of any program trying to generate tests or fault simulate tests for this kind of design would be impractical.

Therefore, the industry, for many years, has clung to the single Stuck-At fault assumption. That is, a good machine will have no faults. The faulty machines that are assumed will have one, and only one, of the stuck faults. In other words, all faults taken two at a time are not assumed, nor are all faults taken three at a time, etc. History has proven that the single

Stuck-At fault assumption, in prior technologies, has been adequate. However, there could be some problems in LSI—particularly with CMOS using the single Stuck-At fault assumption.

The problem with CMOS is that there are a number of faults which could change a combinational network into a sequential network. Therefore, the combinational patterns are no longer effective in testing the network in all cases. It still remains to be seen whether, in fact, the single Stuck-At fault assumption will survive the CMOS problems.

Also, the single Stuck-At fault assumption does not, in general, cover the bridging faults [43] that may occur. Historically again, bridging faults have been detected by having a high level—that is, in the high 90 percent—single Stuck-At fault coverage, where the single Stuck-At fault coverage is defined to be the number of faults that are tested divided by the number of faults that are assumed.

B. The VLSI Testing Problem

The VLSI testing problem is the sum of a number of problems. All the problems, in the final analysis, relate to the cost of doing business (dealt with in the following section). There are two basic problem areas:

1) test generation
2) test verification via fault simulation.

With respect to test generation, the problem is that as logic networks get larger, the ability to generate tests automatically is becoming more and more difficult.

The second facet of the VLSI testing problem is the difficulty in fault simulating the test patterns. Fault simulation is that process by which the fault coverage is determined for a specific set of input test patterns. In particular, at the conclusion of the fault simulation, every fault that is detected by the given pattern set is listed. For a given logic network with 1000 two-input logic gates, the maximum number of single Stuck-At faults which can be assumed is 6000. Some reduction in the number of single Stuck-At faults can be achieved by fault equivalencing [36], [38], [41], [42], [47]. However, the number of single Stuck-At faults needed to be assumed is about 3000. Fault simulation, then, is the process of applying every given test pattern to a fault-free machine and to each of the 3000 copies of the good machine containing one, and only one, of the single Stuck-At faults. Thus fault simulation, with respect to run time, is similar to doing 3001 good machine simulations.

Techniques are available to reduce the complexity of fault simulation, however, it still is a very time-consuming, and hence, expensive task [96], [104], [105], [107], [110], [112]–[114].

It has been observed that the computer run time to do test [80] generation and fault simulation is approximately proportional to the number of logic gates to the power of 3;[1] hence, small increases in gate count will yield quickly increasing run times. Equation (1)

---

[1] The value of the exponent given here (3) is perhaps pessimistic in some cases. Other analyses have used the value 2 instead. A quick rationale goes as follows: with a linear increase k in circuit size comes an attendant linear increase in the number of failure mechanisms (now yielding k squared increase in work). Also, as circuits become larger, they tend to become more strongly connected such that a given block is effected by more blocks and even itself. This causes more work to be done in a range we feel to be k cubed. This fairly nebulous concept of connectivity seems to be the cause for debate on whether the exponent should be 3 or some other value.

$$T = KN^3 \qquad (1)$$

shows this relationship, where T is computer run time, N is the number of gates, and K is the proportionality constant. The relationship does not take into account the falloff in automatic test generation capability due to sequential complexity of the network. It has been observed that computer run time just for fault simulation is proportional to N^2 without even considering the test generation phase.

When one talks about testing, the topic of functional testing always comes up as a feasible way to test a network. Theoretically, to do a complete functional test ("exhaustive" testing) seems to imply that all entries in a Karnaugh map (or excitation table) must be tested for a 1 or a 0. This means that if a network has N inputs and is purely combinational, then 2^N patterns are required to do a complete functional test. Furthermore, if a network has N inputs with M latches, at a minimum it takes 2^{N+M} patterns to do a complete functional test. Rarely is that minimum ever obtainable; and in fact, the number of tests required to do a complete functional test is very much higher than that. With LSI, this may be a network with $N = 25$ and $M = 50$, or 2^{75} patterns, which is approximately 3.8×10^{22} Assuming one had the patterns and applied them at an application rate of 1 μs per pattern, the test time would be over a billion years (10^9).

C. Cost of Testing

One might ask why so much attention is now being given to the level of testability at chip and board levels. The bottom line is the cost of doing business. A standard among people familiar with the testing process is: If it costs \$0.30 to detect a fault at the chip level, then it would cost \$3 to detect that same fault when it was embedded at the board level; \$30 when it is embedded at the system level; and \$300 when it is embedded at the system level but has to be found in the field. Thus if a fault can be detected at a chip or board level, then significantly larger costs per fault can be avoided at subsequent levels of packaging.

With VLSI and the inadequacy of automatic test generation and fault simulation, there is considerable difficulty in obtaining a level of testability required to achieve acceptable defect levels. If the defect level of boards is too high, the cost of field repairs is also too high. These costs, and in some cases, the inability to obtain a sufficient test, have led to the need to have "Design for Testability."

II. DESIGN FOR TESTABILITY

There are two key concepts in Design for Testability: controllability and observability. Control and observation of a network are central to implementing its test procedure. For example, consider the case of the simple AND block in Fig. 1. In order to be able to test the "A" input Stuck-At 1, it was necessary to control the "A" input to 0 and the "B" input to 1 and be able to observe the "C" output to determine whether a 0 was observed or a 1 was observed. The 0 is the result of the good machine, and the 1 would be the result, if you had a faulty machine. If this AND block is embedded into a much larger sequential network, the requirement of being able to control the "A" and "B" inputs to 0 and 1, respectively, and being able to observe the output "C," be it through some other logic blocks, still remains. Therein lies part of the problem of being able to generate tests for a network.

Because of the need to determine if a network has the attributes of controllability and observability that are desired, a number of programs have been written which essentially give analytic measures of controllability and observability for different nets in a given sequential network [69]–[73].

After observing the results of one of these programs in a given network, the logic designer can then determine whether some of the techniques, which will be described later, can be applied to this network to ease the testing problem. For example, test points may be added at critical points which are not observable or which are not controllable, or some of the techniques of Scan Path or LSSD can be used to initialize certain latches in the machine to avoid the difficulties of controllability associated with sequential machines. The popularity of such tools is continuing to grow, and a number of companies are now embarking upon their own controllability/observability measures.

III. AD HOC DESIGN FOR TESTABILITY [10]

Testing has moved from the afterthought position that it used to occupy to part of the design environment in LSI and VLSI. When testing was part of the afterthought, it was a very expensive process. Products were discarded because there was no adequate way to test them in production quantities.

There are two basic approaches which are prevalent today in the industry to help solve the testing problem. The first approach categorized here is Ad Hoc, and the second approach is categorized as a Structured Approach. The Ad Hoc techniques are those techniques which can be applied to a given product, but are not directed at solving the general sequential problem. They usually do offer relief, and their cost is probably lower than the cost of the Structured Approaches. The Structured Approaches, on the other hand, are trying to solve the general problem with a design methodology, such that when the designer has completed his design from one of these particular approaches, the results will be test generation and fault simulation at acceptable costs. Structured Approaches lend themselves more easily to design automation. Again, the main difference between the two approaches is probably the cost of implementation and hence, the return on investment for this extra cost. In the Ad Hoc approaches, the job of doing test generation and fault simulation are usually not as simple or as straightforward as they would be with the Structured Approaches, as we shall see shortly.

A number of techniques have evolved from MSI to LSI and now into VLSI that fall under the category of the ad hoc approaches of "Design for Testability." These techniques are usually solved at the board level and do not necessarily require changes in the logic design in order to accomplish them.

A. Partitioning

Because the task of test pattern generation and fault simulation is proportional to the number of logic gates to the third power, a significant amount of effort has been directed at approaches called "Divide and Conquer."

There are a number of ways in which the partitioning approach to Design for Testability can be implemented. The first is to mechanical partition by dividing a network in half. In essence, this would reduce the test generation and fault simulation tasks by 8 for two boards. Unfortunately, having two boards rather than one board can be a significant cost disadvantage and defeats the purpose of integration.

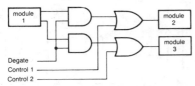

Fig. 2. Use of degating logic for logical partioning.

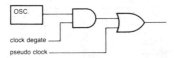

Fig. 3. Degating lines for oscillator.

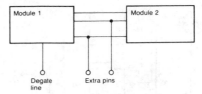

Fig. 4. Test points used as both inputs and outputs.

Fig. 5. "Bed of Nails" test.

Another approach that helps the partitioning problem, as well as helping one to "Divide and Conquer" is to use jumper wires. These wires would go off the board and then back on the board, so that the tester and the test generator can control and observe these nets directly. However, this could mean a significant number of I/O contacts at the board level which could also get very costly.

Degating is another technique for separating modules on a board. For example, in Fig. 2, a degating line goes to two AND blocks that are driven from Module 1. The results of those two AND blocks go to two independent OR blocks one controlled by Control Line 1, the other with Control Line 2. The output of the OR block from Control Line 1 goes into Module 2, and the output of Control Line 2 goes into Module 3. When the degate line is at the 0 value, the two Control Lines, 1 and 2, can be used to drive directly into Modules 2 and 3. Therefore, complete controllability of the inputs to Modules 2 and 3 can be obtained by using these control lines. If those two nets happen to be very difficult nets to control, as pointed out, say, by a testability measure program, then this would be a very cost-effective way of controlling those two nets and hence, being able to derive the tests at a very reasonable cost.

A classical example of degating logic is that associated with an oscillator, as shown in Fig. 3. In general, if an oscillator is free-running on a board, it is very difficult, and sometimes impossible, to synchronize the tester with the activity of the logic board. As a result, degating logic can be used here to block the oscillator and have a pseudo-clock line which can be controlled by the tester, so that the dc testing of all the logic on that board can be synchronized. All of these techniques require a number of extra primary inputs and primary outputs and possibly extra modules to perform the degating.

B. Test Points

Another approach to help the controllability and observability of a sequential network is to use test points [23], [24]. If a test point is used as a primary input to the network, then that can function to enhance controllability. If a test point is used as a primary output, then that is used to enhance the observability of a network. In some cases, a single pin can be used as both an input and an output.

For example, in Fig. 4, Module 1 has a degate function, so that the output of those two pins on the module could go to noncontrolling values. Thus the external pins which are dotted into those nets could control those nets and drive Module 2.

On the other hand, if the degate function is at the opposite value, then the output of Module 1 can be observed on these external pins. Thus the enhancement of controllability and observability can be accommodated by adding pins which can act as both inputs and outputs under certain degating conditions.

Another technique which can be used for controllability is to have a pin which, in one mode, implies system operation, and in another mode takes N inputs and gates them to a decoder. The 2^N outputs of the decoder are used to control certain nets to values which otherwise would be difficult to obtain. By so doing, the controllability of the network is enhanced.

As mentioned before, predictability is an issue which is as important as controllability and observability. Again, test points can be used here. For example, a CLEAR or PRESET function for all memory elements can be used. Thus the sequential machine can be put into a known state with very few patterns.

Another technique which falls into the category of test points and is very widely used is that of the "Bed of Nails" [31] tester, Fig. 5. The Bed of Nails tester probes the underside of a board to give a larger number of points for observability and controllability. This is in addition to the normal tester contact to the board under test. The drawback of this technique is that the tester must have enough test points to be able to control and observe each one of these nails on the Bed of Nails tester. Also, there are extra loads which are placed on the nets and this can cause some drive and receive problems. Furthermore, the mechanical fixture which will hold the Bed of Nails has to be constructed, so that the normal forces on the probes are sufficient to guarantee reliable contacts. Another application for the Bed of Nails testing is to do "drive/sense nails" [31] or "*in situ*" or "in-circuit" testing, which, effectively, is the technique of testing each chip on the board independently of the other chips on the board. For each chip, the appropriate nails and/or primary inputs are driven so as to prevent one chip from being driven by the other chips on the board. Once this state has been established, the isolated chip on the board can now be tested. In this case, the resolution to the failing

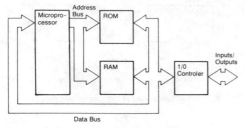

Fig. 6. Bus structured microcomputer.

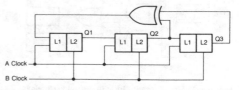

Fig. 7. Counting capabilities of a linear feedback shift register.

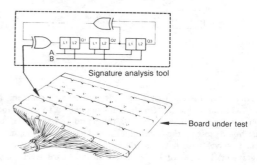

Fig. 8. Use of signature analysis tool.

chip is much better than edge connector tests, however, there is some exposure to incomplete testing of interconnections and care must be taken not to damage the circuit when overdriving it. Design for testability in a Bed of Nails environment must take the issues of contact reliability, multiplicity, and electrical loading into account.

C. Bus Architecture

An approach that has been used very successfully to attack the partitioning problem by the microcomputer designers is to use a bus structured architecture. This architecture allows access to critical buses which go to many different modules on the computer board. For example, in Fig. 6, you can see that the data bus is involved with both the microprocessor module, the ROM module, the RAM module, and the I/O Controller module. If there is external access to the data bus and three of the four modules can be turned off the data bus—that is, their outputs can be put into a high-impedance state (three-state driver)—then the data bus could be used to drive the fourth module, as if it were a primary input (or primary output) to that particular module. Similarly, with the address bus, access again must be controlled externally to the board, and thus the address bus can be very useful to controlling test patterns to the microcomputer board. These buses, in essence, partition the board in a unique way, so that testing of subunits can be accomplished. A drawback of bus-structured designs comes with faults on the bus itself. If a bus wire is stuck, any module or the bus trace itself may be the culprit. Normal testing is done by deducing the location of a fault from voltage information. Isolating a bus failure may require current measurements, which are much more difficult to do.

D. Signature Analysis

This technique for testing, introduced in 1977 [27], [33], [55] is heavily reliant on planning done in the design stage. That is why this technique falls between the Ad Hoc and the Structured Approaches for Design for Testability, since some care must be taken at the board level in order to ensure proper operation of this Signature Analysis of the board [12]. Signature Analysis is well-suited to bus structure architectures, as previously mentioned and in particular, those associated with microcomputers. This will become more apparent shortly.

The integral part of the Signature Analysis approach is that of a linear feedback shift register [8]. Fig. 7 shows an example of a 3-bit linear feedback shift register. This linear feedback shift register is made up of three shift register latches. Each one is represented by a combination of an $L1$ latch and an $L2$ latch. These can be thought of as the master latch being the $L1$ latch and the slave latch being the $L2$ latch. An "A" clock clocks all the $L1$ latches, and a "B" clock clocks all the

$L2$ latches, so that turning the "A" and "B" clocks on and off independently will shift the shift register 1-bit position to the right. Furthermore, this linear shift register has an EXCLUSIVE-OR gate which takes the output, $Q2$, the second bit in the shift register, and EXCLUSIVE-OR's it with the third bit in the shift register, $Q3$. The result of that EXCLUSIVE-OR is the input to the first shift register. A single clock could be used for this shift register, which is generally the case, however, this concept will be used shortly when some of the structured design approaches are discussed which use two nonoverlapping clocks. Fig. 7 shows how this linear feedback shift register will count for different initial values.

For longer shift registers, the maximal length linear feedback configurations can be obtained by consulting tables [8] to determine where to tap off the linear feedback shift register to perform the EXCLUSIVE-OR function. Of course, only EXCLUSIVE-OR blocks can be used, otherwise, the linearity would not be preserved.

The key to Signature Analysis is to design a network which can stimulate itself. A good example of such a network would be microprocessor-based boards, since they can stimulate themselves using the intelligence of the processor driven by the memory on the board.

The Signature Analysis procedure is one which has the shift register in the Signature Analysis tool, which is external to the board and not part of the board in any way, synchronized with the clocking that occurs on the board, see Fig. 8. A probe is used to probe a particular net on the board. The result of that probe is EXCLUSIVE-OR'ed into the linear feedback shift register. Of course, it is important that the linear feedback shift register be initialized to the same starting place every time, and that the clocking sequence be a fixed number, so that the tests can be repeated. The board must also have some initialization, so that its response will be repeated as well.

After a fixed number of clock periods—let's assume 50—a particular value will be stored in $Q1$, $Q2$, and $Q3$. It is not necessarily the value that would have occurred if the linear feedback shift register was just counted 50 times—Modulo 7.

The value will be changed, because the values coming from the board via the probe will not necessarily be a continuous string of 1's; there will be 1's intermixed with 0's.

The place where the shift register stops on the Signature Analysis Tool—that is, the values for $Q1$, $Q2$, and $Q3$ is the Signature for that particular node for the good machine. The question is: If there were errors present at one or more points in the string of 50 observations of that particular net of the board, would the value stored in the shift register for $Q1$, $Q2$, and $Q3$ be different than the one for the good machine? It has been shown that with a 16-bit linear feedback shift register, the probability of detecting one or more errors is extremely high [55]. In essence, the signature, or "residue," is the remainder of the data stream after division by an irreducable polynomial. There is considerable data compression—that is, after the results of a number of shifting operations, the test data are reduced to 16 bits, or, in the case of Fig. 8, 3 bits. Thus the result of the Signature Analysis tool is basically a Go/No-Go for the output for that particular module.

If the bad output for that module were allowed to cycle around through a number of other modules on the board and then feed back into this particular module, it would not be clear after examining all the nodes in the loop which module was defective—whether it was the module whose output was being observed, or whether it was another module upstream in the path. This gives rise to two requirements for Signature Analysis. First of all, closed-loop paths must be broken at the board level. Second, the best place to start probing with Signature Analysis is with a "kernel" of logic. In other words, on a microprocessor-based board, one would start with the outputs of the microprocessor itself and then build up from that particular point, once it has been determined that the microprocessor is good.

This breaking of closed loops is a tenant of Design for Testability and for Signature Analysis. There is a little overhead for implementing Signature Analysis. Some ROM space would be required (to stimulate the self-test), as well as extra jumpers, in order to break closed loops on the board. Once this is done, however, the test can be obtained for very little cost. The only question that remains is about the quality of the tests—that is, how good are the tests that are being generated, do they cover all the faults, etc.

Unfortunately, the logic models—for example, microprocessors—are not readily available to the board user. Even if a microprocessor logic model were available, they would not be able to do a complete fault simulation of the patterns because it would be too large. Hence, Signature Analysis may be the best that could be done for this particular board with the given inputs which the designer has. Presently, large numbers of users are currently using the Signature Analysis technique to test boards containing LSI and VLSI components.

IV. Structured Design for Testability

Today, with the utilization of LSI and VLSI technology, it has become apparent that even more care will have to be taken in the design stage in order to ensure testability and produceability of digital networks. This has led to rigorous and highly structured design practices. These efforts are being spearheaded not by the makers of LSI/VLSI devices but by electronics firms which possess captive IC facilities and the manufacturers of large main-frame computers.

Most structured design practices [14]–[16], [18]–[21], [25], [31], [32], [34], [35] are built upon the concept that if the

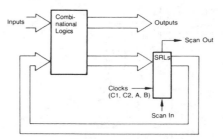

Fig. 9. Classical model of a sequential network utilizing a shift register for storage.

values in all the latches can be controlled to any specific value, and if they can be observed with a very straightforward operation then the test generation, and possibly, the fault task, can be reduced to that of doing test generation and fault simulation for a combinational logic network. A control signal can switch the memory elements from their normal mode of operation to a mode that makes them controllable and observable.

It appears from the literature that several companies, such as IBM, Fujitsu Ltd., Sperry-Univac, and Nippon Electric Co., Ltd. [14]–[16], [18]–[21], [31], [32], [35] have been dedicating formidable amounts of resources toward Structured Design for Testability. One notes simply by scanning the literature on testing, that many of the practical concepts and tools for testing were developed by main-frame manufacturers who do not lack for processor power. It is significant, then, that these companies, with their resources, have recognized that unstructured designs lead to unacceptable testing problems. Presently, IBM has extensively documented its efforts in Structured Design for Testability, and these are reviewed first.

A. Level-Sensitive Scan Design (LSSD)

With the concept that the memory elements in an IC can be threaded together into a shift register, the memory elements values can be both controlled and observed. Fig. 9 shows the familiar generalized sequential circuit model modified to use a shift register. This technique enhances both controllability and observability, allowing us to augment testing by controlling inputs and internal states, and easily examining internal state behavior. An apparent disadvantage is the serialization of the test, potentially costing more time for actually running a test.

LSSD is IBM's discipline for structural design for testability. "Scan" refers to the ability to shift into or out of any state of the network. "Level-sensitive" refers to constraints on circuit excitation, logic depth, and the handling of clocked circuitry. A key element in the design is the "shift register latch" (SRL) such as can be implemented in Fig. 10. Such a circuit is immune to most anomalies in the ac characteristics of the clock, requiring only that it remain high (sample) at least long enough to stabilize the feedback loop, before being returned to the low (hold) state [18], [19]. The lines D and C form the normal mode memory function while lines I, A, B, and $L2$ comprise additional circuitry for the shift register function.

The shift registers are threaded by connecting I to $L2$ and operated by clocking lines A and B in two-phase fashion. Fig. 11 shows four modules threaded for shift register action. Now note in Fig. 11 that each module could be an SRL or, one level up, a board containing threaded IC's, etc. Each level of pack-

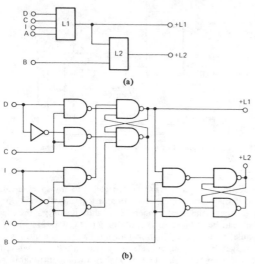

(a)

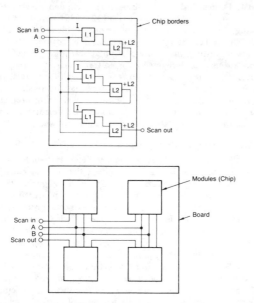

(b)

Fig. 10. Shift register latch (SRL). (a) Symbolic representation. (b) Implementation in AND-INVERT gates.

Fig. 11. Interconnection of SRL's on an integrated circuit and board.

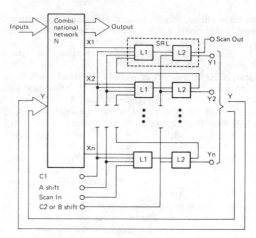

Fig. 12. General structure of an LSSD subsystem with two system clocks.

aging requires the same four additional lines to implement the shift register scan feature. Fig. 12 depicts a general structure for an LSSD subsystem with a two-phase system clock. Additional rules concerning the gating of clocks, etc., are given by Williams and Eichelberger [18], [19]. Also, it is not practical to implement RAM with SRL memory, so additional procedures are required to handle embedded RAM circuitry [20].

Given that an LSSD structure is achieved, what are the rewards? It turns out that the network can now be thought of as purely combinational, where tests are applied via primary inputs and shift register outputs. The testing of combinational circuits is a well understood and (barely) tractable problem. Now techniques such as the D-Algorithm [93] compiled code Boolean simulation [2], [74], [106], [107], and adaptive random test generation [87], [95], [98] are again viable approaches to the testing problem. Further, as small subsystems are tested, their aggregates into larger systems are also testable by cataloging the position of each testable subsystem in the shift register chain. System tests become (ideally) simple concatenations of subsystem tests. Though ideals are rarely achieved, the potential for solving otherwise hopeless testing problems is very encouraging.

In considering the cost performance impacts, there are a number of negative impacts associated with the LSSD design philosophy. First of all, the shift register latches in the shift register are, logically, two or three times as complex as simple latches. Up to four additional primary inputs/outputs are required at each package level for control of the shift registers. External asynchronous input signals must not change more than once every clock cycle. Finally, all timing within the subsystem is controlled by externally generated clock signals.

In terms of additional complexity of the shift register hold latches, the overhead from experience has been in the range of 4 to 20 percent. The difference is due to the extent to which the system designer made use of the $L2$ latches for system function. It has been reported in the IBM System 38 literature that 85 percent of the $L2$ latches were used for system function. This drastically reduces the overhead associated with this design technique.

With respect to the primary inputs/outputs that are required to operate the shift register, this can be reduced significantly by making functional use of some of the pins. For example, the scan-out pin could be a functional output of an SRL for that particular chip. Also, overall performance of the subsystem may be degraded by the clocking requirement, but the effect should be small.

The LSSD structured design approach for Design for Testability eliminates or alleviates some of the problems in designing, manufacturing and maintaining LSI systems at a reasonable cost.

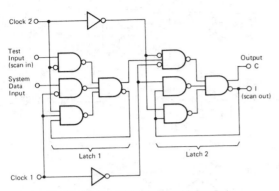

Fig. 13. Raceless D-type flip-flop with Scan Path.

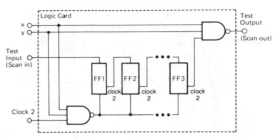

Fig. 14. Configuration of Scan Path on Card.

B. Scan Path

In 1975, a survey paper of test generation systems in Japan was presented by members of Nippon Electric Co., Ltd. [21]. In that survey paper, a technique they described as Scan Path was presented. The Scan Path technique has the same objectives as the LSSD approach which has just been described. The Scan Path technique similarities and differences to the LSSD approach will be presented.

The memory elements that are used in the Scan Path approach are shown in Fig. 13. This memory element is called a raceless D-type flip-flop with Scan Path.

In system operation, Clock 2 is at a logic value of 1 for the entire period. This, in essence, blocks the test or scan input from affecting the values in the first latch. This D-type flip-flop really contains two latches. Also, by having Clock 2 at a logic value of 1, the values in Latch 2 are not disturbed.

Clock 1 is the sole clock in system operation for this D-type flip-flop. When Clock 1 is at a value of 0, the System Data Input can be loaded into Latch 1. As long as Clock 1 is 0 for sufficient time to latch up the data, it can then turn off. As it turns off, it then will make Latch 2 sensitive to the data output of Latch 1. As long as Clock 1 is equal to a 1 so that data can be latched up into Latch 2, reliable operation will occur. This assumes that as long as the output of Latch 2 does not come around and feed the system data input to Latch 1 and change it during the time that the inputs to both Latch 1 and Latch 2 are active. The period of time that this can occur is related to the delay of the inverter block for Clock 1. A similar phenomenon will occur with Clock 2 and its associated inverter block. This race condition is the exposure to the use of only one system clock.

This points out a significant difference between the Scan Path approach and the LSSD approach. One of the basic principles of the LSSD approach is level-sensitive operation—the ability to operate the clocks in such a fashion that no races will exist. In the LSSD approach, a separate clock is required for Latch 1 from the clock that operates Latch 2.

In terms of the scanning function, the D-type flip-flop with Scan Path has its own scan input called test input. This is clocked into the $L1$ latch by Clock 2 when Clock 2 is a 0, and the results of the $L1$ latch are clocked into Latch 2 when Clock 2 is a 1. Again, this applies to master/slave operation of Latch 1 and Latch 2 with its associated race with proper attention to delays this race will not be a problem.

Another feature of the Scan Path approach is the configuration used at the logic card level. Modules on the logic card are all connected up into a serial scan path, such that for each card, there is one scan path. In addition, there are gates for selecting a particular card in a subsystem. In Fig. 14, when X and Y are both equal to 1—that is the selection mechanism—Clock 2 will then be allowed to shift data through the scan path. Any other time, Clock 2 will be blocked, and its output will be blocked. The reason for blocking the output is that a number of card outputs can then be put together; thus the blocking function will put their output to noncontrolling values, so that a particular card can have unique control of the unique test output for that system.

It has been reported by the Nippon Electric Company that they have used the Scan Path approach, plus partitioning which will be described next, for systems with 100 000 blocks or more. This was for the FLT-700 System, which is a large processor system.

The partitioning technique is one which automatically separates the combinational network into smaller subnetworks, so that the test generator can do test generation for the small subnetworks, rather than the larger networks. A partition is automatically generated by backtracing from the D-type flip-flops, through the combinational logic, until it encounters a D-type flip-flop in the backtrace (or primary input). Some care must be taken so that the partitions do not get too large. To that end, the Nippon Electric Company approach has used a controlled D-type flip-flop to block the backtracing of certain partitions when they become too high. This is another facet of Design for Testability—that is, the introduction of extra flip-flops totally independent of function, in order to control the partitioning algorithm.

Other than the lack of the level sensitive attribute to the Scan Path approach, the technique is very similar to the LSSD approach. The introduction of the Scan Path approach was the first practical implementation of shift registers for testing which was incorporated in a total system.

C. Scan/Set Logic

A technique similar to Scan Path and LSSD, but not exactly the same, is the Scan/Set technique put forth by Sperry-Univac [31]. The basic concept of this technique is to have shift registers, as in Scan Path or in LSSD, but these shift registers are not in the data path. That is, they are not in the system data path; they are independent of all the system latches. Fig. 15 shows an example of the Scan/Set Logic, referred to as bit serial logic.

The basic concept is that the sequential network can be

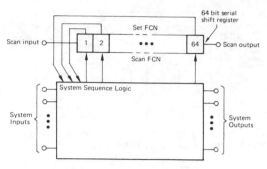

Fig. 15. Scan/Set Logic (bit-serial).

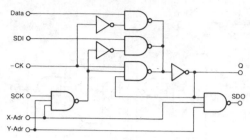

Fig. 16. Polarity-hold-type addressable latch.

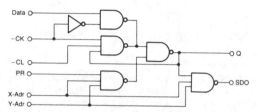

Fig. 17. Set/Reset type addressable latch.

sampled at up to 64 points. These points can be loaded into the 64-bit shift register with a single clock. Once the 64 bits are loaded, a shifting process will occur, and the data will be scanned out through the scan-out pin. In the case of the set function, the 64 bits can be funneled into the system logic, and then the appropriate clocking structure required to load data into the system latches is required in this system logic. Furthermore, the set function could also be used to control different paths to ease the testing function.

In general, this serial Scan/Set Logic would be integrated onto the same chip that contrains sequential system logic. However, some applications have been put forth where the bit serial Scan/Set Logic was off-chip, and the bit-serial Scan/Set Logic only sampled outputs or drove inputs to facilitate in-circuit testing.

Recently, Motorola has come forth with a chip which is T^2L and which has I^2L logic integrated on that same chip. This has the Scan/Set Logic bit serial shift registers built in I^2L. The T^2L portion of the chip is a gate array, and the I^2L is on the chip, whether the customer wants it or not. It is up to the customer to use the bit-serial logic if he chooses.

At this point, it should be explained that if all the latches within the system sequential network are not both scanned and set, then the test generation function is not necessarily reduced to a total combinational test generation function and fault simulation function. However, this technique will greatly reduce the task of test generation and fault simulation.

Again, the Scan/Set technique has the same objectives as Scan Path and LSSD—that is, controllability and observability. However, in terms of its implementation, it is not required that the set function set all system latches, or that the scan function scan all system latches. This design flexibility would have a reflection in the software support required to implement such a technique.

Another advantage of this technique is that the scan function can occur during system operation—that is, the sampling pulse to the 64-bit serial shift register can occur while system clocks are being applied to the system sequential logic, so that a snapshot of the sequential machine can be obtained and off-loaded without any degradation in system performance.

D. Random-Access Scan

Another technique similar to the Scan Path technique and LSSD is the Random-Access Scan technique put forth by Fujitsu [14]. This technique has the same objective as Scan Path and LSSD—that is, to have complete controllability and observability of all internal latches. Thus the test generation func-

tion can be reduced to that of combinational test generation and combinational fault simulation as well.

Random-Access Scan differs from the other two techniques in that shift registers are not employed. What is employed is an addressing scheme which allows each latch to be uniquely selected, so that it can be either controlled or observed. The mechanism for addressing is very similar to that of a Random-Access Memory, and hence, its name.

Figs. 16 and 17 show the two basic latch configurations that are required for the Random-Access Scan approach. Fig. 16 is a single latch which has added to it an extra data port which is a Scan Data In port (SDI). These data are clocked into the latch by the SCK clock. The SCK clock can only affect this latch, if both the X and Y addresses are one. Furthermore, when the X address and Y address are one, then the Scan Data Out (SDO) point can be observed. System data labeled Data in Figs. 16 and 17 are loaded into this latch by the system clock labeled CK.

The set/reset-type addressable latch in Fig. 17 does not have a scan clock to load data into the system latch. This latch is first cleared by the CL line, and the CL line is connected to other latches that are also set/reset-type addressable latches. This, then, places the output value Q to a 0 value. A preset is directed at those latches that are required to be set to a 1 for that particular test. This preset is directed by addressing each one of those latches and applying the preset pulse labeled PR. The output of the latch Q will then go to a 1. The observability mechanism for Scan Data Out is exactly the same as for the latch shown in Fig. 16.

Fig. 18 gives an overall view of the system configuration of the Random-Access Scan approach. Notice that, basically, there is a Y address, an X address, a decoder, the addressable storage elements, which are the memory elements or latches, and the sequential machine, system clocks, and CLEAR function. There is also an SDI which is the input for a given latch, an SDO which is the output data for that given latch, and a scan clock. There is also one logic gate necessary to create the preset function.

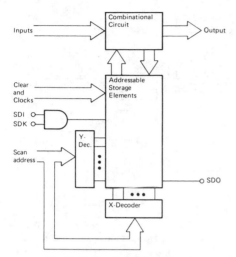

Fig. 18. Random-Access Scan network.

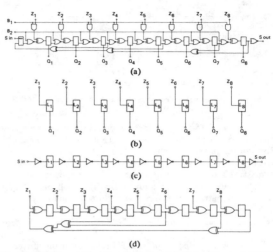

Fig. 19. BILBO and its different modes. (a) General form of BILBO register. (b) $B_1 B_2 = 11$ system orientation mode. (c) $B_1 B_2 = 00$ linear shift register mode. (d) $B_1 B_2 = 10$ signature analysis register with m multiple inputs ($Z_1, Z_2, \cdots, Z_8$).

The Random-Access Scan technique allows the observability and controllability of all system latches. In addition, any point in the combinational network can be observed with the addition of one gate per observation point, as well as one address in the address gate, per observation point.

While the Scan Path approach and the LSSD approach require two latches for every point which needs to be observed, the overhead for Random-Access Scan is about three to four gates per storage element. In terms of primary inputs/outputs, the overhead is between 10 and 20. This pin overhead can be diminished by using the serial scan approach for the X and Y address counter, which would lead to 6 primary inputs/outputs.

V. SELF-TESTING AND BUILT-IN TESTS

As a natural outgrowth of the Structured Design approach for "Design for Testability," Self-Tests and Built-In Tests have been getting considerably more attention. Four techniques will be discussed, which fall into this category, BILBO, Syndrome Testing, Testing by Verifying Walsh Testing Coefficients, and Autonomous Testing. Each of these techniques will be described.

A. Built-In Logic Block Observation, BILBO

A technique recently presented takes the Scan Path and LSSD concept and integrates it with the Signature Analysis concept. The end result is a technique for Built-In Logic Block Observation, BILBO [25].

Fig. 19 gives the form of an 8-bit BILBO register. The block labeled L_i ($i = 1, 2, \cdots, 8$) are the system latches. B_1 and B_2 are control values for controlling the different functions that the BILBO register can perform. S_{IN} is the scan-in input to the 8-bit register, and S_{OUT} is the scan-out for the 8-bit register. Q_i ($i = 1, 2, \cdots, 8$) are the output values for the eight system latches. Z_i ($i = 1, 2, \cdots, 8$) are the inputs from the combinational logic. The structure that this network will be embedded into will be discussed shortly.

There are three primary modes of operation for this register, as well as one secondary mode of operation for this register. The first is shown in Fig. 19(b)—that is, with B_1 and B_2 equal to 11. This is a Basic System Operation mode, in which the

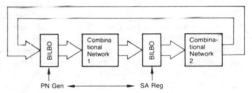

Fig. 20. Use of BILBO registers to test combinational Network 1.

Z_i values are loaded into the L_i, and the outputs are available on Q_i for system operation. This would be your normal register function.

When $B_1 B_2$ equals 00, the BILBO register takes on the form of a linear shift register, as shown in Fig. 19(c). Scan-in input to the left, through some inverters, and basically lining up the eight registers into a single scan path, until the scan-out is reached. This is similar to Scan Path and LSSD.

The third mode is when $B_1 B_2$ equals 10. In this mode, the BILBO register takes on the attributes of a linear feedback shift register of maximal length with multiple linear inputs. This is very similar to a Signature Analysis register, except that there is more than one input. In this situation, there are eight unique inputs. Thus after a certain number of shift clocks, say, 100, there would be a unique signature left in the BILBO register for the good machine. This good machine signature could be off-loaded from the register by changing from Mode $B_1 B_2 = 10$ to Mode $B_1 B_2 = 00$, in which case a shift register operation would exist, and the signature then could be observed from the scan-out primary output.

The fourth function that the BILBO register can perform is $B_1 B_2$ equal to 01, which would force a reset on the register. (This is not depicted in Fig. 19.)

The BILBO registers are used in the system operation, as shown in Fig. 20. Basically, a BILBO register with combinational logic and another BILBO register with combinational logic, as well as the output of the second combinational logic network can feed back into the input of the first BILBO regis-

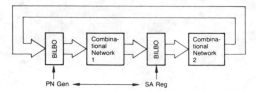

Fig. 21. Use of BILBO registers to test combinational Network 2.

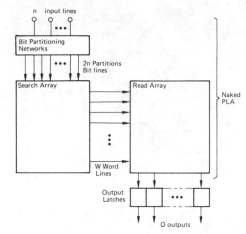

Fig. 22. PLA model.

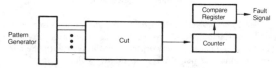

Fig. 23. Syndrome test structure.

ter. The BILBO approach takes one other fact into account, and that is that, in general, combinational logic is highly susceptible to random patterns. Thus if the inputs to the BILBO register, $Z_1, Z_2, \cdots, Z_8$, can be controlled to fixed values, such that the BILBO register is in the maximal length linear feedback shift register mode (Signature Analysis) it will output a sequence of patterns which are very close to random patterns. Thus random patterns can be generated quite readily from this register. These sequences are called Pseudo Random Patterns (PN).

If, in the first operation, this BILBO register on the left in Fig. 20 is used as the PN generator—that is, its data inputs are held to fixed values—then the output of that BILBO register will be random patterns. This will then do a reasonable test, if sufficient numbers of patterns are applied, of the Combinational Logic Network 1. The results of this test can be stored in a Signature Analysis register approach with multiple inputs to the BILBO register on the right. After a fixed number of patterns have been applied, the signature is scanned out of the BILBO register on the right for good machine compliance. If that is successfully completed, then the roles are reversed, and the BILBO register on the right will be used as a PN sequence generator; the BILBO register on the left will then be used as a Signature Analysis register with multiple inputs from Combinational Logic Network 2, see Fig. 21. In this mode, the Combinational Logic Network 2 will have random patterns applied to its inputs and its outputs stored in the BILBO register on the far left. Thus the testing of the combinational logic networks 1 and 2 can be completed at very high speeds by only applying the shift clocks, while the two BILBO registers are in the Signature Analysis mode. At the conclusion of the tests, off-loading of patterns can occur, and determination of good machine operation can be made.

This technique solves the problem of test generation and fault simulation if the combinational networks are susceptible to random patterns. There are some known networks which are not susceptible to random patterns. They are Programmable Logic Arrays (PLA's), see Fig. 22. The reason for this is that the fan-in in PLA's is too large. If an AND gate in the search array had 20 inputs, then each random pattern would have $1/2^{20}$ probability of coming up with the correct input pattern. On the other hand, random combinational logic networks with maximum fan-in of 4 can do quite well with random patterns.

The BILBO technique solves another problem and that is of test data volume. In LSSD, Scan Path, Scan/Set, or Random-Access Scan, a considerable amount of test data volume is involved with the shifting in and out. With BIBLO, if 100 patterns are run between scan-outs, the test data volume may be reduced by a factor of 100. The overhead for this technique is higher than for LSSD since about two EXCLUSIVE-OR's must be used per latch position. Also, there is more delay in the system data path (one or two gate delays). If VLSI has the huge number of logic gates available than this may be a very efficient way to use them.

B. Syndrome Testing

Recently, a technique was shown which could be used to test a network with fairly minor changes to the network. The technique is Syndrome Testing. The technique requires that all 2^n patterns be applied to the input of the network and then the number of 1's on the output be counted [115], [116].

Testing is done by comparing the number of 1's for the good machine to the number of 1's for the faulty machine. If there is a difference, the fault(s) in the faulty machine are detected (or Syndrome testable). To be more formal the Syndrome is:

Definition 1: The *Syndrome S* of a Boolean function is defined as

$$S = \frac{K}{2^n}$$

where K is the number of minterns realized by the function, and n is the number of binary input lines to the Boolean function.

Not all Boolean functions are totally Syndrome testable for all the single stuck-at-faults. Procedures are given in [115] with a minimal or near minimal number of primary inputs to make the networks Syndrome testable. In a number of "real networks" (i.e., SN74181, etc.) the numbers of extra primary inputs needed was at most one (<5 percent) and not more than two gates (<4 percent) were needed. An extension [116] to this work was published which showed a way of making a network Syndrome testable by adding extra inputs. This resulted in a somewhat longer test sequence. This is accomplished by holding some input constant while applying all 2^k inputs ($k < n$) then holding others constant and applying 2^l input patterns to l inputs. Whether the network is modified or not, the test data volume for a Syndrome testable design is extremely low. The general test setup is shown in Fig. 23. The structure requires a pattern generator which applies all possible patterns once, a counter to count the 1's, and a com-

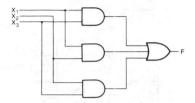

Fig. 24. Function to be tested with Walsh coefficients.

TABLE I
EXAMPLES OF WALSH FUNCTIONS AND WALSH COEFFICIENTS

$X_1 X_2 X_3$	W_2	$W_{1,3}$	F	$W_2 F$	$W_{1,3} F$	W_{All}	$W_{All} F$
0 0 0	−1	+1	0	+1	−1	+1	+1
0 0 1	−1	−1	0	+1	+1	−1	−1
0 1 0	+1	+1	0	−1	−1	−1	−1
0 1 1	+1	−1	1	+1	−1	+1	−1
1 0 0	−1	−1	0	+1	+1	−1	−1
1 0 1	−1	+1	1	−1	+1	+1	+1
1 1 0	+1	−1	1	+1	−1	+1	−1
1 1 1	+1	+1	1	+1	+1	−1	+1

$$C_{ALL} = 4$$

pare network. The overhead quoted is necessary to make the CUT Syndrome testable and does not include the pattern generator, counter, or compare register.

C. Testing by Verifying Walsh Coefficients

A technique which is similar to Syndrome Testing, in that it requires all possible input patterns be applied to the combinational network, is testing by verifying Walsh coefficients [117]. This technique only checks two of the Walsh coefficients and then makes conclusions about the network with respect to stuck-at-faults.

In order to calculate the Walsh coefficients, the logical value 0 (1) is associated with the arithmetic value −1(+1). There are 2^n Walsh functions. W_0 is defined to be 1, W_i is derived from all possible (arithmetic) products of the subject of independent input variables selected for that Walsh function. Table I shows the Walsh function for W_2, $W_{1,3}$, then $W_2 F$, $W_{1,3} F$, finally W_{all} and $W_{all} F$. These values are calculated for the network in Fig. 24. If the values are summed for $W_{all} F$, the Walsh coefficient C_{all} is calculated. The Walsh coefficient C_0 is just $W_0 F$ summed. This is equivalent to the Syndrome in magnitude times 2^n. If $C_{all} \neq 0$ then all stuck-at-faults on primary inputs will be detected by measuring C_{all}. If the fault is present $C_{all} = 0$. If the network has $C_{all} = 0$ it can be easily modified such that $C_{all} \neq 0$. If the network has reconvergent fan-out then further checks need to be made (the number of inverters in each path has a certain property); see [117]. If these are successful, then by checking C_{all} and C_0, all the single stuck-at-faults can be detected. Some design constraints maybe needed to make sure that the network is testable by measuring C_{all} and C_0. Fig. 25 shows the network needed to determine C_{all} and C_0. The value p is the parity of the driving counter and the response counter is an up/down counter. Note, two passes must be made of the driving counter, one for C_{all} and one for C_0.

D. Autonomous Testing

The fourth technique which will be discussed in the area of self-test/built-in-test is Autonomous Testing [118]. Autonomous Testing like Syndrome Testing and testing Walsh coefficients requires all possible patterns be applied to the network inputs. However, with Autonomous Testing the outputs of

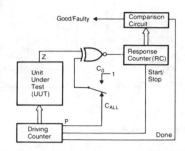

Fig. 25. Tester for veryfying C_0 and C_{all} Walsh coefficients.

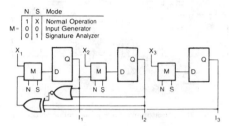

Fig 26. Reconfigurable 3-bit LFSR module.

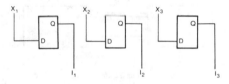

N = 1: Normal Operation

Fig. 27. Reconfigurable 3-bit LFSR module.

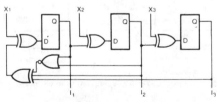

N = 0, S = 1: Signature Analyzer

Fig. 28. Reconfigurable 3-bit LFSR module.

the network must be checked for each pattern against the value for the good machine. The results is that irrespective of the fault model Autonomous Testing will detect the faults (assuming the faulty machine does not turn into a sequential machine from a combinational machine). In order to help the network apply its own patterns and accumulate the results of the tests rather than observing every pattern for 2^n input patterns, a structure similar to BILBO register is used. This register has some unique attributes and is shown in Figs. 26–29. If a combinational network has 100 inputs, the network must be modified such that the subnetwork can be verified and, thus, the whole network will be tested.

Two approaches to partitioning are presented in the paper "Design for Autonomous Test" [118]. The first is to use

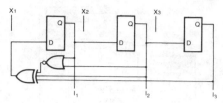

N = 0, S = 0: Input Generator

Fig. 29. Reconfigurable 3-bit LFSR module.

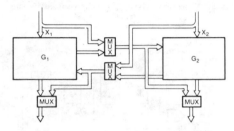

Fig. 30. Autonomous Testing—general network.

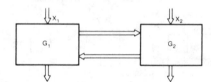

Fig. 31. Autonomous Testing—functional mode.

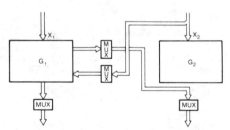

Fig. 32. Autonomous Testing—configuration to test network G_1.

multiplexers to separate the network and the second is a Sensitized Partitioning to separate the network. Fig. 30 shows the general network with multiplexers, Fig. 31 shows the network in functional mode, and Fig. 32 shows the network in a mode to test subnetwork G_1. This approach could involve a significant gate overhead to implement in some networks. Thus the Sensitized Partitioning approach is put forth. For example, the 74181 ALU/Function Generator is partitioned using the Sensitized Partitioning. By inspecting the network, two types of subnetworks can be partitioned out, four subnetworks N_1, one subnetwork N_2 (Figs. 33 and 34). By further inspection, all the L_i outputs of network N_1 can be tested by holding $S_2 = S_3 =$ low. Further, all the H_i outputs of network N_1 can be tested by holding $S_0 = S_1 =$ high, since sensitized paths exist through the subnetwork N_2. Thus far fewer than 2^n input patterns can be applied to the network to test it.

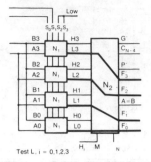

Fig. 33. Autonomous Testing with sensitized partitioning.

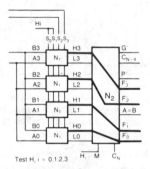

Fig. 34. Autonomous Testing with sensitized partitioning.

VI. CONCLUSION

The area of Design for Testability is becoming a popular topic by necessity. Those users of LSI/VLSI which do not have their own captive IC facilities are at the mercy of the vendors for information. And, until the vendor information is drastically changed, the Ad Hoc approaches to design for testability will be the only answer.

In that segment of the industry which can afford to implement the Structured Design for Testability approach, there is considerable hope of getting quality test patterns at a very modest cost. Furthermore, many innovative techniques are appearing in the Structured Approach and probably will continue as we meander through VLSI and into more dense technologies.

There is a new opportunity arriving in the form of gate arrays that allow low volume users access to VLSI technology. If they choose, structured design disciplines can be utilized. Perhaps "Silicon Foundries" of the future will offer a combined package of structured, testable modules and support software to automatically provide the user with finished parts AND tests.

ACKNOWLEDGMENT

The authors wish to thank D. J. Brown for his helpful comments and suggestions. The assistance of Ms. B. Fletcher, Ms. C. Mendoza, Ms. L. Clark, Ms. J. Allen, and J. Smith in preparing this manuscript for publication was invaluable.

REFERENCES

General References and Surveys

[1] M. A. Breuer, Ed., *Diagnosis and Reliable Design of Digital Systems.* Rockville, MD: Computer Science Press, 1976.
[2] H. Y. Chang, E. G. Manning, and G. Metze, *Fault Diagnosis of*

Digital Systems. New York: Wiley-Interscience, 1970.
[3] A. D. Friedman and P. R. Menon, *Fault Detection in Digital Circuits.* Englewood Cliffs, NJ: Prentice-Hall, 1971.
[4] F. C. Hennie, *Finite State Models for Logical Machines.* New York: Wiley, 1968.
[5] P. G. Kovijanic, in "A new look at test generation and verification," in *Proc. 14th Design Automation Conf.,* IEEE Pub. 77CH1216-1C, pp. 58–63, June 1977.
[6] E. I. Muehldorf, "Designing LSI logic for testability," in *Dig. Papers, 1976 Ann. Semiconductor Test Symp.,* IEEE Pub. 76CH1179-1C, pp. 45–49, Oct. 1976.
[7] E. I. Muehldorf and A. D. Savkar, "LSI logic testing—An overview," *IEEE Trans. Comput.,* vol. C-30, no. 1, pp. 1–17, Jan. 1981.
[8] W. W. Peterson and E. J. Weldon, *Error Correcting Codes.* Cambridge, MA: MIT Press, 1972.
[9] A. K. Susskind, "Diagnostics for logic networks," *IEEE Spectrum,* vol. 10, pp. 40–47, Oct. 1973.
[10] T. W. Williams and K. P. Parker, "Testing logic networks and design for testability," *Computer,* pp. 9–21, Oct. 1979.
[11] IEEE, Inc., *IEEE Standard Dictionary of Electrical and Electronics Terms.* New York: Wiley-Interscience, 1972.

Designing for Testability

[12] "A designer's guide to signature analysis," Hewlett-Packard Application Note 222, Hewlett Packard, 5301 Stevens Creek Blvd., Santa Clara, CA 95050.
[13] S. B. Akers, "Partitioning for testability," *J. Des. Automat. Fault-Tolerant Comput.,* vol. 1, no. 2, Feb. 1977.
[14] H. Ando, "Testing VLSI with random access scan," in *Dig. Papers Compcon 80,* IEEE Pub. 80CH1491-OC, pp. 50–52, Feb. 1980.
[15] P. Bottorff and E. I. Muehldorf, "Impact of LSI on complex digital circuit board testing," *Electro 77,* New York, NY, Apr. 1977.
[16] S. DasGupta, E. B. Eichelberger, and T. W. Williams, "LSI chip design for testability," in *Dig. Tech. Papers, 1978 Int. Solid-State Circuits Conf.* (San Francisco, CA, Feb. 1978), pp. 216–217.
[17] "Designing digital circuits for testability," Hewlett-Packard Application Note 210-4, Hewlett Packard, Loveland, CO 80537.
[18] E. B. Eichelberger and T. W. Williams, "A logic design structure for LSI testability," *J. Des. Automat. Fault-Tolerant Comput.,* vol. 2, no. 2, pp. 165–178, May 1978.
[19] ——, "A logic design structure for LSI testing," in *Proc. 14th Design Automation Conf.,* IEEE Pub. 77CH1216-1C, pp. 462–468, June 1977.
[20] E. B. Eichelberger, E. J. Muehldorf, R. G. Walter, and T. W. Williams, "A logic design structure for testing internal arrays," in *Proc. 3rd USA-Japan Computer Conf.* (San Francisco, CA, Oct. 1978), pp. 266–272.
[21] S. Funatsu, N. Wakatsuki, and T. Arima, "Test generation systems in Japan," in *Proc. 12th Design Automation Symp.,* pp. 114–122, June 1975.
[22] H. C. Godoy, G. B. Franklin, and P. S. Bottoroff, "Automatic checking of logic design structure for compliance with testability groundrules," in *Proc. 14th Design Automation Conf.,* IEEE Pub. 77CH1216-1C, pp. 469–478, June 1977.
[23] J. P. Hayes, "On modifying logic networks to improve their diagnosability," *IEEE Trans. Comput.,* vol. C-23, pp. 56–62, Jan. 1974.
[24] J. P. Hayes and A. D. Friedman, "Test point placement to simplify fault detection," in *FTC-3, Dig. Papers, 1973 Symp. on Fault-Tolerant Computing,* pp. 73–78, June 1973.
[25] B. Koenemann, J. Mucha, and G. Zwiehoff, "Built-in logic block observation techniques," in *Dig. Papers, 1979 Test Conf.,* IEEE Pub. 79CH1509-9C, pp. 37–41, Oct. 1979.
[26] M. D. Lippman and E. S. Donn, "Design forethought promotes easier testing of microcomputer boards," *Electronics,* pp. 113–119, Jan. 18, 1979.
[27] H. J. Nadig, "Signature analysis-concepts, examples, and guidelines," *Hewlett-Packard J.,* pp. 15–21, May 1977.
[28] M. Neil and R. Goodner, "Designing a serviceman's needs into microprocessor based systems," *Electronics,* pp. 122–128, Mar. 1, 1979.
[29] S. M. Reddy, "Easily testable realization for logic functions," *IEETC Trans. Comput.,* vol. C-21, pp. 1183–1188, Nov. 1972.
[30] K. K. Saliya and S. M. Reddy, "On minimally testable logic networks," *IEEE Trans. Comput.,* vol. C-23, pp. 1204–1207, Nov. 1974.
[31] J. H. Stewart, "Future testing of large LSI circuit cards," in *Dig. Papers 1977 Semiconductor Test Symp.,* IEEE Pub. 77CH1261-7C, pp. 6–17, Oct. 1977.
[32] A. Toth and C. Holt, "Automated data base-driven digital testing," *Computer,* pp. 13–19, Jan. 1974.
[33] E. White, "Signature analysis, enhancing the serviceability of microprocessor-based industrial products," in *Proc. 4th IECI*

Annual Conf., IEEE Pub. 78CH1312-8, pp. 68–76, Mar. 1978.
[34] M.J.Y. Williams and J. B. Angell, "Enhancing testability of large scale integrated circuits via test points and additional logic," *IEEE Trans. Comput.,* vol. C-22, pp. 46–60, Jan. 1973.
[35] T. W. Williams, "Utilization of a structured design for reliability and serviceability," in *Dig., Government Microcircuits Applications Conf.* (Monterey, CA, Nov. 1978), pp. 441–444.

Faults and Fault Modeling

[36] R. Boute and E. J. McCluskey, "Fault equivalence in sequential machines," in *Proc. Symp. on Computers and Automata* (Polytech. Inst. Brooklyn, Apr. 13–15, 1971), pp. 483–507.
[37] R. T. Boute, "Optimal and near-optimal checking experiments for output faults in sequential machines," *IEEE Trans. Comput.,* vol. C-23, no. 11, pp. 1207–1213, Nov. 1974.
[38] ——, "Equivalence and dominance relations between output faults in sequential machines," Tech. Rep. 38, SU-SEL-72-052, Stanford Univ., Stanford, CA, Nov. 1972.
[39] F.J.O. Dias, "Fault masking in combinational logic circuits," *IEEE Trans. Comput.,* vol. C-24, pp. 476–482, May 1975.
[40] J. P. Hayes, "A NAND model for fault diagnosis in combinational logic networks," *IEEE Trans. Comput.,* vol. C-20, pp. 1496–1506, Dec. 1971.
[41] E. J. McCluskey and F. W. Clegg, "Fault equivalence in combinational logic networks," *IEEE Trans. Comput.,* vol. C-20, pp. 1286–1293, Nov. 1971.
[42] K.C.Y. Mei, "Fault dominance in combinational circuits," Tech. Note 2, Digital Systems Lab., Stanford Univ., Aug. 1970.
[43] ——, "Bridging and stuck-at faults," *IEEE Trans. Comput.,* vol. C-23, no. 7, pp. 720–727, July 1974.
[44] R. C. Ogus, "The probability of a correct output from a combinational circuit," *IEEE Trans. Comput.,* vol. C-24, no. 5, pp. 534–544, May 1975.
[45] K. P. Parker and E. J. McCluskey, "Analysis of logic circuits with faults using input signal probabilities," *IEEE Trans. Comput.,* vol. C-24, no. 5, pp. 573–578, May 1975.
[46] K. K. Saliya and S. M. Reddy, "Fault detecting test sets for Reed-Muller canonic networks," *IEEE Trans. Comput.,* pp. 995–998, Oct. 1975.
[47] D. R. Schertz and G. Metze, "A new representation for faults in combinational digital circuits," *IEEE Trans. Comput.,* vol. C-21, no. 8, pp. 858–866, Aug. 1972.
[48] J. J. Shedletsky and E. J. McCluskey, "The error latency of a fault in a sequential digital circuit," *IEEE Trans. Comput.,* vol. C-25, no. 6, pp. 655–659, June 1976.
[49] ——, "The error latency of a fault in a combinational digital circuit," in *FTCS-5, Dig. Papers, 5th Int. Symp. on Fault Tolerant Computing* (Paris, June 1975), pp. 210–214.
[50] K. To, "Fault folding for irredundant and redundant combinational circuits," *IEEE Trans. Comput.,* vol. C-22, no. 11, pp. 1008–1015, Nov. 1973.
[51] D. T. Wang, "Properties of faults and criticalities of values under tests for combinational networks," *IEEE Trans. Comput.,* vol. C-24, no. 7, pp. 746–750, July 1975.

Testing and Fault Location

[52] R. P. Batni and C. R. Kime, "A module level testing approach for combinational networks," *IEEE Trans. Comput.,* vol. C-25, no. 6, pp. 594–604, June 1976.
[53] S. Bisset, "Exhaustive testing of microprocessors and related devices: A practical solution," in *Dig. Papers, 1977 Semiconductor Test Symp.,* pp. 38–41, Oct. 1977.
[54] R. J. Czepiel, S. H. Foreman, and R. J. Prilik, "System for logic, parametric and analog testing," in *Dig. Papers, 1976 Semiconductor Test Symp.,* pp. 54–69, Oct. 1976.
[55] R. A. Frohwerk, "Signature analysis: A new digital field service method," *Hewlett-Packard J.,* pp. 2–8, May 1977.
[56] B. A. Grimmer, "Test techniques for circuit boards containing large memories and microprocessors," in *Dig. Papers 1976 Semiconductor Test Symp.,* pp. 16–21, Oct. 1976.
[57] W. A. Groves, "Rapid digital fault isolation with FASTRACE," *Hewlett-Packard J.,* pp. 8–13, Mar. 1979.
[58] J. P. Hayes, "Rapid count testing for combinational logic circuits," *IEEE Trans. Comput.,* vol. C-25, no. 6, pp. 613–620, June 1976.
[59] ——, "Detection of pattern sensitive faults in random access memories," *IEEE Trans. Comput.,* vol. C-24, no. 2, Feb. 1975, pp. 150–160.
[60] ——, "Testing logic circuits by transition counting," in *FTC-5, Dig. Papers, 5th Int. Symp. on Fault Tolerant Computing* (Paris, France, June 1975), pp. 215–219.
[61] J. T. Healy, "Economic realities of testing microprocessors," in *Dig. Papers, 1977 Semiconductor Test Symp.,* pp. 47–52, Oct. 1977.
[62] E. C. Lee, "A simple concept in microprocessor testing," in *Dig.*

Papers, 1976 Semiconductor Test Symp., IEEE Pub. 76CH1179-1C, pp. 13–15, Oct. 1976.

[63] J. Losq, "Referenceless random testing," in *FTCS-6, Dig. Papers, 6th Int. Symp. on Fault-Tolerant Computing* (Pittsburgh, PA, June 21–23, 1976), pp. 81–86.

[64] S. Palmquist and D. Chapman, "Expanding the boundaries of LSI testing with an advanced pattern controller," in *Dig. Papers, 1976 Semicondctor Test Symp.*, pp. 70–75, Oct. 1976.

[65] K. P. Parker, "Compact testing: Testing with compressed data," in *FTCS-6, Dig. Papers, 6th Int. Symp. on Fault-Tolerant Computing* (Pittsburgh, PA, June 21–23, 1976).

[66] J. J. Shedletsky, "A rationale for the random testing of combinational digital circuits," in *Dig. Papers, Compcon 75 Fall Meet.* (Washington, DC, Sept. 9–11, 1975), pp. 5–9.

[67] V. P. Strini, "Fault location in a semiconductor random access memory unit," *IEEE Trans. Comput.*, vol. C-27, no. 4, pp. 379–385, Apr. 1978.

[68] C. W. Weller, in "An engineering approach to IC test system maintenance," in *Dig. Papers, 1977 Semiconductor Test Symp.*, pp. 144–145, Oct. 1977.

Testability Measures

[69] W. J. Dejka, "Measure of testability in device and system design," in *Proc. 20th Midwest Symp. Circuits Syst.*, pp. 39–52, Aug. 1977.

[70] L. H. Goldstein, "Controllability/observability analysis of digital circuits," *IEEE Trans. Circuits Syst.*, vol. CAS-26, no. 9, pp. 685–693, Sept. 1979.

[71] W. L. Keiner and R. P. West, "Testability measures," presented at AUTOTESTCON '77, Nov. 1977.

[72] P. G. Kovijanic, "testability analysis," in *Dig. Papers, 1979 Test Conf.*, IEEE Pub. 79CH1509-9C, pp. 310–316, Oct. 1979.

[73] J. E. Stephenson and J. Grason, "A testability measure for register transfer level digital circuits," in *Proc. 6th Fault Tolerant Computing Symp.*, pp. 101–107, June 1976.

Test Generation

[74] V. Agrawal and P. Agrawal, "An automatic test generation system for ILLIAC IV logic boards," *IEEE Trans. Comput.*, vol. C-21, no. 9, pp. 1015–1017, Sept. 1972.

[75] D. B. Armstrong, "On finding a nearly minimal set of fault detection tests for combinational logic nets," *IEEE Trans. Electron. Comput.*, vol. EC-15, no. 1, pp. 66–73, Feb. 1966.

[76] R. Betancourt, "Derivation of minimum test sets for unate logical circuits," *IEEE Trans. Comput.*, vol. C-20, no. 11, pp. 1264–1269, Nov. 1973.

[77] D. C. Bossen and S. J. Hong, "Cause and effect analysis for multiple fault detection in combinational networks," *IEEE Trans. Comput.*, vol. C-20, no. 11, pp. 1252–1257, Nov. 1971.

[78] P. S. Bottorff et al., "Test generation for large networks," in *Proc. 14th Design Automation Conf.*, IEEE Pub. 77CH1216-1C, pp. 479–485, June 1977.

[79] R. D. Eldred, "Test routines based on symbolic logic statements," *J. Assoc. Comput. Mach.*, vol. 6, no. 1, pp. 33–36, 1959.

[80] P. Goel, "Test generation costs analysis and projections," presented at the 17th Design Automation Conf., Minneapolis, MN, 1980.

[81] E. P. Hsieh et al., "Delay test generation," in *Proc. 14th Design Automation Conf.*, IEEE Pub. 77CH1216-1C, pp. 486–491, June 1977.

[82] C. T. Ku and G. M. Masson, "The Boolean difference and multiple fault analysis," *IEEE Trans. Comput.*, vol. C-24, no. 7, pp. 691–695, July 1975.

[83] E. I. Muehldorf, "Test pattern generation as a part of the total design process," in *LSI and Boards: Dig. Papers, 1978 Ann. Semiconductor Test Symp.*, pp. 4–7, Oct. 1978.

[84] E. I. Muehldorf and T. W. Williams, "Optimized stuck fault test patterns for PLA macros," in *Dig. Papers, 1977 Semiconductor Test Symp.*, IEEE Pub. 77CH1216-7C, pp. 89–101, Oct. 1977.

[85] M. R. Page, "Generation of diagnostic tests using prime implicants," Coordinated Science Lab. Rep. R-414, University of Illinois, Urbana, May 1969.

[86] S. G. Papaioannou, "Optimal test generation in combinational networks by pseudo Boolean programming," *IEEE Trans. Comput.*, vol. C-26, no. 6, pp. 553–560, June 1977.

[87] K. P. Parker, "Adaptive random test generation," *J. Des. Automat. Fault Tolerant Comput.*, vol. 1, no. 1, pp. 62–83, Oct. 1976.

[88] ——, "Probabilistic test generation," Tech. Note 18, Digital Systems Laboratory, Stanford University, Stanford, CA, Jan. 1973.

[89] J. F. Poage and E. J. McCluskey, "Derivation of optimum tests for sequential machines," in *Proc. 5th Ann. Symp. on Switching Circuit Theory and Logic Design*, pp. 95–110, 1964.

[90] ——, "Derivation of optimum tests to detect faults in combinational circuits," in *Mathematical Theory of Automation*. New York: Polytechnic Press, 1963.

[91] G. R. Putzolu and J. P. Roth, "A heuristic algorithm for testing of asynchronous circuits," *IEEE Trans. Comput.*, vol. C-20, no. 6, pp. 639–647, June 1971.

[92] J. P. Roth, W. G. Bouricius, and P. R. Schneider, "Programmed algorithms to compute tests to detect and distinguish between failures in logic circuits," *IEEE Trans. Electron. Comput.*, vol. EC-16, pp. 567–580, Oct. 1967.

[93] J. P. Roth, "Diagnosis of automata failures: A calculus and a method," *IBM J. Res. Devel.*, no. 10, pp. 278–281, Oct. 1966.

[94] P. R. Schneider, "On the necessity to examine D-chairs in diagnostic test generation—An example," *IBM J. Res. Develop.*, no. 11, p. 114, Nov. 1967.

[95] H. D. Schnurmann, E. Lindbloom, R. G. Carpenter, "The weighted random test pattern generation," *IEEE Trans. Comput.*, vol. C-24, no. 7, pp. 695–700, July 1975.

[96] E. F. Sellers, M. Y. Hsiao, and L. W. Bearnson, "Analyzing errors with the Boolean difference," *IEEE Trans. Comput.*, vol. C-17, no. 7, pp. 676–683, July 1968.

[97] D. T. Wang, "An algorithm for the detection of tests sets for combinational logic networks," *IEEE Trans. Comput.*, vol. C-25, no. 7, pp. 742–746, July 1975.

[98] T. W. Williams and E. E. Eichelberger, "Random patterns within a structured sequential logic design," in *Dig. Papers, 1977 Semiconductor Test Symp.*, IEEE Pub. 77CH1261-7C, pp. 19–27, Oct. 1977.

[99] S. S. Yau and S. C. Yang, "Multiple fault detection for combinational logic circuits," *IEEE Trans. Comput.*, vol. C-24, no. 5, pp. 233–242, May 1975.

Simulation

[100] D. B. Armstrong, "A deductive method for simulating faults in logic circuits," *IEEE Trans. Comput.*, vol. C-22, no. 5, pp. 464–471, May 1972.

[101] M. A. Breuer, "Functional partitioning and simulation of digital circuits," *IEEE Trans. Comput.*, vol. C-19, no. 11, pp. 1038–1046, Nov. 1970.

[102] H.Y.P. Chiang et al., "Comparison of parallel and deductive fault simulation," *IEEE Trans. Comput.*, vol. C-23, no. 11, pp. 1132–1138, Nov. 1974.

[103] E. B. Eichelberger, "Hazard detection in combinational and sequential switching circuits," *IBM J. Res. Devel.*, Mar. 1965.

[104] E. Manning and H. Y. Chang, "Functional technique for efficient digital fault simulation," in *IEEE Int. Conv. Dig.*, p. 194, 1968.

[105] K. P. Parker, "Software simulator speeds digital board test generation," *Hewlett-Packard J.*, pp. 13–19, Mar. 1979.

[106] S. Seshu, "On an improved diagnosis program,". *IEEE Trans. Electron. Comput.*, vol. EC-12, no. 1, pp. 76–79, Feb. 1965.

[107] S. Seshu and D. N. Freeman, "The diagnosis of asynchronous sequential switching systems," *IRE Trans, Electron. Compat.*, vol. EC-11, no. 8, pp. 459–465, Aug. 1962.

[108] T. M. Storey and J. W. Barry, "Delay test simulation," in *Proc. 14th Design Automation Conf.*, IEEE Pub. 77CH1216-1C, pp. 491–494, June 1977.

[109] S. A. Szygenda and E. W. Thompson, "Modeling and digital simulation for design verification diagnosis," *IEEE Trans. Comput.*, vol. C-25, no. 12, pp. 1242–1253, Dec. 1976.

[110] S. A. Szygenda, "TEGAS2—Anatomy of a general purpose test generation and simulation system for digital logic," in *Proc. 9th Design Automation Workshop*, pp. 116–127, 1972.

[111] S. A. Szygenda, D. M. Rouse, and E. W. Thompson, "A model for implementation of a universal time delay simulation for large digital networks," in *AFIPS Conf. Proc.*, vol. 36, pp. 207–216, 1970.

[112] E. G. Ulrich and T. Baker, "Concurrent simulation of nearly identical digital networks," *Computer*, vol. 7, no. 4, pp. 39–44, Apr. 1974.

[113] ——, "The concurrent simulation of nearly identical digital networks," in *Proc. 10th Design Automation Workshop*, pp. 145–150, June 1973.

[114] E. G. Ulrich, T. Baker, and L. R. Williams, "Fault test analysis techniques based on simulation," in *Proc. 9th Design Automation Workshop*, pp. 111–115, 1972.

[115] J. Savir, "Syndrome—Testable design of combinational circuits," *IEEE Trans. Comput.*, vol. C-29, pp. 442–451, June 1980 (corrections: Nov. 1980).

[116] ——, "Syndrome—Testing of 'syndrome-untestable' combinational circuits," *IEEE Trans. Comput.*, vol. C-30, pp. 606–608, Aug. 1981.

[117] A. K. Susskind, "Testing by verifying Walsh coefficients," in *Proc. 11th Ann. Symp. on Fault-Tolerant Computing* (Portland, MA), pp. 206–208, June 1981.

[118] E. J. McCluskey and S. Bozorgui-Nesbat, "Design for autonomous test," *IEEE Trans. Comput.*, vol. C-30, pp. 866–875, Nov. 1981.

Part VII
International Aspects

THIS part starts with a paper by T. Sudo, T. Ohtsuki, and S. Goto on the aspects of CAD systems developed for IC design and manufacture in Japan. It describes the current status of VLSI-CAD systems and technologies, from device to system levels. It comprises the description and evaluation of most of the respective CAD tools used in Japan and discusses the standardization issue, which has become indispensable for the efficient usage of the various CAD resources. For future VLSI-CAD systems, research and development in the following areas emerge: 1) more intelligent CAD algorithms and methodologies; 2) CAD-dedicated machine or usage of supercomputer in CAD area; 3) highly interactive design environment; and 4) vertically integrated CAD system covering system concept to the device fabrication process. Japan is clearly determined to take the lead in these fields.

The next paper, by A. B. Bhattacharyya, deals with VLSI problems in the developing countries and the various options of these countries for the acquisition of VLSI. While the author chooses to illustrate those topics with India as an example, most of his findings relate in similar manner to other developing countries. The developing nations have yet to decide how appropriate and sustainable VLSI is in the context of their urge for modernization and the problems of an unemployment explosion, weak technological and scientific infrastructure, rural and agricultural bias, etc. Governments in developing nations will have to nourish the induction of new technology either in application or production through market protection, subsidy, and incentive for a prolonged period. For industrial development, microelectronics is essential. Low volume of an internal market will be the most serious inhibiting factor for a rapid VLSI development. Therefore, only a gradually increasing awareness of the downstream application of VLSI in basic tools will slowly evolve in these countries in the immediate future.

CAD Systems for VLSI in Japan

TSUNETA SUDO, TATSUO OHTSUKI, SENIOR MEMBER, IEEE, AND SATOSHI GOTO, MEMBER, IEEE

Invited Paper

Abstract—With the advent of the VLSI era, computer-aided design (CAD) is increasing its importance, and much effort is now being expended on CAD by many IC manufacturers and laboratories in Japan. This paper reviews the historical aspect of the CAD systems developed in this field, and describes the current status of VLSI CAD systems and technologies, from device to system levels, in Japan. The CAD development activities for IC's were initiated in the late 1960's. At present, VLSI CAD systems and related CAD technologies in Japan seem to be in the adolescent stage—partly capable of practical use and partly still in the immature state.

I. INTRODUCTION

AT THE BEGINNING of the 1960's, the development of computer-aided design (CAD) systems started in the electronic industry in Japan. CAD programs were recognized as essential to support the design and manufacture of electronic equipment for 1) design turn-around time reduction, 2) elimination of human errors, and, as a result, 3) reduction in design and manufacturing costs. At the earliest stage, efforts were expended mainly toward developing logic simulators for large electronic circuits and physical design programs for printed-circuit or back-wiring boards, which were used in mainframe computers or electronic switching systems. These CAD systems, as well as the fundamental algorithms, were developed originally by Japanese people.

As soon as the large-scale integrated circuit (LSI) concept appeared in the late 1960's, CAD tools for LSI design were also recognized to be essential for efficient LSI design, and manufacturing or development efforts have been made since then. In developing CAD programs for LSI design, LSI CAD designers have made use of numerous technologies and extensive know-how derived from their predecessors. The LSI placement and routing problem was considered to be one of the main subjects in the LSI CAD area, and various kinds of layout programs have been developed by many IC manufacturers and laboratories. In the early LSI development stage, numerous kinds of LSI layout design approaches were proposed such as planar layout, masterslice, building-block, multichip LSI, etc. The planar layout approach, which features a single metal layer for routing, offered interesting themes to theorists, but soon proved to be impractical because of the rapid progress in LSI technologies which has made possible the use of two or more layers for signal wiring. The masterslice and building-block LSI's have shown themselves to be more practical approaches in conjunction with the development of layout CAD programs, and, at present, have become the most popular LSI's

Manuscript received April 15, 1982; revised October 5, 1982.
T. Sudo is with the Nippon Telegraph and Telephone Public Corporation, Tokyo, Japan.
T. Ohtsuki is with the Department of Electronics and Communication Engineering, Waseda University, Tokyo, Japan.
S. Goto is with C & C Systems Research Laboratories, Nippon Electric Co., Ltd., 1-1 Miyazaki Yinchome, Miyamae-ku, Kawasaki, Japan 213.

in Japan. The multichip or hybrid LSI is also in practical use in mainframe computers. At the beginning, the masterslice approach was dedicated to bipolar technologies, while building-block approaches were used only for MOS LSI's. However, such a distinction disappeared as both the LSI fabrication and CAD technologies progressed, and, currently, either approach is being applied to both bipolar and MOS technologies. For these layout design systems, Japan was always a technical leader in the world, as the first papers on these topics were published by Japanese researchers.

Entering the 1970's, research and development on LSI CAD programs flourished over a wider range, including device, circuit and logic simulations, placement and routing, artwork verification, and test generation. Although strenuous efforts have been made to develop LSI CAD programs, CAD designers always faced a great many difficulties in putting their programs into practical use because the automatically designed results were often of lower quality than manually designed ones. Among the layout programs, CAD programs for masterslice LSI's containing several hundred gates were successfully applied to the design of "semicustom" LSI's for mainframe computers or electronic switching systems at that time.

With in-house CAD system development efforts being made, the so-called stand-alone interactive design systems were introduced in many IC manufacturing plants and laboratories, and mass-produced LSI's, such as memories, calculators, and microprocessors, which have severe requirements for high packing density to hold the fabrication cost down as low as possible, have mainly been designed manually with the aid of these interactive graphic systems. In most cases, these stand-alone systems have magnetic tape interfaces with mainframe computers to share design tasks. According to a report [1] by the Research Committee on Electronic Equipment Design Technology of the Information Processing Society of Japan (IPSJ) regarding the status of design automation in Japan, about 40 percent of the CAD systems used for LSI layout design are such stand-alone interactive design systems purchased from outside vendors, while the remaining 60 percent of the CAD systems were developed in house. Along with the introduction of interactive stand-alone graphic systems, CAD application programs have also been introduced and applied for practical use, in combination with in-house originally developed CAD programs. SPICE [2], SLIC [3], and ASTAP [4] have been used for circuit analysis of LSI circuits, and TEGAS [5] for logic verification and test generation in several companies.

At present, the greatest concern is for the development of CAD systems, covering from device to system levels, for VLSI, which is always increasing in scale and complexity and creating numerous kinds of design difficulties. These technical problems are summarized as follows: 1) enlargement of design ob-

Reprinted from *Proc. IEEE*, vol. 71, pp. 129–143, Jan. 1983.

255

TABLE I
DESIGN STAGES AND DESIGN AUTOMATION (DA) RESOURCES

	Process Design	Device Design	Circuit Design	Logic Design	Layout	Test Pattern Generation
Verification	Process Siml.	o Device Siml.	o Circuit Siml.	o Logic Siml. Function Siml.	o Design Rule Checker o Connectivity Checker o Timing Siml.	o Fault Siml.
Automatic Design	Process Optimizer	Device Optimizer	Circuit Optimizer	RTL → gate translator o μ program assembler PLA minimizer	o Placer o Router	o Test Pattern Generator
DA hardware	———	———		o TSS terminal Graphic System Logic Diagram Reader	o Graphic System	———
DA-oriented LSI Structure	———	———	o DA-oriented Cell	o PLA	o Building Block o Master Slice o PLA	o Scan Path

o --- most popular

jectives from device to system level; 2) increase of the amount of design data contained on a single chip; 3) overall optimization requirements with respect to logical and physical design factors; 4) strict requirements regarding design result quality; and 5) ever-progressing LSI technologies.

A hierarchical design concept is considered to be indispensable to alleviating these technical problems. Extensive efforts are being made toward the establishment of hierarchical CAD systems for VLSI design in many IC manufacturing companies and laboratories. As an example of hierarchically oriented CAD systems for VLSI design, an outline of the VLSI DA system developed by NTT is described in Section VI. It seems that VLSI CAD systems and related CAD technologies in Japan have reached the "adolescent" stage—partly capable of practical use and partly still in the immature state. Table I shows the present status regarding VLSI CAD–VLSI design stages and available CAD resources for each design phase.

Surveys on CAD systems in the electronic industry in Japan have been presented several times at various international conferences [6]–[14]. They will complement this paper, furnishing more information on CAD development in various fields of the electronic industries in Japan.

II. LOGIC DESIGN AND TEST GENERATION TOOLS

Logic design aids are mainly divided into three parts—synthesis, verification, and design methodology. Logic synthesis is finding an automatic way to realize in logic a set of Boolean expressions or a representation of a sequential machine. However, there is currently a great deal of human intervention in the synthesis process and models used in the synthesis process are not complete. At this moment, verification plays an important role to guarantee the logic function before the chip is built (simulation) and after (testing).

A. Logic Design

Fig. 1 shows the logic design tools which are used in Japan (Figs. 1–5 are taken from [1] and [11]). Logic simulators,

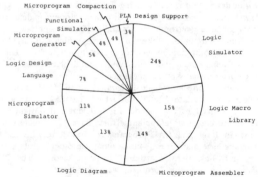

Fig. 1. Logic design tool.

hardware design languages, and microprogram support tools are now mainly used.

Logic simulators are the most popular logic design tools and have been used by many organizations. Most logic simulators used in Japan have been developed individually by the organizations which use them and improved year by year. Some are imported from the United States. Among these TEGAS [5] is a typical program. The input data for logic elements are shown in Fig. 2. Table II summarizes the logic simulators developed in Japan.

Gate-level simulators are the most commonly used in logic design. LOGOS [15], developed by the Nippon Electric Company (NEC), is a typical gate-level simulator, based on an event-driven method with mapping mechanism. It can handle unit, maximum, minimum, rise, fall, or wire delay time with 3 values. Recently, it was extended for simulating complex MOS circuits, including analog or bidirectional circuits with 4 values [16]. Toshiba first developed a 7-value logic simulator for MOS LSI circuits, which can treat transmission gates, clocked gates, and tri-state buffers successfully [17].

In the past few years, functional-level simulators have been

TABLE II
LOGIC STIMULATORS DEVELOPED IN JAPAN

System Name	Developer	Year	Logic Hierarchy	Function
LOGOS [15]	NEC	1977	Gate	3-value Simulator
ALEPH [18]	Hitachi	1979	RTL, Gate	Simulator
DDL [21]	Fujitsu	1979	RTL → Gate	Translator
ALS-4 [17]	Toshiba	1980	Gate	7-value Simulator for MOS
BINARY [19]	Oki	1980	RTL, Gate, Timing	Simulator, Verifier
MIXS [20]	NEC	1980	RTL, Gate	Mixed Level Simulator
FOREST [35]	NTT	1981	RTL, Gate	Simulator

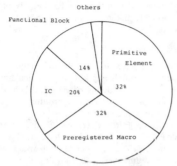

Fig. 2. Logic simulator input data.

Fig. 3. Test application circuit size.

developed by computer manufacturers. Hitachi has developed a logic simulator [18], called ALEPH, which can handle register-transfer-level logic descriptions in addition to gate-level ones with capability of 750 000 gates. Oki's logic simulator [19], BINARY, can simulate logic circuits with three levels, functional, logic, and timing, in a hierarchical structure.

Functional-level, or register-transfer-level simulators can handle a logic circuit almost 10 times larger in half the computation time, compared to gate-level simulators. On the other hand, gate-level simulators are able to simulate logic circuits with more accurate delay time. Recently, mixed-level simulators have been developed to incorporate the features of the functional and gate-level simulators. Recently, NEC has developed a mixed-level simulator [20], called MIXS, suitable for a hierarchical or top-down support of large digital systems. It has realized a unified simulation mechanism for both gate- and functional- or register-transfer-level models, based on time-wheel and selective-trace algorithms.

In order to integrate the design and the verification stages, Fujitsu Labs has developed a DDL system [21] which can support register-transfer-level simulation, translation from DDL description to gate-level logic, and automatic logic verification. Also, an automatic input and interactive editing system for logic circuit diagrams has been developed [22].

"Array logic" was conceived to reduce design time and cost in comparison to random logic, so the popularity of the PLA is steadily increasing. NEC [23], [24] and Nippon Telegraph and Telephone (NTT) [25] have made a large effort in this area. They established the CAD system which first performs Boolean minimization and then automatically maps the logic function into the PLA personality matrix, together with the logic verifier. As we enter the VLSI era, the advantage of regularity is increasingly emphasized, and as device sizes scale down and chip area may be plentiful, the PLA or regular structural design will be more popular and practical in use.

Universities are active in the research and development of logic design [7], [26], [27]. The University of Tokyo has developed a logic simulation system using a data flow machine, which achieves a high-speed parallel logic simulation [28].

B. Test Generation

Testing and diagnosis of digital logic circuits (IC cards) have been studied actively for the past decades in Japan [29]. Recently, with the appearance of LSI's or VLSI's, a greater effort in research and development has enthusiastically been made by universities, public corporations, and manufacturers. The bulk of digital testing can be summarized as using single stuck-at fault models, generating test patterns, and using fault simulation to find all the faults which can be detected by these test patterns. This procedure is iterated until an acceptable percentage of all faults is covered.

The logic circuit size, to which testing tools can be applied, is shown in Fig. 3. Most tools are applied to combinatorial circuits but are rarely applied to sequential ones. Also, more than half of them can treat asynchronous circuits.

The test generation methods used are shown in Fig. 4. Full automatic generation is quite rare, but most methods are combined with manual and automatic methods. The generation algorithm is either a D-algorithm or path-sensitizing method. For fault simulation, the parallel method is most popular, but concurrent or deductive methods are also adopted (see Fig. 5). In 1968, NEC first proposed a method to convert sequential circuits to combinatorial circuits by evaluating circuits clock by clock, which facilitated the easy generation of test patterns for complicated sequential circuits [30].

257

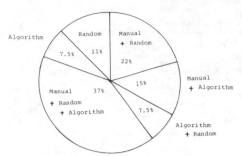

Fig. 4. Test generation method.

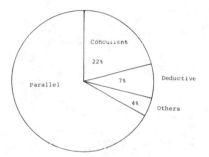

Fig. 5. Fault simulation method.

Now, let us look at the test systems in more detail. Oki has developed an automatic test generation system called FUNTASY by using Muth's 9-value method [19]. Hitachi has also developed a diagnostic system [31], consisting of an automated test generator, a fault simulator, and a fault locator. Its technique is based on a 9-value D-algorithm and a 6-value concurrent fault simulator with functional modeling. NEC has developed a test generation system [32], called TESTA, whose newly proposed algorithm is particularly efficient for large asynchronous and highly sequential circuits. It can handle up to 2000 gate sequential circuits, and can also be applied to MOS dynamic circuits.

Basic research efforst have been made in universities. Hiroshima and Saga Universities have jointly developed a test generator for combinatorial circuits using the structured description function and Boolean difference approach [33]. Recently, Osaka University devised an efficient generating algorithm for combinatorial circuits by introducing the testability measure [34].

The testing problems increase exponentially with the circuit chip complexity. Partitioning and hierarchical structure of VLSI design help to keep the testing problem within control. The major techniques used for testability are circuit partitioning or module design, the scan-path method, and built-in self-testing.

NTT has developed a test generation system [35] called FOREST which generates test patterns block by block. This system can treat a very large logic circuit efficiently by using a block-sensitizing algorithm in a hierarchical manner.

The scan-path method has been used practically by NEC for the first time [36] to improve the design testability (controllability and observability), while avoiding situations which cannot be tested easily. The method uses a serial shift register

approach, which converts sequential circuits to combinatorial circuits. It has been applied to system-level test generation and testing, in addition to chip and printed-circuit assembly levels. FTT-700 has been developed by NEC and can handle up to 100K block digital systems [37].

Built-in self-testing research is now going on in several organizations.

III. CIRCUIT AND TIMING SIMULATORS

An electrical circuit simulator performs simulation wherein detailed electrical waveforms are taken into account. It comprises two main simulator categories, a "general circuit simulator" (Section III-A), and a "MOS timing simulator" (Section III-B). A considerable number of papers have been written by researchers in NTT and electronics manufacturers. However, there is very little activity in this field by the universities. This seems to be a notable difference when Japan is compared with the United States.

A. General Circuit Simulator

General circuits simulators, or circuit analysis programs, were developed to simulate any kind of electrical network and are capable of detailed modeling of electrical behavior. However, the simulation often becomes prohibitively expensive, particularly in this VLSI era.

Circuit analysis programs, developed in the United States, such as ASTAP [4] and SPICE [2], have been widely used in Japan. Also, NTT and electronics manufacturers have modified the programs originally developed in the United States or developed new programs for their own use. NTT's ECSS [38], Fujitsu's FNAP [39], NEC's ANAP (formerly called "NECTAR") [40], etc., summarized in Table III, are the programs developed in Japan. These programs are either unpublished or are available only to users who have installed computers produced by the program developers.

Among these programs, some of them have remarkable features, which those developed in the United States do not have. For example, NEC's COSMOS is a program dedicated to only MOS logic circuits. Although the class of applicable circuits is limited, COSMOS is reported to run much faster than any other existing circuit analysis program. NEC's ANAP [40] has another such feature in that convergence of DC analysis is guaranteed by exploiting the piecewise-linear technique [41], unlike the programs using Newton–Raphson type iteration.

Even in this VLSI era general circuit simulators are still used for verification of circuit design. However, the present research efforts focus primarily on development of timing simulators, which are capable of analyzing larger scale circuits.

B. MOS Timing Simulator

MOS timing simulators, such as MOTIS [42] and MOTIS-C [43], attempt to compromise between "speed," as in logic simulation, and "accuracy," as in general circuit simulation. An MOS device is essentially unidirectional, which leads to a decoupling of successive stages in MOS combinatorial logic. Also, the physics of the MOS device is much simpler than that of a bipolar device. Taking advantage of the simplicity of MOS circuits, together with pertinent decomposition and approximation techniques, MOS timing simulators are reported to perform transient analysis faster than general circuit simulators by a factor of one hundred. To maintain accuracy, however, the class of applicable circuits is reduced considerably.

TABLE III
CIRCUIT AND TIMING SIMULATORS DEVELOPED IN JAPAN

System Name	Developer	Year	Function			
			DC	AC	Transient	Timing
ECSS [38]	NTT	1973	o	o	o	
LILAS	Mitsubishi	1973	o		o	
FNAP [39]	Fujitsu	1973	o	o	o	
ANAP6 [40]	NEC	1975	o	o	o	
ECAP	Hitachi	1976	o	o	o	
ECAP 6	Toshiba	1976	o		o	
COSMOS 2	NEC	1976	o		o	
NAP II	Oki	1977	o		o	
MATIS [44]	Toshiba	1978				o
FNAP (Extended) [46]	Fujitsu	1979				o
LOTAS [47]	NTT, NEC	1979				o
LNAP	NTT	1980	o		o	
MOSTAP [48]	NEC	1980				o

Japanese LSI designers were stimulated by the development of MOTIS [42] and MOTIS-C [43]. The basic ideas included in these programs have affected the direction of their research and development activities. As it turned out, however, developers were not satisfied with the accuracy and class of applicable MOTIS or MOTIS-C circuits. NTT and electronics manufacturers have developed or are now developing their own timing simulators [44]–[50], which are summarized in Table III. These activities include fundamental research on high-speed simulation techniques, such as a bypass technique for latent or inactive gates, macro modeling for logic gates, circuit decomposition, and a direct table lookup technique for the calculation of MOS device equations.

Japanese LSI designers have started to use their MOS timing simulators for transient analysis of large-scale circuits, including hundreds or thousands of transistors, which are beyond the capability of general circuit simulators. It is reported that degradation of accuracy compared with general circuit simulators can be restrained to within a few percent by careful device modeling. For example, a cascade circuit including ten inverters was simulated by both a general circuit simulator (COSMOS) and a timing simulator (MOSTAP). Results are compared in Fig. 6.

At present, some engineers are still reluctant to use MOS timing simulators, because the technologies are not yet as mature as those in general circuit simulation. However, the authors expect that timing simulators will be further improved and used by many more engineers in the near future.

IV. LAYOUT SYSTEM AND ARTWORK CHECKING TOOLS

In the layout design automation field, several important contributions have been made by Japanese researchers. The line search method [57] proposed by Mikami and Tabuchi greatly improved the efficiency of the Lee-type maze routing algorithm for Printed-Circuit Board (PCB) and LSI, and the algorithm has been widely used in many layout systems. Aiming at efficiency and quality improvement of routing for PCB, Hashimoto and Stevens' two-phase routing method [52] was proposed, and its concept has been implemented in various routing systems for VLSI as well as PCB. NEC people have

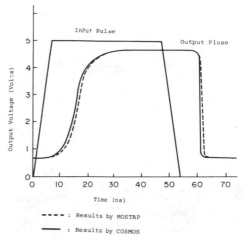

Fig. 6. Transient analysis by a general circuit simulator (COSMOS) and an MOS timing simulator (MOSTAP).

proposed an algorithm to pack a set of rectangles into a rectangle for a planar electrical circuit as small as possible [53]. This approach, again, is looked at as a useful technique for building-block LSI's.

The routing method reported in COMPAS [54], a routing system for multichip or hybrid LSI, adopted almost the same method as the Hashimoto and Stevens method.

A. Building-Block Layout Systems

In the VLSI layout design process, chip mask patterns are generally constructed by using predefined cells. These cells correspond to gates or more complex logic blocks. They are placed in several rows on a chip, and the interconnections between cells are wired within the channel regions. A channel router is generally applied to interconnections between two rows of cells. This layout design style is called the building-

TABLE IV
AUTOMATIC LAYOUT SYSTEMS DEVELOPED IN JAPAN

System Name	Developer	Years	Layout Style	Application	Routing Method	Placement Method
LILAC [55]	Hitachi	1972	Building block	MOS	Channel router 2-layer	Clustering
Advanced-LILAC [56]	Hitachi	1974	Building block	MOS	Channel router 2-layer	
— [69]	Oki	1974	Masterslice		Line search method Maze router 2-layer	Partitioning by a seeding algorithm Iterative improvement
ROBIN [57]	NEC	1976	Building block	MOS	Global router Channel router 2-layer	Manual placement
CAD75 [70]	Hitachi	1976	Masterslice	ECL	Maze router 2-layer	Random method Pair interchange
MARC [72]	Musashino ECL NTT	1978	Masterslice	ECL MOS	Global router Line search method 2-layer	Attractive and repulsive (AR) method
MIRAGE [61]	Mitsubish	1979	Hierarchical layout		Global router Channel router 2-layer	Manual placement
MASTER [77]	NEC	1979	Masterslice	Bipolar	Global router Line search method 2-layer/3-layer	SORG GFDR
— [60]	Osaka University	1980		MOS	Left edge method	Clustering Iterative improvement
— [76]	Fujitsu	1980	Masterslice	CMOS	Global router Channel 2-layer	Min-cut placement One-dimensional improvement
PLASMA/COSMIC — [67]	Musashino ECL NTT	1980	Hierarchical layout	CMOS Bipolar	Channel router 3-layer	Linear placement Pseudo 2-dimensionalization
MARS-M3 [74]	Mitsubishi	1981	Masterslice	ECL	Global router Channel router 2-layer	Top-down placement FDPR
MILD [63]	Mitsubishi	1981	Hierarchical layout	NMOS CMOS	Global router Grid-free Channel router 2-layer	2-dimensional placement Linear placement
SHARPS [65]	Sharp	1981	Hierarchical layout		Global router Channel router 2-layer	Clustering Linear placement FDR
ALPHA [68]	Musashino ECL NTT	1982	Hierarchical layout		Global router Channel router 3-layer	Linear placement Pairwise exchange Shift insertion
LAMBDA [80]	NEC	1982	Masterslice		Global router Maze router Dynamic router	SORG GFDR Two level hierachical placement

SORG = Sub - Optimum - Random - Generation
GFDR = Generalized - Force - Directed - Relaxation
FDPR = Force - Directed - Pairwise - Relaxation
FDR = Force - Directed - Relaxation

block or polycell layout approach, and has mainly been applied to MOS LSI's.

Automatic layout systems for building-block LSI's were developed at a relatively early stage in Japan. LILAC [55], Advanced LILAC [56], and ROBIN [57] are layout systems of this type, as shown in Table IV. In the LILAC system [55], an algorithm for minimizing the number of tracks needed in practical routing is used. The LILAC system is considered to be the first polycell-type layout design system in the world. In the Advanced LILAC system [56], in addition to standard cells, nonstandard cells like PLA's are allowed. A wiring model is proposed where channel routing is always guaranteed in a predefined sequence. In addition, the strategy is implemented which can eliminate cyclic loops in the constraint graph without the rearrangement of cells.

ROBIN [57] is a layout system applicable to more general building-block LSI's. A chip structure used in ROBIN is shown in Fig. 7. A group, which usually consists of a row of cells, is used as a layout unit. Besides these usual groups, some large predefined blocks, such as ROM's, RAM's, and PLA's, are also treated as a group. The determination of interconnection routes between these groups is performed according to the following procedure [58], [59]: 1) for a given topological layout, a mapping process sequence is determined, which can be applied to each street without contradiction; 2) by a heuristic algorithm, the interconnection nets are assigned to streets, aiming to minimize the chip area (routing process); and 3) using a heuristic approach, the physically precise positions of wire segments are also determined in order to minimize the width of streets (mapping process). The graph-

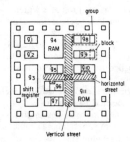

Fig. 7. Chip structure of ROBIN [57].

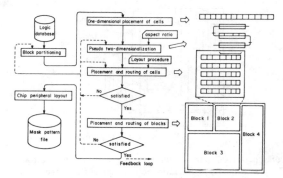

Fig. 10. Layout process flow in PLASMA/COSMIC [67].

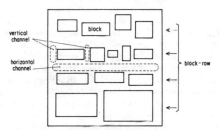

Fig. 8. Layout model of MIRAGE [61].

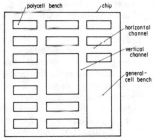

Fig. 9. Chip structure of MILD [63].

theoretical model proposed in ROBIN is the first such publication [58] in the world. Since its publication, many papers on the general building-block or hierarchical layout problems which are based on the ROBIN model have appeared.

A layout system [60] developed by Osaka University is used for the layout of the random logic portion of MOS LSI, which is based on the one-dimensional MOS complex gate-array ordering technique.

B. Hierarchical Layout Systems

MIRAGE [61] is the first hierarchical layout system developed in Japan. Fig. 8 shows a layout model of the MIRAGE system. In this system, in order to simplify the placement and routing process, the following restrictions are imposed [62]: 1) blocks are placed in rows called "block rows"; and 2) pin location of each block is allowed only at the upper and lower edges of the block. The vertical channels are used only for the vertical feedthrough lines.

MILD [63] is an automatic layout system for custom-made LSI's. This system can treat general cells, such as memory blocks (i.e., RAM's, PLA's, and ROM's) as well as standard cells. The chip structure for MILD is shown in Fig. 9. "Bench" is defined as an area in which cells are placed. The placement

process consists of the following three steps: 1) element assignments in benches; 2) determination of the intrabench positions of elements; and 3) improvements in the results in 2) within individual benches. The routing process is achieved by the global routing and grid-free channel router [64].

SHARPS [65] is a hierarchical layout system for fully custom-made LSI's. This system has the following specific features: 1) rectangular functional blocks of arbitrary size and shape can be treated; 2) contradictions in the channel processing order can be automatically dissolved by a new shrinking operation; and 3) in the track assignment process, relative positions of blocks adjacent to the current channel are determined so as to minimize the channel area, and a modified dogleg channel router [66] is adopted. The system also has interactive utilities, such as maze-running router and initial-placement program, based on a constructive approach.

PLASMA/COMIC [67] is an automatic layout system recently announced. A hierarchical layout procedure is also provided with this system. The chip structure in each hierarchical layout stage is simplified to the polycell layout style. This restriction does not cause serious damage in respect to chip density. Fig. 10 shows the layout process flow in PLASMA/COSMIC. In this system, the layout process is divided into four stages, namely, one-dimensional placement by COSMIC; pseudo two-dimensionalization, placement, and routing of functional blocks by PLASMA; and chip peripheral routing. In each step, a designer can select various kinds of placement and routing strategies aiming toward higher density. An appropriate hierarchical structure for optimal layout can be selected in each step. Also, not only higher density but also better electrical performance can be realized in the placement and routing procedures.

A new layout system, ALPHA [68], presented recently uses the hierarchical top-down layout design method. A global route assignment process reduces the redundant interblock wiring area. Routing in a single path over the whole chip enables one to use chip area more efficiently.

C. Masterslice or Gate Array Layout Systems

Automatic layout systems for masterslice or gate array LSI's in Japan are shown in Table IV. A layout design system [69] is the first announced system for masterslice LSI in Japan. The automatic layout system reported in [70] is also one of these systems. In the routing process, a modified Lee algorithm [71] is used, and rerouting is also tried.

MARC [72] places functional blocks on a chip and wires between these blocks for masterslice LSI's. It is impossible to

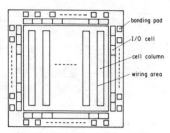

Fig. 11. Masterslice structure [76].

guarantee 100 percent wiring completion in the masterslice LSI, in which the interconnection area is fixed and limited. Therefore, in the MARC system, manual modification can be performed through the stand-alone graphic system interfaced with the main computer.

The three afore mentioned automatic layout systems use the Lee algorithm [71] and the line search algorithm [51] as routing algorithms. However, to deal with VLSI chip complexity, channel routing algorithms have been widely adopted recently.

MARS-M3 [73], [74] is an automatic layout system for ECL and MOS gate array LSI's using two metal layer levels. In the placement phase, hierarchical placement and top-down initial placement techniques are utilized [75]. The routing is also hierarchically achieved in two phases. The first phase is a global routing called channel assignment. The second is a local routing, which assigns tracks by modified dogleg channel router.

Similarly, an automatic layout program [76] also uses channel routing algorithm. The system has been applied to the layout design for CMOS masterslice LSI's. Fig. 11 shows a masterslice structure treated by this system. The placement process is performed as follows. First, the initial placement is determined by the min-cut placement algorithm. Next, in order to avoid local congestion, a one-dimensional placement improvement process is iterated for the initial placement. The routing process consists of two phases, i.e., topological routing and channel routing.

MASTER [77] is also an automatic layout system for masterslice LSI's. In this system, a new placement algorithm [78] is adopted, which is considered to be the most efficient iterative improvement method in the world. The routing process consists of two phases—global routing and detailed routing—in order to avoid local wiring congestion. Detailed routing is performed by using a line search method [51] with a few modifications, which can be applied to three-layer wiring.

LAMBDA [79], [80] is the newest automatic/interactive layout design system for masterslice LSI's developed in Japan. In this system, automatic and interactive functions are completely integrated and, therefore, can achieve complete net connectivity in a quick design time. The placement algorithm consists of two kinds of heuristic methods, a constructive one called SORG and an iterative improvement one called GFDR [78]. A maze algorithm is adopted with some modifications to find the exact wiring pattern. And the dynamic router iterates by removing routes and putting them back to improve the connection rate.

D. Design Rule, Connection, and Electrical Performance Checker

Many artwork verifiers have been developed in the last half decade, and development efforts are being continued in Japan.

Although automatic layout programs which produce error-free layout patterns from logic descriptions have been developed, an artwork verifier is of primary importance because most memory LSI's and general-purpose logic LSI's are still being designed manually, in combination with automatic programs or with the so-called interactive graphic systems. Generally speaking, there are two kinds of verifiers. One is a checker for geometrical design rules, and the other is a checker for interconnections and electrical performances.

1) Design Rule Checker: A design rule checker has been developed in many companies. Many simple function programs reside in interactive graphic systems and are used for checking small-size blocks. An elaborated checker was reported from Toshiba in 1977 [81] which can perform a rather sophisticated function like a Boolean operation between layout patterns, a high-speed expansion/shrinking operation, and a design-rule violation checking. Since then, intensive investigations have been made in many companies [82], [83] about how to easily and speedily handle a great deal of geometrical data. New technologies and data structures have been applied not only to checking but also to more general data-handling purposes.

2) Interconnection and Electrical Performance Checker: Interconnection and electrical performance check verifiers can be classified into several groups. The most primitive verifier checks only the consistency of interconnections between block terminals identified with names. More general checking capability for connections is provided as a part of the other kinds of verifiers presented in the following.

Electrical performance checkers, which derive various circuit parameters from layout patterns, have been widely developed for MOS LSI's [84], [85] because the MOS circuit performance is very sensitive to parasitic capacitances, which directly depends on the layout patterns. Similar function programs for an analog bipolar LSI have also been developed in Matsushita [86] and Toshiba. These programs derive circuit-level descriptions from layout patterns, draw circuit diagrams, and calculate circuit parameters such as transistor sizes and capacitance values. The circuit parameters obtained by these programs can be directly input into circuit simulators, and a detailed circuit performance analysis can be achieved.

Resistance calculation is another function requested especially for the estimation of long wirings or analog circuits. One of the difficulties in this calculation lies in the fact that it is necessary to recognize networks which are only implicitly expressed in layout patterns. Multiterminal interconnections have to be broken up into many two-terminal networks because resistance calculation is essentially performed between a couple of terminals. For this purpose, a center line extraction algorithm for any geometrical pattern shape has been reported by Matsushita [86]. Another problem for resistance calculation is in regard to accuracy. A complex potential method has been proposed recently by NTT and Hitachi which can offer an accurate resistance calculation with a comparatively small memory. The finite element method reported by Toshiba also seems promising. Practically, especially for MOS LSI's, resistance calculation is needed only for a few long wirings on critical paths. Therefore, a simple and interactive program developed by NTT [87], which can calculate resistances within a limited condition, is also very useful from the practical point of view.

A logic function consistency verifier has become one of the indispensable tools for logic LSI design. The most popular and widely used method is one that takes advantage of identification marks given on each gate and terminal in advance [88]. In order to eliminate the possibility of giving marks incorrectly

TABLE V
ARTWORK VERIFIERS DEVELOPED IN JAPAN

Program	Developer	Year	Design Rule Check	Connection Check	Electrical Performance Check	Application
MAICAP [87]	NTT	1978			o	MOS
PAS [84]	NTT	1978		o	o	MOS
PALLEQ	Mitsubishi	1979		o		MOS
PALMS [88]	NEC	1979		o		MOS
IVS	Hitachi	1979		o		MOS
EMAP [85]	NTIS	1980	o	o	o	MOS
PANAMAP [86]	Matsushita	1980		o	o	Bipolar
LAS	Hitachi, NTT	1980		o	o	Bopolar/MOS
LIVES [91]	NTT	1981		o		MOS
MIAS	Oki	1981		o	o	MOS

and to remove such laborious work, the program developed by NTIS makes use of a logic simulation technology [85], [89]. For the same purpose, employment of the graph isomorphism to this problem has been attempted by NEC [88] and Osaka University [90]. A new verifier for a logic consistency check using this graph isomorphism technology has been reported recently by NTT [91].

As with other CAD tools, it is also desirable for verifier programs to be free from device change as well as fabrication technology changes. If they are not free from changes, continuous version upgrading efforts become inevitably necessary due to technological changes with rapid LSI progress. In order to avoid this problem, a library concept has been implemented into several programs [81], [85]. In these programs, a user defines the relationship between device technologies and desired operations in the form of a library with the prepared definition language.

Artwork verifiers, which have been developed in Japan, are summarized in Table V. Though there are many well-designed programs already, continuous efforts are being made to develop new verifiers having enough capabilities to deal with much larger LSI data in less computing time. They will be closely combined to the other CAD programs and will become an indispensable part of total CAD systems for future VLSI design.

V. DEVICE AND PROCESS SIMULATORS

The device simulator has become an indispensable tool for device design. Also, a process simulator, such as SUPREM [92], has been widely used in process evaluation prior to fabrication. Furthermore, a device simulator coupled to a process simulator [93] has also played a significant role as a method for predicting device parameter variations from process specifications.

In Japan, much effort has been made to develop device simulators applicable to various devices, including bipolar [94]–[96] and unipolar devices [97]–[101]. Two-dimensional device simulators are widely used for device design.

Three-dimensional simulators for very small device analysis [102], [103] have now been reported. A two-dimensional simulator, applicable to transient conditions, has also been investigated [104]. Process simulator developments have also become active [105], [106]. As a basic approach, a process/device optimization simulator [107], which can obtain optimum process conditions for realizing desired device perfor-

mance, has been developed. Device and process simulators developed in Japan are summarized in Table VI.

A. General-Purpose Device Simulators and FET Device Simulators

1) General-Purpose Device Simulators: General-purpose device simulators are capable of analyzing a wide variety of bipolar and unipolar devices, wherein Gummel's iteration method [108] is applied to linearized Poisson's equation and the continuity equations. These partial-differential equations are formulated by using the finite difference or finite element method suitable for a nonrectangular grid. To solve the resulting matrix, the relaxation [109], [110] or direct method is adopted, according to its matrix structure.

Physical models and boundary conditions are implemented, corresponding to device material, such as Si or GaAs, and corresponding to device structure, such as MOSFET, MESFET, or bipolar devices, respectively. Application examples of these simulators for bipolar devices are presented as follows.

Current–voltage characteristics can easily be obtained, corresponding to impurity profiles. In addition, the junction capacitance and cutoff frequency are numerically calculated. Therefore, the transistor parameters are precisely calculated and served for the Gummel–Poon model [111] or for a table lookup model, instead of a test element device for the model parameter determination. Device performance can be evaluated through a circuit simulator, based on the above model. This application example for IIL is reported, including the experiments [96]. However, phenomena such as current spreading due to the extrinsic base region in bipolar devices can be analyzed with only a three-dimensional simulator. Fig. 12 shows the current–voltage characteristics calculated by a three-dimensional simulator [102]. These results suggest that the three-dimensional effects are dominated in the higher current region, compared with two-dimensional results.

As another example of a bipolar device simulator, IIL analysis with multistream function was investigated [94]. In this simulator, in order to solve the continuity equations with multistream function, the currents are divided into recombination current component and electron/hole current components injected into each electrode.

2) FET Device Simulators: FET device simulators are capable of analyzing only FET devices based on unipolar approximation with shorter CPU time. These simulators use

TABLE VI
DEVICE AND PROCESS SIMULATORS DEVELOPED IN JAPAN

Program	Developer	Year	Function	Feature	Application	Algorithm
TRANAL [95],[96],[102],[104]	NTT	1977	D.S.	2D, 2D-transient, 3D	General	FDM, FEM
FEDAS [99],[103]	NTT	1979	D.S.	2D, 3D	FET	FDM
POSEIDON [107]	NTT	1981	D.P.O.	SUPREM+FEDAS	FET	Flecher-Powell
CADDET [94],[97],[98]	Hitachi	1978	D.S.	2D	FET, Bipolar	FDM
———	Hitachi	1981	D.O.	SUPREM+CADDET	FET	
MODEST [101]	Toshiba	1981	D.S.	2D	FET	FDM
TOPICS [106]	Toshiba	1980	P.S.	2D	FET	FDM
SUBMODAN [113]	Toshiba	1981	D.O.	SUPREM+MODEST	FET	
PIEECHPIE [105]	NEC	1980	P.S.	1D	FET	
——— [115]	NEC	1981	D.O.	PIEECHPIE+D.S.(2D)	FET	
——— [100]	Fujitsu	1979	D.S.	2D	FET	FDM

D.S. --- Device Simulator   D.O. --- Device Optimizing simulator

P.S. --- Process Simulator   D.P.O. --- Device and Process Optimizing simulator

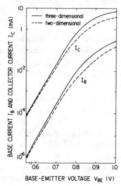

Fig. 12. Forward base and collector current as a function of base-to-emitter bias using TRANAL [102].

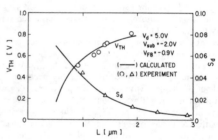

Fig. 13. Threshold voltage V_{TH} and its sensitivity for drain voltage S_d versus channel length L characteristics. Open circles and triangles denote experimental results for V_{TH} and S_d, respectively. Solid lines indicate calculated results [99].

Mock's algorithm [112] to solve the continuity equations with stream function and Gummel's method, which linearizes Poisson's equation. The difference equations are solved by the relaxation method.

Device parameters such as voltage–current, g_m–V_G and C_G–V_G characteristics, can be easily deduced in a manner similar to a bipolar device and serve for circuit analysis on device parameters. The other parameters—for example, threshold sensitivities based upon profiles—are estimated numerically, as shown in Fig. 13 [99]. Moreover, avalanche breakdown analysis for short channel NMOS was also investigated by a two-dimensional simulator [98]. A two-dimensional simulator cannot easily handle performance variations in a small-size MOSFET whose width is similar to that of the channel length. A three-dimensional simulator was successfully applied to examination of short and narrow channel effects [103].

B. Device and Process Optimization

Process-oriented device design is an inevitable state in order to reduce fabrication costs. Table VI also shows the process simulators developed in Japan, including those coupled with the device simulators.

There are two trends for process modeling. One is a one-dimensional simulator, which has advantages in regard to wide application and savings in computational time. For example, PIEECHPIE [105] and modified SUPREM II [92] in oxidation-rate and depth-dependent diffusion coefficient, etc., are commonly used. However, these methods have limitations in accuracy under the very small device dimensions. The other one is two-dimensional process modeling, taking into account lateral spreading. TOPICS [106], for example, has been developed for MOSFET process design and reported two-dimensional implanted Boron distribution.

In either case, if the device structure is closely related to the fabrication process simulator, it would be possible to design desired device performance through an optimized fabrication process and device structure. Therefore, the integration of the device simulator and the process simulator is considered to make overall device and process optimization, as shown in Table VI. Much work has been accomplished in MOSFET's synthesizing pseudo-two-dimensional impurity profile. Then process sensitivities for device characteristics can be analyzed using a coupled simulator. Although problems involving the

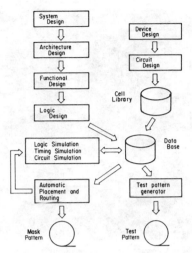

Fig. 14. VLSI design process flow.

short-channel effects remain to be solved, these simulators can be applicable to submicron devices [113]. Coupling the device simulator with a two-dimensional process simulator, instead of a one-dimensional simulator, enables the design of a device with shorter channel length.

The afore mentioned optimization procedure depends upon the engineer's capability or work load. On the contrary, the computer-aided process/device optimization method POSEIDON has been reported [107] owing to the progress in computer facilities. The Flecher–Powell method [114], commonly used in circuit design, is applicable to calculating the process sensitivity for device characteristics.

The optimization simulator is expected to be a very effective tool for process/device optimum design through the use of an array processor.

VI. INTEGRATED VLSI DESIGN SYSTEM

A. Overview

In this section, a VLSI CAD system [116], [117] developed by NTT is described as an example of hierarchical-oriented CAD systems. Several main features of this system are as follows:

1) A hierarchical and structural design method is adopted throughout the design phases from LSI specification to mask pattern data.

2) The LSI design language (HSL) is extensively used as common input data.

3) A hierarchical design process is mainly achieved by the iterative interactiveness of the placer and the router (COSMIC/PLASMA).

4) A design database controller (HIDEMAP) administrates logical and physical data.

5) In addition to highly automatic processes, man–machine interfaces are provided to facilitate an interactive design.

B. General VLSI Design Flow

The VLSI design process flow is shown in Fig. 14. After the VLSI system architectural design is accomplished, functional specifications for each functional block are fixed. Then the logical design for each block follows, and the resultant logical design data are registered into the VLSI design database. On the other hand, standard function cells are designed, confirmed through circuit simulations, and provided within a cell library in the database.

After the logic expansion, the logical data is verified using logic and circuit simulations. Then automatic placement and routing programs are executed. After the layout process, the resultant patterns are evaluated through critical path check and timing simulation. If the critical path delay exceeds a specified value, the routing parameters are changed and the layout programs are rerun. Placement and routing are repeated until the given specifications are satisfied. Finally, the resultant data are converted to a format file for mask fabrication. In addition, test patterns are also generated, using a test pattern generator from the verified logical design data.

C. Hierarchical Specification Language: HSL

The Hierarchical specification language (HSL) is used as a common input language to the VLSI design system. HSL has been developed, based on the structure description language (SDL) [118] developed by vanCleemput of Stanford University, which is appropriate for hierarchical LSI design methodology. In HSL, the language specification is extended with respect to the following items:

1) For verification purposes, module function specification items are added.

2) Gate and media delay parameters are added.

3) Pin function and attribute can be specified.

4) Schematic information is added.

5) Database management information is provided.

The VLSI cannot be designed by using only VLSI structural information since the verification and evaluation processes require accurate design data. For example, in the case of circuits with bidirectional buses or wired gates, the physical structure of the network becomes different from the logical one. Therefore, the design language has to be provided with appropriate functions to deal with these problems.

In HSL, the DEFAULT statement is introduced to overcome these problems. If the DEFAULT statement is specified, a circuit with dotting function is automatically converted to a circuit with no dotting function. The stack values of unconnected pins are also specified by the DEFAULT statement.

D. Hierarchical Structure

The VLSI CAD system consists of three major subsystems, as shown in Fig. 15, i.e., language processing, verification, and placement and routing subsystems. The language processing subsystem, especially, has a unique feature. It is integrated into the program called HIDEMAP (Hierarchical design database manipulator), which has the following functions: 1) HSL compiler and decompiler; 2) macro expander; 3) scissor (block divider); 4) wired function (dot) and bidirectional bus processor; 5) database manager; and 6) interface between database and application programs.

1) Compiler: The HSL compiler checks for a syntax error in input data described by HSL and converts it to the object file which consists of a collection of modules directly accessible by module names or its data items. The object file can be directly registered into the database, and broken down and converted back to the HSL source file or list.

2) Database Manager and Macro Expander: In the database, modules are managed by name and management items. The

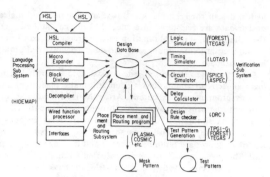

Fig. 15. VLSI design system configuration [116], [117].

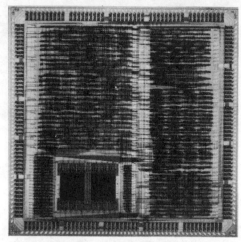

Fig. 17. Microphotograph of an automatically designed 32-bit VLSI processor chip (containing 20K gates) [119].

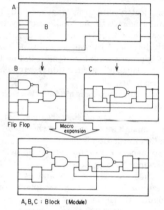

Fig. 16. Macro expansion.

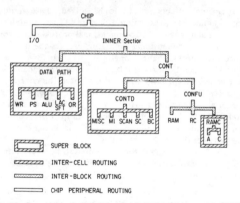

Fig. 18. Layout hierarchy of the 32-bit VLSI processor chip [119].

database consists of library, project, and user file. The library file which keeps cell libraries is accessible by any user who has access permission. The design data can be shared among several users working on the same project. Database control commands are provided to handle the collection of modules and get statistical information easily.

The macro expander program transforms higher level modules to lower level modules. An example is shown in Fig. 16. Macro expansion is also controlled by HIDEMAP commands specifying top module, and stop level name or stop module names. By using this function, designers can set up network data which are necessary for the hierarchical layout program. Input data to the macro expander can be retrieved from the database by specifying only top module name or management item priority.

3) Block Divider: The block divider is also a useful tool for the hierarchical VLSI design approach. In the hierarchical-oriented system, since the design is made in a top-down manner, it often occurs that some blocks are too large and other blocks are too small to be processed in a single run of the layout program. Therefore, it is desirable that the block structure is reorganized into a proper size for the routing process. The block divider (or scissor) is provided with such a function, which can automatically change structures by simple commands.

4) Layout Program: After the hierarchical structure is reorganized, a layout process takes place. At first, functional

cells are automatically routed. Then intercells are routed to build functional blocks. These functional blocks are then routed and compose the whole chip. In the hierarchical layout method, the layout quality is controlled by: i) block partitioning; ii) block shape and location; iii) interblock wiring channel location; and iv) external pin locations within each block.

E. System Application Example of VLSI CAD System

The VLSI CAD system has been applied to a number of VLSI designs [119], [120] since 1979. Fig. 17 shows a micro-photograph of a 32-bit CMOS VLSI processor chip containing a 17K gate random logic and a 2304-bit RAM, which has been designed by using the above CAD system. In this particular circuit, the logic hierarchy consists of three levels—cell, block, and chip. The cell size is 3 gates on an average, and each block contains about 100 to 300 cells or 300 to 1000 gates.

The original three-level hierarchy was extended to seven levels, as shown in Fig. 18, such that it becomes well fitted to the automatic layout process. The RAM block was designed manually, while RC block, DATA PATH, CONTD and RAMC superblocks were automatically designed by using the cell placer and intercell router. Layout design efforts were within two man–months for the particular circuit which contains 78K transistors and 17K interconnection nets. The CAD system has achieved a high packing density of 542 Trs/mm^2 for random logic circuits. This result is considered equal to higher layout quality, compared to a manual design.

VI. Conclusion

The developmental aspect and the present status of CAD systems for VLSI design in Japan have been presented. With the explosive increase in VLSI scale and complexity, CAD will play an unprecedentedly important role. To meet future VLSI design requirements, great efforts must be continued for the development of CAD systems and technologies. In order to effectively aid 50K-gate or larger VLSI design, in addition to improvements in traditional CAD systems, technological breakthroughs are keenly needed. In the research and development on VLSI CAD hereafter, the following subjects will be the principal themes: 1) more intelligent CAD algorithms and methodologies; 2) CAD-dedicated machine or usage of supercomputer in CAD area; 3) highly interactive design environment; and 4) vertically integrated CAD system covering system concept to the device fabrication process.

With the remarkable progress in LSI technologies, the LSI world is widening its boundary and the population of LSI designers, i.e., CAD users, is rapidly increasing as a result. Under these circumstances, standardization becomes indispensable for the efficient usage of CAD resources among numerous users at various levels and with different backgrounds. Consequently, it is earnestly desirable that strenuous efforts are made toward standardization as well as accomplishment of CAD systems for future VLSI design.

Acknowledgment

The authors wish to thank K. Ueda, T. Watanabe, T. Adachi, M. Nagatani, M. Tomisawa, T. Hoshino, H. Miyashita, and K. Yokoyama of Musashino ECL, NTT for preparing the manuscript. We would also like to thank A. Yamada, T. Kurobe, and N. Tanabe of Nippon Electric Co., Ltd. for their valuable suggestions. Finally, the authors are greatly indebted to the Research Committee on the Design Technology of Electronics Equipment of IPSJ for providing the data on design automation status in Japan.

References

[1] Research Committee on the Design Technology of Electronics Equipment, "Computer aided design of electronic equipment (4)—the CAD system in use or under development," *J. Inform. Process. Soc. Japan*, vol. 21, no. 2, pp. 165–167, Feb. 1980 (Japanese).

[2] L. W. Nagel and C. O. Pederson, "Simulation program with integrated circuit emphasis," in *Proc. 16th Midwest Symp. Circuit Theory* (Waterloo, Ont., Canada, Apr. 1973).

[3] T. E. Idleman, F. S. Jenkins, W. J. McCalla, and D. O. Pederson, "SLIC—a simulator for linear integrated circuits," *IEEE J. Solid State Circuits*, vol. SC-6, pp. 188–204, Aug. 1971.

[4] W. T. Weeks, A. J. Jimenez, G. W. Mahoney, D. Mehta, H. Qassemzadeh, and T. R. Scott, "Algorithms for ASTAP—a network analysis program," *IEEE Trans. Circuit Theory*, vol. CT-20, pp. 628–634, Nov. 1973.

[5] S. A. Szygenda and E. W. Thompson, "Digital logic simulation in a time based table driven environment," *Computer*, Mar. 1975.

Survey on CAD Systems in Japan

[6] K. Kusunoki, "DEX-design automation system cooperation development," in *Proc. 10th Design Automation Workshop*, 1973, pp. 187–192.

[7] T. Moto-Oka, T. Kurachi, T. Shiino, and M. Sugimoto, "Logic design system in Japan," in *Proc. 12th Design Automation*

Conf., June 1975, pp. 241–250.

[8] K. Ueda, "Computer-aided layout design for LSI; state of the art," *Proc. 2nd USA-Japan Computer Conf.*, 1975, pp. 556–561.

[9] K. Kani, A. Yamada, and M. Teramoto, "CAD in the Japanese electronics industry," presented at the Symp. CAD of Digital Electronic Circuits and Systems, Brussels, Belgium, Nov. 1978.

[10] M. Watanabe, "CAD tools for designing VLSI in Japan," in *Proc. ISSCC 79*, Feb. 1979, pp. 242–243.

[11] A. Yamada, "Design automation status in Japan," in *Proc. 18th Design Automation Conf.*, 1981, pp. 43–50.

[12] T. Hosaka, K. Ueda, and H. Matsuura, "A design automation system for electronic switching systems," in *Proc. 18th Design Automation Conf.*, 1981, pp. 51–58.

[13] T. Sudo, "VLSI and CAD," *Proc. IPSJ*, vol. 22, no. 8, 1981 (Japanese).

[14] T. Sudo, "Present status of CAD technologies in Japan," to be published.

Logic Design

[15] T. Kurobe, S. Nemoto, Y. Shikata, and K. Kani, "Logic simulation system; LOGOS 2," in *Monograph of Technical Group on DA of Inform. Process. Soc. Japan*, DA31-2, 1977 (Japanese).

[16] Y. Fujinami, N. Yasuda, H. Sakuma, and T. Kurobe, "A logic simulation system for MOS LSI circuits with bidirectional elements," in *Monograph of Technical Group on Circuits and Systems of Inst. Electron. Commun. Eng. Japan*, Feb. 1982.

[17] J. Watanabe, J. Miura, T. Kurachi, and I. Suetsugu, "Seven value logic simulation for MOS LSI circuits," in *Proc. IEEE Inter. Conf. Circuits and Computers 80*, Oct. 1980, pp. 941–944.

[18] Y. Ohno, M. Miyoshi, and K. Sato, "Logic verification system for very large computers using LSI's," in *Proc. 16th Design Automation Conf.*, June 1979, pp. 367–374.

[19] M. Murakami, N. Shiraki, and K. Hirakawa, "Logic verification and test generation for LSI circuits," in *Proc. Test Conf.*, Nov. 1980, pp. 467–472.

[20] T. Sasaki, A. Yamada, S. Kato, T. Nakazawa, K. Tomita, and N. Nomizu, "MIXS: a mixed level simulator for large digital system logic verification," in *Proc. 17th Design Automation Conf.*, June 1980, pp. 626–633.

[21] N. Kawato, T. Saito, F. Maruyama, and T. Uehara, "Design and verification of large-scale computers by using DDL," in *Proc. 16th Design Automation Conf.*, June 1979, pp. 360–366.

[22] M. Ishii, Y. Ito, M. Iwasaki, M. Yamamoto, and S. Kodama, "Automatic input and interactive editing systems of logic circuit diagrams," in *Proc. 18th Design Automation Conf.*, June 1981, pp. 639–645.

[23] K. Hayamizu and T. Nanya, "An automatic design system for PLA," in *Proc. Nat. Conf. Inform. Process. Soc. Japan*, 5G-4, 1978 (Japanese).

[24] M. Tsuboya, T. Takagi, M. Teramoto, and T. Nanya, "PLA design support system," in *Proc. Nat. Conf. Inform. Process. Soc. Japan*, 5G-5, 1978 (Japanese).

[25] H. Miyashita and Y. Sugiyama, H. Sakuma, and H. Ishizuka, "PLACAD: PLA design automation system," in *Proc. Nat. Conf. Inst. Electron. Commun. Eng. Japan*, 410, 1981 (Japanese).

[26] M. Tokoro, M. Sato, M. Ishigami, E. Tamura, T. Ishimitsu, and H. Ohara, "A module level simulation technique for systems composed of LSIs and MSIs," in *Proc. 15th Design Automation Conf.*, June 1978, pp. 418–427.

[27] M. Itoh, G. Kohno, T. Makita, and R. Tadenuma, "A logic design automation system," in *Monograph of Technical Group on Design Technology of Electronics Equipment of Inform. Process. Soc. Japan*, 4-3, Mar. 1980 (Japanese).

[28] T. Fukazawa, K. Kurihara, T. Suzuki, H. Tanaka, and T. Moto-Oka, "Logic simulator by data flow machine," in *Monograph of Technical Group on Design Technology of Electronics Equipment of Inform. Process. Soc. Japan*, 6-3, Oct. 1980 (Japanese).

Test Generation

[29] S. Funatsu, N. Wakatsuki, and T. Arima, "Test generation system in Japan," in *Proc. 12th Design Automation Conf.*, June 1975, pp. 112–114.

[30] H. Kubo, "A procedure for generating test sequence to detect sequential circuit failures," *NEC Res. Develop.*, no. 12, pp. 69–78, 1968.

[31] S. Goshima, T. Kozawa, Y. Oka, T. Mori, Y. Takeguchi, and Y. Ohno, "Diagnostic system for large scale logic cards and LSIs," in *Proc. 18th Design Automation Conf.*, June 1981, pp. 256–259.

[32] T. Yamada, M. Saisho, and Y. Kasuya, "TESTA-1: test generation system using state diagram tracing approach," *NEC Res. Develop.*, no. 65, pp. 68–73, Apr. 1982.

[33] K. Kinoshita, Y. Takamatsu, and M. Shibata, "Test generation for combinatorial circuits by structure description functions," *FTCS-10*, pp. 152–154, Oct. 1980.

[34] T. Shimono, H. Fujiwara, and H. Ozaki, "An efficient test generating algorithm based on testability measurements," in *Monograph of Technical Group on Design Technology of Electronics Equipment of Inform. Process. Soc. Japan*, 13-4, Feb. 1982 (Japanese).

[35] T. Hoshino, Y. Wada, and T. Sudo, "A test pattern generation system by using a block sensitizing method," in *Monograph of Technical Group on Design Technology of Electronics Equipment of Inform. Process Soc. Japan*, 9-3, June 1981 (Japanese).

[36] A. Kobayashi, S. Matsue, and H. Shiba, "Flip-flop circuit with FLT capability," in *Proc. Nat. Conf. Inst. Electron. Commun. Eng. Japan*, no. 892, 1968.

[37] A. Yamada, N. Wakatsuki, T. Fukui, and S. Funatsu, "Automatic system level test generation and fault location for large digital systems," in *Proc. 15th Design Automation Conf.*, June 1978, pp. 347–352.

Circuit and Timing Simulators

[38] M. Sugimori, "DEMOS E circuit analysis program: ECSS," in *Proc. Nat. Conf. Inst. Electron. Commun. Eng. Japan*, 1974, p. 1784 (Japanese).

[39] T. Kojima and K. Watanabe, "CARD (computer assisted research and development) for electrical circuit," *Fujitsu*, vol. 24, no. 7, pp. 175–189, 1973 (Japanese).

[40] K. Kawakita and T. Ohtsuki, "NECTAR-2—circuit analysis program based on piecewise linear approach," in *Proc. IEEE Inter. Conf. Circuits and Systems*, 1975, pp. 46–51.

[41] T. Ohtsuki, T. Fujisawa, and S. Kumagai, "Existence theorems and a solution algorithm for piecewise-linear resistor networks," *SIAM J. Math. Anal.*, vol. 8, pp. 69–99, 1977.

[42] B. R. Chawla, H. K. Gummel, and P. Kozak, "MOTIS—an MOS timing simulator," *IEEE Trans. Circuits Syst.*, CAS-22, vol. 12, pp. 901–910, 1975.

[43] S. P. Fan, M. Y. Hsueh, A. R. Newton, and D. O. Pederson, "MOTIS-C: a new circuit simulator for MOS LSI circuits," in *Proc. IEEE Inter. Conf. Circuits and Systems*, 1977, pp. 700–703.

[44] K. Hirabayashi and J. Watanabe, "MATIS—macromodel timing simulator for large scale integrated MOS circuits," in *Proc. 3rd USA-Japan Computer Conf.*, 26-1-1, 1978.

[45] T. Shikage and H. Sato, "A circuit simulation method based on macro-modeling of circuit blocks," in *Proc. Nat. Conf. Semiconductors of Inst. Electron. Commun. Eng. Japan*, 1979, p. 62 (Japanese).

[46] J. Watanabe, "Macro-model timing simulator—MATIS'" in *Proc. Nat. Conf. Semiconductors of Inst. Electron. Commun. Eng. Japan*, 1979, p. 63 (Japanese).

[47] J. Yamada, T. Takeya, N. Miyahara, and H. Nakamura, "A large-scale circuit simulator (LOTAS)," in *Proc. Nat. Conf. Semiconductors of Inst. Electron. Commun. Eng. Japan*, 1979, p. 65 (Japanese).

[48] N. Tanabe, H. Nakamura, and K. Kawakita, "MOSTAP: an MOS circuit simulator for LSI circuits," in *Proc. IEEE Inter. Conf. on Circuits and Systems*, 1980, pp. 1035–1038.

[49] N. Tanabe, M. Endo, and N. Miyahara, "Timing simulation: a fast analysis method," in *Proc. Nat. Conf. Inst. Electron. Commun. Eng. Japan*, 450, 1981, p. 215 (Japanese).

[50] N. Miyahara, M. Endo, N. Tanabe, and H. Nakamura, "Timing simulator (LOTAS)," in *Monograph of Technical Group on Electron Devices of Inst. Electron. Commun. Eng. Japan*, EDD82-13, 1982, pp. 61–69 (Japanese).

Automatic Layout Design

[51] K. Mikami and K. Tabuchi, "A computer program for optimal routing of printed circuit conductors," in *Proc. IFIP Cong. 68*, 1968, pp. 1475–1478.

[52] A. Hashimoto and J. Stevens, "Wire routing by optimal channel assignment within large apertures," in *Proc. 8th Design Automation Workshop*, 1971, pp. 158–169.

[53] N. Sugiyama, T. Ohtsuki, S. Nemoto, K. Kani, and H. Watanabe, "An integrated circuit layout design program based on graph-theoretical approach," *ISSCC*, 1970.

[54] Y. Sugiyama, K. Ueda, K. Kani, and M. Teramoto, "Routing program for multichip LSIs," in *Proc. USA-Japan Design Automation '75*, Aug. 1975, pp. 87–94.

[55] T. Kozawa, H. Horino, K. Watanabe, M. Nagata, and H. Fukuda, "Block and track method for automated layout generation of MOS LSI array," *ISSCC*, 1972, pp. 62–63.

[56] T. Kozawa, H. Horino, T. Ishiga, and S. Sato, "Advanced LILAC—an automated layout generation system for MOS/LSIs," in *Proc. 11th Design Automation Workshop*, 1974, pp. 26–46.

[57] K. Kani, H. Kawanishi, and A. Kishimoto, "ROBIN: a building block LSI routing program," in *Proc. 1976 IEEE Inter. Conf. on Circuits and Systems*, 1976, pp. 658–661.

[58] H. Kawanishi, S. Goto, T. Oyamada, H. Kato, and K. Kani, "A routing method of building block LSI," in *Proc. 7th Asilomar Conf. on Circuits, Systems and Computers*, 1973, pp. 119–124.

[59] H. Kato, H. Kawanishi, and S. Goto, "On automated wire routing for building-block LSI," in *Proc. 1974 IEEE Inter. Conf. on Circuits and Systems*, 1974, pp. 309–313.

[60] I. Shirakawa, N. Okuda, T. Harada, S. Tani, and H. Ozaki, "A layout system for the random logic portion of MOS LSI," in *Proc. 17th Design Automation Conf.*, 1980, pp. 92–99.

[61] K. Sato, T. Nagai, H. Shimoyama, and T. Yahara, "MIRAGE—a simple model routing program for the hierarchical layout design of IC masks," in *Proc. 16th Design Automation Conf.*, 1979, pp. 297–304.

[62] K. Sato and T. Nagai, "A method of specifying the relative locations between blocks in a routing program for building block LSI," in *Proc. 1979 IEEE Inter. Conf. on Circuits and Systems*, 1979, pp. 673–676.

[63] K. Sato, T. Nagai, M. Tachibana, H. Shimoyama, M. Ozaki, and T. Yahara, "MILD—A cell based layout system for MOS LSI," in *Proc. 18th Design Automation Conf.*, 1981, pp. 828–836.

[64] K. Sato, H. Shimoyama, T. Nagai, M. Ozaki, and T. Yahara, "A grid-free channel router," in *Proc. 17th Design Automation Conf.*, 1980, pp. 22–31.

[65] T. Chiba, N. Okuda, T. Kambe, I. Nishioka, T. Inufushi, and S. Kimura, "SHARPS: a hierarchical layout system for VLSI," in *Proc. 18th Design Automation Conf.*, 1980, pp. 820–827.

[66] D. N. Deutsch, "A dogleg channel router," in *Proc. 13th Design Automation Conf.*, 1976, pp. 425–433.

[67] M. Nagatani, H. Miyashita, H. Okamoto, K. Tansho, and Y. Sugiyama, "An automated layout system for LSI functional blocks: PLASMA," in *Monograph of Technical Group of Electronics Equipment of Inform. Process. Soc. Japan*, 41, 1980, pp. 1–10.

[68] T. Adachi, H. Kitazawa, M. Nagatani, and T. Sudo, "Hierarchical top-down layout design method for VLSI chip," presented at 19th Design Automation Conf., 1982.

[69] Y. Ozawa, M. Murakami, and K. Suzuki, "Master slice LSI computer aided design system," in *Proc. 11th Design Automation Conf.*, 1974, pp. 19–25.

[70] R. Kamikawai, K. Kishida, A. Osawa, I. Yasuda, and T. Chiba, "Placement and routing program for masterslice LSIs," in *Proc. 13th Design Automation Conf.*, 1976, pp. 245–250.

[71] C. Y. Lee, "An algorithm for path connections and its applications," *IRE Trans. Electron. Comput.*, vol. EC-10, no. 3, pp. 346–364, 1961.

[72] K. Ueda, Y. Sugiyama, and K. Wada, "An automated layout system for masterslice LSI: MARC," *IEEE J. Solid State Circuits*, vol. SC-13, no. 5, pp. 716–721, 1978.

[73] C. Tanaka, S. Murai, S. Nakamura, T. Ogihara, M. Terai, and K. Kinoshita, "An integrated computer aided design system for gate array masterslices: part 1 logic reorganization system LORES-2," in *Proc. 18th Design Automation Conf.*, 1981, pp. 59–65.

[74] C. Tanaka, Su. Murai, H. Tsuji, T. Yahara, K. Okazaki, M. Terai, R. Katoh, and M. Tachibana, "An integrated computer aided design system for gate array masterslices: part 2 the layout design system for master-slice LSIs," presented at 19th Design Automation Conf., 1982.

[75] S. Murai, M. Kakinuma, M. Imai, and H. Tsuji, "The effects of initial placement techniques on the final placement results constructive vs. top-down techniques," in *Proc. 1980 IEEE Inter. Conf. on Circuits and Computers*, 1980, pp. 80–82.

[76] H. Shiraishi and F. Hirose, "Efficient placement and routing techniques for master slice LSI," in *Proc. 17th Design Automation Conf.*, 1980, pp. 458–464.

[77] H. Yoshizawa, H. Kawanishi, S. Goto, A. Kishimoto, Y. Fujinami, and K. Kani, "Automatic layout algorithms for master slice LSI," in *Proc. 1979 IEEE Inter. Conf. on Circuits and Systems*, 1979, pp. 470–473.

[78] S. Goto, "An efficient algorithm for two dimensional placement problem in electrical circuit layout," *IEEE Trans. Circuits and Syst.*, vol. CAS-28, no. 1, pp. 12–18, Jan. 1980.

[79] S. Goto, "An automated layout design system for masterslice LSI chip," in *Proc. Europ. Conf. on Circuit Theory and Design '81*, 1981, pp. 631–635.

[80] T. Matsuda, T. Fujita, K. Takamizawa, H. Mizumura, H. Nakamura, F. Kitajima, and S. Goto, "LAMBDA: a quick, low cost layout design system for master-slice LSIs," presented at 19th Design Automation Conf., 1982.

Artwork Verifier

[81] K. Yoshida, T. Mitsuhashi, Y. Nakada, T. Chiba, H. Ogita, and S. Nakatsuka, "A layout checking system for large scale integrated circuit," in *Proc. 14th Design Automation Conf.*, 1977, pp. 322–330.

[82] T. Kozawa, A. Tsukizoe, J. Sakemi, C. Miura, and T. Ishii, "A

concurrent pattern operation algorithm for VLSI mask data," in *Proc. 18th Design Automation Conf.*, 1981, pp. 563–570.

[83] H. Kawanishi, T. Nishide, and T. Masuda, "An algorithm on graphical manipulation of LSI mask pattern," *Trans. Inst. Electron. Commun. Eng. Japan*, vol. J65-A, pp. 611–618, 1980 (Japanese).

[84] S. Yamada and T. Watanabe, "A mask pattern analysis system for LSI (PAS-1)," in *Proc. IEEE Inter. Conf. on Circuits and Systems*, 1979, pp. 858–861.

[85] T. Mitsuhashi, T. Chiba, M. Takashima, and K. Yoshida, "An integrated mask artwork analysis system," in *Proc. 17th Design Automation Conf.*, 1980, pp. 277–284.

[86] J. Yoshida, T. Ozaki, and Y. Goto, "PANAMAP-B: a mask verification system for bipolar IC," in *Proc. 18th Design Automation Conf.*, 1981, pp. 690–695.

[87] H. Yoshimura, K. Tansho, N. Ohwada, and T. Nishide, "An algorithm for resistance calculation from IC mask pattern information," in *Proc. IEEE Inter. Conf. on Circuits and Systems*, pp. 478–481, 1979.

[88] A. Kishimoto, H. Kawanishi, H. Yoshizawa, H. Ohno, Y. Fujinami, and K. Kani, "An interconnection check algorithm for mask pattern," in *Proc. IEEE Inter. Conf. on Circuits and Systems*, 1978, pp. 669–672.

[89] K. Hirabayashi and M. Kawamura, "MACLOS—mask checking logic simulator," *IEEE J. Solid State Circuits*, vol. SC-15, no. 3, pp. 368–370, 1980.

[90] N. Kubo, I. Shirakawa, and H. Ozaki, "Algorithm for testing graph isomorphism, " in *Proc. IEEE Inter. Conf. on Circuits and Systems*, pp. 641–644, 1979.

[91] N. Miyahara, T. Watanabe, M. Endo, and S. Yamada, "A new CAD system for automatic logic interconnection verification," in *Proc. IEEE Inter. Conf. on Circuits and Systems*, 1981, pp. 114–117.

Device and Process Simulators

[92] D. A. Antoniadis, S. E. Hanson, and R. W. Dutton, "SUPREM— a program for IC process modeling and simulation," Stanford Electronics Labs, Stanford Univ., Stanford, CA, Tech. Rep., SEL78-020, 1978.

[93] R. W. Dutton, D. A. Divekar, A. G. Gonzales, S. E. Hansen, and D. A. Antoniadis, "Correlation of fabrication process and electrical device parameter variations," *IEEE J. Solid-State Circuits*, vol. SC-12, pp. 349–355, Aug. 1977.

[94] T. Toyabe, M. S. Mock, T. Okabe, K. Ujiie, and M. Nagata, "A two-dimensional analysis of I²L with multi-stream function technique," in *Proc. NASECODE 1st Conf.*, 1979, pp. 290–292.

[95] T. Adachi, A. Yoshii, and T. Sudo, "Two-dimensional semiconductor analysis using finite-element method," *IEEE Trans. Electron Devices*, vol. ED-26, pp. 1026–1031, July 1979.

[96] M. Tomizawa, H. Kitazawa, A. Yoshii, S. Horiguchi, and T. Sudo, "An accurate design method of bipolar device using a two-dimensional device simulator," *IEEE Trans. Electron. Devices*, vol. ED-28, pp. 1148–1153, Oct. 1981.

[97] K. Yamaguchi, S. Asai, and H. Kodera, "Two-dimensional analysis of stability criteria of GaAs FET's," *IEEE Trans. Electron Devices*, vol. ED-23, pp. 1283–1290, Dec. 1976.

[98] T. Toyabe and S. Asai, "Analytical models of threshold voltage of short-channel MOSFET's derived from two-dimensional analysis," *IEEE J. Solid-State Circuits*, vol. SC-14, pp. 375–383, Apr. 1979.

[99] K. Yokoyama, A. Yoshii, and S. Horiguchi, "Threshold sensitivity minimization of short-channel MOSFET's by computer simulation," *IEEE Trans. Electron Devices*, vol. ED-27, pp. 1509–1514, Aug. 1980.

[100] H. Oka, K. Nishiuchi, T. Nakamura, and H. Ishikawa, "Computer analysis of a short-channel BC MOSFET," *IEEE Trans. Electron Devices*, vol. ED-27, pp. 1514–1520, Aug. 1980.

[101] M. Konaka, K. Natori, and R. Dang, "Development of an MOS device simulator (MODEST) and some related problems in the two-dimensional numerical calculation," *Inst. Electron. Commun. Eng. Japan*, Tech. Rep. SSD81-10, 1981 (Japanese).

[102] A. Yoshii, H. Kitazawa, M. Tomizawa, S. Horiguchi, and T. Sudo, "A three-dimensional analysis of semiconductor devices," *IEEE Trans. Electron Devices*, vol. ED-29, pp. 184–189, Feb. 1982.

[103] R. Kasai, K. Yokoyama, A. Yoshii, and T. Sudo, "Threshold voltage analysis of short and narrow channel MOSFET's by three-dimensional computer simulation," *IEEE Trans. Electron Devices*, to be published.

[104] M. Tomizawa, K. Yokoyama, A. Yoshii, and T. Sudo, "Two-dimensional device simulator for gate level characterization," *Solid-State Electron.*, to be published.

[105] Y. Ohno and Y. Okuto, "Computer aided Si-MOSFET process designing," in *Proc. 11th Conf. Solid State Devices* (Tokyo, Japan), vol. 19, sup. 19-1, 1980, pp. 65–69.

[106] K. Taniguchi, M. Kashiwagi, and H. Iwai, "Two-dimensional computer simulation models for MOSLSI fabrication process," *IEEE Trans. Electron Devices*, vol. ED-28, May 1981.

[107] K. Yokoyama, A. Yoshii, T. Adachi, and R. Kasai, "Application of Fletcher–Powell's optimization method to process/device simulation of MOSFET characteristics," *Solid-State Electron.*, vol. 25, pp. 201–203, Mar. 1982.

[108] H. K. Gummel, "A self-consistent iterative scheme for one-dimensional steady-state transistor calcualtion," *IEEE Trans. Electron Devices*, vol. ED-11, pp. 455–465, Oct. 1964.

[109] H. L. Stone, "Iterative solution of implicit approximations of multidimensional partial differential equations," *SIAM J. Numer. Anal.*, vol. 5, pp. 530–558, Sept. 1968. . . . .

[110] J. A. Meijerink and H. A. van der Vorst, "An interactive solution method for linear systems of which the coefficient matrix is a symmetrical M-matrix," *Math. Comput.*, vol. 31, pp. 148–162, Jan. 1977.

[111] H. K. Gummel and H. C. Poon, "An integral charge control model of bipolar transistors," *Bell Syst. Tech. J.*, vol. 49, pp. 827–852, May–June 1970.

[112] M. S. Mock, "A two-dimensional mathematical model of the insulated-gate field effect transistor," *Solid-State Electron.*, vol. 16, pp. 601–609.

[113] R. Dang, T. Shibata, M. Konaka, S. Onga, and M. Kashiwagi, "Complete process/device simulation system and its application to the design of sub-micron MOSFET," in *Proc. 1981 Symp. VLSI Technology*, 1981, pp. 86–87.

[114] R. Flecher and M.J.D. Powell, "A rapid convergence descent method for minimization," *Comput. J.*, vol. 6, pp. 163–168, June 1963.

[115] Y. Okuto, Y. Ohno, and M. Fukuma, "Device process designing aids for MOS LSIs," in *Proc. 2nd NASECODE Conf.*, 1981.

Integrated VLSI CAD System

[116] T. Sudo, "VLSI Design Methodology," *Monograph of Technical Group on Design Technology of Electronics Equipment of Inform. Process. Soc. Japan*, 1-1, 1979 (Japanese).

[117] T. Sudo and Y. Sugiyama, "Custom VLSI design system," in *Proc. Inform. Process. Soc. Japan*, vol. 22, no. 8, pp. 791–796, 1981 (Japanese).

[118] W. M. vanCleemput, "An hierarchical language for the structural description of digital systems," *Proc. 14th Design Automation Conf.*, pp. 378–385, June 1977.

[119] S. Horiguchi, H. Yoshimura, R. Kasai, and T. Sudo, "An automatic designed 32b CMOS VLSI processor," *ISSCC82*, pp. 54–55, 1982.

[120] Y. Sugiyama, M. Suzuki, Y. Kobayashi, and T. Sudo, "A sub-nano second 12K gate bipolar 32 bit VLSI processor," in *Proc. of Custom Integrated Circuit Conf.*, pp. 73–77, 1981.

VLSI—The Technological Giant—and the Developing Countries

A. B. BHATTACHARYYA, MEMBER, IEEE

Invited Paper

Abstract—At a time when developing nations, after centuries of drift, are in search of an appropriate technology, they are confronted with a technological giant—Very Large Scale Integrated (VLSI) Circuit Technology—which seems to be gripping various aspects of the industrial sector and areas of human activity in the developed nations. In VLSI, the latest happens to be the most appropriate technology. The developing nations are yet to decide how appropriate and sustainable the VLSI technological edifice is in the context of their urge for modernization and the problems of an unemployment explosion, weak technological and scientific infrastructure, rural and agricultural bias, etc.

The author believes that the developing countries will be involved in repeated technology transfer from developed nations in the area of VLSI through systems related to industry, defense, communication, instrumentation, etc. The various options of VLSI technology acquisition have been analyzed with their attendent problems.

Downstream applications of VLSI to problems characteristic of developing nations, education and training in hardware and software, silicon foundry to serve as a technological listening post, and custom-design capability are some of the possible short- and long-term options for the developing nations to make optimum use of VLSI.

INTRODUCTION

THE WORLD is at the threshold of the third industrial revolution with the LSI/VLSI chips set to trigger human civilization to a new structure with respect to production, consumption, and even cultural values. The industrialized world has traveled through various phases of evolution under the impact of different technological forces, but in a long and memorable growth, few developments have been identified as revolutionary and fewer earned the epithet "ubiquitous." This description is now being applied to microelectronics in general, however, and to VLSI chips in particular. If the steam engine was the soul of the first industrial revolution and electromechanics was at the root of the second industrial revolution, VLSI microchips are destined to be the transformation agents for the third industrial revolution.

Any revolution brings with it a set of new forces and establishes a new order. The first industrial revolution witnessed the growing domination of England, which fathered it. The second one, engineered by the U.S.A. gave her the leadership which she still enjoys, to a large extent. It is quite natural that a bitter battle is in progress amongst the developed nations to wrest the initiative for the third industrial revolution through VLSI. Hence, VLSI technology is now not merely a technical issue for most countries; it has assumed an important global perspective and political shade. It is no wonder, then, that the leading industrial countries have worked out their own master plans [1]–[6] or set up task forces for recommending a strategy for coping with the VLSI implications.

Manuscript received June 28, 1982; revised September 14, 1982.
The author is with the Centre for Applied Research in Electronics, Indian Institute of Technology, New Delhi 110016, India.

While even many of the so-called developed countries find the transition to the new VLSI era rather agonizing, it is obvious that the developing nations, which are perhaps yet to be tuned fully to the structural environment of the second industrial revolution, find themselves outpaced and watching from the sideline the onset of a third industrial revolution. It is unfortunate that VLSI technology—the wonder microchip technology for future social and economic transformation—is based on such a technological superstructure and level of sophistication that it is beyond the immediate comprehension of most of the developing countries.

On the other hand, it is certain that the destiny of human civilization will be decisively microelectronics dominated in the future. With the existing status of industrial evolution, the developed world plans to utilize the new opportunity for the creation of their world, aiming at gross national satisfaction, intellectual creation, and self-realization and leaving all that is associated with labor to machines. This will invariably be taken care of by microelectronics, i.e., VLSI. For the developing world, the priorities and perspectives are different. They have to respond to the challenge of VLSI—the emerging technological giant—with two prime motivations: i) a technology, by definition, being useful and applied knowledge, is a vehicle for quick social transformation and hence, cannot be ignored, and ii) history has taught them that the other name of technology is freedom.

A general reaction of most of the developing nations will be that, in the present context, technology—even high technology—like the demon of the second law of thermodynamics, is an irreversible process, and the only way to live with it is to master and use it in an appropriate manner to realize socio-economic benefits without unduly affecting the core cultural ethos and social equilibrium. Like developed countries, the developing countries have their own characteristic evolutionary backgrounds, diversity in size, phases of development, and constraints. Hence, the developing countries can have neither a unique approach in responding to the new technological challenge nor the same assessment as developed countries of adoption of a new technological culture. "Self-reliance" is a highly emotional term in the developing world, and the attitude to VLSI would reflect this feeling and would follow the same line as reactions to other types of high technology. Self-reliance is envisaged and comprehended at the national level of each developing country as the determination to attain the capability for autonomous decision-making and implementation of a development process embracing all aspects of science and technology.

The developing countries are occupied today with debates about and identification of the so-called appropriate technol-

Reprinted from *Proc. IEEE*, vol. 71, pp. 144–148, Jan. 1983.

270

ogy. In VLSI what is latest seems to be the most appropriate. How appropriate the latest technology is, is not a trivial question for most of the developing nations. The present article examines the various options available to the developing countries for the development of VLSI, and identifies the problems inherent in the possible options. A case study is made for a possible strategy by developing nations, with the Indian approach as an example.

OPTIONS, OPPORTUNITIES, AND OBSTACLES

A developing country has the following options for the development of VLSI technology.

A. Indigeneous Research and Development

This is an option which is perhaps the dream of all the developing countries, if situations permit. The arguments in favor of local development of technology are these.

1) A country should have its own technology base even to import a technology and assimilate it.

2) VLSI technology has become a highly messy affair. It has all the characteristics of being obsolete even before preparations are made to adopt the technology. Hence, the only solution is to retain the initiative through local research and development so that repeated and continuous dependence on imported technology is avoided.

3) As VLSI technology is acknowledged to be all pervasive, ignoring this area will mean surrendering control over all the industrial sectors.

4) VLSI is due for restructuring the future of military electronics. On one hand, defense requirements cannot always be shared even between friendly nations; on the other hand, the classified nature of defense electronics provides local research and development the necessary government support and captive market. If defense expenditure has become a reality for every nation in the world, VLSI technology development becomes inseparable from the defense burden.

5) Most of the developing nations would be required to start with such a small scale of economy and volume to initiate VLSI technology, that it will not attract involvement of advanced industries in technology transfer. If a domestic facility is available, marginal involvements are distinctly possible which may be adequate for many purposes.

6) Developing countries have one asset, that is, relatively inexpensive labor which can be utilized to advantage. However, as attractive as it might be for a developing country, an indigenous VLSI technology development has an uphill task for the following reasons.

7) The characteristic features of VLSI technology are: Required heavy financial outlay associated with significant risk, dependence on the learning curve, highly evolved technical nature of the enterprise, cutthroat competition, sensitivity to mass production and market volume, and dependence on market forces, marketing backup, and synergy with users. The developing countries, unfortunately, would find most of the conditions difficult to satisfy. The hard realities are:

1) Even to absorb and assimilate a new technology requires as much investment as generating the new technology itself.

2) VLSI technology is highly capital intensive. Further, it is not a one time investment but requires dynamic updating.

3) VLSI technology is a high-risk venture even in developing countries. The evolution and characteristics of industrial management in developing countries make them too cautious and conservative to fit into VLSI enterprise.

4) Automation and VLSI are almost synonymous today. In most of the developing countries where there is a large surplus of human forces the concept of "robotization" may lead to social and political stress and upheaval.

5) Most of the developing countries do not have the experience to develop VLSI technology suited to local conditions; they generally follow the groove etched by the developed nations, whose priorities are different. This difference in priorities would render local technology developed at prohibitive cost almost totally irrelevant to local needs.

6) There is an acute shortage of manpower even in developed countries in the area of VLSI because of sudden, massive investments in all the developed nations. This situation is likely to continue for a long time in future. In the wake of such openings and prospects, a large proportion of the potentially capable manpower is sure to migrate to the developed nations. It usually happens that those who migrate are the ones who could play an important role in their own country. The traffic is one way—from developing to developed nations.

7) Last but not least, the volume of internal market is totally inadequate for the scale of investment required.

B. Technology Importation

Direct importation of VLSI technology may be considered a viable alternative by many developing countries. The positive points are these.

1) If the receiving country can negotiate a front-end technology, a much higher take-off plane is ensured and leap-frogging to new technology can be attained.

2) The importation of technology could be associated with an understanding that the receiving country would be entitled to have access to future developments on preferential terms and conditions. This would save considerable investment on exploratory research which a developing country can ill afford to spare. Further, if as a part of a TOT (Transfer of Technology) deal, buy-back can be negotiated, economic viability is perhaps more reasonable.

3) The developing countries can benefit considerably from "hands on" training agreements in such deals.

Though attractive at the first consideration, importation of microelectronics technology has evoked mixed reactions among many developing countries. Some samples of negative aspects are these.

1) In a true sense, technology being vital to any nation, is never transferred in full; it is bought and sold only in parts, unless the price paid is too exorbitant to be commercially acceptable. As a rule, the technology exported by advanced countries in the area of microelectronics is the one which is on its way to obsolescence.

2) It is quite possible that some of the developing countries receive VLSI technology under bilateral trade agreement through a product. In the name of a product, they inherit a process technology which is neither viable nor economically sound.

3) VLSI technology would usually demand that the receiving country ensure large production capacity to make the industry viable. If there is no domestic market to absorb the production, or there is no export potential, even the latest technology may lead to a financial disaster.

4) There may be built-in resistance in the developing country itself to acquiring the latest LSI technology if there are microelectronics industries already operating. There will be a natural fear that the latest technology will displace the existing market of the local industry; hence, the resistance.

5) Another common resistance to the transfer of the latest technology to developing countries is the claim from local research and development organizations that a particular tech-

271

nology already exists. It is little realized that evolution from laboratory stage to production is a long, drawn-out affair. However, more often such a dilemma of choice between exploitation of domestic claim and import delays initiation of technology. It is catastrophic when one has to run to be at the same place.

C. Multinational Enterprise

Some developing countries prefer inviting multinational enterprises to set up their VLSI industry—in full or parts—with the following considerations.

1) A package deal with MNE directly transplants capital, technology, managerial skill, engineers, and marketing apparatus into the host country and helps to appreciate the potential of latest developments, which would not be possible otherwise.

2) Continuous access to advancements is ensured.

3) It is possible that sooner rather than later local entrepreneuers, having been exposed to the whole range of problems, venture to set up industries which would become more viable for local requirements.

As in other options, inviting MNE has its own bane, part of which is outlined below:

1) An MNE never establishes a local R and D center; hence, even if the industry operates in a viable way, it hardly provides technological capability to the host country. It also drives the receiving country to complacence in technology development.

2) Cost mechanism followed by an MNE is usually found to be irrational, and terms are never revealed.

3) The technological base in developing countries is so weak that it usually frustrates any effort to start competing organizations; hence, MNE sometimes becomes identified as a symbol of perpetual technological enslavement.

4) There are instances in which developing countries are sometimes taken for a ride by multinationals. For instance, VLSI has made it possible to make telephone switches available for $150.00 or less per subscriber line. They can easily be assembled and looked after in most of the developing nations. But there are many instances where multinationals are installing mechanical switches even though they are perhaps ten times more costly. This is done with the logic that mechanical switches are more appropriate to the competence (or incompetence) of developing nations. Such situations are typical in such categories where suppliers are limited in number. Developing countries need to be realistic to recognize that MNE's are governed by the stark realities of business interest, and they are not expected to subsidize, whatever might be the problems of the developing countries. A weak technological base in developing countries increases the possibility of such instances.

D. Joint Venture

It is a hybrid approach with mixed fallout followed by even some of the developed nations, though the experience has not shown unqualified success. One of the reasons for established industries to attempt joint ventures is to make use of the research base of the host country in view of either skill clusters or economy. Whether a partnership with a developing nation with weak base in science and technology is of any attraction in the area of VLSI/LSI is an open question. For developing nations, further, the infrastructural and political considerations will be the key factors to decide this course. Many countries hold the view that there is nothing alien about technology and what is most prudent for developing nations is to adopt the latest available and absorb it.

Whatever option is chosen by a developing country, the major task before them all will be to achieve a changeover to VLSI in all the existing electronics sectors—communication, control, transportation, medical, defense, etc.—sooner rather than later if these systems intend to be anywhere near up to date and self-reliant. There will be three possible routes for this transformation: a) a revolution strategy where immediate updating and modernization of all the electronics systems are envisaged. This is rather an unlikely step in most countries because of the enormous pressure on funds, manpower, training, etc.; b) an inert strategy of waiting till an electronics system has completely outlived its utility and then replace it by systems based on VLSI; and c) an evolution strategy which is a mean path between these two and calls for updating the system that will meet present and future requirements and at the same time remains compatible with present environment.

Development of VLSI technology revolves round a wide base of science and technology which needs to be kept in view before a development course is selected. Developing nations set for the domestic development of VLSI would do well to take note of the following involvements such as: a wide range of process and technology development, modeling, computer-aided design, analysis and testing, metallurgy for package development, automated optical and electron-optical equipments, software for application, operation systems and languages, quality control and failure analysis, etc.

This covers almost the whole range of scientific and technological activity requiring a strong base. Further, if the experience of Europe is any indication, even a strong scientific base without emphasis on development and marketing structure will hardly render VLSI economically effective, or even sustainable, in developing countries. One area where VLSI technology will play the most effective role in developing countries is information processing, where software development assumes considerable importance. It is human skill intensive; hence, it is more adaptable to developing nations.

For the most of the developing nations, contrary to the general belief that technology, equipment, or resources are the biggest hurdle in LSI development, the manpower shortage could be the single factor inhibiting the planning and launching of the VLSI era.

INDIAN STRATEGY—AN ILLUSTRATION

It is extremely interesting to observe the strategy adopted by India—one of the largest among the developing nations—though not in production of electronics components [7], [8].

The growth rate and total value is much less than that of countries such as South Korea, Singapore, and Taiwan or even Sri Lanka due to the overpowering demands from other sectors such as steel, agriculture, health, etc. In spite of a depressing past record in the electronics component sector, India has decided to enter VLSI enterprises based on the following considerations.

1) The example of some developing countries in allowing multinational companies freely to set up assembly shops is not a viable choice because of two reasons: i) labor in India has high individual skill rather than collective productivity and ii) in a pure assembly operation, real technology flow will not arise and, hence, it is not in the long-term interest of the country.

2) The country is large and has the third largest technical manpower strength in the world. It has acquired fair amount of industrial infrastructures to support an LSI venture.

3) She attaches utmost priority to communication and

information processing, which is vital for a country of India's size and diversity. If communication has to be revolutionized, there is an optimistic domestic market to sustain a national LSI program.

4) Even if she cannot achieve state-of-the-art LSI technology in the short term, in a large number of industrial sectors where she has her own system-design capability, significant cost-benefit can be accomplished by mere customization rather than by the induction of latest technology.

5) Although in VLSI technology change seems to be the only constant in many systems, the half-life period is relatively long. While for a developed nation, a quick changeover may be necessary for developing countries, the priority of changing the system may not be so desperate. But an in-house domestic capacity is necessary to support spares, etc., to operate the existing system effectively. Such a capability would also ease difficulties here in procuring these vital components which are not industry standard and sometimes single-source dependent.

6) In research a judicious strategy of wait and watch should minimize risks in product development.

7) A newcomer, or for that matter, a late comer in semiconductor technology sometimes stands to benefit from others' mistakes and, hence, has an implicit advantage.

A partial overview of the market, infrastructure, and skill in Indian context is the following:

A. Market

For the viability of a VLSI venture in any country, the availability of an internal or external market becomes a vital consideration. If for the year 1990 an ad hoc figure of production capacity worth 60 billion dollars is assumed in the USA, 20 billion dollars in Japan, 4 billion dollars in Western Europe, and 1 billion dollars in the rest of the world (excluding the USSR), India has a projected production capacity of 100 million dollars with the existing organizations. Another fact is that at the present level the electronics production output is less than 1 percent of GNP (Gross National Product) in India as against 5 to 7 percent in advanced countries. With modernization, therefore, there is naturally a projection of an optimistic demand figure.

A conservative estimate predicts that the demand for indigeneously produced LSI's by 1990 is expected to be worth 100 million dollars with the present level of use of only 1 percent LSI chips in the systems. It is believed that within a decade an advanced system design should contain about 20 percent LSI chips. Assuming that our learning curve enables us to use a modest 10 percent LSI chips, the market for indigeneous LSI chips should grow up to 500 million dollars. The above target excludes defense requirements.

At the present level, India has no export in LSI's, and overtaking the USA, Japan, or Western Europe in any area seems improbable. Even a modest aspiration of a share of 25 percent of the rest of the world market should raise its market volume worth another 400 million dollars in LSI.

B. Available Infrastructure

The above figures show that if India has to keep up with this stimulated market, however small the market may look in the global context, even the modest target would demand an eight- to ten-fold increase in the production capacity in LSI/VLSI chips. For a developing country this is a serious strain on its infrastructure for design, technology, and materials.

The approach to meet the emerging situation in LSI/VLSI is as follows:

C. Design

Since low volume is a potential problem, it is the customization which is identified as the key for market stimulation. India has a network of about 120 universities and five institutes of technology producing about six thousand professional electronic engineers per year and a number of R and D organizations. It should be possible to expand the existing design base to 20 percent of these institutions. Very few developing or even developed nations have access to such an enormous human resource which has intrinsic design potential. The estimated cost of providing CAD facilities for decentralized design activity in these establishments is not prohibitive. In addition, India has a Joint Development Team agreement with American Microsystems, Inc. (AMI) for embarking on LSI system design both for domestic and international markets.

D. Technology

India has a twin strategy to acquire 5- and 3-μm Si-gate NMOS and CMOS technology as a take-off plane through importation and develop it further through indigeneous development. While the available local technology is geared for further research and development, the imported technology from AMI (USA) could act as a technological "listening post." The local technology may be geared to act as a silicon foundry to provide necessary experience to the chain of design centers and to experiment on process innovations and simulations.

E. Application

India has a skill cluster in application technology. Among the alternatives of a) the component route, b) the prefabricated module route, and c) the packaged system route, the prefabricated module with route has been the preferred approach with considerable success [9]. Till she acquires more competence in custom design, the first route, i.e., the customized component route which is the target for the system designers, has to be abandoned.

The country has a chain of about a dozen State Electronic Corporations to provide thrust in specialized sectors such as agroelectronics, mining electronics, transport electronics, and avionics, in addition to well-recognized areas in communication, computers, consumer sectors, etc. It is expected that these corporations would provide increasing scope for LSI growth.

The industrial, economic, and political conditions of each developing nation are so different that the Indian approach may not be the ideal strategy for others. It is significant to note that most of the developing countries which have done remarkably well in production of electronics components have relatively little domestic volume requirement in professional LSI's and are mostly entertainment oriented. Their industries are based on 70 percent export. India, on the other hand, so far has little export balance to its credit and has much wider support for its LSI industry for its own professional requirement. For LSI/VLSI development, all the developing nations shall have one common and formidable handicap: low volume of internal market-to-make VLSI technology development economically logical.

CONCLUSIONS

It is obvious from the above discussion that the realities of the developing nations are heavily weighted against their rapid adoption of microelectronics or VLSI technology. Nevertheless, in view of the enormous potential of this technology, they cannot remain in isolation or afford to be uncommitted. The most important task for the developing nations should be generating awareness of the downstream application of VLSI chips in improving basic tools which can carry large untapped resources into the service of decentralized rural society. In the emerging future, socio-techno-economic infrastructure will be decided by the range of tools used by an individual, community, or nation. There is a strong case for building up an inventory of information regarding the nature of current and future applications. Such a document will help the policy makers of various sectors to decide priorities.

It is expected that until the developing countries become relatively mature, frequently, technology transfer will take place under the cover of purchase of systems. To ensure maximum benefit the developing countries would do well to buy a process and integrate design into it rather than a product.

Whatever route is adopted by a developing country, the most crucial immediate task is launching an education and training program in broad aspects of VLSI electronics including software for selection, adaptation, use, and management of downstream applications.

There is endless scope for cooperation among developing nations themselves to innovate VLSI applications affecting rural areas, agricultural sectors, medium- and small-scale industries. The improvement in communication infrastructure would immensely benefit the developing countries in removing the isolation of the rural community from the mainstream of national life [11].

VLSI leads to machanization of jobs and consumerism. Both these would create attendent social problems. Applications have to be oriented to useful activities of productivity and not senseless illusions of affluence. In many developing countries, mere electronics assembly operation has opened up significant job potential at minimum investment. To cite a typical figure, at present the electronics industry in India provides maximum employment with minimum investment—something like 500 jobs for a 10-million-dollar investment—an aspect unmatched by other heavy investment sectors such as steel, fertilizer, etc. Whether this feature can be sustained with VLSI systems would be a major consideration in developing countries in arriving at decisions on investments.

The governments in the developing nations will have to nourish the induction of new technology either in application or production through market protection, subsidy, and incentive for a prolonged period. They would find an ambiguous situation. For industrial development, microelectronics induction is essential. On the other hand, without industrial development microelectronics technology cannot be stimulated. Low volume of an internal market for a given type of product will be the most serious inhibiting factor for VLSI development. Direct or indirect government subsidy has been the key factor in the development of VLSI even in developed countries.

It may be sheer coincidence that the emergence of VLSI synchronizes with the worldwide energy crisis, ecological pollution, population explosion, and North–South disparity. The VLSI revolution has the potential to bring all the nations together to face the above problems through cooperation between the developed and developing nations. While developing nations would desperately depend on developed countries for the benefits of the new technological giant, an LSI/VLSI-conscious developing world should provide a growing market to the developing nations. In fact, it is estimated that growth rate in electronics components is likely to be higher in the developing world compared to that in developed nations. It is here that an international program on cooperation in microelectronics is highly relevant and calls for urgent attention.

REFERENCES

[1] T. Matsumara, "Tomorrow's major manufacturing capability," *Microelectron.*, Infotech state of the art report, series 8, no. 2, pp. 329–344.
[2] R. Mac Donald, "The case for European manufacturing capability: a multinational's view," *Microelectron.*, Infotech state of the art report, series 8, no. 2, pp. 315–328.
[3] J. F. Mason, "VLSI goes to school," *IEEE Spectrum*, vol. 17, no. 11, pp. 48–52, 1980.
[4] R. R. Heikes, "Electronics—strategies for failure," *Microelectron.*, vol. 12, no. 4, pp. 30–32, 1981.
[5] G. M. Badger, "A report to the prime minister by the Australian Science and Technology Council," 1981.
[6] P. S. Bonelli, "Microelectronics and Data Processing in the next five years: the French case," *Microelectron.*, Infotech state of the art report, series 8, no. 2, pp. 45–53.
[7] S. C. Mehta, "Semiconductor device industry in India," *Electronics Information and Planning*, vol. 6, no. 2, pp. 195–211, 1978.
[8] C. R. Subramanian, "Commercial and Technical aspects of IC development and production," *Electronics Information and Planning*, vol. 6, no. 9, pp. 783–794, 1979.
[9] V. P. Bhatkar, Personal Communication.
[10] C. Mead and L. Conway, *Introduction to VLSI Systems*. Reading, MA: Addison-Wesley, 1980.
[11] United Nations Industrial Development Organization, "Implications of technological advances in micro-electronics for developing countries," Vienna, Austria, June 1981.

Part VIII
Outlook

THE final part of this book will give an outlook to the future of VLSI. In the paper entitled "Managing VLSI Complexity: An Outlook," by C. H. Séquin, the positive aspects of VLSI complexity as a way to increase performance and reduce chip size are presented. The evolution of the VLSI system design environment is outlined for the near-, medium-, and long-term future. The changing role of the designer is discussed in view of the increasing use of automatic and semi-automatic tools. Recommendations are made for the education of next-generation designers with skills to enable them to cope with the increasing VLSI complexity.

In the last paper of this book, by O. G. Folberth, the obstacles for the further miniaturization of digital Si-VLSI and the fundamental limits of this technology are discussed. If everything else with less fundamental character is sorted out, there remain essentially three limitations of this kind: geometrical limitations, thermal limitations, and signal propagation limitations. An attempt is made to quantify these limits as far as possible. In some cases, however, only rough estimates can be given. A hypothetical "ultimate" silicon chip technology is discussed considering these limits and their interdependencies.

Managing VLSI Complexity: An Outlook

CARLO H. SÉQUIN, FELLOW, IEEE

Invited Paper

Abstract—The nature of complexity in the context of VLSI circuits is examined, and similarities with the complexity problem in large software systems are discussed. Lessons learned in software engineering are reviewed, and the applicability to VLSI systems design is investigated. Additional difficulties arising in integrated circuits such as those resulting from their two-dimensionality and from the required interconnections are discussed. The positive aspects of VLSI complexity as a way to increase performance and reduce chip size are reviewed.

With this discussion as a basis, the evolution of VLSI system design environments is outlined for the near-term, medium-term, and long-term future. The changing role of the designer is discussed. Recommendations are made for enhancements to our engineering curriculums which would provide the next generation of designers with skills relevant to managing VLSI complexity.

I. INTRODUCTION

VERY-LARGE-SCALE-INTEGRATION (VLSI) will soon make it economically viable to place 1 000 000 devices on a single chip, and the technological evolution will continue to double this number every 1-2 years for at least another decade [1]. According to G. Moore [2], the major hurdle faced in the construction of ever larger integrated systems is a *complexity barrier*. In order to exploit fully the technological potential of VLSI, new ways of managing the information associated with the design of a VLSI chip must be developed.

Why is it that complexity and its management have suddenly become such popular concerns? Mankind is routinely building systems with more than a million components: skyscrapers, air planes, telephone systems. . . . System complexity and the associated engineering issues do not seem to differ markedly for alternative implementations, e.g., whether a circuit is contained within a cabinet, on a printed-circuit board, or on a single silicon chip.

Packaging *does*, however, have an impact because of the partitioning that it enforces. Nobody would dare to insert a million discrete devices into a large chassis using discrete point-to-point wiring. Large systems built from discrete devices are broken down into subchassis, mother boards, and module boards carrying the actual components. This physical partitioning encourages careful consideration of the logical partitioning and of the interfaces between the modules at all levels of the hierarchy. Since such systems are typically designed by large teams, early top-down decisions concerning the partitioning and

the interfaces must be made and enforced rather rigidly—for better or for worse. This keeps the total complexity in the scope of each individual designer limited in magnitude, and thus manageable.

VLSI permits the whole system to be concentrated in the basically unstructured domain of a single silicon chip which does not *a priori* force any partitioning or compartmentalization. On the positive side, this freedom may be exploited for significant performance advantages. On the negative side, it may result in a dangerous situation where the complexity within a large, unstructured domain simply overwhelms the designer. A similar crisis was faced by software engineers when unstructured programs started to grow to lengths in excess of 10 000 lines of code. The crisis was alleviated by the development of suitable design methodologies, structuring techniques, and documentation styles. Many of the lessons learned in the software domain are also applicable to the design of VLSI systems.

Much as programming was done throughout the 1950's by small groups of highly qualified people solving problems in their own style, integrated circuit design in the 1970's was still done by small clusters of layout wizards. This often led to intricate, if not mysterious, circuits. This "cottage industry" style of creating systems [3] starts to fail once programs approach tens of thousands of lines of code or once circuits end up with 100 000 devices. More formal and organized methods are required to create larger systems.

Sections II and III explore the nature of complexity in general and analyze methods to deal with complexity that were developed in the framework of software engineering. In Sections IV and V the point is made that the problems associated with VLSI designs are even harder than those encountered in large programs.

Section VI presents general developments in the emerging VLSI system design tools that address the discussed problems, and Section VII tries to predict the evolution of such tools for three different time frames. In Sections VIII and IX the role of the designer is re-evaluated in the face of this changing design environment, and some recommendations are made for the education of the next generation of designers.

Most sections are relatively self-contained and can be read as a sequence of minipapers. On the whole, they should not be viewed as the final word on the subject of VLSI complexity, but rather as food for thought and a nucleus for further discussion.

II. THE NATURE OF COMPLEXITY

VLSI is more than just "a lot of LSI"—in the same sense that a city is not just a large village and the human brain is not just a large collection of ganglions. The 256-kbit RAM's

Manuscript received April 23, 1982; revised November 8, 1982. This work was sponsored by the Defense Advance Research Projects Agency (DOD) under ARPA Order 3803; monitored by the Naval Electronic System Command under Contract N00039-81-K-0251.

The author is with the Computer Science Division, Electrical Engineering and Computer Sciences, University of California, Berkeley, CA 94720.

Reprinted from *Proc. IEEE*, vol. 71, pp. 149–166, Jan. 1983.

(random-access memories) of 1982 are quite different from the first 1-kbit RAM's that appeared on the market a decade ago. As the scale of any system is increased by orders of magnitude, its organization typically changes because different issues become relevant. Internal structuring starts to appear, specialized subparts emerge, communication between the different parts gains importance, and, at some level, the *complexity* of the system becomes an explicitly stated concern.

The introduction of new design methodologies to deal with this concern requires an understanding of complexity and its special demands. Webster's Dictionary gives the following definition:

> complex: referring to that which is made up of many elaborately interrelated or interconnected parts, so that much study or knowledge is needed to understand or operate it.

This section tries to provide some insight into the notion of system complexity. It will emerge that it is useful to distinguish between explicit (apparent) complexity and implicit (hidden) complexity.

A. Explicit Complexity

Unlike the information content of a transmitted message, there is no formal absolute measure for complexity. In general one tends to call those systems more complex that need more words or more bytes to be adequately described or specified. Thus a comparison of the lengths of the corresponding descriptions can be used as a measure for the *relative* complexities of two or more *similar* systems. In order for such a comparison to make sense, the systems to be compared must be described in the same language and in terms of the same primitive elements.

This *apparent* or *explicit* complexity of a system depends strongly on the language or notation used for its description. By using suitable abstractions, the details of the subcomponents of the system can be hidden, and the apparent complexity can be reduced dramatically. It is equally important to exploit any structure or regularity to reduce the length of the description and to express more succinctly the "essence" of a particular system. This can be achieved with the use of suitable notations designed to express repetition, symmetry, and other regularities in an efficient and compact manner. In this light, an early microprocessor such as the 8008, with only a few thousand transistors, is more complex than one of the large memory chips with, say, 16 384 bits. Because of its regularity, the latter can be grasped and described more easily.

B. Implicit Complexity

However, complexity is not simply proportional to the number of different parts or the length of an optimally encoded layout description. The interactions between the parts play an important role. Steward [4] defines complexity in the following way:

> Given the parts and their behaviors, complexity is the difficulty involved in using the relations among the parts to infer the behavior of the whole.
> Or phrased another way:
> Complexity is how much more the whole is than just the sum of its parts.

This *hidden* or *implicit* complexity of a system involves issues such as the behavior of the system and the way in which it achieves a particular function. A collection of gates that im-

TABLE I
MEASURES OF COHESION IN COMPOUND MODULES

Name	Explanation	Example
functional	all parts contribute to function.	operational amplifier
sequential	portion of a data-flow diagram	filter cascade
communicational	data abstraction, same data used	LIFO stack
spatial	need to be physically close	sensor array
procedural	same procedural block	bus controller
temporal	used at a similar time	start-up circuitry
logical	a group of similar functions	I/O-pad library
coincidental	random collection	miscellaneous wiring

plement the well-defined Boolean function of an adder is far less complex than some historical radio receiver stage with a single vacuum tube which simultaneously amplifies the incoming HF signal, demodulates the LF component, and preamplifies the sound signal.

These intricate aspects of a system's behavior could, in principle, be reduced to the previously defined measure of explicit complexity. One would have to take into account the complete systems documentation, including: all its functional specifications, a description of its operation, the plans for its physical realization, and the set of repair instructions. Since it is normally impractical to sum up all this diverse information, one needs some other guidelines to evaluate this more elusive notion of implicit complexity. Looking at the way in which systems are composed from smaller components is a suitable approach.

C. Complexity in a Structured System

Few systems are described or documented in a hierarchically flat manner. Large systems are viewed as being composed of subsystems, which, in turn, consist of components on a lower hierarchical level. *Cohesion* and *coupling* are two useful concepts for a more detailed evaluation of the complexity of a module at a particular level of the system hierarchy. They address the nature by which components are combined into modules at the next higher level of the description.

Cohesion: Cohesion is a measure of how closely the internal parts that make up a module belong together when seen from different perspectives. In general, a high level of cohesion is desirable, since it leads to a simpler description at the next higher level and thus reduces its explicit complexity. High cohesion can be derived from functional similarity, from logical or physical grouping, or from the fact that all subparts work on the same data. Yourdon and Constantine [5] define several different criteria by which the cohesion of a compound software module can be judged. They can readily be extended to the domain of integrated circuits as demonstrated by the examples in Table I.

Spatial cohesion is something that is unique to the hardware domain and plays a big role in analog VLSI components such as capacitor arrays or optical sensor systems. Temporal, logical, or coincidental cohesion are very weak and are primarily used to keep things ordered from an organizational point of view.

Coupling: Coupling measures how much the submodules interact. Good structuring and clever systems partitioning aim at reducing implicit complexity by minimizing the amount of interaction between subparts. The interaction patterns should be simple and regular. This leads to independence of design, simple layout, high testability, and easy modifiability. Table II gives some measures by which the degree of coupling can be judged.

TABLE II
MEASURES OF COUPLING BETWEEN SUBMODULES

Perspective	Degree of Coupling	Example
Topology:	linear flow-through	filter chain
	hierarchical tree	carry look-ahead
	lattice modularity	memory array
	irregular mosaic	processor control
Interaction:	continuous	light sensor
	periodic	timer
	occasional	reset
Bandwidth:	high	video signal
	bursty	disk head
	low	voice signal

Minimal coupling, using explicit communications between submodules rather than parasitic interactions, supports modularity and makes possible plug-compatible replacements. The topology of the interactions should be kept as simple as possible. Clean modularization reduces implicit complexity since self-contained modules are easier to specify than a collection of highly interacting components.

III. DEALING WITH COMPLEXITY

Complexity is an integral part of large, "interesting" systems. In this section, general techniques for managing this complexity will be discussed. Most of them have been developed or refined in the context of large programs and form the basis of good software engineering. They are also applicable to the design of complex VLSI systems.

A. Design Equals Documentation

A complex system often can be understood more easily when viewed from the proper perspective. This is the role of good documentation. *Design* and *documentation* should become synonymous.

Software maintenance costs usually exceed initial production costs by a significant factor [6]. Software systems are constantly being modified, upgraded, and expanded [7]. This means that other people must be able to thoroughly understand what the original developer(s) had in mind. A similar issue is emerging in VLSI design as the development cycle of many products starts to exceed the average time an employee spends with the same company, and thus designs have to be passed from one designer to the next one.

Among good software designers, it is now common practice to make the documentation an integral part of the program. It has been realized that a separately kept documentation folder is never up-to-date and, before long, describes something quite different from the actual code. Documentation for a typical integrated circuit, however, is still normally scattered over several different media and/or several organizational groups, including the systems architects, the logic designers, and the layout crew. Often some pieces of the documentation are lacking entirely, making the circuit a mystery to all but the original design group. Modifying or even just debugging of such a system by anybody but the original designer(s) tends to be a real nightmare.

Notations and Representations: An important step in minimizing the *apparent* complexity of a system at any level of its description is to use suitable languages and/or notations, tailored to the particular issue that needs to be documented. Hoare emphasizes the importance of the proper notation by pointing out that the history of mathematics is, to a large degree, the story of improvements of notation [8]. The use of bad, hard-to-decipher notation is not only unproductive, it breaks the thought process aimed at finding problem solutions.

One should use all possibilities of the representation medium to enhance the clarity of the constructs that are being used: suitable mnemonic labels, symbolic shapes, differentiating colors, sound. . . . To simply ask for more extended English descriptions for each item is not the right way to go. Abstract, terse symbols are crucial to making the "grand picture" visible.

B. Use of Abstraction

Humans can effectively deal with only one problem at a time and can concern themselves with only a few constraints simultaneously [9]. This necessitates judicious use of hierarchy and abstraction. If the representation of a system can be rendered more succinct, one has taken a big step towards managing its complexity. Abstraction in the form of *user-defined macros* or *parameterized subroutine or cell calls* permits one to focus on the few qualities that are essential at a particular phase of the design process. It hides internal interactions and irrelevant details that contribute nothing to the solution but would clutter the picture and thus hamper the relevant thought processes.

Examples from the world of VLSI are: lumped devices hiding the complicated physical processes inside a contiguous piece of silicon; logic gates abstracting from a particular realization; register-transfer modules showing the basic data operations while hiding details of timing; and instruction-set descriptions for computer architectures hiding all but the primitives that the programmer has to deal with.

In addition, abstraction permits the creation of *generic modules*, usable with different data types or implementable with different technologies. Abstract encapsulation of modules in well-defined interfaces is the basis for efficient design of large systems. Well-defined modules, properly documented and made available through module libraries, can be used repeatedly by many designers. Design systems for integrated circuits often provide several plug-compatible versions of such modules which vary in a few parameters such as power and speed, or the availability of an explicit testing interface. Efficient construction of large systems is not possible without a library of well-designed modular components.

C. High-Level Descriptions

High-level languages lead to shorter and more readable programs. They make it easier to understand the organization and behavior of programs or systems and result in designs that are more likely to be free of errors, easier to debug and modify.

Programmer Productivity: Long-term average productivity in a commercial software production environment is about 10 lines of code per day. One arrives at this number by dividing the total number of lines in the final program by the amount of programmer time used for its development. The number is surprisingly independent of the language used—but the resulting net programmer effectiveness is not. A high-level language statement such as CASE or a complicated algebraic expression assignment is more powerful than an assembler-level LOAD instruction. Thus the net programmer productivity in terms of the functional effect produced by his/her code scales strongly with the power of the primitives employed. Similarly, in integrated circuit design, designers can place on average only five to ten *items* per day [10]. If ten *processors* rather than ten *transistors* are inserted into the layout per day, the effective productivity is increased dramatically.

Compilers versus Code Efficiency: High-level descriptions must be mapped down to the level of the actual implementation. Traditionally, coding in lower level languages has resulted in more compact and faster-executing code than what can be produced by a compiler. However, compiler technology is improving. Present-day compilers for high-level programming languages will do an adequate job for most applications and will do it far more quickly and reliably than any programmer. Of course, skilled programmers, willing to devote a large amount of time, can still outperform them by a factor 2–3 in small program segments, but this effort is only justified if there are hard constraints such as real-time requirements or the need to fit a program into a limited amount of on-chip memory.

High-level languages are now being introduced to the development of VLSI systems. There are several long-term research efforts in VLSI design aimed at the construction of a *silicon compiler* [11]–[13]. Driven by high-level specification of the desired circuit, these automated design systems are expected to translate high-level systems descriptions into correct circuit implementations in a particular technology. These layout compilers are still in their infancy and produce relatively inefficient results for all but narrowly defined, highly structured subsystems.

However, when the rising development costs for VLSI systems become comparable to the fabrication costs of ten thousands of devices, a faster development cycle at the price of a less efficient implementation becomes an attractive alternative for many systems. The increasing market share of gate arrays [14] and macro cells [15] must be seen in this light.

D. Partitioning

Problems that are too large to be handled as a whole must be partitioned into smaller, more manageable parts. Section III-E reviews some formal methods for finding suitable partitionings. In any such subdivision, the interactions between the subparts must be given particular attention.

Intermediate Decisions and Specifications: When a module is partitioned into submodules, the latter must be specified in enough details so that one can verify that the partitioning step does not violate any of the original specifications. In carrying out the successive refinement steps, one must also assure that the implementation of every module agrees with the abstract view used at the higher level. The properties of the composition of the new submodules must be assured for *all* possible concerns, e.g., functional correctness, timing constraints, signal levels, and even testability.

If *formal* verification is not possible—and it may be a long time before this becomes practical in the domain of circuit design—another solution has to be found. Intermediate system simulation, using proper models for the submodules, is a usable approach. VLSI system design tools must have the means to create, retain, and make use of such intermediate models. They should readily permit partial and mixed-mode simulations [16], [17] of a system in a top-down manner, making use of the abstractions for the subparts. Such a simulation can cut off all branches of the design hierarchy for which suitable simulation models exist. The resulting savings in simulation efforts are considerable.

Separation of Functionality and Implementation: The specifications of a system are normally separated into a description

of what the system is supposed to do plus a list of performance objectives. This provides another boundary along which a problem can be partitioned.

During the design of a system it is also useful to separate the concern for functional correctness from the details of the actual implementation, which must often include an optimization step; the number of packages is minimized or a set of packages is distributed evenly on a few printed circuit boards. Constantine refers to this optimization and packaging step as clustering pieces of a problem solution into physical constraints without unduly compromising the integrity of the original design [5]. Such packaging optimizations should be made as the final step and only after the algorithmic optimizations have been exploited to the fullest. Once the design has been compromised by low-level packaging optimizations, it loses a lot of its generality, portability, and durability in the face of emerging technologies. Such optimization tricks are difficult to comprehend and to reverse at a later time.

Conceptually, the design process should thus contain the following three concerns:

1) functional design: guaranteeing proper behavior;
2) implementation: finding a suitable structure;
3) optimization: fine tuning the physical arrangement.

These basic steps should also be taken in the design of a VLSI system. However, several iterations through these three steps may be required to make sure that the nature of the implementation medium has been properly taken into account in the high-level design decisions.

E. Structuring Methods

Structuring is a key approach to large programs, systems, or problems in general. Good structuring implies partitioning. Many of the concepts suitable for judging the structure of programs [18] are also applicable to VLSI systems. As a start, one can demand that a well-designed subsystem implement a single, independent function, have only a few "low-bandwidth" entry or exit points, be separately testable from the module boundaries, and be itself constructed of a limited number of submodules that obey the same criteria.

Unfortunately it is often not clear *how* one should partition a particular problem or system; it can involve the most important and most difficult decisions a designer must face. This section reviews some program structuring strategies and discusses their applicability for VLSI systems design.

Functional Decomposition: Functional Decomposition is an application of the very general and popular *divide-and-conquer technique*. It consists of a recursive subdivision into parts, so that the joint operation of the properly interconnected parts performs the specified operation of the whole.

It can be used in a top-down manner, splitting a large system into cohesive blocks [19]. The recursive refinement step to be executed in this design strategy is as follows. Start from the definition of the function to be performed and its desired interface. Identify logical subparts, define the function and interfaces of these parts, and specify their interactions. Then verify that when the subparts are interconnected in the specified manner, their overall behavior corresponds to the original specification at the previous level. Unfortunately, this last step is nontrivial in programming and even harder in VLSI systems design.

Any significant design effort will have to iterate between top-down and bottom-up techniques because the characteristics of the medium used in the final implementation might not be visible at the top. Functional decomposition also plays a role in conjunction with the bottom-up phase. The natural building blocks of a particular technology and effective implementations thereof are derived in a bottom-up manner. The overall problem specification is then scanned for the usage of such blocks and partitioned accordingly.

The advantage as well as the problem with functional decomposition lie in its generality. If there is a large gap between the top-level problem specification and the natural building blocks dictated by the technology, the methodology will not provide guidelines for reproducible implementations and an excessive variety of possible decompositions results. The quality of the final result will then depend strongly on the intuitive insights of the designer. This is equally true for VLSI systems and for large programs.

Flow Graph Design: A more specific way to decompose a problem is to follow its *flow of data or of control.* In the first approach, the *data* flowing through the system are viewed as the primary ingredients, and all functional blocks are viewed as filters transforming the data as they pass through [20]–[22]. This approach suggests a further decomposition of each module into input circuitry, transformation circuitry, and output circuitry. Particular concern has to be given to synchronization, flow control, and possibly to buffering of intermediate data at the interfaces.

This is a particularly important and suitable approach for integrated circuits since it deals explicitly with the communication between blocks and puts proper emphasis on spatial ordering as dictated by the flow of data. It is being used in signal-processing devices and is particularly well exemplified in systolic arrays [23]. The formal data-flow graph of a system is a good starting point for a layout. Even in laying out the datapath of a microprocessor, the flow of data and of control often form the basis for the floor plan. Typically, they are assigned to the directions of the two coordinate axes so that the two flows cross at right angles [24], [25], [13].

The price to formally partition each "filtering module" into input circuitry, transformation circuitry, and output circuitry appears to be too high for present-day VLSI systems. In regular structures, such as systolic arrays [23] implemented as an iteration of identical cells, it is preferable to design outputs and inputs as matched pairs. Significant savings in power and layout area result from this optimization step. For modules that are used more randomly and are combined with a variety of other modules, the extra overhead of buffering provides abstraction and modifiability. So far, the control flow of a system has been used less directly to produce a structured circuit layout, except possibly for the case of a microcoded control section.

Data-Structure Design: Another successful structuring method in software engineering is to start with the *data structures.* The idea is to describe a problem through its associated objects, and to specify these objects through suitable abstractions and their interactions [20], [26]. This technique applies particularly well to small subsystems performing a specific function. Because there are fewer arbitrary and different ways to find data structures that correspond to a particular model of a subsystem, the resulting system structuring is more reproducible than with other methods. However, it is not so clear how this approach can be used for large systems.

The application of this method to VLSI systems design is also difficult. Direct mappings into hardware have been realized for only a rather limited number of data structures. The parallelism desired in VLSI circuits is a further difficulty. The inter-actions between objects and their spatial ordering are crucial. There is a high price on interactions between submodules, which is normally not considered in the setup of data structures.

There is plenty of room for innovation. VLSI will provide ever more sophisticated and efficient implementations for such data structures as trees, queues, and content-addressable memories. Such structures can either be implemented directly with special hardware primitives, e.g., an array of associative memory cells, or they can be built using standard RAM's with suitable control structures. In either case, these VLSI data structures should be properly encapsulated so that the user sees only the desired external behavior, regardless of implementation.

Programming Calculus: Perhaps the most intellectually satisfying approach to the construction of correct and reliable software is to prove correctness during construction of the program [27], [28]. The design freedom is deliberately limited so that program and proof can be constructed hand-in-hand. This design strategy requires that the system to be built has solid, unambiguous specifications. One way to do this formally is to state the required result as an assertion in predicate calculus. Each top-down refinement step is then carried out with rigorous strength to guarantee that the specifications are still met and to produce the specifications for the next lower level of modules. Till now this approach has been limited to fairly small program segments.

There is some expectation that in the long run the circuits resulting from silicon compilers (Section III-C) can be shown to be correct by construction. However, the day is still far in the future when such generators will produce correct and economically viable solutions for arbitrary systems for all sensible combinations of input parameters, and formal proofs of correctness should not be expected in this century.

F. Restriction to a Limited Set of Constructs

Böhm and Jacopini [29] have shown that the logic of any program can be represented as a hierarchical arrangement of three basic constructs: *sequence, iteration,* and *selection.* Others [30], [31], [20] have also recommended that the number and type of control flow constructs in programs be limited to these few well-defined constructs and that unstructured control flow, as resulting from indiscriminate use of the controversial GOTO statement, should be minimized. For software systems, Jackson [20], Brooks [32], and Dijkstra [33] recommend the use of a rather limited set of allowable structuring topologies and even suggest restriction to pure *tree structures.*

For the structuring of integrated circuits, such a formal restriction to tree structures leads to implementations that are too inefficient. However, in general, restriction to few robust, well-understood constructs has many advantages. In particular, the use of standard modules that have been proven to work previously can make a system more modular and easier to understand, and reduces the possibility for errors. This comes at the price of some inefficiency and associated performance loss; thus the degree to which one can adhere to that philosophy depends on the application. Here is a sample of possible restrictions in VLSI design:

1) At the geometrical layout level, one might restrict oneself to only "Manhattan" geometry, i.e., only rectilinear features. This simplifies the required design tools and results in substantial speedup of such operations as layout rule checking for the price of some loss in layout density.

2) At the logic level, one could rely exclusively on pretested standard cells interconnected in a standardized automatic or

semiautomatic way. This leads quickly to relative risk-free implementations; but the chips are large and dominated by wiring area.

3) At the register level, one can avoid problems with hazards and race conditions by using strictly synchronous sequential circuits with no unclocked feedback loops.

4) At the large system level, hung flip-flops and similar synchronization problems can be avoided with a self-timed sequencing approach.

At all levels, the improvement in testability and understandability gained from such restrictions in the types of constructs used will make the introduced inefficiencies well worthwhile, if overall systems constraints can still be met.

G. Testing the Design

Testing is an integral part of the design process. Every design decision must be checked for its appropriateness. Any large system designed in an "open-loop" manner has a very small chance to work correctly.

There are many different ways in which people can convince themselves that a part or a design "works." Two extreme approaches are:

1) by running the part in its intended application environment;
2) by formally proving the correctness of the design from its specifications.

Both approaches have obvious drawbacks. The first one corresponds to driving a car around the block to see whether it works. In a complicated system this can never give full confidence that there are no undiscovered flaws; there is nothing to tell the designer what has *not* been tested yet. The second approach is like taking a lawyer's affidavit based on an inspection of the car assembly line; unless the inspection is complete and the conclusions are derived in an impeccable manner, the result is just as questionable.

Any test requires exact knowledge of what the system is supposed to do. However, at the onset of the design of a system, its specifications are seldom completely defined. As the design is refined and the constraints become better understood, specifications get added and fine tuned. In the end, specifications must become an exact description of what the designer believes that the system will do so that this information can then become the basis for tests or design verifications. The formulation of exact systems specifications is thus another important part of the *design* effort.

Testing should be kept in mind during the design of any system, program, or VLSI part. The designer should constantly ask questions of the kind: What is this part supposed to do? How will it be used? What are the extremes of the input parameters or operating conditions it will have to withstand? How can it be asserted that the completed part will be doing what it is supposed to do? Asking these tough questions and trying to provide answers to them will lead to cleaner and safer designs, which are also more amenable to debugging and testing.

H. Tools and Design Methodologies

Of crucial importance in the construction of large and complex systems is a good set of tools and a suitable design method.

Design Tools: The user interface is an important part of any design tool, be it for program development or the design of VLSI circuits. As computer time becomes relatively less expensive than the designer's time, the tools become more interactive in nature. Batch jobs should be used only for large

program runs where the interaction of the designer is not required. Program development, on the other hand, should be done in an environment where the programmers get all the help they need to be most productive, such as syntax directed editors [34] and powerful high-level debuggers [35]. An equivalent set of tools in the domain of integrated circuit design would include design stations with built-in design rule checking, automatic layout compaction, and tight coupling to a set of simulators.

Most currently available tools fall short of the designer's expectations in many ways. Here is a list of frequently heard complaints about today's commercially available design tools for integrated circuits. Similar criticism has been voiced for software development tools [36].

1) *Cumbersome commands.* Too many actions (key strokes or cursor moves) are required to invoke frequently used operations such as placing a rectangle in a layout.

2) *Not responsive enough.* Manipulations on a graphics screen should be at least as fast as the corresponding manipulations with pencil and paper.

3) *Lack of uniformity.* Design tools reside on several machines with quite different accessing methods and interfacing protocols; this discourages the effective and frequent use of these tools.

4) *Poor integration with other tools.* Tools use different data formats or different hierarchical structuring; this makes it cumbersome to use different tools on the same design.

5) *Capabilities too narrow.* Some tools, efficiently tailored to a specific approach such as Gate Arrays [14], [37] do not permit the integration of other useful devices or functional blocks, even when these devices are compatible with the fabrication technology.

Support for Good Methodologies: An even more serious, general shortcoming is that most tools do not support a clean design methodology. Layouts done on a graphics editor can be rather ad hoc, since there is nothing to enforce high-level structuring disciplines. Normally there is no place where the designer can capture semantic information, either for the benefit of other designers re-using a particular cell or for other tools such as circuit extractors or logic simulators. Graphics editors and design tools centered around layout information alone are not sufficient for the design of complex VLSI systems.

The analysis of tradeoffs, resolution of conflicting demands, and finding the best structure are at the heart of the design process. According to Parnas [38], this leads to three key criteria by which different design methodologies should be compared:

1) In what order are decisions made?
2) How are these decisions recorded?
3) When is their correctness verified?

The search continues for good formal structuring methods giving consistent results. The search for the right design methodology for VLSI systems and for tools that properly support the latter has only just begun.

Consistency of Style: A good design methodology is one that reproducibly generates a particular system implementation, independent of whoever is applying it. So far, no design method, even in the field of software engineering, automatically produces unique solutions. As a result, one can find widely differing programming or layout styles. Even if the advantages of one style over another are hard to quantify, adherence to a consistent style in the design of a large system is important from the point of view of clarity and maintainability.

TABLE III
DIFFERENT REPRESENTATIONS OF A SUBSYSTEM

Particular Aspect	Description Format
Semantic behavior:	English text
Test specification:	text, tables
Logic function:	equations, state diagram
Timing behavior:	waveforms
Geometrical area:	graphics display
Connection diagram:	display, wire list
Power consumption:	text, tables

Representations, too, should use a consistent notation to make understanding easy. The use of familiar constructs greatly enhances understandability. The pattern-matching processes in the human brain are very powerful and can be trained to quickly find relevant patterns. This should be exploited in the selection of the notations for the various representations of a problem.

For similar reasons, interactive tools also should have consistent user interfaces. A particular command such as *delete* should have a corresponding effect in all tools in a design environment, regardless whether it is used in a graphics layout tool, in a text editor, or in a file manager. A uniform design environment will greatly enhance designer productivity.

IV. ADDITIONAL DIFFICULTIES IN VLSI SYSTEMS DESIGN

The general problems associated with complex systems that were discussed in the previous sections also occur in VLSI systems design. The related techniques developed in the field of software engineering can thus readily be applied to VLSI design. However, VLSI systems cause additional problems based primarily on the two-dimensional nature of integrated circuits and the need for physical interconnections between modules, i.e., the inability to "jump" to a "submodule." This section will outline problems that go beyond those that are normally faced by the software engineer.

A. Multiple Views and Representations

In VLSI systems, the number of different concerns is quite large and diverse. This necessitates a much richer set of views and representations than is normally used to document a software system. First, there is a larger spectrum of hierarchical abstractions, ranging from functional specifications to machine-level layout descriptions. Secondly, for a particular level of detail, several different representations may be used to optimally capture a particular concern of the designer. For instance, at the module level of a digital system, a pipelined piece of logic might be described by:

1) its logic function and test patterns for switch-level functional simulation;
2) suitable delay models to be used in signal-independent worst case timing verification;
3) separate logic gates with timing parameters useful for timing simulation and checking for glitches.

The different representations cannot always be fit into a single hierarchical ordering. Table III gives a sampling of various concerns in VLSI systems and possible notations to capture these concerns. This set of representations is richer than the one normally encountered in software engineering.

Unfortunately, these many different representations do not easily follow from one another. In a VLSI chip, most information can be computed from a final layout, but this is a very time-consuming and computation-intensive task. In order to provide an interactive design environment, most derived information should be stored explicitly in a database once it has been computed, so that it is readily available to the designer. Other information, such as functional specification, is provided top-down before any layout exists. This must be stored and later compared against the information derived from the actual implementation.

Keeping the various representations up-to-date and consistent in the face of daily changes is a major task. The search continues for a centralized representation from which most of the other representations can be derived quickly and inexpensively. Conversions between the different representations are particularly difficult if the designers do not relinquish part of their freedom and do not restrict themselves to a subset of well-defined modules and constructs.

B. Partitioning a VLSI System

Section III-E dealt with the difficulties in top-down design methods related to the fact that it is not clear *how* a large system should be partitioned into smaller blocks. In highly integrated systems, such as a VLSI chip, there are additional difficulties. Because of the lack of explicit interfaces, the partitioning step is often done in an *ad hoc* manner, improperly documented, and never formally verified to meet the original specifications of the overall system. Specifications that might have been precise at the higher level become more fuzzy or may even be violated in the intermediate partitioning steps. It is often not until the whole partitioning hierarchy has been instantiated, and a global systems simulation is being performed, that such errors get noticed. At this late stage it is often no longer clear *who* was responsible for the original violation, and an innocent group of people may have to sweat to correct the problem.

Clean and precise specifications are needed *at all levels* of the design hierarchy and in all transformations of representations. This is tedious and difficult, but unless it is done properly, the original problem has not *really* been partitioned; at best, a more terse and economical notation has been found for something that is still functionally unstructured. As an example, consider a switched-capacitor filter comprising some switches and capacitors and five identical operational amplifiers, each with, say, 30 transistors. In any reasonable description, the amplifier will be factored out as some kind of macro cell. But unless a simpler and more abstract model is used to represent it in the systems simulation, i.e., as long as the filter circuit is presented to the simulator with all 200-odd components visible, the circuit has not been partitioned functionally. Proper functional partitioning is accomplished only if each amplifier is viewed as a new lumped element with its own higher level simulation model.

There is a lot more work involved in creating satisfactory models in *all* relevant representations of a physical component than what it takes to give an abstract description of a cleanly designed program subroutine.

C. Optimization and Packaging

Because of constraints on implementation, physical and logical hierarchy need not have a direct one-to-one correspondence. The logical design hierarchy results from a suitable partitioning into significant functional blocks. The physical hierarchy may be determined by packaging constraints or by geometrical placement restrictions.

In present-day integrated circuits, functional solution and technical implementation are rather narrowly intertwined.

The performance loss resulting from the separation of the two concerns and from the use of automated implementation has been considered too high by most companies producing high-volume integrated circuits. The emergence of integrated, customized systems of VLSI complexity will force us to rethink this issue. The intertwining of functional solution and implementation should be considered an optimization step that has to be justified, rather than being the default approach.

To make these tradeoffs wisely, a better understanding needs to be developed of where the boundary between functional solutions and implementation can be drawn. The special nature of VLSI technology and its physical realities must be considered already at the system level. Algorithmic changes may be called for when one switches from a software solution to a printed-circuit board implementation and later to a VLSI chip. Yet, at the same time, one cannot afford to tie a design exclusively to a single fabrication process.

Many of the high-level partitioning steps are relatively implementation independent; e.g., the decomposition of a large processor into register–transfer level modules is independent of whether the system will be implemented in NMOS or in CMOS technology. Thus the top end of such a design system can be common to many different technologies. In principle, one could decompose a computer down to the gate level and then simply use either the NMOS or CMOS gate implementations. However, that would lead to highly inefficient realizations of such functions as an operand shifter for which compact, technology-specific realizations exist. The more one wants to push performance and optimize an implementation, the higher up the technology-specific concerns have to enter the selection of the algorithm and the structuring process. This optimization step is crucial for the fabrication of present-day VLSI chips and will result in a certain loss of clarity in the design.

D. Layout

A particularly important set of constraints stems from the two-dimensional nature of integrated circuits.

Electrical Connectivity: Whereas high-level language programmers normally need not concern themselves with the overhead of jump instructions, communication between modules in a physical machine is expensive, both in terms of space and time. For components interacting with high frequency, physical proximity is crucial since the penalties for long, high-bandwidth interconnections are severe. In large integrated circuits, the partitioning into blocks and their location on the chip must be chosen carefully since the physical distances between components and the total bandwidth between them remains frozen once the chip is made; there is no equivalent of a memory hierarchy managed by an operating system which can move frequently used information closer to the point where it is used, e.g., into a cache memory.

The communications overhead is particularly severe if the signals must travel from chip to chip or from one printed-circuit board to another. This results in a substantial expense in power and in loss of bandwidth. In addition, the number of pins is often strictly limited. (In the software domain this would correspond to the situation where the number of parameters that can be passed to a subroutine is limited to, say, two integers or one floating-point variable!) The physical packaging hierarchy must thus be chosen with particular care.

Two-Dimensionality: The concern with interconnectivity and geometrical placement is particularly intensive in VLSI systems since the implementation is restricted to the two-dimen-

TABLE IV
DEGREES OF CONCURRENCY

Type	Example
Bit concurrency:	n-bit parallel adder
Vector operations:	matrix multiplication
Pipelining:	overlapped instruction execution
Set concurrency:	evaluation of alternatives
Specialist functions:	co-processors
Task concurrency:	communicating processes
Random concurrency:	everything else ...

sional space of the surface of a silicon wafer. The signal paths to other modules compete with the computational elements themselves for the rather limited chip surface. This places severe topological restrictions on implementation. A particular module can have only a very small set of close neighbors, and it is often hard to decide which of several contenders should get the preferred spot. By comparison, the sequence and ordering of the definitions of subroutines is rarely a concern to a programmer (except when forward references are disallowed).

Furthermore, changing the placement of a module in a layout is a much harder task than rearranging software modules. Very few design tools reroute the attached wires automatically when a circuit block is moved to a different corner of the chip floor plan; i.e., the equivalent of a link editor for two-dimensional layouts is still in the research stage. Moreover, no really good language exists for expressing topology.

E. Exploiting Concurrency

To realize their true potential, VLSI systems should be designed for as much concurrent action as possible. Ideally, one would like to see all the gates on a chip do useful work most of the time. But so far, the concurrency exploited on VLSI chips has been of a relatively simple and straightforward nature. That is not surprising since the problem of exploiting concurrency in a general manner is not even solved in the software domain.

A first goal must be to find adequate high-level descriptions for highly parallel but irregular operations. Timing sheets with multiple traces, a method typically employed by integrated circuit designers, does not scale effectively to the VLSI level. Table IV gives an overview over various levels of concurrency, ordered by their generality and, alas, by their difficulty of implementation.

The simplest kind is bit concurrency. Parallel operation on the bits of fixed-sized operands, such as parallel addition, is routinely employed in microprocessors and normally implemented in a straightforward manner by iteration of the proper 1-bit cells.

The next level, the lock-step concurrency, as employed in single-instruction multiple-data vector machines, is conceptually not much harder. Problems arise when the number of data components exceeds the available hardware resources, and the job has to be done partly parallel, partly serial.

Control for the third level, pipelining, is more complicated. The execution times in the various stages have to be matched carefully in order to efficiently process different data elements through the same basic functional blocks. Particular problems arise at discontinuities in the data stream where the pipeline has to be refilled with relevant information.

Really difficult problems arise with the higher levels of concurrency, such as set, task, or random concurrency. At this level, one tries to extract concurrency from a problem in such a manner that different operations may be performed simultaneously on different data. The potential improvements in functional throughput resulting from an exploitation of parallelism in this most general form are tremendous. This problem is still unsolved even at the algorithmic level and remains one of the major challenges for this decade.

F. Technology Changes

VLSI designs are aimed at a moving target. Because of the length of the development cycle, a new design is often aimed at a presently emerging, still rather speculative implementation process, with the hope that the process will be mature by the time that the design is finished. As the envisioned process changes, the emerging layout has to be adjusted, demanding modular and modifiable designs.

Because the technology changes so fast, the adaptation to a new process must occur in a reasonably short time span. If the design takes longer than this period, it will have missed a fast moving target. This also speaks for the usage of higher level, and thus more technology-independent descriptions. If the system design has been carried out at too low a level of representation, it will not be usable with new fabrication processes. High-level language descriptions with suitable layout compilers will be more adaptable.

G. Debugging and Testing a VLSI Chip

Debugging the prototype design of a VLSI system involves all the problems that the software engineer faces and then some additional ones. Because a VLSI chip is a rather monolithic system, it cannot be easily tested in bits and pieces, i.e., one subroutine at a time—unless explicit measures have been taken to partition the system for debugging or testing purposes. Because of the small physical features on the chip, it is very tedious and costly to gain access to the inner parts of a VLSI circuit. Only signals that are brought out to the terminals of the chip are readily observable. In other words, the equivalent of a debugger with breakpoints and monitoring of variables has not yet been invented for VLSI chips.

Checking a monolithic system becomes exponentially harder with increasing size [39] and the amount of complexity that can be packed into a single VLSI chip is far beyond the maximum reasonable size of a testable block. Special measures are thus necessary to break the overall system into smaller, testable parts, such as providing internal access points or scan-in scan-out registers [40].

Imperfect Implementation: In addition to debugging, i.e., verifying that the *design* of a chip is correct, there is also the problem of testing each copy to make sure that it is acceptable. This problem can usually be ignored in software, since a simple redundancy check is normally sufficient to guarantee that the copy is a perfect replica of the original.

When writing a program, one typically assumes that there will be a system that guarantees, often by complicated means, that all instructions are properly executed in the sequence specified. The VLSI designer faces a less ideal world. Signal voltages are only defined in certain *ranges;* in addition, they are subject to *noise* that may well exceed the stated tolerances. Alpha particles can change the contents of a memory cell. Temporary voltage surges occur on the supply lines when large numbers of signal lines change state simultaneously.

The overall system has to be immune against such erratic behavior. Overdesign, redundancy, checking, and recovery mechanisms have to be built into larger functional blocks and subsystems so that they can present a more nearly ideal picture to the observer at the next higher level of abstraction. In debugging the design as well as in testing the final product, a particular operation has to be checked over a range of "environmental" conditions, such as supply voltage variations, temperature ranges, and processing parameter deviations. This adds an extra dimension to the debugging/testing problem.

V. TRADEOFFS IN VLSI CHIP COMPLEXITY

In software systems there is a clear trend to higher level languages. With ever faster processors and cheaper memories, the inefficiencies in code density and execution speed in a compiled program become insignificant in comparison to the advantages associated with the usage of high-level languages (Section III-C). Hand optimization at the assembly language level is reserved for critical inner loops, often-used routines, or for applications with real-time constraints.

The issue of layout density is more important for VLSI chips than code density is for programs because of the severe technological restrictions on maximum chip size. Efficiency of implementation cannot be ignored. It will be necessary to sacrifice a certain amount of modularity and modifiability in order to fit a system on an economically viable chip. This section considers these tradeoffs.

A. Hardware versus Software

In designing a complete system based primarily on some VLSI chips, a new tradeoff has to be considered: what part of the function should be implemented in silicon and what part can be done with software? This tradeoff actually spans a whole spectrum of possibilities. Consider the example of a microprocessor: should a complicated instruction be wired into the decoding logic, should it be programmed into the microcode memory, or should the compiler compose this function from a collection of more primitive instructions? These decisions are of particular importance in VLSI system design, since the individual chip is an entity that must work as a whole. If the chip design is too ambitious, the chip cannot be fabricated economically. Thus at any given point in time, the number of active devices of a certain type that can be used economically on a single chip represents a rather rigid resource limitation. One must decide very carefully how to best use this resource.

B. Simplicity to Get the Job Done

A very direct approach to managing complexity is to question whether the complexity asked for in a set of specifications is indeed reasonable and necessary. Some recent studies into instruction sets and organizations of microprocessors showed that evolving products need not necessarily follow a trend to ever increasing complexity [41]. Complexity introduced to provide rarely used instructions may not be worth the extra costs in terms of increased chip area, a slower overall machine cycle due to the delays through more complicated decoders or micro stores, and delayed market entry because of a prolonged design cycle. Worse yet, such additional circuitry may run against the hard limit of resources on the chip and thus take away devices from other functions that might have made a larger contribution to the overall performance of the system. In the domain of integrated circuits, unnecessary functionality as well as irregularity [42] comes at a much higher price than in software engineering.

285

C. Complexity for Higher Yield

Beyond a certain point, the yield of good integrated circuits emerging from the fabrication process drops off exponentially with increasing active chip area [43]. Due to these hard constraints on chip size, a reduction in the number of devices on the chip is well worth some increase in complexity.

In large regular arrays such as memory blocks, groups of two or four adjacent cells are often designed jointly so that proper rotation and mirroring can be used to share contacts or power bus lines. Such a cluster of two or four cells is then repeated to produce the overall array. Similarly, large amounts of random logic are typically not implemented as a single, large, and sparsely populated programmed logic array (PLA), but are broken down into several smaller PLA's [44]. In both cases, while apparent complexity is slightly increased, considerable area savings may result.

As integrated circuit technology evolves, chip functionality will increase. But the limit of how many fully functional devices can be placed on a single chip cannot rise indefinitely. To make significant improvements in the total functionality of a chip, new methods have to be exploited. The emerging 64-kbit memory parts already employ redundant memory cells and circuit elements which take over for the devices that have fabrication flaws [45]. So far, the parts have to be tested individually, and the proper rewiring or reprogramming has to be done from the outside. It is reasonable to expect that at some point in the future there will be more complex, self-testing circuits that reconfigure themselves internally to portray to the outside a flawless function of a given specification.

D. Complexity for Better Performance

Among the reasons for casting systems in silicon is the aim of compactness and performance. This implies a certain degree of system optimization. Simply taking the most regular and straightforward implementation might result in an intolerably bulky or slow chip.

Even RISC [41] is not just a simple Turing machine. Instruction fetch and execution are overlapped. This pipelining increases the system complexity, but no microprocessor designer would give up the resulting performance gain at the present time. New commercial microprocessors go even further and use more sophisticated pipelining schemes. Increased complexity and increased performance need to be carefully evaluated to find the optimum approach. Similarly, increasing the richness of the instruction set leads to a point of diminishing return. A general guideline on this issue has been given by Wulf [46]. He demands that instruction sets offer *primitives, not solutions.*

A look into the future sometimes justifies cramming more complexity and functionality onto a particular chip than is justified by present-day resource limitations. First, one expects that these limits will expand, and that the decision to add extra features will be right in the light of future developments. Secondly, computer architectures tend to be around for a long time. A company that plans to launch a whole family of processors of various performance ranges needs to accommodate the basic instruction set even in the lowest performer; this might distort the proper balance of resource allocation for this particular member of the family.

VI. General Trends in VLSI Systems Design

Many of the techniques for complexity management reviewed in Section III are slowly being integrated into presently emerging VLSI circuit design systems. This section summarizes the main trends and explores how the discussed methods are adapted to the special problems of VLSI systems design.

TABLE V
Comparison of Languages

IC DESIGN and	PROGRAMMING
Functional specifications	Specification languages
Self-generating layouts	APL, ...
Protected, abstract modules	Ada, ...
Subcircuits, explicit connections	Pascal, ...
Symbolic description	Basic, ...
λ-based conceptual features	Intermediate code
Mask geometry	Assembler language
Mann or MEBES format	Machine language

A. Towards High-Level Languages for VLSI Systems

There is a rich spectrum of possible views which can be used to discuss the design of a VLSI system. Table V shows the most important hierarchical levels in a high-to-low order and attempts to put them in perspective by pairing these levels with representations from the world of programming languages.

In the 1970's, the practice of laying out integrated circuits corresponded to assembly language programming. Even today, most designers still have an overriding concern for density in order to end up with a chip that is small enough to be manufactured economically. Traditional designers feel that the compactness and performance achievable with good hand layout are worth the tediousness of the approach.

In the domain of software engineering, high-level languages are now used routinely for system developments of substantial size. Assembly language code is reserved for small, high-volume systems with limited memory, such as games and controllers, or for real-time systems with absolute timing constraints. The same trends towards high-level languages seen in software engineering are also apparent in the domain of integrated circuit design. As integrated circuit technology progresses, it will soon be possible to place more than a million devices on a single chip. For random control circuits, this is an inordinate amount—far more than any designer can reasonably handle manually. In such complicated systems, efficiency is a lesser issue than achieving correct operation.

High-level languages also reduce development time. This is even more important in the fast-changing field of integrated circuit fabrication. Earlier market entry will translate into large economical advantages in this highly competitive field. The evolution of single-chip VLSI systems creates a demand for more personalized systems that fit the customer's needs exactly; multiyear development times are no longer tolerable in this context. Minimizing the size of integrated circuits will only pay off for high-volume products (more then 100 000 samples). For customized VLSI applications, some layout inefficiencies can normally be tolerated; the most important consideration is to get the job done correctly and on time.

B. Partitioning of Concerns and Problem-Specific Representation

The development of a VLSI system involves even more diverse considerations than writing a large software system. If possible, the various concerns should be addressed independently. Jackson recommends the separation of problem-oriented concerns from machine-oriented ones [20]. The use of two complementary languages is suggested: a programming language to solve the problem, and an execution language to specify how to compile and execute with efficiency. The notation for the two languages should be optimized for the task at hand.

Similarly, in VLSI design, different languages and notations should be used at different points of the abstraction hierarchy.

Representations and notations must be matched to the problems that one tries to solve. In the design of VLSI systems there is a large variety of different concerns; a rich spectrum of notations is thus necessary. The proper definition of these representations is important because notations not only determine the form of the final solution, but also shape the way we think about a problem [47].

This issue has recently been addressed by Stefik et al. [48]. They define several representations and develop appropriate notations and composition rules. Each one deals with only a few concerns and is thus most effective in avoiding a particular class of bugs:

"*Linked Module Abstraction*" deals with event sequencing at the systems or subsystem level. Modules get started by accepting a token; they do exactly one task at a time; when finished they emit a token to the next module. This representation helps avoid deadlocks and the sampling of data that are not ready.

"*Clocked Registers and Logic*" are concerned with the details of timing. This abstraction tries to eliminate errors such as race conditions in unclocked feedback loops, e.g., by using strictly alternating two-phase clocking.

"*Clocked Primitive Switches*" try to assure proper digital behavior by addressing the ratios of digital NMOS inverters and avoiding passive charge sharing on intermediate nonrestoring nodes.

"*Layout Geometry*" is concerned with geometrical layout rules and tries to prevent spacing errors or unrealizable mask features.

Stefik et al. [48] point out that such problem-specific representations need not fall into a strict hierarchical ordering. The relative ranking of the abstractions along different axes of concern might well be permuted.

C. Emphasis on Structure and Abstraction

Without the introduction of some structure, i.e., hierarchy and regularity, the problem of VLSI system design would be unmanageable. As the organizational problems start to overshadow the fabricational difficulties, the use of a *constrained hierarchy* [49] becomes more attractive. Additional restrictions are imposed on the structuring process:

1) The hierarchical partitioning is truly functional with proper abstractions at each node.

2) The hierarchies in the various representations (geometrical, logical) must correspond to one another.

These restrictions on the designer's freedom result in a higher degree of clarity and in more efficient operation of most design tools, at the price of some loss of layout density.

Regularity, i.e., reusing the same submodules as often as possible, also increases effectiveness. Lattin has introduced the *regularity factor*, derived by dividing the total number of features (transistors, rectangles) by the number of features actually drawn by the designer. Present-day microprocessor chips have regularity factors ranging around 5 for commercial products [10] and reaching about 20 for experimental devices [50].

Traditional Logic Cell Macros: A traditional approach to structuring large digital circuits relies on the logical abstractions of the well-known small- and medium-scale components, such as gates, flip-flops, and registers. This approach is used in the *standard cell* and *gate array* systems. The *standard cell* or *polycell* approach [15] relies on a library of layouts of such logic components and on some automatic or semiautomatic procedure to place the cells and to route the interconnections. The *macro cell* or *gate array* approach [14], [37] uses a combination of preprocessed wafers and libraries of predefined

wiring options to generate the same standard logic functions. The design systems normally contain powerful routing algorithms that wire most of the chip automatically. The designer has to help only when there are special timing or area constraints. The increasing market share of such products indicates that these are indeed practical approaches. In both cases, engineers can approach the VLSI design in the traditional manner and map their logic designs onto a silicon chip with relatively little effort.

The drawback with these approaches is that they use the wrong weighting factors. They encourage the designer to minimize the number of logic gates, assuming that wires are free, whereas on VLSI chips, they dominate the layout area as well as the timing delays. Suitable representations for VLSI must properly address the interconnections at all levels of the partitioning hierarchy.

Advanced systems permit the integration of custom-designed macro cells into the final layout like any other library cell. This approach has the advantage that higher level functional blocks, such as the datapath of a microprocessor or a control PLA, can be designed by alternative design methods, leading to more compact implementations.

Hierarchical Analysis Tools: As regularity and hierarchy is empasized in the synthesis of our designs, the design tools also need to be restructured to exploit this new methodology in the analysis phase. Design rule checkers or circuit extractors that walk rectangle by rectangle through a regular array are no longer tolerable for 64-kbit memory chips. The generating cells and their generic constellations in the array should be checked *once*; repeated instances of checked constellations can then be skipped. This requires some sophisticated book-keeping, but the performance advantages of hierarchical circuit extractors and design rule checkers are well worth it [51]–[54].

A well thought-out abstraction hierarchy must also be exploited in the simulation tools. Once a low-level module, such as a 1-bit adder, has been constructed and checked to behave correctly, that information must be tightly linked to the definition of that cell. System simulations then no longer need to work all the way to the level of the physical differential equations but can stop at the module level and use a more abstract model describing the behavior of the module at that level.

The use of hierarchical analysis tools can only succeed if it can be guaranteed that the introduced abstractions remain valid. In particular, the cell has to be protected so that its behavior cannot be changed accidentally. In the layout domain, some kind of protection frame can be employed so that accidental interference into inner parts of a cell can be detected. There are some inefficiencies associated with this approach; cells cannot be packed as tightly as they could be in an unrestricted environment. However, this mechanism should only be invoked for cells of a reasonable size, where introducing a new level of abstraction is appropriate. The protection frames serve the same roles as the *module* construct in some high-level languages; across module boundaries all interactions have to be declared explicitly. At that level, the loss in packing density can be tolerated.

D. Separation of Design and Implementation

Another application of abstraction and partitioning of concerns occurs in the transition from design to implementation. Traditionally, the layout engineer had to stay in close contact with the fabrication line and the mask makers in order to understand what exact geometrical patterns (what polarity, suitably grown or shrunk) had to be submitted in order to receive the desired physical features on the fabricated silicon wafer. Certain process variations force the designer to rework one or more mask levels. In addition, the selection of the proper processing test structures and alignment marks was also a responsibility of the designer.

The experiments with multiproject chips shared among many designers at several different universities [55] demonstrated that design and implementation can indeed be separated. The designer is responsible only for his or her own design and need not worry about mask polarity, alignment marks, process compensation, or monitors for critical dimensions. The designs are submitted in a standardized low-level geometrical descriptive form such as CIF2.0, the Caltech Intermediate Form [56]. A centralized service organization will then merge the different designs onto several reasonably sized chips together with a *starting frame* containing the alignment marks and some process control monitors. These chips, in turn, are assembled into a suitable tiling pattern, which also contains a few slots for gross registration marks and more extensive test structures, to cover a whole wafer. The same service organization will arrange and coordinate mask making and the actual fabrication of the silicon wafer and will subsequently redistribute the fabricated and possibly packaged chips to the original designers. This approach distributes the costs of mask making and wafer fabrication among all the designers and brings the cost per design down to an affordable range for small volume silicon systems; such services have been called "silicon foundries" [57].

This approach shields the occasional designer from the time-consuming and confusing details that one has to consider when submitting a design for fabrication. The silicon foundry approach abstracts the implementation process to a single "module" with a well-defined interface. The designer specifies the physical features that should appear on the final chip. All the expand/shrink operations necessary to compensate for the actual processing are performed by the implementation service. Only chips originating from wafers that pass the process control tests will be returned to the customers. This approach can only be successful with well-established, stable fabrication technologies. Again, the additional abstractions and the corresponding reduction in complexity in the design process comes at the price of somewhat lower performance.

E. Procedural Generation of Modules and Systems

While a silicon compiler for complete systems is still some time off in the future, procedural generators for special, frequently used, functional blocks become commonplace. The most important ones produce PLA's and read-only memories (ROM's). These module generators take a set of parameters or, in the case of ROM's and PLA's, the Boolean equations of the desired logic function, and then compose the complete layout from predefined low-level cells. Because these blocks are so important and used so frequently, a lot of effort has been spent to optimize the basic cells from which the final layout is composed.

Other, more complicated functional blocks, are special data processing elements, such as the datapath of a typical microprocessor forming a linear arrangement of registers, shifter elements, incrementers, or complete arithmetic/logic units [24], [13]. Hewlett–Packard claims [58] that about 90 percent of its data processing chips could be cast in the format of such a generalized datapath.

The first set of these module generators is aimed at a specific process and a specific set of layout rules. In later versions, more fabrication independence will be gained by performing the cell composition at the logic level and passing the result through a fabrication-rule-dependent circuit compactor [59]–[61].

Eventually there will be module generators that handle many *diverse* fabrication technologies (NMOS, CMOS, SOS, ...). However, because the most suitable topology for a PLA is different for these different implementation technologies, only the higher levels of these generators, e.g., the algebraic minimization and the optimizations through folding and splitting, can be shared. To be most effective, these module generators must be fully integrated with the layout system. Their output must have the complete documentation of a typical macro module. This requires that the module generator produce all necessary representations, ideally including test specifications.

F. Enhanced Use of Graphics and Interactive Tools

VLSI system design is strongly tied to the two-dimensional nature of the implementation medium. Because of the lack of suitable languages to express the relative geometrical arrangements of individual modules and the wiring between them, the use of graphics plays an important role. Presently graphics display hardware is becoming inexpensive enough, so that there is no reason not to provide every tool that can profit from it with a graphics interface. A highly responsive, interactive graphics display is going to be the core of every integrated circuit design station.

The success of the module generators discussed in the previous section has led many people to postulate that *all* design work should be done in a procedural manner. This approach would have two major drawbacks:

1) The description of the geometry of low-level cells is rather tedious.

2) Without a two-dimensional representation the designer lacks an important element in the feedback from the design system.

Graphics is an invaluable aid at many levels of the design. For the geometrical layout of complicated leaf cells, graphics is clearly the preferred medium of interaction. At the higher levels, where a procedural description of the modules is more appropriate, graphics still plays an important role for checking the results of the procedural constructions. A good interactive graphics system can also play an important role in the strategic planning of the chip layout. It permits the presentation of the problem to a human in a format where the designer's intuition can be tapped most effectively.

On the other hand, it seems more appropriate to use a procedural approach to specify the placement of the "1"-cells in a large PLA. Because of these different tradeoffs, there is an ongoing dispute of the use of "Pictures versus Parentheses" [62]. Both approaches are optimal for certain tasks, and a good design system thus cannot ignore either one of them.

A major disadvantage with present-day procedural design tools stems from their "batch-processing" nature. It is often necessary to make small changes in a nearly finished design. If placement or routing is specified in a procedural manner, the introduction of a small change in the specifications may result in a completely different layout. This will invalidate the simulation and performance verification efforts expended on the 95 percent of the chip that were correct beforehand. Restating the constraints in such a manner that only the *desired* changes take place is normally not possible.

In the future, these procedural tools need to be integrated into a design system with interactive interfaces on which desired changes in placement or routing can be specified in a natural manner. New algorithms are required that make only *incremental* changes and derive the next solution as a *minimal change* from the previous solution. Many problems need to be solved to create such an integrated system in which the designer gets the best benefits from both approaches.

VII. EVOLUTION OF DESIGN TOOLS

To a large degree, the evolution of design environments for systems on silicon will follow the evolution of programming environments [63]-[66]. However, future tools need to take into account the special demands of VLSI design discussed in Section IV. This section attempts to project how this will be achieved in three different time frames. Tomorrow's design tools already exist in prototype form in many research laboratories, and so one can have a fairly clear idea what they will look like. The remarks concerning future design environments are based on work that is currently in active pursuit in several research institutions with the goal of creating prototypes within the next couple of years. The last subsection on ultimate ways of creating solid-state systems is a rather speculative extrapolation of some ideas currently being discussed in research papers and workshops.

A. Tomorrow's Design Tools

The trends discussed in Section VI will gradually make their way into the emerging design tools. Based on the work currently in progress in many research and development organizations, one can have the following expectations about tomorrow's design systems: they will have strongly improved human interfaces, addressing most of the issues discussed in Section III-H. The tools for layout planning, module placement, and routing will make use of ever more powerful algorithms to do a large fraction of the task, but retain a strong interactive nature to permit the designers to make full use of their intuition and judgment.

There will be an increased use of higher level symbolic descriptions coupled with more and more automatic generation of frequently needed modules. Explicit design methodologies, such as the use of a constrained hierarchy, will gain preference, and the analysis tools will start to exploit the hierarchy used in the design process.

The two main components of tomorrow's design system will be a modular set of tools and a database.

A Modular Set of Tools: The same considerations that apply to large programs or VLSI systems also apply to the development of the design environment itself: the latter should also be highly structured and composed of modular components with simple, well-defined interfaces.

The art of VLSI design is still not fully understood, and new methodologies are still evolving. It is thus too early to specify a rigid design system that performs the complete design task; quite likely, such a system would be obsolete by the time it becomes available to the user. It is more desirable to create a framework that permits the usage of many common tools in different approaches and that supports a variety of different design methods and styles. In short, the environment should provide *primitives* rather than *solutions* or, in other words, *mechanisms* rather than *policies*.

Intricate interaction between the various tools must be avoided. Every tool should do one task well and with reasonable efficiency [36]. Compatible data formats are needed to make possible ready exchange of information among the tools

or direct piping of data through a whole chain of tools. These formats should be comprehensive enough to carry all relevant information for various tools working on a particular design.

At Berkeley such a collection of tools [67] is being developed, embedded in the UNIX [64] operating system. UNIX already provides many of the facilities needed for our planned environment; a suitable hierarchical *file structure*, a powerful monitor program in the form of the UNIX *shell* [68] and convenient mechanisms for *piping* the output of one program directly into the input of a successor program.

Database and Data Management: All information concerning a particular design should be kept in one place, ideally in some *database* readily accessible to designers and design tools. In an emerging system at Berkeley [67], a VLSI design is mapped onto the structure of the UNIX file and directory system. Each module of the system under development is represented as a directory of files on the computer's storage system. Submodules are represented as immediate subdirectories or as files in special library directories. Each such directory may contain a varying number of files corresponding to different representations of this module. There may be files describing layouts, circuit diagrams, symbolic representations, suitable models for high-level simulation, sets of test vectors for this module, and possibly some plain English documentation. The number of files at each node is potentially unlimited.

Currently, many design systems for custom circuitry use the geometrical layout information to "glue" everything together. It is from this low-level description that other representations are derived; many of the analysis tools work from that level, e.g., circuit extraction and design rule checking. This is an unsatisfactory approach. Too much of the designer's intent has been lost in that low-level representation and has to be pieced together again by the analysis tools. If there is to be a "core" description from which other representations are derived, it has to be at a higher level. The trend is to move to a symbolic description [59] that is still close enough to the actual geometry so that ambiguities in the layout specification can be avoided. Yet at the same time, this description must have provisions to specify symbolically the electrical connections and functional models of subcircuits [69], [70].

Regardless of the exact structure of the database, the various different representations of a design should be at the fingertips of the designer so that one can readily go back and forth to the one representation that best captures the problem formulation with which the designer is grappling at the moment.

B. Future Design Environments

Based on the improved tools discussed in the previous section, five to ten years from now one will see the emergence of integrated yet flexible development *environments* for solid-state systems. Major parts of such future environments are currently in the active research stage at several institutions.

Design Management: An ever larger fraction of VLSI systems will be generated in a semiautomatic manner in which the tedious low-level operations are performed automatically. Just as future programming environments will tend to deemphasize programming by end users [71], the system design environments of the 1990's will encourage most users to work at a higher level. These environments will contain parameterized components in a variety of the technologies available at that time and the necessary tools to place and interconnect them semiautomatically. The designs will be described at much higher levels and significant parts of them will be compiled into the layouts for the chosen technology. "Design *management* tools" rather than design tools will play an increasingly important role.

Tools to help with the management of the overall design effort, including task distribution, activity scheduling, and design reviews, will gain importance with respect to the tools that just support the technical aspects of the design. Some utilities that have proven beneficial in the domain of software engineering have started to make inroads into solid-state systems design. One such utility, the Source Code Control System (SCCS) [72], plays a role when a system is too big for a single designer. It maintains a record of versions of a file or a system. This is useful when several people work together on a project and thus need to make changes to a document that is jointly used by all of them. SCCS keeps a record with each set of changes of what the changes are, why they were made, by whom, and when. Old versions of the document can be recovered, and different versions can be maintained simultaneously. It also assures that two persons are not editing the same file at the same time, which could lead to the loss of one person's modifications.

In the realm of VLSI system design, a more formal *configuration management* [73] discipline should be adopted to control modification of the specification files, the emerging microcode, or the lists of the intermodule connections. These are typical examples of documents that change continuously throughout the design phase and which may have to receive input from several people.

Design Data Base and Module Libraries: The file system containing the information about a design will evolve into a full database. This database containing the emerging custom design will be complemented by a library of cells that will be shared by many designers working on different designs. For custom designs using hand layout, these libraries have only been moderately successful. There is a lot of reinventing the wheel. Weinberg [74] noted that the problem with program libraries is that "everyone wants to put something in, but no one wants to take anything out." Most of this is caused by cumbersome access methods, inadequate documentation, poor adaptability of the modules, and a "not invented here" mentality [75], [76].

The libraries of the next decade must evolve into database systems that include convenient, interactive search procedures, employing hierarchical menus or the possibility of querying in a subset of a natural language to find the desired function. For the selected cells, the system must produce layers of more and more detailed documentation so that the designer can unambiguously determine whether a particular cell will suit his needs or will have to be modified. All relevant design information must also be available on-line so that modifications can be done easily.

Such a library should contain all regularly used, generic, functional units, such as memory blocks, stacks, ALU's, analog-to-digital converters—to name just a few. These components should be suitably parameterized to span a wide range of possible applications and should be available in a range of different technologies. In addition, they should be properly encapsulated and provided with unambiguous, easy-to-use, standardized interfaces by which they can be fit together without a need for the designer to pay attention to the device-level details of this interface. The effort needed to create, document, maintain, and adapt all these modules to an evolving

technology can be prohibitive for small companies. It is conceivable that such libraries will be sold or leased on a commercial basis by special companies.

Automatic Consistency Checking: As outlined in the previous section, the various pieces that make up the whole VLSI system will be designed at a higher level and stored in that form to increase the designer's productivity and to maintain some technology independence. A rich set of representations is thus associated with each module. Special software is needed to maintain the consistency of the various views of each module. While such consistency checks could be built into the database, it is preferable to put the know-how of this task into special tools. As more sophisticated tools become available, they can readily be introduced without affecting the structure of the database.

By 1990 silicon compilers will have made a lot of progress. They will then hopefully be able to handle fairly complex subsystems. However, they will still not be mature enough to produce guaranteed correct results from a set of functional specifications. It may not even be possible to prove that they produce proper results for all sensible parameter combinations. A substantial amount of checking will, therefore, still be needed.

A mechanism to alleviate this situation and to catch many possible errors at compile time is to rely on built-in assertions. These assertions verify that certain restrictions hold; they can perform bounds checking on parameters or combination of parameters, monitor current densities, or control module dimensions. Today, assertions are frequently used to verify timing constraints in large systems [77], [78]. They will play an ever increasing role in future systems.

In the design of a large system, individual modules are separately constructed. For a specific implementation, these descriptions have to be compiled into a representation that unambiguously describes the information to be passed to the fabrication line. Some simulation and performance checks may have to be done after this transformation. Rather than doing these steps jointly for a whole VLSI system, it will become more practical to do it on a per-module basis. This corresponds to the notion of separate compilation of the modules of large programs; the required facilities for a suitable environment for VLSI design [79] would be rather similar. A good model is the *make* facility [80] in UNIX. A *makefile* at each node in the file system describes the dependencies between the various data descriptions which may exist at that node, as well as the rules by which a desired description can be obtained from the information on which it depends. In addition, all files carry a time stamp. When the *make* facility is invoked, all files which have predecessors with more recent time stamps will be regenerated. In this manner, incremental updates propagate through the hierarchy.

At all levels, submodules can be tested or verified independently and then protected against further accidental changes. If a deliberate change is made inside such a module, then the flags indicating that the module has been verified are reset to false. An automatic sequence of test programs will recheck the new version and assert the corresponding flags if the specified tests are passed. Thus recompilation or rechecking of modules is required only if something changes inside. Small corrections in a large layout may thus be contained to a small fraction of the overall design.

Testing and Debugging: The areas that are most in need of

advancement are debugging and testing of VLSI systems. Because of the monolithic structure of integrated circuits, more than ever before, debugging and testing must be carefully planned during the design of the system [81]. The key issue is to subdivide the VLSI system into smaller parts that are easier to test. The controllability and observability of internal nodes can be greatly improved with such scan-in scan-out techniques as LSSD [40]. This methodology can be integrated into the design systems that rely on logic gates and register-transfer components. In such a system, a special type of latch is used for every flip-flop, unless explicitly told otherwise, which can then be strung together into scan-in scan-out registers. This approach is particularly powerful if for every encapsulated module the design environment automatically generates a set of test vectors, or, if that is not possible, prompts the designer for the delivery of such a set to encourage him or her to address the issue.

In the same context, better and more technology-specific fault models will have to be developed. It is too simplistic just to deal with stuck-at faults in a solid-state system that is dominated by interconnects. *Shorts* between different wires need to be considered. The simulation of the effect of such faults *per se* is no problem. However, it is impractical to test all possible pairs of nodes for the effect of a short between them. With circuit extractors operating from the layout or from a suitable symbolic description that defines the topology unambiguously, all adjacencies can be determined, and short simulation can thus be limited to relevant pairs. Broken wires, creating *open circuits* can be reduced to corresponding stuck-at faults.

C. Ultimate Ways for Creating Systems

This section is rather speculative; it is not expected that the concepts discussed herein will become reality in this century.

Specification-Driven System Generation: There is a possibility that ultimately routine system design will be driven directly by very-high-level language system specifications. This goal has been pursued in the software domain for the last two decades; but automatic, specification-driven software generation has yet to be demonstrated on a *general* program of substantial size.

In the VLSI domain, such specification-driven designs might emerge as an outgrowth of ever more sophisticated module generators. PLA generators currently require only a few specifications concerning their intended logic functions, constraints on the ordering of inputs and outputs, and some indication to what degree minimization, splitting, and folding should be performed. As these generators evolve, one may soon be able to select from several different structural variants to cover a wide range of delay/power tradeoffs, and to map the resulting design into most common integrated circuit fabrication processes. Once such facilities have been created, a specification-driven system is not too far away. The provision of such facilities for *arbitrary* VLSI systems, however, will lag many years behind. Here, as in software engineering, the difficulty of providing exact, unambiguous specifications is a major part of the problem.

Formal verification for programs [82]–[84] has been discussed for more than a decade. However, it is still impractical, too cumbersome, and mathematically too difficult for most programmers [85]. Application to the domain of VSLI design lies even further in the future because of the more complicated medium and its "analog" behavior. However, most inventions that have revolutionized our lives, have required 20 to 50 years from first demonstration to the point where they started to have a significant impact [71]. This is true for the telegraph, the steam engine, photography, as well as for television. More readable specification languages will be developed, and most of the tedium of grinding through the formal verification steps will be automated to the point where the computer is taking care of the details under high-level directions by the designer. So, while verification methods have not yet become a smashing success in their first 15 years, it may be well before the turn of the century that they will affect the way in which large designs will be approached.

Knowledge Engineering and Expert Systems: Techniques developed in the field of Artificial Intelligence are expected to have a major influence on our development environments for software engineering as well as for VLSI design. The goal is to capture the essence of the design process and establish a formal design methodology. Once VLSI design is well enough understood that we can start to express explicitly some of the plans followed by good designers, some of that reasoning and background knowledge can be incorporated into *Expert Systems* [86]. Such expert systems combined with rich databases of suitable software tools or electronic subsystems will then be able to piece together reasonable solutions to routine problems. The specially constrained, high-performance systems will be left to the human experts for a long time to come.

Self-Testing and Self-Reorganizing Systems: Even on that day far in the future, when the emerging designs will be provably correct because of the methodology that produced them, fabrication yields will still be less than 100 percent. Testing of the fabricated circuits will thus still be a necessity. When done in the traditional way, it can become a major, if not the dominant, part of their costs. More of the testing chore has to be off-loaded to the VLSI system itself.

Here is a possible scenario. The wafer carries, in addition to the desired VLSI chips, a grid of power and control lines that connects all chips through some suitable circuitry to a few external connectors. In the testing phase, the whole array is powered up and some control signal will initiate a self-test in all the chips on the wafer. Bad chips that draw an excessive amount of power will automatically trip a circuit that disconnects them from the power grid. The remaining circuits will start a small internal state machine that tests a local ROM. If the first test is successful, a second phase will be initiated, in which these registers and the tested ROM from a more sophisticated testing machine that now can test systematically all major parts of the associated chip. If necessary, more layers of this testing hierarchy can be introduced. The final result of all those tests, a single bit of information, will be written nondestructively into an easily readable spot; this might be done by selectively blowing a small fuse, so that good and bad chips can be identified by visible inspection.

This general idea can be extended to systems that continue to perform self-checks while they are in operation. A collection of multiple redundant blocks, constantly monitoring themselves and each other, may be a way to move into wafer scale integration. Failing blocks will be disconnected from the power supplies and spare parts will be turned on instead. This approach is only viable if the blocks themselves are large enough (more than a 100 000 devices) so that the control and monitoring overhead can be tolerated. The size of these blocks, in turn, requires a more mature technology so that blocks of a few hundred thousand devices can be built with reasonable yield.

VIII. THE ROLE OF THE DESIGNER

A. The Design Tool Manager

Just as evolving programming environments show a trend away from programming, designers of solid-state systems will spend an ever smaller fraction of their time designing at the solid-state level. The general trend has already started. The low-level layout functions get off-loaded to tools of increasing sophistication. The "tall, thin designer" [87] who carries the design from the top-level down to the layout will be a short-lived phenomenon. Solid-state systems engineers who work too much at the layout level neglect the more important design decisions that need to be made at the higher levels of abstraction. A lot of the low-level technical tasks can soon be left to computer-based design tools. The systems designer will be able to rely on tools and on prototype modules generated by expert designers. He or she will thus change from being a technical designer to being a *manager of design tools*. At the same time, *computer-aided design* will evolve into synergistic *designer-directed semiautomatic design.*

A good manager, rather than doing the job himself, will concentrate on creating an environment in which the job can get done most efficiently. This requires an attitude change on the part of the typical engineer. The most leverage out of human ingenuity can be obtained if the latter is used to build new and better tools, which then can do the job more or less automatically. In this mode, the impact of the work of individual engineers can be compounded.

B. The Expert Designer

In all the excitement about the potential of these sophisticated design environments and the power of the proposed tools, one should not overlook the role of the technical expert designer. As technology scales down, the medium gets more difficult, devices are dominated by edge effects and parasitics, and more design parameters have to be considered. It takes an expert to know whether the constrained design space provided for the average designer should be left, where it pays to cross abstraction boundaries, and when large advantages can be gained by violating the rules. Feedback from various tools can be used to check the intuitive insights of the expert.

Experts, too, will rely heavily on design tools. Even a less sophisticated tool can be used to survey the design space in order to decide which approaches are worth studying in detail. The layout expert who plans to hand-pack a certain array structure to the limit possible in a given technology, will be well advised to use a less skillful, automatic compaction program first to quickly find promising topologies that can then be optimized further by hand. Without such an exploratory search of the design space, the expert designer might get "trapped in a local minimum," overlooking a deeper global minimum resulting from a different topology. Seeing a succession of many possible solutions also leads to a better understanding of the tradeoffs, and develops heuristics that permit homing-in on desirable solutions more quickly.

Designers most interested and skilled in low-level design will make their contributions by improving the basic cells on which the solid-state systems compilers must rely. They will formalize their knowledge and incorporate it into the systems that drive the design tools. The support by the expert designer will be vital in keeping the automatic design environment from becoming obsolete.

C. Multi-Designer Teams

Even with a very powerful set of almost fully automatic design tools, large VLSI systems will very likely still require the help of more than one designer. A big problem, well known in the area of software engineering, lies in the management of a design team. Too large a team can become completely ineffective [32] if so much time is spent in meetings discussing *what should be done*, that there is no time left for *actually doing* something. Computers can alleviate this situation in two ways. First, by providing more sophisticated tools, computers will allow the individual designer to achieve more, and this will reduce the size of design teams. Secondly, properly set up electronic communication can also increase the efficiency of the interactions between designers.

The foundation is provided by a sophisticated electronic mail system. A lot of time is wasted when busy people try to get in touch with each other in real time. Forwarding messages to an electronic mailbox that is read when the other party next uses the computer permits more frequent interaction. In addition, electronic messages tend to be relatively terse and devoid of a lot of the additional overhead encountered in many telephone conversations. Most people can deal with an order of magnitude more computer messages than phone conversations per unit time.

Such a system can be expanded readily to contain interest-oriented mailing lists for semipublic announcements and electronic bulletin boards that store relevant information about an emerging system design or a family of design tools. By browsing through these bulletin boards periodically, every member of a large design department can keep informed about issues of general concern.

Electronic mailboxes and bulletin boards can be integrated with the design system itself. Analysis tools, such as geometrical design rule checkers, or update tools such as the described *make* facility, may do some of their tedious work during the night and then send the results and suitable diagnostics to the mailbox of the designer. Changes to cells in a common library may be announced on the bulletin board, and reported to every designer employing these cells in a system that is currently in the active design stage.

Computers can also help formalize the tools used in the management of the design team. They can keep records of the formal distribution of tasks and responsibilities, and of planned and actual project schedules. They can record design decisions, preserve the specifications of the various subsystems and their interfaces, and use them to verify the design in functional simulations. Such a system could even initiate group meetings for design reviews and structured walk-throughs.

IX. RECOMMENDATIONS FOR ENGINEERING CURRICULA

Currently the more innovative design systems are being developed by people with a strong background in computer science, software engineering, or artificial intelligence. The tools required as well as the VSLI systems to be built require an explicit methodology to cope with the complexity involved; ad hoc methods are no longer sufficient.

Hands-on Experience with Complexity Management: It is thus recommended that courses be introduced into the engineering curriculum that explicitly and implicitly teach some of the techniques already well established in software engineering. Courses that concentrate on one big project, demonstrating how the techniques can be used to subdivide a large task into manageable parts, will prove highly beneficial. At the University of California at Berkeley several courses that give the students experience in complexity management exist in the area of Computer Science, even at the undergraduate level. These are courses in which the students build major parts of a compiler, modify significant pieces of an operating system, or design complete subsystems in a VLSI layout course. In an advanced course sequence, a small group of students has recently built a complete microprocessor [41]. On the other hand, such courses are much sparser in the traditional engineering schools, where the emphasis is typically more on design at the "component" level. There is, for instance, rarely a course on how to design a complete television set or a frequency spectrum analyzer.

Emphasis on Specification and Testing: Functional partitioning goes hand in hand with properly specifying the resulting submodules. To emphasize this point, all designers should be forced to specify precisely what it is that they are going to design or implement, be it hardware or software. Before they write a single line of code or draw a single circuit schematic, they should write down exactly how they are going to check whether their product fits certain specifications.

They should also have prepared a complete debugging plan and hand in their test files with their project proposal. Such a debugging plan starts with the simplest possible test, e.g., measuring the power consumption, for the case when chips come back in which not a single recognizable signal sequence appears at the output. Then, in case that this simple test works, there is a sequence of incrementally more sophisticated experiments building on the results of earlier tests. Thinking about testing early in the design process and doing the thorough preparations outlined above will strongly influence the design. The changes that such discipline enforces will be most appreciated when the prototype chips come back from fabrication.

X. CONCLUSION

Many of the techniques that are needed to manage the complexity of VLSI system design are already known. During the last decade, several of them have reached a stage of maturity in the domain of software engineering. However, they are only slowly entering the domain of integrated circuit design; they have not yet appeared as integral parts of commercial VLSI design tools.

The introduction of these new design techniques and their emergence in VLSI design tools will change the style in which VLSI systems will be produced in the future. The bulk of the products will no longer be designed by circuit wizards who, by ad hoc methods based on their experience and intuition, will come up with chip designs that do miraculous and mysterious things. More circuits will be specified by high-level descriptions and by functional specifications from which the lower level descriptions and ultimately the layout will be compiled in an automatic or semiautomatic manner. The time will soon come where a systems engineer can draw on a set of sophisticated semiautomatic tools that will produce a properly structured, understandable, and testable chip that will adhere to specifications and has a good chance to work the first time.

To make this happen sooner rather than later requires primarily a change in attitude. Such a change is taking place in many research laboratories. It can gain momentum if the engineering schools in their curricula put proper emphasis on explicit and practical instruction in complexity management.

ACKNOWLEDGMENT

The thoughts expressed in this paper have clearly been influenced by my environment: the many colleagues at UC Berkeley and other academic and industrial institutions with whom I interact during my work, at conferences, and indirectly through publications and correspondence. I am sure that many of my friends will recognize their models and metaphors appearing implicitly or explicitly in this text. I would like to express to all of them my sincere gratitude for the stimulating environment and the fruitful personal interactions that make it so exciting to work in this rapidly evolving field. Special thanks go to S. C. Johnson, H. T. Kung, J. K. Ousterhout, R. L. Russo, S. Trimberger, P. W. Verhofstadt, and A. I. Wasserman who have given me a lot of constructive criticism on earlier drafts.

REFERENCES

[1] G. E. Moore, "Progress in digital integrated electronics," presented at the IEEE Int. Electron Devices Meet., Talk 1.3 (Washington, DC, Dec. 1975).
[2] G. E. Moore, Quote at the First Caltech Conference on VLSI, Pasadena, CA, Jan. 1979.
[3] J. N. Buxton, "Software engineering," in *Programming Methodology*, D. Gries, Ed. New York: Springer, 1978, pp. 23–28.
[4] D. V. Steward, "Analysis and complexity," in *Systems Analysis and Management*. New York: Petrocelli Books, 1981, p. 2.
[5] E. Yourdon and L. L. Constantine, *Structured Design*. Englewood Cliffs, NJ: Prentice-Hall, 1979.
[6] P. Freeman and A. I. Wasserman, *Tutorial: Software Design Techniques*, 3rd ed. Los Alamitos, CA: IEEE Computer Society, 1980.
[7] L. A. Belady and M. M. Lehman, "Characteristics of large systems," in *Research Directions in Software Technology*, P. Wegner, Ed. Cambridge, MA: MIT Press, 1979, pp. 106–142.
[8] C.A.R. Hoare, "Hints on programming language design," Memo AIM 224, Stanford Artificial Intelligence Laboratory (Oct. 1973). Reprinted in *Tutorial: Programming Language Design*, A. I. Wasserman, Ed. Los Alamitos, CA: IEEE Computer Society, 1980.
[9] G. A. Miller, "The magical number seven, plus or minus two: Some limitations on our capacity for processing information," *Psychol. Rev.*, vol. 63, pp. 81–97, 1956.
[10] W. W. Lattin, J. A. Bayliss, D. L. Budde, J. R. Rattner, and W. S. Richardson, "A methodology for VLSI chip design," *Lambda*, vol. 2, no. 2, pp. 34–44, 2nd quarter, 1981.
[11] D. L. Johannsen, "Bristle blocks: A silicon compiler," in *Proc. Caltech Conf. VLSI* (Pasadena, CA), pp. 303–310, Jan. 1979.
[12] J. M. Siskind, J. R. Southard, and K. W. Couch, "Generating custom high performance VLSI designs from succinct algorithmic descriptions," in *Proc. Conf. on Adv. Research in VLSI* (MIT, Cambridge, MA), pp. 28–40, Jan. 1982.
[13] H. E. Shrobe, "The data path generator," in *Proc. Conf. on Adv. Research in VLSI* (MIT, Cambridge, MA), pp. 175–181, Jan. 1982.
[14] R. J. Blumberg and S. Brenner, "A 1500 gate, random logic, large-scale integrated masterslice," *IEEE J. Solid-State Circuits*, vol. SC-14, pp. 818–823, 1979.
[15] B. W. Kernighan, D. G. Schweikert, and G. Persky, "An optimum channel routing algorithm for polycell layouts of integrated circuits," in *Proc. 10th Design Automation Workshop* (Portland, OR), pp. 50–59, June 1973.
[16] V. D. Agrawal *et al.*, "The mixed mode simulator," in *Proc. 17th Design Automation Conf.*, pp. 618–625, June 1980.
[17] A. R. Newton, "Timing, logic, and mixed mode simulation for large MOS integrated circuits," NATO Advanced Study Institute on Computer Design Aids for VLSI Circuits, Sogesta-Urbino, Italy, 1980.
[18] G. D. Bergland, "A guided tour of program design methodologies," *Computer*, vol. 14, no. 10, pp. 13–36, Oct. 1981.
[19] N. Wirth, "Program development by stepwise refinement," *Commun. ACM*, vol. 14, no. 4, pp. 221–227, Apr. 1971.
[20] M. A. Jackson, *Principles of Program Design*. New York: Academic Press, 1975.
[21] T. DeMarco, *Structured Analysis and System Specification*. Englewood Cliffs, NJ: Prentice-Hall, 1979.
[22] C. Gane and T. Sarson, in *Structured Systems Analysis: Tools and Techniques*. Englewood Cliffs, NJ: Prentice-Hall, 1979.
[23] H. T. Kung and C. E. Leiserson, "Algorithms for VLSI processor arrays," in *Introduction to VLSI Systems*. C. A. Mead and L. A. Conway, Eds. Reading, MA: Addison-Wesley, 1980.
[24] D. L. Johannsen, "Our machine: A microcoded LSI processor," Display File 1826, Dept. Comp. Science, Caltech, Pasadena, CA, July 1978.
[25] R. W. Sherburne, M.G.H. Katevenis, D. A. Patterson, and C. H. Séquin, "Datapath design for RISC," in *Proc. Conf. on Adv. Research in VLSI* (MIT, Cambridge, MA), pp. 53–62, Jan. 1982.
[26] J. D. Warner, *Logical Construction of Programs*. New York: Van Nostrand, 1974.
[27] E. W. Dijkstra, *A Discipline of Programming*. Englewood Cliffs,

NJ: Prentice-Hall, 1976.

[28] D. Gries, "An illustration of current ideas on the derivation of correctness proofs and correct programs," *IEEE Trans. Software Eng.*, vol. SE-2, no. 4, pp. 238–244, Dec. 1976.

[29] C. Böhm and G. Jacopini, "Flow diagrams, turing machines and languages with only two formation rules," *Commun. ACM*, vol. 9, no. 5, pp. 366–371, May 1966.

[30] H. D. Mills, "Mathematical foundations for structured programming," IBM Tech. Rep. FSC 72-6012, Federal Syst. Div., Gaithersburg, MD, 1972.

[31] D. E. Knuth, "Structured programming with goto statements," *Computing Surveys*, vol. 6, no. 4, pp. 261–301, Dec. 1974.

[32] F. P. Brooks, Jr., *The Mythical Man-Month*. Reading, MA: Addison-Wesley, 1975.

[33] E. W. Dijkstra, "The humble programmer," *Commun. ACM*, vol. 15, no. 10, pp. 859–866, Oct. 1972.

[34] T. Teitelbaum and T. Reps, "The Cornell program synthesizer: A syntax-directed programming environment," *Commun. ACM*, vol. 24, no. 9, pp. 563–573, Sept. 1981.

[35] M. Linton, "A debugger for the Berkeley Pascal system," Master's Report, U.C. Berkeley, June 1981.

[36] S. Gutz, A. I. Wasserman, and M. J. Spier, "Personal development systems for the professional programmer," *Computer*, vol. 14, no. 4, pp. 45–53, Apr. 1981.

[37] D. Hightower and F. Alexander, "A mature I^2L/STL gate array layout system," in *Dig. Papers, COMPCON*, pp. 149–155, Feb. 1980.

[38] D. L. Parnas, "The use of precise specifications in the development of software," in *Information Processing 77 (Proc. IFIP Congress)*. Amsterdam, The Netherlands: North Holland, 1977, pp. 861–867.

[39] G. J. Myers, *The Art of Software Testing*. New York: Wiley, 1980.

[40] E. B. Eichelberger and T. W. Williams, "A logic design structure for LSI testability," *J. Des. Automat. Fault-Tolerant Comput.*, vol. 2, pp. 165–178, May 1978.

[41] D. A. Patterson and C. H. Séquin, "RISC I: A reduced instruction set VLSI computer," in *Proc. 8th Int. Symp. on Computer Architecture* (Minneapolis, MN), pp. 443–457, May 1981.

[42] W. A. Wulf, "Compilers and computer architecture," *Computer*, vol. 14, no. 7, pp. 41–47, July 1981.

[43] A. B. Glaser and G. E. Subak-Sharpe, "Failure, reliability and yield of integrated circuits," in *Integrated Circuit Engineering*. Reading, MA: Addison-Wesley, 1978, pp. 746–799.

[44] R. Ayres, "Silicon compilation—Hierarchical use of PLAs," in *Proc. Caltech Conf. on VLSI* (Pasadena, CA), pp. 311–326, Jan. 1979.

[45] S. S. Eaton, D. Wooton, W. Slemmer, and J. Brady, "Circuit advances propel 64-k RAM across the 100 ns barrier," *Electronics*, vol. 55, no. 6, pp. 132–136, Mar. 24, 1982.

[46] W. A. Wulf, "Keynote address," presented at the Symp. on Arch. Supp. for Prog. Lang. and Operat. Syst., Palo Alto, CA, Mar. 1982.

[47] ——, "Trends in the design and implementation of programming languages," *Computer*, vol. 13, no. 1, pp. 14–25, Jan. 1980.

[48] M. Stefik, D. G. Bobrow, A. Bell, H. Brown, L. Conway, and C. Tong, "The partitioning of concerns in digital systems design," in *Proc. Conf. on Adv. Research in VLSI* (MIT, Cambridge, MA), pp. 43–52, Jan. 1982.

[49] M. Tucker and L. Scheffer, "A constrained design methodology for VLSI," *VLSI Des.*, vol. 3, no. 3, pp. 60–65, May 1982.

[50] D. T. Fitzpatrick, J. K. Foderaro, M.G.H. Katevenis, H. A. Landman, D. A. Patterson, J. B. Peek, Z. Peshkess, C. H. Séquin, R. W. Sherburne, and K. S. VanDyke, "VLSI implementation of a reduced instruction set computer," in *Proc. CMU Conf. on VLSI Systems and Computations* (Pittsburgh, PA), pp. 327–336, Oct. 1981.

[51] M. E. Newell and D. T. Fitzpatrick, "Exploiting structure in integrated circuit design analysis," in *Proc. Conf. on Adv. Research in VLSI* (MIT, Cambridge, MA), pp. 84–92, Jan. 1982.

[52] L. K. Scheffer, "A methodology for improved verification on VLSI designs without loss of area," in *Proc. 2nd Caltech Conf. on VLSI* (Jan. 19–21, 1981).

[53] T. Whitney, "A hierarchical design analysis front end," in *Proc. VLSI81, Int. Conf. on Very Large Scale Integration* (Edinburgh, Scotland), pp. 217–225, 1981.

[54] S. C. Johnson, "Hierarchical design validation based on rectangles," in *Proc. Conf. on Adv. Research in VLSI* (MIT, Cambridge, MA), pp. 97–100, Jan. 1982.

[55] L. A. Conway, A. Bell, and M. E. Newell, "MPC79: A large-scale demonstration of a new way to create systems in silicon," *Lambda*, vol. 1, no. 2, pp. 10–19, 2nd quarter, 1980.

[56] B. Hon and C. H. Séquin, *Guide to LSI Implementation* (2nd

revised and extended edition), Xerox PARC, Palo Alto, CA, Jan. 1980.

[57] W. D. Jansen and D. G. Fairbairn, "The silicon foundry: Concepts and reality," *Lambda*, vol. 2, no. 1, pp. 16–26, 1st quarter, 1981.

[58] W. J. Haydamack, Public Lecture, University of California, Berkeley, Fall 1981.

[59] J. D. Williams, "STICKS—A graphical compiler for high level LSI design," in *AFIPS Conf. Proc., NCC*, vol. 47, pp. 289–295, 1978.

[60] A. Dunlop, "SLIP—Symbolic layout of integrated circuits with compaction," *Computer-Aided Des.*, vol. 10, pp. 387–391, Nov. 1978.

[61] M. Y. Hsueh and D. O. Pederson, "Computer-aided layout of LSI circuit building blocks," in *Proc. IEEE Int. Solid-State Circuits Conf.* (Tokyo, Japan), pp. 474–477, 1979.

[62] C. H. Séquin, "Pictures versus parentheses: Design methodologies of the 1980's," Panel Discussion at COMPCON, San Francisco, CA, Feb. 1982.

[63] A. I. Wasserman, "Automated development environments," *Computer*, vol. 14, pp. 7–10, Apr. 1981.

[64] B. W. Kernighan and J. R. Mashey, "The UNIX programming environment," *Computer*, vol. 14, no. 4, pp. 12–22, Apr. 1981.

[65] W. Teitelman and L. Masinter, "The INTERLISP programming environment," *Computer*, vol. 14, no. 4, pp. 25–33, Apr. 1981.

[66] A. I. Wasserman and S. Gutz, "The future of programming," *Comm. ACM*, vol. 25, no. 3, pp. 196–206, Mar. 1982.

[67] A. R. Newton, D. O. Pederson, A. L. Sangiovanni-Vincentelli, and C. H. Séquin, "Design aids for VLSI: The Berkeley perspective," *IEEE Trans. Circuits Syst.*, vol. CAS-28, no. 7, pp. 666–680, July 1981.

[68] S. R. Bourne, "UNIX time-sharing system: The UNIX shell," *Bell Syst. Tech. J.*, vol. 57, no. 6, pp. 1971–1990, Jul.–Aug. 1978.

[69] C. H. Séquin and A. R. Newton, "Description of STIF 1.0," in *Design Methodologies for VLSI*. Groningen, The Netherlands: Noordhoff, Jan. 1982, pp. 147–171.

[70] S. A. Ellis, K. H. Keller, A. R. Newton, D. O. Pederson, A. L. Sangiovanni-Vincentelli, and C. H. Séquin, "A symbolic layout design system," presented at Int. Symp. on Circuits and Systems, Rome, Italy, May 1982.

[71] A. K. Graham, "Software design: Breaking the bottleneck," *IEEE Spectrum*, vol. 19, no. 3, pp. 43–50, Mar. 1982.

[72] M. J. Rochkind, "The source code control system," *IEEE Trans. Software Eng.*, vol. SE-1, no. 4, pp. 364–370, Dec. 1975.

[73] E. H. Bersoff, V. D. Henderson, and S. G. Siegel, "Software configuration management: A tutorial," *Computer*, vol. 12, no. 1, pp. 6–14, Jan. 1979.

[74] G. M. Weinberg, *The Psychology of Computer Programming*. New York: Van Nostrand-Reinhold, 1971.

[75] L. A. Belady, "Evolved software for the 80's," *Computer*, vol. 12, no. 2, pp. 79–82, Feb. 1979.

[76] A. I. Wasserman and L. A. Belady *et al.*, "Software engineering: The turning point," *Computer*, vol. 11, no. 9, pp. 30–41, Sept. 1978.

[77] T. M. McWilliams, "Verification of timing constraints on large digital systems," in *Proc. 17th Design Automation Conf.* (Minneapolis, MN), pp. 139–147, June 1980.

[78] W. E. Cory and W. M. VanCleemput, "Development in verification and design correctness," in *Proc. 17th Design Automation Conf.* (Minneapolis, MN), pp. 156–164, June 1980.

[79] A. R. Newton, "The VLSI design challenge of the 80's," in *Proc. 17th Design Autom. Conf.*, pp. 343–344, June 1980.

[80] S. I. Feldman, "Make—A program for maintaining computer programs," *Software—Practice and Experience*, vol. 9, pp. 255–265, Apr. 1979.

[81] J. Grason and A. W. Nagle, "Digital test generation and design for testability," in *Proc. 17th Design Automation Conf.* (Minneapolis, MN), pp. 175–189, June 1980.

[82] P. Naur, "Proof of algorithms by general snapshot," *BIT*, vol. 6, pp. 310–316, 1966.

[83] R. Floyd, "Assigning meaning to programs," in *Proc. Symp. in Applied Mathematics*, vol. 19, pp. 19–32, American Math. Soc., Providence, RI, 1967.

[84] C.A.R. Hoare, "An axiomatic basis for computer programming," *Commun. ACM*, vol. 12, no. 10, pp. 576–583, Oct. 1969.

[85] R. DeMillo, R. Lipton, and A. J. Perlis, "Social processes and proofs of computer programs," *Commun. ACM*, vol. 22, no. 5, pp. 271–280, May 1979.

[86] M. Stefik, J. Aikins, R. Balzer, J. Benoit, L. Birnbaum, F. Hayes-Roth, and E. Sacerdoti, "The organization of expert systems: A perspective tutorial," Tech. Rep., Xerox PARC, Palo Alto, CA, Jan. 1982.

[87] C. A. Mead, "VLSI and technological innovation," Keynote Address, presented at the Caltech Conf. on VLSI, Pasadena, CA, Jan. 1979.

Miniaturization of Digital Si VLSI—Obstacles and Limits

OTTO G. FOLBERTH

I. INTRODUCTION

IT was 25 years ago that this journal[1] made its appearance as a periodical. In that same year, integrated circuits were conceived, but hardly anyone realized at that time how vastly they would affect the further evolution of digital electronics. Integrated circuits—the cornerstone of present-day microelectronics—have proliferated during the past 25 years with an astonishing speed into every part of the globe.

The major driving force of this development was the continuously advancing miniaturization of component functions, which, in turn, permitted an ever-increasing number of components to be accommodated on an ever-diminishing area of silicon. Simultaneously, it was possible to practically improve all the other essential properties of electronic circuits by orders of magnitude. In addition to the already mentioned integration density (packing density), such improvements were made with regard to the power dissipation, the performance, the reliability, and—last but not least—the cost. All of this combined led to an ever-increasing technological and economical application of electronic devices, and hence to the frequently invoked "third industrial revolution."

This evolution was largely synergetical: each advance in miniaturization led to improved systems, which in turn stimulated new applications and created new markets. Such achievements justified increased efforts towards further miniaturization and improved circuits, and so on [1].

During this evolution, however, there were occasionally delays and setbacks: at every new stage of miniaturization, physical and technological effects and phenomena were encountered, which either had been previously unknown or could be neglected as being insignificant and which posed—at least temporarily—obstacles to further progress. Only by increased and dedicated research and development efforts, novel and feasible—and superior—solutions could be accomplished, which, in turn, enabled the development of superior systems.

In a straightforward manner it is easy to imagine that this tendency is going to continue: with each newly achieved level of miniaturization, further effects and phenomena will pop up, which have either been unknown or could be neglected as insignificant at larger dimensions, but which have suddenly become of decisive importance at the new miniaturization level. One can further visualize that these obstacles are going to become higher—and consequently more difficult to overcome—the closer one gets to the ultimate limitations of the technology.

Obstacles of this kind will be discussed in more detail in Section III. The following sections will treat the fundamental limitations of the digital silicon VLSI. The final section will deal with some perspectives and conclusions. To begin with,

however, the present state-of-the-art and the current major problems and trends will be outlined briefly.

II. STATE-OF-THE-ART AND DEVELOPMENT TRENDS

At present, generally speaking, the technology of integrated electronics finds itself at the beginning of the VLSI (very large-scale integration) era. The expression VLSI is used for integration levels exceeding several thousand circuits per chip. Whether or not it will become generally acceptable and commonly agreeable to introduce a further stage of advancement, i.e., ULSI (ultimate large-scale integration) remains to be seen. If so, the integration levels as described in Section IV would have to be classified as ULSI.

Today, silicon chips are produced almost exclusively in the so-called planar technology with the aim of photolithographic processes. Routinely, this enables the mastering of the smallest element sizes of 3 μm with fairly good yields. For chip sizes of up to 50 mm^2, it is possible to achieve integration levels of approximately 10^5 circuits per chip. (This holds predominantly for memory chips and microprocessors, which require relatively few contact pads).

Presently, improved optical equipment for smaller dimensions is being introduced by most manufacturers. In order to enhance the resolution, either projection with ultraviolet light is being used and/or the original 1:1 projection of the mask onto the entire wafer is being replaced by a reducing projection of a mask with larger dimension onto partial fields of the wafer, whereby field after field is sequentially exposed step-by-step. (direct-step-on-wafer-method) [2]. By means of such improved photolithographic processes, structural elements with minimal linear dimensions of little more than 1 μm can be resolved reproducibly. For chip sizes of approximately 70 mm^2, it is thus possible to obtain integration levels of up to 10^6 circuits per chip. Such chips will reach the production stage within the next few years.

As has already happened at former points in time in the history of microelectronics, several major and minor obstacles are impeding further development. Among others, these are the physical effects caused by the miniaturization of the components per se [3]. Miniaturization means that perimeter effects increase relatively with regard to surface effects and that surface effects increase compared to volume effects. The lower dimension effects are often unwanted perturbational "parasitic" effects of the wanted—functional—higher dimension effects. Such parasitic effects, which can be neglected at larger dimensions, have a tendency to become of importance when the dimensions are reduced, and thus they impede the feasibility of the functional elements. Typical effects of this kind are the well-known short-channel and narrow-channel effects in MOSFET's. By means of appropriate scaling rules, however, the deteriorating influences of such effects can be

The author is with IBM Deutschland GmbH, Stuttgart, Germany.
[1]This paper was originally published in the 25th anniversary issue of *Elektronische Rechenanlagen*.

A revised version of a paper published in German in *Elektronische Rechenanlagen*, vol. 25, no. 6, pp. 45–55, 1983.
Printed with permission of R. Oldunburg Verlag GmbH.

overcome (partially or completely) [4]. Overall, the prevailing expert opinion says that it should be possible to master a 0.5 μm technology around 1990 (with minimal effective channel lengths for MOSFET's of approximately 0.25 μm), which should enable the development and production of chips of about 1 cm^2 effective chip area containing several million circuits.

However, such an evolution encounters—among others—four major obstacles, which should be surmountable by means of dedicated efforts. The following section will deal with these obstacles.

III. THE FOUR MAJOR OBSTACLES TO THE FURTHER EVOLUTION OF VLSI

A. Technology

As already pointed out, it will be possible to achieve resolutions for a 1 μm technology with modern photolithographic processes. For smaller structural elements, light (including invisible UV light) is too "coarse" a tool. There are, however, various types of radiation with shorter wavelengths—and hence more delicate tools—on hand, namely X-, electron, and ionic rays. Very likely it will be able to achieve resolution improvements of at least one further order of magnitude by means of processes based on such rays, i.e., a lithography for smallest linear dimensions of approximately 0.1 μm seems to be achievable. Each of the three above mentioned types of radiation (including the corresponding specific resist system) has its typical advantages and disadvantages [5]. Which one will eventually succeed (may be in combination with others) remains to be seen.

The problems of the "overlay" should not be underestimated. Not only must the patterns of one layer be of high precision, but the following lithographic steps (in certain instances up to 20 and more!) must match with each other at every part of the silicon wafer too. This will necessitate sophisticated self-registration and self-correction schemes, which require substantial electronic control.

The structural transfer of the lithographically created patterns into the silicon and into the conducting and insulating layers on top of the silicon surface is a further major problem for such extreme miniaturization levels. Only with well-tuned and precisely controlled modern methods, like ion implantation, dry-etching, low-temperature deposition, and oxydation etc., may it become possible to produce such minute structures in a reproducible manner. Substantial efforts in equipment engineering will be a prerequisite for the successful mastering of these problems.

Although major, these technological obstacles are probably not insurmountable, since on a large, world-wide scale, concentrated and dedicated efforts with major investments of manpower, machinery, and capital are being applied to further improve this technology.

B. Complexity of VLSI-Chip Design

The expenditures for VLSI design have increased at an alarming rate. High as this rate is, however, it is less than the rate with which the corresponding integration level has increased. According to G. E. Moore [6], the integration level has doubled every $1\frac{1}{3}$ year, while the expenditures for chip layout and chip design have doubled only every $2\frac{2}{3}$ years, i.e., with only about half of that rate ("Moore's law no. 2") [7]. This means that although the design expenditures *per circuit* are declining, these expenditures *per chip* are still increasing exponentially. This reduction of the design costs (per circuit) was only achievable by applying economizing design tools and design principles. In order to keep these costs at a bearable level, however, further substantial efforts are required in the field.

Design tools comprise, in particular, various CAD programs for automatic or semiautomatic design [8]. Among others, these include programs for analysis, simulation, modeling, design, checking, placement, wiring, the generation of mask sets, test programs, documentation, etc. All this is done with the aim of computers. It is therefore obvious that the development of future electronics depends largely on the efficient application of the presently available electronics. In other words, the future equipment generation is based on the utilization of the available generation. In the past, mainly generic ("general-purpose") computers with specifically developed programs were used for this purpose. There are indications, however, that—at least in some CAD applications, especially for simulation and checking programs and the tedious placement and routing programs—the growing chip complexity requires excessive computing power. Possible solutions for this problem, on which several competence centers are working with high priority, is the conception, construction, and operation of special computers (or computer networks), which—due to their specialization—will be able to achieve processing efficiencies that are higher by several order of magnitude (compared to solutions which apply general-purpose hardware). There are indications that such special-purpose hardware will enable the mastering of VLSI chip designs with higher integration levels and with increased complexity, by one or more orders of magnitude.

In order to facilitate the design task and lower the costs, it is helpful to maximize the utilization of modular and hierarchical design methods. For a modular multiple application of the same "cell," only the design of *one* cell and its automatic repetitive placement is required. This modular design principle, of course, is particularly well suited for memories, since they have a natural "cellular" structure. But logic circuits, too, can be built modularly. The so-called "gate arrays" are popular examples of this kind.

The structuring and partitioning of complex networks into several hierarchic levels ("gates," "cells," "blocks," "macros") simplifies the design effort considerably. The design and the structuring of the various hierarchic levels are simpler and less complex compared to the unpartitioned treatment of the system as a whole. In most cases, the hierarchic structuring is done heuristically, refraining thereby from a complete optimization of the whole system, in favor of a tradeoff with regard to a considerable reduction in design effort. Such suboptimizations are quite often reasonable compromises.

C. The Testing of VLSI Chips

Analogous to the design expenditures for VLSI chips, which increase with increasing integration levels, the testing expenditures, too, increase exponentially. Therefore, the attempt to test VLSI chips exhaustively became illusory and impractible long ago. The customary test strategies, therefore, try to obtain maximum detection, localization, and identification of faults by applying a combination of as few as possible and as powerful as possible complementary individual tests.

With increasing integration levels, the localization of faults becomes more and more difficult: an ever-increasing number of circuits can no longer be directly accessed via the test probes, since they are embedded into other circuits and therefore are only indirectly connectable with probes. Such embedded circuits can neither be set individually by means of input signals, nor can they be observed separately via output signals. The modular concept, which proves beneficial for the design of VLSI chips, offers solutions for this problem, too: the input and output states of embedded modular units are duplicated in additionally built-in storage units. By reorganizing these additional storage cells as shift registers, characteristic states of the modular unit can be transferred sequentially to special test pads so that the units now become testable. This method, however, requires additional circuits (which have no functional use), and consequently an increased silicon area. All in all, this leads to a lower effective integration density, in tradeoff for an improved testability, which is very often a reasonable compromise, too.

With an appropriate layout, such additional circuits may be used for diagnostic purposes as well, preventively, or for actual circuit failures during regular operations. Furthermore, the partitioning of VLSI networks into smaller decoupled modular units will facilitate engineering changes, since such impending changes do not necessarily affect the entire network, but may be confinable to one or a few of the subunits.

"Intelligent" VLSI chips (particularly microprocessors) are increasingly equipped with self-testing functions. Test programs executed within fractions of a second during switch-on (or during intermissions of normal operations), are loaded in a part of the usual ROM's. Such programs test the functionality of the most important units, such as memories, registers, processors, etc. Most of the frequent errors will be discovered and displayed automatically. On the other hand, a self-test with no errors found is a high-probability indication for a fully functional unit.

The test strategy for VLSI chips should already be determined during the design stage and, if necessary, provision must be made for specific additional circuits to facilitate and improve the testing. In addition to the method described above, there are further similar techniques, which are described elsewhere in this volume [9].

Design and testability are closely interrelated. With a suitable and carefully structured design, the mastering of the testing problems should be possible even for higher integration levels. Increased sophistication and increased expenditures, however, will become mandatory.

D. Economic Considerations

The phenomenal success of microelectronics is based on the extreme cost reduction for the individual functions. Such low-cost functions, however, are available only if used in large quantities in integrated chips and if these chips can be mass produced and mass marketed. The individual discrete transistor has *not* seen such a dramatic cost reduction.

In this context, occasionally the following misleading comparison can be found in newspapers and magazines: "If the automobile industry had experienced progress in technology similar to the computer industry, a Volkswagen would cost only 5 deutsche marks." More appropriately, however, this comparison should read: "A Volkswagen would cost only 5 deutsche marks, provided that one purchased 10 000 of them at a time, with all of them rigidly coupled together, each one providing room for midgets only." Some comparisons just have a tendency to limp!

Increasing integration levels mean decreasing manufacturing costs per function in spite of slightly increasing manufacturing costs per chip, which become larger and more complex. In addition, the progress in miniaturization requires more elaborate and hence more expensive manufacturing equipment. Consequently, these overall increasing manufacturing costs per chip can only be amortized with a large-scale production series.

Furthermore, development costs no longer play a minor role in the whole cost-pictures as in the old days of small-scale integration. At lower integration levels the development costs were of little importance and could be covered by minor additions to the manufacturing costs. The advent of VLSI has changed the situation significantly: due to the trend described in Sections III-B and III-C, the development costs increase rapidly and can no longer be considered as just a small correction to the overall expenses—particularly not for the small production series. With increasing integration levels, these expenditures—even with highly automated processing—will eventually become so large that a sound profitability is harder and harder to achieve. This trend will lead to a slowdown of the evolution, i.e., the time between the emergence of new chip families is being stretched, a tendency which is already apparent today.

Such overall enormous expenditures, which will only be profitable in the case of huge quantities of marketable chips, lead to a concentration within the semiconductor industry, since only very few companies or associations, well provided with capital, will be able to muster such extraordinary means. In addition, this leads to an increased trend towards "vertical integration": major systems manufacturers are establishing their own component development and manufacturing facilities for the population of their system products. At the same time, some of these companies market these components directly in the component marketplace. Particularly, the major Japanese electronics companies fit into this pattern.

From this economical viewpoint it is obvious that only "front-end electronics" for leading edge equipment can afford to utilize advanced technologies. The larger chunk of "everyday" or "utility" electronics will be based more on low-cost components of more mature development stages produced in largely depreciated, less advanced, manufacturing facilities. Front-end electronics of today will eventually become everyday electronics of tomorrow. The state-of-the-art is progressing for both branches; the relative distance, however, may remain about the same, for quite some time to come.

While chip technology is influenced by regular cyclical economic trends, it still remains one of the most expansive growth industries. Although the obstacles described here are serious and can only be overcome with great effort, they probably do not constitute insurmountable barriers. The present growth trend—perhaps in a somewhat subdued form—is most certainly going to continue until, at least, the turn of the millenium.

IV. LIMITATIONS OF DIGITAL ELECTRONICS

The obstacles discussed in Section III are practical difficulties, but they are not fundamental limitations. It goes without saying, however, that there are "hard" physical limits, indeed, which cannot be overcome, even with unlimited means. Eventually, when these limits are reached, the evolution of the silicon chip technology will come to an end. If everything else with less fundamental character is sorted out, there remain essentially three limitations of this kind: geometrical limitations; thermal limitations; signal propagation limitations. These limits will be discussed subsequently, including their interdependencies and their significance for the "ultimate" silicon chip technology.

An attempt will be made to quantify these limits as far as possible. It should be realized, however, that in most cases only rough estimates can be given.

A. Geometrical Limitations

The progress of miniaturization will reduce the dimensions of components further and further, as far as they can be shaped by the manufacturing process. In addition to such shapable elements there are, however, critical dimensions, which will remain essentially unaffected by such measures. This holds particularly for the thickness of depletion layers of p-n junctions, which are essential entities for every semiconductor device, contributing decisively to their function. The thickness of those depletion layers (order of magnitude: 0.03 μm) cannot be influenced by lithographic or other production methods. Eventually, the miniaturization process will be limited by these "nonscalable" dimensions, which lastly, will determine the minimum dimensions of ultraminiaturized devices.

The area requirement of transistors for which, for the reasons stated above, no further size reduction is possible—even with the most sophisticated production methods—is a few μm^2 [10]. For reasons of simplicity, the following estimation will be performed with a specific value for the minimal transistor size— namely, 2 μm^2—realizing that this figure is only a rough estimate and that it might be somewhat smaller for ultimate MOSFET's and somewhat larger for ultimate bipolar transistors.

An elementary logic gate with a fanout of about 4 requires the area of approximately two transistors, provided that area-saving "super-integrated" structures are used (e.g., I^2L, polysilicon resistors above active elements, "stacked" CMOS gates, etc.). This would result in a maximum geometrical integration density of $D_{max} = 2.5 \times 10^7$ gates/cm^2 [11]. The present state-of-the-art is about 2.5 $\times$ 10^5 gates/cm^2; therefore, a further increase of the integration density of approximately two orders of magnitude is possible before this fundamental limit has been reached. Some qualifying remarks, however, are in order at this point.

1) VLSI chips only rarely contain exclusively logic circuits. Generally, they are made up of circuits of various types. This especially holds for microprocessors. It is customary and widely accepted, however, to express the area requirement for all circuits in "equivalent gates." For every specific circuit family, each particular circuit is characterized by a numerical value which represents the number of elementary logic gates for which the area requirement is equivalent to that of the respective circuit.

2) Such a procedure is particularly suitable for assessing the area requirement of memory circuits, which are used in large quantities and which are of major significance in all digital systems. For static storage cells (flip-flops), which consist essentially of two cross-coupled inverters, the same area requirement as for one logic gate (maybe somewhat more) can be assumed. For the largely used dynamic storage cells, however, which consist essentially of a capacitance and a "valve" transistor, the area requirement is less, about one-third to one-half of an elementary gate. The further miniaturization of dynamic cells, however, encounters additional specific problems, which are caused by the radiation sensitivity of the dynamically (i.e., capacitively) stored information. Such "soft errors" result from the cosmic radiation or from the α-radiation of minute traces of radioactive impurities in the materials in-

volved. This sensitivity increases more than proportionally with increasing miniaturization. In addition, the valve function of the transistors deteriorates with increasing miniaturization so that refreshing operations become impractical because they would have to be carried out too often. It is therefore assumed that with further miniaturization the present density advantage of dynamic cells over static cells will diminish or even disappear. Therefore, very roughly, the maximum ultimate integration density of memory circuits may be estimated to about 2.5 $\times$ 10^7 bits/cm^2, the same numerical value as for logic gates.

3) In most designs, the wirability of the densely packed devices impairs the practically achievable integration density. Different results may be obtained, depending on layout, system function, wiring mechanism, wiring algorithm (e.g., automatic or "manual" wiring, respectively), etc. In view of the discussion of final limits, however, it may be justified to assume that a multitude of wiring layers will be available on the chip surface, so that these wiring constraints can be neglected. It is understood, however, that this is a "best case" assumption and that in all practical cases some fraction of the circuits will remain nonwirable.

4) Usually, input and output circuits (receiving and driving circuits) cannot be designed with minimum dimensions. This holds particularly true for off-chip drivers, which have to produce higher currents. Therefore, the area requirement of such circuits is frequently overproportional higher and must be considered in the layout accordingly. Overall, of course, this leads to a reduction in the theoretically possible maximum integration density also, so that the value given here of 2.5 $\times$ 10^7 circuits/cm^2 must be considered as an upper limit, indeed.

B. Thermal Limitations

The ohmic heat generated at the operation of electronic circuits must be removed in order to prevent undue overheating of the hardware. With forced air cooling, about 2 W/cm^2 thermal power can be removed from planar chips, without exceeding the maximal critical temperature of about 100°C. With the means of "cold plates" and similar more elaborate cooling arrangements, up to about 10 W/cm^2 can be removed, particularly if the heat is carried away from the primary cooling elements by streaming (precooled) water. Presently, techniques of this type are customary for larger mainframe computers. With boiling liquids, about 20 W/cm^2 may be removed from the chip surface [12].

Recently, a new scheme was proposed and experimentally proven using forced liquid cooling with a liquid streaming along microfins etched directly into the backside of chips [13]. This scheme would allow removal of up to 1000 W/cm^2. It would be a substantial improvement over the present state-of-the-art and could boost the performance of future computers significantly.

C. Interdependence of Integration Density, Performance, and Power Dissipation

It is convenient to characterize the performance of digital circuits with a figure of merit, the so-called power delay product: the smaller this figure is, the higher the switching speed is and the lower the power dissipation of the circuits is. Within certain limits, characteristic for each circuit family, it is possible to "drive" the circuits more or less hard; i.e., they can be operated slower at lower power and faster at higher power. Furthermore, there are typical application ranges for the various families; e.g., bipolar circuits are customary in the high-speed range, while for lower power dissipation (and consequently lower speed), MOSFET circuits are very popular.

For state-of-the-art circuits this figure of merit is on the order of

$$K = P \cdot t_d = 5 \times 10^{-13} \text{ [W} \cdot \text{s/circuit]}$$

with P = power dissipation per circuit and t_d = signal delay time per logic step.

In order to minimize K (and thereby maximize the performance), the capacitances of the circuits (including the wiring capacitances) which are charged and discharged during the switching operations should be made as small as possible. Furthermore, the signal level should be reduced as much as possible [11]. A lower limit for the signal level is given by the requirement for noise immunity; it must be distinctly above the thermal noise of about 25 mV at room temperature.

Approximations for ultraminiaturized circuits [11], [14] reveal a minimum power delay product of approximately

$$K_{min} = 5 \times 10^{-16} \text{ [W} \cdot \text{s/circuit]}.$$

This means an improvement of about three orders of magnitude over the present state-of-the-art, but barely two orders over best laboratory results [15].

While the power delay product is a rather useful figure of merit for individual circuits, it is, unfortunately, less useful for the characterization of logic networks comprising a multitude of circuits. With increasing integration levels (circuit per chip), the properties of the wiring determine more and more the performance of the network, while the switching properties of the individual circuits become of lesser and lesser importance [24], [25].

For moderate integration levels it has become customary to modify the power delay product by adding the wiring capacities to the device capacities, resulting in an overall increased (less favorable) power delay figure [16].

Estimations of this kind yield useful results as long as the operation can be described essentially as the charging and discharging of capacitances through resistive lines. In other words, as long as a "short-line" RC approach is applicable. Such an approach is reasonable as long as the pulse length is large compared to the wire length, which means large compared to the chip dimensions. The pulse length, on the other hand, depends on the internal transistor switching time t_i. In general, the shortest possible pulse requires several time elements t_i, say 5. Consequently, an RC line has the length of such a pulse if its time constant $t_{RC} = 2.3 \times RC$ equals $5 \cdot t_i$. Assuming state-of-the-art ground rules and switching times, the pulse lengths—according to the above given approximation—are on the order of 10 cm.

This means present-day chips are small compared to the pulse lengths, and the usual RC calculations and approximations (including the modified power delay product) are, therefore, justified and will yield meaningful and useful results.

This situation will change, however, if the miniaturization and the integration density progress: assuming an "ultimate technology" with ultraminiaturized fast devices and ultradense chips with 0.1 μm ground rules and t_i = 100 ps, the same approximation scheme as before leads to pulse lengths in the order of 0.03 cm. This is considerably smaller than the chip dimensions (which will certainly even increase over the presently usual ones), and therefore a "short-line" (RC) approach yields grossly misleading and unacceptable (too pessimistic) results. This holds especially for the power delay product—

based essentially on RC models—which will loose its usefulness as a figure of merit for the characterization of such large and ultradense logic networks [17].

D. The Transmission-Line Model

To overcome this problem, it is advisable to restart with approximations "from the other end," so to say. This means, to consider the wiring as the *essential* part of the network and to add the switching elements as *small corrections* later on, if needed. In this alternative approach, the wiring is considered as being composed of "long lines" and the signal propagation on these long lines is treated with the transmission-line theory [18], [19]. It is further assumed that on those hypothetical ultradense chips all long signal-lines are materialized in upper metallization layers with nearly ideal transmission-line properties, while only the short lines, especially for intracircuit connections, are realized within lower levels, especially first-level metal lines. (Please remember that we assumed that a multitude of wiring layers is available on the chip surface).

The signal propagation time on the short lines is relatively short, in spite of the fact that the signal propagation velocity is low (about 10^9 cm/s), due to the so-called "slow wave mode" operation [18]. The signal propagation times on the long signal-lines are longer, in spite of the fact that the signals travel in the fast TEM-mode with about 10^{10} cm/s, since these lines are much longer. Therefore, for the estimation of the clock frequency and cycle time of digital systems, these longer propagation times are of significance.

Assuming a synchronous operation of the network, the so-called "Wallmark synchronization condition" [19] applies, which requires that all pulses at every fan-in point of the network must be in phase within one tenth of the cycle time t_c (t_c = $1/f_c$, with f_c being the clock frequency of the system). Hence, the longest signal propagation time (and consequently the longest line) determines the maximum clock frequency of the network. If no design restrictions are imposed, the longest line L_{max} is usually a connection across the entire chip, for example from the lower left corner to the upper right corner. Accordingly, the maximal area of a square chip would be $F_{max} = L_{max}^2/4$, and hence, the maximum integration level[2] $I_{max} = D_{max} \times F_{max}$. Fig. 1 shows these functional dependencies for a meaningful parameter range for a maximal integration density of $D_{max} = 2.5 \times 10^7$ gates/cm^2 and a signal propagation time (on the "long lines") of $v_s = 1 \times 10^{10}$ cm/s. The corresponding maximum switching time t_{max} is marked on the abscissa, too. This is the longest tolerable switching time, which the circuits may have in order to be compatible with the corresponding clock frequencies. This switching time must not exceed $t_{max} = 1/5f_{max}$, otherwise this time factor as such would limit the clock frequency. (This argument is in essence the same as the one used earlier for the approximation of the pulse lengths).

From Fig. 1 it can be seen, for instance, that for a chip size of 1 cm^2 the upper frequency limit for synchronous operations is $f_{max} = 5 \times 10^8$ Hz. Higher clock frequencies are only possible with shorter lines, i.e., smaller chips. For example, an operation of 1 GHz is only compatible with chips that are smaller than 0.25 cm^2, corresponding to a maximum of 6.25 $\times$ 10^6 gates/chip; an operation of 10 GHz is only compatible with chips that are smaller than 0.25 mm^2, corresponding to a

---

[2]Please note the different definitions: integration density D: circuits/cm^2; integration level I: circuits/chip.

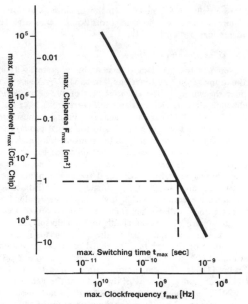

Fig. 1. Maximal integration level as a function of the maximal clock frequency for ultraminiaturized logic chips.

maximum of 6.25×10^4 gates/chip. In these cases, the internal transistor switching times should be shorter than 200 ps and 20 ps, respectively. This requirement will probably pose no serious problem for ultraminiaturized transistors, since their switching times may be on the order of a few picoseconds [11].

Consequently, it looks fairly appropriate and meaningful to neglect—in a first approximation—the switching properties of the switching elements altogether since for this "ultimate technology" the performance of digital chip networks will be determined essentially by the lines rather than by the switching elements themselves.

E. The Power Delay Relation for "Ultimate" Chips

It was pointed out earlier that circuits can be switched faster, if harder driven, i.e., by using higher currents and hence, a higher power dissipation (see Section IV-C). In the case of RC models, this behavior is reflected in the linear relationship of a constant power delay product. It can reasonably be assumed that a similar relation may also exist in the regime of the transmission-line models (at least up to f_{max}). The classic power delay product, however, is no longer applicable as explained in Section IV-C.

Here, again, a "global approach" [20] seems more appropriate and might be more suitable for ultraminiaturized transistors and ultradense chips. In this approach, the maximum power dissipation per gate P is related to the maximum power dissipation density Q and the cycle time t_c by the equation

$$P \times t_c^2 = \frac{(\Lambda V^2)^2}{Q}.$$

In this equation V is the voltage swing and $\Lambda \approx 10^{-10}$ F/cm is an entity related to the dielectric constant of the free space ϵ_0, but about 10^3 times larger. Unfortunately, this approach is only a rough estimate due to a fairly large uncertainty of Λ and

a strong dependency from V (fourth power) so that small deviations in the assumption of the minimum voltage swing have great effects. The numerical value assumed for Λ in [20] seems reasonable as far as the order of magnitude is concerned, but the value for V (i.e., $V = 1$ V) does seem rather high. A more appropriate value should be on the order of $V = 0.4$ V [14], [21].

Analogous to the power delay product, the above equation may be considered as the definition of a figure of merit, too, with $P \times t_c^2$ = constant and $(\Lambda V^2)^2/Q$ as the respective figure of merit.

Again, power delay tradeoffs can be accomplished by varying the impedance of the circuits and networks in a similar manner as customary with the "constant power delay approach." The performance, however, no longer increases linearly with the increasing power—as in the case of the validity of a constant power delay product—but slower, namely with f_c (or $1/t_c$) proportional to $\sqrt{P}$.

Without analyzing this relationship in detail, there is, nevertheless, some plausibility for such a "less than linear" increase of the performance as a function of power: in order to drive harder one needs lower impedencies; these are only achievable with larger cross sections and therefore lower integration densities; this means larger capacities, which, in turn, mean even more current (power) for charging and discharging. This extra power does not contribute to the performance improvement. Overall, a f_c proportional to $\sqrt{P}$ relation looks plausible and can be justified more rigorously as described here [20]. Basically responsible for this less favorable tradeoff is the "wrong" scaling of the resistivities, i.e., the fact that the overall resistivity of a network increases with decreasing dimensions [18], [22]. This is the well-known "resistivity problem of microelectronics."

F. Interdependency of the Various Limitations

The so far listed and discussed limitations are shown in consolidated form in Figs. 2 and 3 as power delay density diagrams. These diagrams are composed and are to be read analogously to the customary power delay representations:

• The performance is marked on the horizontal axis, with increasing clock frequency, i.e., decreasing switching delays (cycle times) towards the left (as in Fig. 1).

• The power dissipation per circuit (P) is marked on the vertical axis, with higher power dissipations in the upper portion and lower power dissipations in the lower portion.

• Therefore, power delay figures corresponding to the state-of-the-art are located in the upper right portion of the diagram, with improvements pointing towards the lower left corner.

• The maximal—thermally limited—integration density is

$$D_{th} = Q/P \text{ [Gates/cm}^2\text{]}$$

with Q the maximal power density according to Section IV-B and P the power dissipation per gate, as marked on the vertical axis. Therefore, the thermally limited maximal integration density D_{th} can be marked on the same axis as P, with higher densities pointing down and lower densities pointing up. The product of two figures (each one from the two different scales, but taken from the same point of the axis) is then always Q.

• In Fig. 2, a value of 20 W/cm^2 is used for Q (corresponding to cooling with boiling liquids); in Fig. 3, Q has been selected as 1000 W/cm^2, corresponding to a forced liquid cooling with microfins on the backside of the chips (see Section IV-B).

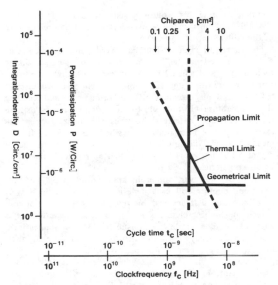

Fig. 2. Power delay density diagram (for power dissipation density $Q = 20$ W/cm^2).

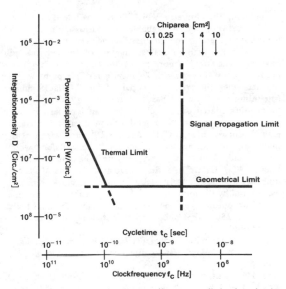

Fig. 3. Power delay density diagram (for power dissipation density $Q = 1000$ W/cm^2).

• By lowering P (the power dissipation per gate), the thermally limited integration density will increase, but only up to the geometrically limited integration density $D_{\max} = 2.5 \times 10^7$ gates/cm^2. This is a "hard" limit, independent of thermal effects, and it is represented in Figs. 2 and 3 by a horizontal straight line.

• As pointed out previously (Section IV-D), the performance limit is essentially determined by the signal propagation times and is independent of the integration density and of the power dissipation, but dependent on the length of the longest signal line, and therefore on the chip size. Hence, this limit is represented by a straight vertical line in the power delay density diagrams. In Figs. 2 and 3, respectively, this limit is marked for a 1 cm^2 sized chip. This line moves to the left (higher frequencies) for smaller chips and to the right (lower frequencies) for larger chips. For some selected chip sizes, the position of this vertical line is indicated by arrows.

• The thermally limited power delay relation is of the form $P/f_c^2 =$ constant (see Section IV-E). Therefore, in the double logarithmic power delay diagrams this relation is a straight line with an inclination of 116.5° (a constant power delay product would have a 135° inclination). The corresponding lines marked in Figs. 2 and 3 represent the limits according to the approximations given in Section IV-E.

In the case of $Q = 20$ W/cm^2, a 1 cm^2 sized chip will be limited in various regions by different effects:

• At low integration densities and high power dissipation per gate, the performance is limited by signal propagation delays. This holds, of course, only if the transistors per se are ultraminiaturized (with very short switching times t_i) and the low integration density is due to an artificial "thinning out." Should, however, the low integration density occur due to an obsolete technology with large, relatively slow transistors, then these slow switching elements themselves are the determining elements for the achievable switching speeds, and hence, the

classic relationship of the standard constant power delay product is naturally applicable.

• For medium densities and medium power dissipation per gate, the equation $P/f_c^2 =$ constant, i.e., the thermal limit becomes the governing relation. This range is larger for smaller chips and smaller for larger chips; it increases—will move towards the upper right—for inefficient cooling, i.e., with lower values for the power dissipation density Q.

• At 2.5×10^7 gates/cm^2 the geometrical density limit is reached forming a solid limit regardless of other parameters.

Further progress in cooling techniques (e.g., forced liquid cooling) may shift the maximal power dissipation density to, say, 1000 W/cm^2 (Section IV-B). Accordingly, the thermal limit shifts to the left in the diagram and—for the same integration densities—the maximum power dissipation per gate is higher. This means that the two scales of the vertical axis have to be shifted with regard to each other. In such cases, the geometrical limitations and, even more so, the propagation delay limitations will become more predominant and will pose stringent limits for future VLSI circuits operated under such conditions.

V. SYSTEM ASPECTS

With increasing integration densities, subsystems and even entire systems fit on a chip (microprocessors). In the not too distant future, this will become possible even for medium and larger mainframe computers.

The efficiency of computers—measured, for example in MIPS (million instructions per second)—is usually enhanced by adding more hardware, providing them with functions for simultaneous ("pipelining") and parallel processing. In addition, ever faster circuits will be used in order to increase the clock frequencies. Once, however, the signal propagation delay times become essential for the determination of the processing speed, a further increase of the clock frequency can only be achieved by reducing the chip size, which, in turn, will lead to a reduction in the number of available circuits (assuming that the maximum integration density has been achieved).

Under these assumptions, an increase of the network will have positive effects (more parallelism, more pipelining) *and* negative ones (lower clock frequencies). This point will be reached when the synchronous part of a mainframe computer (including the "internal part" of the memory hierarchy) can be accommodated on one chip. Such an internal computer complex may consist of several million circuits (equivalent gates). For example, a CPU of 6.25×10^6 circuits/chip at the maximum integration density of 2.5×10^7 circuits/cm^2 would fit on a chip of 0.25 cm^2 and may have a maximum clock frequency of 1 GHz. In a first approximation, the MIPS of a uniprocessor can be derived by dividing the clock frequency by 10^6 and by the number of cycles per instruction. Assuming, for instance, four cycles per instruction, such a CPU may therefore have 250 MIPS, about ten times the performance of today's "jumbos."

In order to achieve further performance increases for digital systems, the following two directions may lead to feasible solutions:

1) The partitioning of the network into subunits ("islands"), which should be as small as possible, with many of them located on large chips. Synchronous operations should be restricted to the intra-island traffic, while a loose coupling should govern the inter-island traffic, which should be spread as much as possible time- and space-wise (multiplexing). The smaller the "islands" are, the higher the clock frequencies are feasible since all arguments pertaining to "chip size" in the previous sections are equally valid for "island size" if the "system chip" is partitioned and operated as described.

Chips of this type will contain many islands with memory-type arrays (registers, buffers, caches, etc.); their total area will frequently exceed the area of logic islands. These memory functions have to be matched performance-wise with the logic. Extensive use of the hierarchy techniques is required to achieve such a match, otherwise the overall system performance will suffer.

Various types of auxiliary functions will also be increasingly integrated into the chips. Functions of this kind are error-detection and error-correction circuits, circuits for self-testing, redundant circuits for the automatic replacement of defective circuits, circuits for power supply and control, etc.

2) The transition from uniprocessors to multiprocessors can be considered as a second significant development trend to increase the performance. So far, however, this method has been proven efficient only for the parallel operation of a few uni-processors. Presently, there are, however, intensive worldwide development efforts ongoing, aimed at new multiple parallel architectures [23]. It is too soon to judge which of the various concepts may succeed and how effective the performance increases may be. The progress in VLSI will certainly lead to the emergence of novel, more favorable schemes.

VI. CLOSING REMARKS

In the relatively short period of about 25 years, the silicon chip technology emerged as an important major industry. Microelectronics, which is based on this technology, has grown into an omnipresent bristling business. The extention potential is still substantial. With this paper an attempt was made to assess and discuss the obstacles and limits which will be en-

countered during this evolution. The ultimate limitations will probably not be reached or even approached before the turn of the millenium.

The signal propagation limit is a very universal one, being not only a fundamental limit for the room-temperature silicon technology, (as discussed here) but also, with slight modifications, for any other digital technology using electrical or optical signals. Replacing silicon with other materials and reducing the temperature will not help to move or to remove this limitation. This does not mean, however, that faster devices than those which can be made out of silicon are useless. It only means that for the application described here in ultradense digital VLSI not much can be gained by replacing silicon by an other material, say GaAs.

There are, however, numerous applications in which faster switching circuits will have beneficial effects, particularly if used in "ordered structures" in which line lengths do not constitute the limiting elements and/or for low integration levels with inherently short lines. For such and similar applications, other materials have been proven superior and are being used in unique and complementing applications.

On the other hand, in cases where thermal limitations are predominant, low temperature operations offer quite some relief. The nonlinearities of the I–V characteristics become more pronounced with lower temperatures. Therefore, the operating voltages, and, in turn, the power dissipation can be reduced. This holds especially and prominently for the Josephson technology. However, a discussion of such technologies which have their own particular problems would exceed the scope of this paper.

REFERENCES

[1] R. N. Noyce, "From relays to MPU's," *Computer*, pp. 26–29, Dec. 1976.
[2] See e.g., J. Lyman, "Lithography steps ahead to meet the VLSI challange," *Electronics*, pp. 121–128, July 14, 1983.
[3] K. Hess and N. Holonyak, Jr., "Hot electrons in layered semiconductors," *Phys. Today*, pp. 40–47, Oct. 1980.
[4] J. R. Brews *et al.*, "Generalized guide for MOSFET miniaturization," *IEEE Trans. Electron. Devices Lett.*, vol. EDL-1, pp. 2–4, Jan. 1980.
[5] A. K. Pickar, "Lithography and etching-issues and trends in the 80s," *VLSI Technologies*, IEEE catalog no. EHO 192-5, 1982, pp. 55–61.
[6] G. E. Moore, "Progress in digital integrated electronics," IEDM, Washington, DC, Tech. Dig., 1975, pp. 11–13.
[7] See e.g., *IEEE Spectrum*, p. 36, Apr. 1979.
[8] See e.g., other parts of this book.
[9] W. T. Williams and P. K. Parker, "Design for testability—A survey," this book, pp. 238.
[10] B. Hoeneisen and C. A. Mead, "Fundamental limitations in microelectronics," *Solid State Electron.*, vol. 15, pp. 819–829 and 891–897, 1972.
[11] O. G. Folberth and J. H. Bleher, "Grenzen der digitalen Halbleitertechnik," *Nachrichtentech. Z.*, vol. 30, pp. 307–314, 1977.
[12] R. W. Keyes, "Physical limits in digital electronics," *Proc. IEEE*, vol. 63, pp. 740–767, 1975.
[13] D. B. Tuckerman and R. F. W. Pease, "High-performance heat sinking for VLSI," *IEEE Electron Devices Lett.*, vol. EDL-2, pp. 126–129, 1981.
[14] K. N. Ratnakumar, J. D. Meindl, and D. J. Bartelink, "Performance limits of E/D NMOS VLSI," in *Tech. Dig., IEEE Int. Solid-State Circuits Conf.*, vol. 23, 1980, pp. 72–73.
[15] D. L. Frazer *et al.*, "Gigabit logic circuits with scaled NMOS," in *Dig. Tech. Papers ESSCIRC*, 1981, pp. 202–204.
[16] P. W. Cook, D. L. Critchlow, and L. M. Terman, "Comparison of MOSFET logic circuits," *IEEE J. Solid-State Circuits*, vol. SC-8, pp. 348–355, 1973.
[17] O. G. Folberth, "The interdependence of geometrical, thermal, and electrical limitations for VLSI Logic," *IEEE J. Solid-State Circuits*, vol. SC-16, pp. 51–53, 1981.
[18] ——, "Signalfortpflanzung in integrierten Schaltungen," *Int. Elektron. Rundsch.*, vol. 28, pp. 9–12 and 29–31, 1974.

[19] J. T. Wallmark, "Fundamental physical limitations in integrated electronic circuits," in *Inst. Phys. Conf. Ser.*, vol. 25, 1975, pp. 133–167.

[20] R. W. Keyes, "Physical limits in semiconductor electronics," *Science*, vol. 195, pp. 1230–1235, 1977.

[21] F. Faggin, "How VLSI impacts computer architecture," *IEEE Spectrum*, pp. 28–31, May 1978.

[22] R. W. Keyes, "Physical problems and limits in computer logic," *IEEE Spectrum*, pp. 36–45, May 1969.

[23] See e.g., T. Manuel, "Parallel processing," *Electronics*, pp. 105–114, June 16, 1983.

[24] A. K. Sinha, J. A. Cooper, Jr., and H. J. Levinstein, "Speed limitations due to interconnect time constants in VLSI integrated circuits," *IEEE Electron Devices Lett.*, vol. EDL-3, pp. 90–92, Apr. 1982.

[25] K. C. Saraswat and F. Mohammadi, "Effect of scaling of interconnections on the time delay of VLSI circuits," *IEEE Trans. Electron Devices*, vol. ED-29, pp. 645–650, Apr. 1982.

Author Index

A

Adesida, I., 62
Alles, D. S., 121
Avenier, J. P., 201

B

Ballantyne, J. M., 64
Bhattacharyya, A. B., 270
Brehm, G. E., 148
Buhrman, R. A., 69

C

Chinn, J. D., 62

D

Dirks, H. K., 159
Ditlow, G. S., 183

E

Eastman, L. F., 65
Economou, N. P., 71
Engl, W. L., 159
Everhart, T. E., 59

F

Feuer, M., 19
Folberth, O. G., 295
Frey, J., 67

G

Goto, S., 255
Grobman, W. D., 47

H

Hanson, G. R., 61
Hatzakis, M., 32
Havemann, R. H., 93
Herriott, D. R., 27
Hollman, R. F., 52
Hong, S. J., 209

I

Isaacson, M. S., 61

K

Krusius, J. P., 66

L

Lepselter, M. P., 121
Levinstein, H. J., 121
Lipp, H. M., 228

M

Macksey, H. M., 148
Meinerzhagen, B., 159
Muray, A. J., 61

N

Nair, R., 209
Neidert, R. E., 138
Neureuther, A. R., 82
Niessen, C., 218

O

Ohtsuki, T., 255

P

Parker, K. P., 238
Peckerar, M. C., 138

R

Reisman, A., 3
Ruehli, A. E., 183

S

Saunier, P., 148
Séquin, C. H., 277
Shah, P. L., 93
Siegel, B. M., 61
Smith, G. E., 121
Sonek, G. J., 64
Sudo, T., 255

T

Triplett, B. B., 52

V

Varnell, G. L., 93

W

Watson, H. A., 121
Wicks, G. W., 65
Williams, T. W., 238
Wilson, A. D., 37
Wisseman, W. R., 148
Wolf, E. D., 59, 62
Wood, C. E. C., 65

305

Subject Index

Editors' Biographies

Otto G. Folberth received the degree in physics and the Dr. rer nat. degree from Technical University, Stuttgart, Germany, in 1951 and 1952, respectively.

From 1952 to 1960 he was with the Research Laboratory of the Siemens-Schuckert-Werke AG in Erlangen, Germany, working in the field of semiconductor compounds. He originated numerous publications and patents durng this period. In 1961 he joined IBM Deutschland GmbH in Boeblingen, where he became instrumental in the build-up of a semiconductor research and development facility. This department formed the nucleus for the manufacturing organization of silicon components in IBM in Germany, an activity which comprised a substantial part of the total manufacturing operation of the company in the years to follow. The development department designed and piloted a multitude of advanced IC's, used worldwide in many IBM systems of several generations. In addition to his managerial duties, he performed several part-time jobs internally and externally. From 1968 on, he has served each summer semester as a part-time lecturer at the University of Stuttgart, teaching courses in "Technology of Integrated Semiconductor Circuits." In 1974 he was appointed Honorary Professor. Also, in 1974 he was appointed an IBM Fellow. In 1978 and 1979 he was a member of IBM's Corporate Technical Committee, IBM's supreme technical advisory board. After his return to Germany, he became manager of the component technology organization of the IBM Laboratory in Boeblingen. In October 1983, he was promoted to Director of Science and Technology, IBM Deutschland GmbH. In this position, he is responsible for the Scientific Center in Heidelberg and the scientific programs of IBM Germany, including cooperative projects with German universities.

Dr. Folberth is member of several national and international scientific and technical societies in which he participates actively. For several years he was the Chairman of the steering committee for the organization of solid-state scientific and engineering conferences in Europe. He was also Secretary (1971–72) and Chairman (1973–75) of the European Group of the Program Committee for the International Solid State Circuits Conference (ISSCC).

Warren D. Grobman (M'81) received the B.A. in physics in 1964 from the University of Pennsylvania, Philadelphia, and the M.A. and Ph.D. degrees in physics from Princeton University, Princeton, NJ, in 1966 and 1967, respectively.

He was a member of the technical staff at Bellcomm Inc. from 1967 to 1969, and then he joined IBM as a research staff member. At IBM he has worked in the field of experimental photoemission spectroscopy, and has done theoretical work on the electronic structure of solids and in the area of many-body systems. From 1976 to 1983 he worked in the area of high resolution lithography, including research and development in the fields of electron-beam lithography and X-ray lithography at a storage ring. He now manages groups responsible for materials and processes for semiconductor systems packaging technology.

Dr. Grobman is a member of the proposal review panel of the Stanford Synchrotron Radiation Laboratory, and is a Fellow of the American Physical Society.